APPLIED
PROBABILITY *and*
STATISTICAL
METHODS

APPLIED PROBABILITY *and* STATISTICAL METHODS

George C. Canavos

VIRGINIA COMMONWEALTH UNIVERSITY

LITTLE, BROWN AND COMPANY
Boston   Toronto

To my Mother
and to Athena, Alexis, and Costa

Library of Congress Cataloging in Publication Data

Canavos, George C.
  Applied probability and statistical methods.

  Includes index.
  1. Probabilities.   2. Mathematical statistics.
  I. Title.
QA273.C254   1984   519.2   83-18743
ISBN 0-316-12778-7

Library of Congress Catalog Card No. 83-18743

ISBN 0-316-12778-7

9 8 7 6 5 4 3 2 1

MV

Published simultaneously in Canada
by Little, Brown & Company (Canada) Limited

Printed in the United States of America

Preface

This book is intended as an introduction to probability theory and statistical inference for readers in applied disciplines, such as business and economics, engineering, and the physical and life sciences. No previous exposure to probability and statistics is assumed. Although the reader is expected to be familiar with the essentials of integral and differential calculus, the text focuses on the application of probability and statistics. Mathematical rigor is used only to expound the foundation of probability and statistical inference, which is believed to be a necessary ingredient if one is to apply the methods effectively. The book attempts to provide the applied reader with a more than superficial understanding of probability and statistics without burdening him or her with excessive theory. In this sense, the book gives the reader the opportunity to reinforce the "why" in addition to presenting him or her with the "how" for the application of probability and statistical inference.

Throughout the text, each concept or method is illustrated with realistic examples and is verbalized in such a way that the reader can obtain an intuitive understanding of the concept. For the most part the development of statistical inference is based on the sampling theory approach. The Bayesian point of view is also explored to provide the reader with the proper perspective. The assumptions for the statistical methods are fully explored, and "what if" questions are answered. Moreover, computer packages and simulation techniques are often used to illustrate and reinforce the material presented.

The material covered in the text should prove sufficient for a two-semester sequence in probability and statistical methods. Other configurations are also possible, such as a one-semester course in probability distributions and their applications, using Chapters 1 through 7; a two-quarter course in the essentials of probability and statistical methods, using Chapters 1–10; or a one-semester course in analysis of variance and regression methods, using Chapters 9, 12, 13, and 14. The topical coverage is comprehensive and extensive, providing the instructor with ample opportunity for greater emphasis of certain topics or deletion of others. Depending on the particular needs and backgrounds of readers, the book can be used at both the undergraduate and graduate levels.

After a reasonably thorough discussion of descriptive statistics (Chapter 1), the text is divided into probability (Chapters 2–7) and statistical methods (Chapters

8–15). In Chapters 2 and 3 the basic concepts of probability, random variable, and probability distribution are presented. Chapters 4 and 5 contain a fairly complete treatment of discrete and continuous probability distributions and their applications. In these chapters distributions such as binomial, Poisson, normal, beta, gamma, and Weibull, among others, are fully explored as to their properties, are compared and contrasted, and particular areas of application are given. Because of the ever-increasing role of computers and simulation techniques, a section in Chapter 5 is devoted to methods for generating random values from the various probability distributions presented. In Chapter 6 joint and conditional distributions are discussed. In this context the concepts of prior and posterior distributions for the Bayesian approach are introduced.

Chapter 7 serves as a transition from probability to statistical inference. In this chapter the important concepts of random sample and sampling distribution are discussed. In Chapter 8 methods for point and interval estimation are presented. Distribution-free tolerance limits and those based on the normal distribution are also discussed. The foundation of a statistical hypothesis is explored in Chapter 9, and the testing of hypotheses for means, variances, and proportions is presented. Chapter 10 details the use of the chi-square distribution for goodness of fit and for contingency tables, while Chapter 11 introduces the reader to the basic concepts of statistical quality control and acceptance sampling procedures. In Chapter 12 the design of statistical experiments and the analysis of variance procedure are presented for single-factor and two-factor experiments. A comprehensive treatment of regression analysis topics is provided in Chapters 13 and 14. In these chapters important topics such as autocorrelated errors, analysis of residuals, weighted least squares, multicollinearity, and ways for determining the best set of predictor variables are examined in detail. Finally, Chapter 15 explores and contrasts some of the more useful nonparametric procedures that have been developed.

A review of summation notation is appended to Chapter 1, and a brief review of matrix algebra is given in the appendix to Chapter 13. Proofs of key theorems are provided for theoretically inclined readers in appendices to Chapters 4, 5, and 7. Eleven statistical tables are provided in the book Appendix. Where possible, an attempt has been made to standardize the structure of these tables. For example, the distribution functions are tabulated for the binomial, Poisson, hypergeometric, and normal distributions, and quantile values are given for the chi-square, Student's t, and F distributions. The tables for the binomial, Poisson, normal, chi-square, Student's t, and F distributions have been generated using appropriate subroutines from the International Mathematical and Statistical Libraries (IMSL) package. Agreement with established statistical tables is excellent. Minitab and the Statistical Analysis System (SAS) computer packages are used to illustrate regression analysis techniques (Chapters 13 and 14). It is assumed that the reader has access to these or to comparable packages such as the Statistical Package for the Social Sciences (SPSS) and Biomedical Programs (BMDP).

I am grateful to all the people who over the years, in one way or another, have played direct and indirect roles in making this book possible. I am particularly grateful to the Department of Statistics at Virginia Polytechnic Institute and State

University, where I first learned statistics, to NASA's Langley Research Center, where I was given the opportunity to continue my studies in statistics, and to Virginia Commonwealth University, where I currently teach statistics. I also want to acknowledge the assistance in preparation of this book of John Koutrouvelis, of the Department of Mathematical Sciences at Virginia Commonwealth University, who through his constructive criticism contributed significantly to the chapters on probability. In addition, I extend a special thanks to the following people for providing me with extremely helpful suggestions at various stages in the development of the manuscript: Arlene S. Ash, Boston University; Bruce K. Blaylock, Virginia Polytechnic Institute and State University; George W. Brown, University of California, Irvine; Donald R. Burleson, Rivier College; John M. Burt, University of New Hampshire; Dean H. Fearn, California State University, Hayward; Richard H. Lavoie, Providence College; Stephen Meeks, Boston University; Glenn W. Milligan, Ohio State University; Chester Piascik, Bryant College; Ramona L. Trader, University of Maryland; and George D. Weiner, Cleveland State University. Sincere appreciation is also extended to Carolyn England, K. W. Hall, and Jamie Stokes, who shared the effort in typing the several versions of the manuscript. A special thanks also goes to the editorial staff of Little, Brown and Company and especially to Elizabeth Schaaf for her invaluable assistance. Finally, I thank my family for their patience, understanding, and encouragement while the book was being written.

George C. Canavos

Contents

CHAPTER SIX

Joint Probability Distributions   173

CHAPTER SEVEN

Random Samples and Sampling Distributions   199

CHAPTER EIGHT

Point and Interval Estimation   223

CHAPTER NINE

Testing Statistical Hypotheses   282

CHAPTER TEN

Goodness of Fit Tests and Analysis of Contingency Tables 336

CHAPTER ELEVEN

Methods for Quality Control and Acceptance Sampling 352

CHAPTER TWELVE

Design and Analysis of Statistical Experiments 373

CHAPTER THIRTEEN

Regression Analysis: The Simple Linear Model 411

CHAPTER FOURTEEN

Regression Analysis: The General Linear Model   467

CHAPTER FIFTEEN

Nonparametric Methods   530

APPENDIX   551

CHAPTER ONE

Introduction and Descriptive Statistics

1.1 Introduction

To most people, "statistics" means numerical descriptions. This can be verified easily by listening to a television commentator describe a football game on any given Sunday. In more precise terms, however, statistics is the study of random phenomena. In this sense the science of statistics has a virtually unlimited scope of application over a spectrum of disciplines ranging from the sciences and engineering to law and medicine. The most important aspect of statistics is the process of drawing conclusions based on sample data. Such a process is known as *statistical inference*. Whether a stated conclusion pertains to a key economic indicator or a possibly dangerous concentration of a pollutant, or if it purports to establish a relation between cigarette smoking and the incidence of lung cancer, it is highly likely that the conclusion is based on statistical inference.

To understand the nature of statistical inference, it is necessary to understand the notions of *population* and *sample*. The population is the collection of all possible information that characterizes some phenomenon. In statistics, population is a more general concept than in the ordinary usage of the word. We think of a population as either a collection of a finite number of measurements or as a virtually infinitely large collection of data about something of interest. The sample, on the other hand, is a representative subset selected from the population. The word "representative" is the key to this idea. A good sample must be one that reflects the essential features of the population from which it is drawn. In statistics, objective sampling techniques are used to ensure that each observation in the population has an equal and independent chance of being included in the sample. Such a sampling process leads to a *random sample*. The observations of the random sample are used to compute certain characteristics of the sample called *statistics*. The statistics are then used as the bases of inferences concerning certain characteristics of the population, called *population parameters*. Thus we often analyze the information contained in the random sample for the main

1

purpose of making inferences about the nature of the population from which the sample was drawn.

Inference in statistics is inductive in the sense that we project from the specific (sample) to the general (population). In a procedure of this nature, there is always the possibility of error. We can never be 100 percent certain about a statement based on statistical inference. However, what makes statistics a science (and thus separates it from the art of fortune-telling) is that to every statement based on statistical inference there is attached a measure of the statement's reliability. In statistics, reliability is measured in terms of probability. That is, for each statistical inference, the probability of that inference being correct is identified.

The following four elements characterize many statistical problems:

1. The population of interest and the scientific procedure to sample the population.
2. The sample and the mathematical analysis of its information.
3. The statistical inferences that result from the analysis of the sample.
4. The probability of those inferences being correct.

The preceding approach to statistical inference is based solely on sample evidence. It is called the *sampling-theory* or *classical* approach to statistical inference, and for the most part it will be the approach taken in this book. However, it is also our intention to incorporate from time to time another point of view known as *Bayesian inference*. This approach to statistical inference utilizes a combination of sample evidence with other information, usually provided by the investigator of the problem of interest. Such information is based primarily on the investigator's degree of belief or conviction concerning the uncertainties of the problem before sample evidence is made available. This degree of belief may be based on many considerations such as known results from previous investigations. It is important for the reader to understand that the objective of both classical and Bayesian procedures remains the evaluation of uncertainties based on probability.

To comprehend the essence of random sampling and statistical inference, it is necessary first to understand the nature of a population in the context of probability and probability models. These topics are examined in some detail in Chapters 2 through 6.

The balance of this chapter will present a brief treatment of what are commonly referred to as *descriptive statistics*. Although they are mathematically simple, descriptive statistics are invaluable in many cases where the full population is available and no uncertainty exists, or where large data sets that may or may not be regarded as random samples are available. If a large set is regarded as a random sample from some population, descriptive statistics can go a long way in providing empirical evidence as to the general distribution of values in the population as well as information on other characteristics of the population. Such evidence is often invaluable in affirming certain assumptions that must be made in the application of statistical inference.

1.2 Graphical Description of Data

A highly informative description of any data set is provided by the frequency of occurrence or distributional arrangement of the observations in the data set. To appreciate the necessity of summarizing data in this way, take the example of the Internal Revenue Service, which receives and processes millions of tax returns every year. It is doubtful whether the IRS can uncover the underlying patterns of income and taxes by looking at the gross information contained in those tax returns. Similarly, the Bureau of the Census would not go very far in analyzing census data if all it could do was to visually scan the information. To identify the patterns in a data set, it is necessary to group the observations into a relatively small number of nonoverlapping classes such that there is no ambiguity as to the class in which a particular observation is placed. The number of observations in a class is called the *class frequency*, while the ratio of a single class frequency to the combined number of observations in all classes is called the *relative frequency* of that class. The boundaries of the classes are called *class limits*, and the arithmetic average between the upper and lower limits of a class is the *midpoint* of the class. The relative frequencies of the classes are plotted against their respective class intervals as rectangles to produce what is commonly known as the *relative frequency histogram* or *relative frequency distribution*. It is this distribution that can make the patterns in a data set clear.

To illustrate, the data in Table 1.1 represent frequencies for the number of units sold per day of some product by a company. The relative frequency histogram is constructed by plotting the relative frequency on the vertical axis and the lower boundary of each class on the horizontal axis, as shown in Figure 1.1.

The number of classes used to categorize a data set depends on the total number of observations in the set. If the number of observations is relatively small, the number of classes should be near five, but usually not less than five. If there are a substantial number of observations, the number of classes should be somewhere between eight and twelve; there should almost never be more than 15 classes. An extremely small number of classes may mask the real distribution

TABLE 1.1 Frequencies for the number of units sold of a product

Number of units sold (Class)	Class frequency	Relative frequency
80–89	7	7/100 = 0.07
90–99	20	20/100 = 0.20
100–109	5	5/100 = 0.05
110–119	11	11/100 = 0.11
120–129	11	11/100 = 0.11
130–139	12	12/100 = 0.12
140–149	6	6/100 = 0.06
150–159	23	23/100 = 0.23
160–169	5	5/100 = 0.05
Total	100	1.00

FIGURE 1.1 Relative frequency histogram for the number of units sold

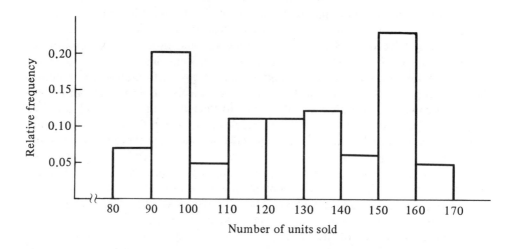

of the data set, while an extremely large number of classes may leave some classes without any observations in them, thus limiting their use. For example, if we were to compress the nine classes of the previous illustration into the three in Table 1.2, the resulting relative frequency histogram, as shown in Figure 1.2, would be different from that in Figure 1.1.

It is usually a good practice to create classes with intervals of equal width. This can be accomplished by taking the difference between the two extreme values of the data set and dividing it by the number of classes; the result should be approximately the width for each class. There are cases, however, in which this rule cannot or should not be applied. For example, if we had the IRS list of the taxes paid by individuals for some year, these amounts might range from $0 to $1,000,000. Even if we had chosen 20 classes for the relative frequency distribution, with equal-width intervals each class would have a range of $50,000. This would create a situation in which nearly all of the observations would fall in the first class. For cases such as this, it is preferable to select class intervals at the lower end of the data scale that are smaller than those at the higher end. Such a selection will make the pattern of the distribution clearer.

TABLE 1.2 Frequencies for the number of units sold of a product

Number of units sold (Class)	Class frequency	Relative frequency
80–109	32	32/100 = 0.32
110–139	34	34/100 = 0.34
140–169	34	34/100 = 0.34
Total	100	1.00

FIGURE 1.2 Modified histogram for the number of units sold

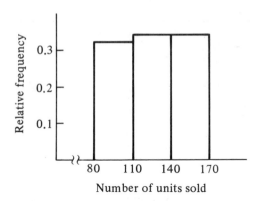

Number of units sold

The following two examples will illustrate these concepts.

Example 1.1 The annual premiums charged by 40 companies for $25,000 term insurance for 35-year-old males, as reported in the February 1980 issue of *Consumer Reports,* are as follows:

$ 82	85	86	87	87	89	89	90	91	91
92	93	94	95	95	95	95	95	97	98
99	99	100	100	101	101	103	103	103	104
105	105	106	107	107	107	109	110	110	111

Establish a grouping scheme for this data set and determine the relative frequencies.

Since the range is only $29, it would be reasonable to group the data into classes with equal-width intervals. Suppose we decide to use six classes; then the class interval is about $5. To establish the boundaries of each class, it is necessary to consider the nearest unit to which the observations are measured. In this example, the premiums are reported to the nearest dollar. Presumably, the premiums are known to the penny but are reported only to the nearest dollar. Thus the premium of, say, $82 is interpreted to mean between $81.50 and $82.49 inclusive, and the six classes and their boundaries are (81.5–86.5), (86.5–91.5), (91.5–96.5), (96.5–101.5), (101.5–106.5), (106.5–111.5).

These boundaries are also known as the *true limits* because they reflect the smallest unit of measurement chosen to record the observations. Since the premiums are reported to the nearest dollar, one may also choose to write the limits of the six classes as (82–86), (87–91), (92–96), (97–101), (102–106), (107–111). These are known as the *written limits* because they reflect the same degree of precision as the reporting of the observations. The class interval is the difference between the true limits of each class, while the class midpoints may be determined by

TABLE 1.3 Grouping and relative frequencies for Example 1.1

Class written limits	Midpoint	Class frequency, f_i	Relative frequency, f_i/n
82–86	84	3	$3/40 = 0.075$
87–91	89	7	$7/40 = 0.175$
92–96	94	8	$8/40 = 0.200$
97–101	99	8	$8/40 = 0.200$
102–106	104	7	$7/40 = 0.175$
107–111	109	7	$7/40 = 0.175$
	Total	40*	1.000

$$*n = \sum_{i=1}^{6} f_i$$

using either the true limits or the written limits. A summary of the pertinent grouping information for this example is given in Table 1.3.

As before, the relative frequency distribution is determined by plotting the relative frequencies on the vertical axis against the written lower limits for each of the classes on the horizontal axis using equal-width rectangles to represent the relative frequencies. The relative frequency histogram for Example 1.1 is given in Figure 1.3. It should be noted that one can just as easily plot the class frequencies rather than the relative frequencies on the vertical axis; the graphs would be identical. If there is a preference for using the relative frequencies, it is because the vertical scale is fixed in the range zero to one.

The main purpose of such a graphical representation of the relative frequencies is to display the distributional shape of the data. Knowledge of the shape is useful in many ways, such as to suggest appropriate analyses that might be

FIGURE 1.3 Relative frequency distribution for the data in Example 1.1

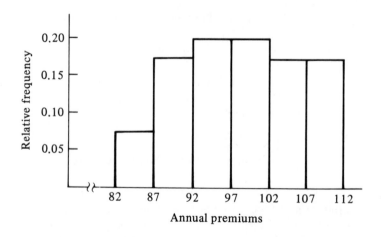

attempted for statistical inference, if the data were a random sample from some population, or to compare the distributional shapes of two or more data sets. For Example 1.1 it is apparent that the distribution of the annual premiums charged by the 40 companies is essentially uniform throughout the range of premium values.

Another useful graphical characterization of a data set is the *cumulative relative frequency distribution,* or *ogive.* The cumulative distribution is obtained by plotting on the vertical axis the cumulative relative frequency of a class against the lower limit of the next class on the horizontal axis and joining all consecutive points by line segments. Table 1.4 lists the cumulative relative frequencies for Example 1.1.

Since the relative frequency of a class reflects the proportion of the observations contained in that class, the cumulative relative frequency of a class is the proportion of the observations with values less than or equal to the upper limit of that class, or equivalently less than the lower limit of the next class. In Example 1.1 and Table 1.4, the proportion of premiums less than $82 is zero, the proportion of premiums less than $87 is 0.075, the proportion less than $92 is 0.250, and so on. The cumulative relative frequency distribution for Example 1.1 is shown in Figure 1.4.

In this context the primary use of the cumulative distribution is to determine what are commonly known as quantile values. With reference to a cumulative relative frequency distribution, a *quantile* is defined as the value below which a certain proportion of the values will fall. The quantile value is read off the horizontal axis opposite the desired proportion on the vertical axis. The most common quantile is the percentile. For example, $q_{0.2}$ is the value below which 20 percent of the distribution of values will fall, and $q_{0.9}$ is the value below which 90 percent of the distribution of values will fall.

Example 1.2   The net incomes per farm for the 50 states for 1976, as reported by the U.S. Department of Agriculture, are as follows:

$ 5,952	63,855	39,362	9,692	27,611
13,647	10,630	6,644	4,438	19,106
8,681	5,332	2,304	6,859	8,141
11,771	9,378	5,992	7,000	12,543
4,963	4,543	11,177	12,292	6,695
10,207	7,627	8,992	23,811	7,657
8,043	8,972	6,480	6,824	9,554
4,626	4,845	10,452	9,922	7,683
5,119	8,621	2,290	4,973	3,904
2,892	5,405	2,789	30	241

Establish a grouping scheme for this data set and determine the relative frequencies.

Suppose we decide to use eight equal-width classes. Since the range of the data set is approximately $64,000, the class width is $8,000 and the class limits are $(-0.5-7,999.5), (7,999.5-15,999.5), ..., (55,999.5-63,999.5)$. The class frequencies

TABLE 1.4 Cumulative relative frequencies of Example 1.1

Class written limits	Class frequency	Cumulative frequency	Cumulative relative frequency
82–86	3	3	3/40 = 0.075
87–91	7	10	10/40 = 0.250
92–96	8	18	18/40 = 0.450
97–101	8	26	26/40 = 0.650
102–106	7	33	33/40 = 0.825
107–111	7	40	40/40 = 1.000

and relative frequencies for this grouping scheme are given in Table 1.5. This grouping scheme is inadequate since 90 percent of the observations fall in the first two classes and two other classes contain no observations at all. Example 1.2 illustrates data sets for which equal-width intervals should not be used because they contain a single highly concentrated cluster of observations with only sparse observations outside that cluster. In Example 1.2 a much heavier concentration exists at the lower end than at the upper end. For this reason, the class widths at the lower end should be much smaller than those at the upper end. Consider, therefore, a grouping scheme comprised of eight classes with limits (−0.5–1,999.5), (1,999.5–3,999.5), (3,999.5–5,999.5), (5,999.5–7,999.5), (7,999.5–11,999.5), (11,999.5–27,999.5), (27,999.5–43,999.5), (43,999.5–75,999.5). Table 1.6 contains

FIGURE 1.4 Cumulative relative frequency distribution for Example 1.1

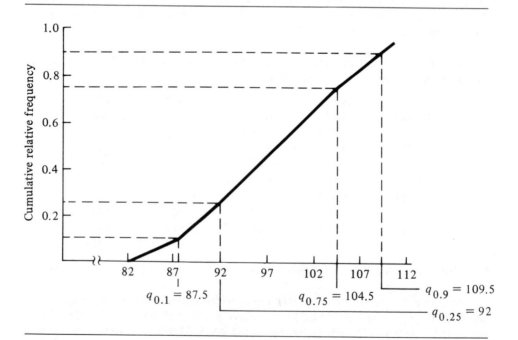

TABLE 1.5 Relative frequencies for Example 1.2 with equal-width intervals

Class written limits	Class frequency	Relative frequency
0–7,999	27	0.54
8,000–15,999	18	0.36
16,000–23,999	2	0.04
24,000–31,999	1	0.02
32,000–39,999	1	0.02
40,000–47,999	0	0
48,000–55,999	0	0
56,000–63,999	1	0.02
Total	50	1.00

the relative frequencies for this grouping scheme, and Figure 1.5 depicts the frequency distribution.

In determining the relative frequency distribution given in Figure 1.5, we have used the height of the rectangle for each class to represent its relative frequency, as we did in Example 1.1. However, because of the unequal-width intervals, Figure 1.5 gives the erroneous impression that, for example, the class (12,000–27,999) contains more than 12 percent of the observations. This is because when we compare geometric figures such as rectangles, we tend to compare their areas rather than their sides. When the class intervals are the same, the areas of the rectangles do represent frequency. However, when the intervals are unequal, as in Example 1.2, the areas do not represent frequency. Consequently, it is

FIGURE 1.5 Relative frequency distribution of farm incomes for 1976

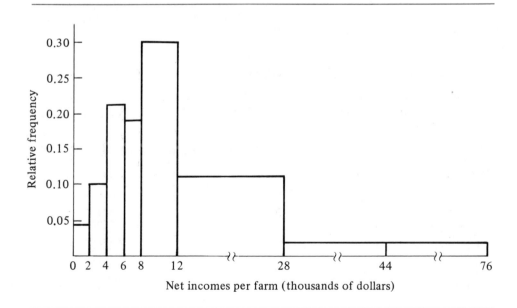

Net incomes per farm (thousands of dollars)

TABLE 1.6   Relative frequencies for Example 1.2 with unequal-width intervals

Class written limits	Class frequency	Relative frequency
0–1,999	2	0.04
2,000–3,999	5	0.10
4,000–5,999	11	0.22
6,000–7,999	9	0.18
8,000–11,999	15	0.30
12,000–27,999	6	0.12
28,000–43,999	1	0.02
44,000–75,999	1	0.02
Total	50	1.00

necessary to adjust the heights of the rectangles to make their areas proportional to frequency. Such a procedure yields a correct representation of frequencies for unequal-width intervals.

To demonstrate this method in Example 1.2, notice that the widths of the first four classes are the same. The last four classes should then be adjusted so that their widths are relative to the common width of $2,000 for the first four classes. That is, the heights of the rectangles for the last four classes are adjusted so that their areas are in the same proportion (2,000) to their respective relative frequencies as the areas of the rectangles for the first four classes. The heights of the first four classes remain as given in the last column of Table 1.6, while the adjusted heights of the last four classes work out to be 0.15, 0.015, 0.0025 and 0.00125, respectively. Note, however, that the sum of these new heights is 0.70875 and not 1.00, as required for relative frequencies. Division by 0.70875 converts these heights to relative frequencies, as desired. The adjusted relative frequencies are given in Table 1.7, and the correct representation of the relative frequency distribution is as given in Figure 1.6.

1.3   Numerical Descriptive Measures

In the last section we discussed graphical techniques for uncovering the underlying distributional patterns of a data set. In this section we shall define some numerical

TABLE 1.7   Adjusted relative frequencies for Example 1.2 with unequal-width intervals

Class written limits	Adjusted relative frequency
0–1,999	0.0564
2,000–3,999	0.1411
4,000–5,999	0.3104
6,000–7,999	0.2540
8,000–11,999	0.2116
12,000–27,999	0.0212
28,000–43,999	0.0035
44,000–75,999	0.0018
Total	1.0000

FIGURE 1.6   Adjusted relative frequency distribution of farm incomes for 1976

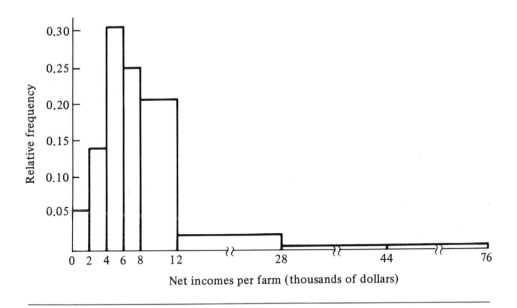

Net incomes per farm (thousands of dollars)

measures that are commonly used to describe data sets. If the data set is a random sample drawn from some population of interest and statistical inference is the ultimate goal, such measures will be used as the bases of the inferences, as will be discussed in Chapters 7 through 9.

Two descriptive items of interest for any data set are the location of its center and its variability. The *central tendency* of a data set is the tendency of the data to cluster or to center about certain numerical values. The *variability* of a data set is the scatter or dispersion of the observations in the set.

There are three primary measures of central tendency: the mean, the median, and the mode.

Definition 1.1   The *mean* of the observations x_1, x_2, ..., x_n is the arithmetic average of these observations and is denoted by

$$\bar{x} = \sum_{i=1}^{n} x_i/n. \tag{1.1}$$

The mean is a highly desirable measure of central tendency for most data sets. However, since every observation of the data set is used in the computation of the mean, the mean can be disproportionately affected by a few extreme values.

Definition 1.2   The *median* of a set of observations is the observation value such that when the observations are arranged in increasing order of magnitude, half of the observations will be less than this value and the other half will exceed this value.

   If the number of observations in a data set is odd, the median is the value of the middle observation in the ordered sequence. If the number of observations is even, the median is taken to be the arithmetic average of the values of the two middle observations in the ordered sequence. Alternatively, the median can be determined from a cumulative distribution. That is, the median is the 50th percentile.

   It should be noted that since the median is a value based on the ordered sequence of the observations in a data set, a relative few extreme observations cannot influence its value. Therefore, if a data set contains a single highly concentrated cluster of observations and a few extreme observations, the median may be a more desirable measure of central tendency than the mean. Usually data sets describing income information fall into this category.

Definition 1.3   The *mode* of a set of observations is the observation value that occurs most frequently in the data set.

   The mode shows where the data tend to concentrate. In relatively small data sets, there may not be even two observations that are identical in value. In such a situation, it is not clear how to define the mode. A situation may also arise in which the highest frequency is shared by two or more observations. In that case, two or more modes exist. Because of these cases, the mode is of limited usefulness as a measure of central tendency. If a relative frequency distribution has been determined, the class with the highest frequency may be called the modal class with the mode taken to be the midpoint of that class. In this case, the modal class serves as the concentration point of the data set.

   For the observations in Example 1.1, the mean is computed to be

$$\bar{x} = \frac{82 + 85 + \cdots + 111}{40} = \$97.90.$$

The mean for Example 1.2 is

$$\bar{x} = \frac{5,952 + 63,855 + \cdots + 241}{50} = \$9,811.34.$$

   The median of Example 1.1 is the arithmetic average of the values of the 20th and 21st observations in the ordered sequence since there are an even number of observations. That is, the median is $(98 + 99)/2 = \$98.50$. Similarly, the median of Example 1.2 is the arithmetic average of the values of the 25th and 26th observations in the ordered sequence, or $(7,627 + 7,657)/2 = \$7,642$. The mode of Example 1.1 is seen to be \$95 since it occurs most frequently; however, for Example 1.2 the mode is not clearly defined since none of the values are duplicated. Note that for Example 1.1 the values of the mean, median, and mode are relatively close to each other. This is because the premiums are fairly evenly distributed over the range of values. For Example 1.2 the mean is substantially larger than the median because the former is disproportionately affected by the farm incomes of a few states, which are extremely large in a relative sense. Thus, for this data set the median of $7,642 would be a more realistic measure of central tendency.

Many times the only information available is a frequency table like Tables 1.3 to 1.6. In such cases only approximate values for the mean, median, and mode — or for any other numerical descriptive measure — are possible; exact values can only be calculated from the individual observations of the data set or the ungrouped data. The approximate computations are based on the midpoints of the classes and the class frequencies. In general, the smaller the class interval and the more evenly the observations of each class are distributed within the class, the closer will be the agreement between descriptive measures based on grouped and ungrouped data.

To compute the mean based on grouped data, let k be the number of classes and let x_i denote the midpoint of the ith class. Then the approximate value of the mean is

$$\bar{x} = \sum_{i=1}^{k} f_i x_i / n, \tag{1.2}$$

where f_i is the frequency of the ith class and $n = \sum_{i=1}^{k} f_i$. Note that in this formula the class frequencies represent the relative importance of the observations within each class. That is, the more observations a class contains, the more weight the class midpoint will have in the computation of the mean. This is generally true for the determination of numerical measures based on grouped data.

We will illustrate the computational procedures for determining numerical descriptive measures using Example 1.1 and, in particular, the class limits and frequencies as given in Table 1.3. The relevant information and the computation of the mean are shown in Table 1.8.

For grouped data, the median is the value that divides the relative frequency distribution into two equal parts. The computational formula is given by

$$Median = L + c(j/f_m), \tag{1.3}$$

TABLE 1.8 Computation of the approximate value of the mean for Example 1.1

Class midpoint x_i	Class frequency f_i	$f_i x_i$	
84	3	252	$n = \sum_{i=1}^{6} f_i = 40$
89	7	623	
94	8	752	$\sum_{i=1}^{6} f_i x_i = 3{,}910$
99	8	792	
104	7	728	
109	7	763	$\bar{x} = \sum_{i=1}^{6} f_i x_i / n = 3{,}910/40 = \$97.75$
Total	40	3,910	

where L is the lower limit of the class into which the median falls, f_m is the frequency of that class, c is the width of that class, and j is the number of observations needed from this class to total $n/2$. To determine the median, this formula in essence interpolates linearly into the class containing the median. Thus it is assumed that the observations are evenly distributed within that class.

The median for the grouped data of Example 1.1 is determined by using the information contained in Table 1.3. The total number of observations is 40 and $n/2$ is 20. Since the sum of the frequencies of the first three classes is 18 and that of the first four is 26, the median will fall in the fourth class, whose lower limit is 97. Of the eight observations in this class, we need two to reach the required value of 20. Thus by using the formula, the median turns out to be

$$Median = 97 + 5(2/8) = \$98.25.$$

As we have already noted, for grouped data the mode is taken to be the midpoint of the class with the highest frequency. In Example 1.1 the highest frequency is shared by the classes (92–96) and (97–101). Thus the mode is taken to be the arithmetic average between the two class midpoints, or $(94 + 99)/2 = \$96.50$.

Whereas a measure of central tendency provides some information about a data set, it does not give any indication about the variability of the observations in the set. For example, consider the following two sets of data, each consisting of four observations: 0, 25, 75, 100; 48, 49, 51, 52. In both cases, *mean* = *median* = 50. These two sets are quite different, however, in that the observations of the first are much more dispersed than those of the second. One of the most useful measures of dispersion or variation is the variance.

Definition 1.4   The *variance* of the observations $x_1, x_2, \cdots, x_n$ is, in essence, the average of the squared distances between each observation and the mean of the set of observations. The variance is denoted by

$$s^2 = \sum_{i=1}^{n}(x_i - \bar{x})^2/(n - 1). \qquad (1.4)$$

The variance is a reasonably good measure of variability since, if many of the differences are large (or small) in magnitude, a large (small) value for s^2 would be determined. However, even more so than the mean, the variance can be disproportionately affected by a relative few extreme values in the data set.

Definition 1.5   The positive square root of the variance is called the *standard deviation* and is denoted by

$$s = \sqrt{\sum_{i=1}^{n}(x_i - \bar{x})^2/(n - 1)}. \qquad (1.5)$$

The variance and the standard deviation are not two distinct measures of variability since the latter cannot be determined unless the former is known.

Often preference is given to the standard deviation, primarily because it is expressed in the same physical units as the observations rather than in units squared.

When the computation of the variance is done by hand or using a low-capability pocket calculator and when either the value of the mean or the values of the observations are not integers, the use of equation (1.4) can lead to an appreciable round-off error. A computational formula for s^2 is derived from (1.4) by using a bit of algebra to make computation more accurate under these conditions:*

$$s^2 = \sum_{i=1}^{n}(x_i - \bar{x})^2/(n - 1)$$

$$= \frac{\sum(x_i^2 - 2\bar{x}\,x_i + \bar{x}^2)}{n - 1}$$

$$= \frac{\sum x_i^2 - 2\bar{x}\sum x_i + n\bar{x}^2}{n - 1}$$

$$= \frac{\sum x_i^2 - \dfrac{2\left(\sum x_i\right)\left(\sum x_i\right)}{n} + \dfrac{n\left(\sum x_i\right)^2}{n^2}}{n - 1}$$

$$= \frac{\displaystyle\sum_{i=1}^{n} x_i^2 - \dfrac{\left(\displaystyle\sum_{i=1}^{n} x_i\right)^2}{n}}{n - 1}. \tag{1.6}$$

Note that for the numerator of equation (1.4) we must first find the mean, subtract it from each observation value, square, and then sum. For the numerator of (1.6) we sum the squares of the observation values, then subtract the square of their sum divided by the number of observations n. Based on equation (1.6), the standard deviation is given by

$$s = \sqrt{\frac{\displaystyle\sum_{i=1}^{n} x_i^2 - \left(\displaystyle\sum_{i=1}^{n} x_i\right)^2 \Big/ n}{n - 1}}. \tag{1.7}$$

We illustrate the steps for the computation of the variance and standard deviation for ungrouped data using Examples 1.1 and 1.2. For Example 1.1,

*For a review of summation notation see the appendix to this chapter.

$$\sum_{i=1}^{40} x_i = 82 + 85 + \cdots + 111 = 3,916$$

$$\sum_{i=1}^{40} x_i^2 = 82^2 + 85^2 + \cdots + 111^2 = 385,756.$$

Using equation (1.6),

$$s^2 = \frac{385,756 - \dfrac{(3,916)^2}{40}}{40 - 1} = 61.0154.$$

It follows from equation (1.7) that the standard deviation is $s = \sqrt{61.0154} = \$7.81$.

For Example 1.2 we have

$$\sum_{i=1}^{50} x_i = 5,952 + 63,855 + \cdots + 241 = 490,567,$$

$$\sum_{i=1}^{50} x_i^2 = 5,952^2 + 63,855^2 + \cdots + 241^2 = 10,000,514,273,$$

and

$$s^2 = \frac{10,000,514,273 - \dfrac{490,567^2}{50}}{50 - 1} = 105,865,196.8.$$

The standard deviation is $s = \$10,289.08$.

For grouped data, the approximate value of the variance may be computed by using the formula

$$s^2 = \frac{\sum_{i=1}^{k} f_i(x_i - \bar{x})^2}{n - 1} \tag{1.8}$$

or

$$s^2 = \frac{\sum_{i=1}^{k} f_i x_i^2 - \dfrac{\left(\sum_{i=1}^{k} f_i x_i\right)^2}{n}}{n - 1}. \tag{1.9}$$

The formula for the standard deviation is

$$s = \sqrt{\sum_{i=1}^{k} f_i(x_i - \bar{x})^2/(n - 1)}. \tag{1.10}$$

In all three formulas, f_i and x_i are the frequency and midpoint, respectively, of the ith class, and n is the sum of all frequencies. It should be noted that the approximation of the variance for grouped data may be unreliable, especially if the observations are not evenly distributed within their classes. The computation for the approximate values of the variance and standard deviation for the grouped data of Example 1.1 is detailed in Table 1.9.

Another useful measure of variability is based on the absolute deviation of the observations x_1, x_2, ..., x_n from either their mean or their median, depending on whether the mean or median is used as the measure of central tendency.

Definition 1.6 The *mean deviation* is the average of the absolute differences between each observation and the mean of the observations. The mean deviation is given by

$$M.D. = \frac{\sum_{i=1}^{n} |x_i - \bar{x}|}{n}. \tag{1.11}$$

For grouped data the mean deviation is approximated by

$$M.D. = \frac{\sum_{i=1}^{k} f_i |x_i - \bar{x}|}{\sum_{i=1}^{k} f_i}. \tag{1.12}$$

The terms in these expressions are as previously defined.

The mean deviation is an appealing measure of variation, especially in the context of empirical evidence, because we are often interested in the magnitudes of the deviations and not their signs. However, from a theoretical point of view, the mean deviation is at a disadvantage as a measure of dispersion because often it is mathematically difficult to obtain. At any rate, the mean deviation is less sensitive to the effect of a relative few extreme observations in a data set than

TABLE 1.9 Computation of the approximate values of the variance and the standard deviation for Example 1.1

Class midpoint x_i	*Class frequency* f_i	x_i^2	$f_i x_i^2$	
84	3	7,056	21,168	
89	7	7,921	55,447	
94	8	8,836	70,688	
99	8	9,801	78,408	
104	7	10,816	75,712	
109	7	11,881	83,167	
Total	40	11,881	384,590	

$\sum_{i=1}^{6} f_i x_i = 3{,}910$ (from Table 1.8)

$\left(\sum_{i=1}^{6} f_i x_i \right)^2 \Big/ 40 = 382{,}202.5$

$\sum_{i=1}^{6} f_i x_i^2 = 384{,}590$

$$s^2 = \frac{384{,}590 - 382{,}202.5}{40 - 1}$$

$$= 61.2179$$

$$s = \sqrt{61.2179} = \$7.82$$

the variance or the standard deviation. Therefore, in the presence of a few extreme values, the mean deviation may provide a more realistic measure of dispersion than the standard deviation provides.

For the ungrouped data given in Example 1.1, the mean deviation is computed from

$$\sum_{i=1}^{40} |x_i - \bar{x}| = |82 - 97.9| + |85 - 97.9| + \cdots + |111 - 97.9| = 264.2$$

to be

$$M.D. = 264.2/40 = \$6.61.$$

Similarly, for Example 1.2 the mean deviation is calculated from

$$\sum_{i=1}^{50} |x_i - \bar{x}| = |5,952 - 9,811.34| + |63,855 - 9,811.34| + \cdots + |241 - 9,811.34|$$

$$= 278,051.48$$

to be

$$M.D. = 278,051.48/50 = \$5,561.03.$$

The computational steps for the approximation of the mean deviation for the grouped data in Example 1.1 are illustrated in Table 1.10.

Definition 1.7   The *median deviation* is the average of the absolute differences between each observation and the median of the observations. The median deviation is given by

$$Md.D. = \frac{\sum_{i=1}^{n} |x_i - Md|}{n}, \qquad (1.13)$$

where *Md* denotes the median.

TABLE 1.10   Computation of the approximate value of the mean deviation for Example 1.1

Class midpoint x_i	Class frequency f_i	$|x_i - \bar{x}|$	$f_i|x_i - \bar{x}|$	
84	3	$\|84 - 97.75\|$	41.25	$\sum_{i=1}^{6} f_i\|x_i - \bar{x}\| = 265$
89	7	$\|89 - 97.75\|$	61.25	
94	8	$\|94 - 97.75\|$	30.00	
99	8	$\|99 - 97.75\|$	10.00	$M.D. = 265/40$
104	7	$\|104 - 97.75\|$	43.75	
109	7	$\|109 - 97.75\|$	78.75	$= \$6.63$
Total	40		265.00	

When the median is used as the measure of central tendency to mollify the effect of a few extreme observations, the median deviation should be the preferred measure of dispersion and for the same reason. When the data are grouped, the approximate median deviation is determined from Equation (1.12), substituting the median for the mean. The median deviations for the observations in Examples 1.1 and 1.2, computed by the same procedure as for the mean deviations, work out to be 6.6 and 5,060.60, respectively. Similarly, the approximate median deviation for the grouped data of Example 1.1 is determined to be 6.575.

The range of the observations in a data set is another measure of variability.

Definition 1.8   The *range R* of the observations in a data set is the difference between the largest value and the smallest value of the observations.

Because of its simplicity, the range provides a quick indication of the variability among the observations in a data set. However, as a measure of dispersion, the range must be used with caution since its value is a function of only the two extreme observations, and it in no way reflects the variability of the other observations. As a general rule, the range should be avoided as a measure of variability whenever the number of observations in a data set is large or when the set contains some observations whose values are relatively extreme. This point can be illustrated by considering the ranges of Examples 1.1 and 1.2, which turn out to be $R_1 = 111 - 82 = \$29$, and $R_2 = 63,855 - 30 = \$63,825$, respectively. For Example 1.1, R_1 appears to be a realistic measure of variability, primarily because the data set does not contain any premium values that are way out of line relative to the others. However, for Example 1.2, R_2 is not a realistic measure of variability since the values of \$30 and \$63,855 are apparently extreme relative to the net farm incomes of most of the other states. For many problems it is more useful to determine the range between two quantile values instead of the range between the two extreme values.

Definition 1.9   The difference between the 75th and 25th percentiles is known as the *interquartile range*.

Definition 1.10   The difference between the 90th and 10th percentiles is known as the *interdecile range*.

The interquartile range reflects the variability within the middle 50 percent of the distribution of values in the data set, and the interdecile range indicates the dispersion within the middle 80 percent of the distribution of values. As a result, neither the interquartile nor the interdecile range is affected by the presence of a few extreme observations.

For grouped data the interquartile and interdecile ranges may be approximated from the cumulative relative frequency distribution. To illustrate, using Figure 1.4 we determine that the approximate values of the interquartile and interdecile ranges for Example 1.1 are $q_{0.75} - q_{0.25} = 104.50 - 92 = \$12.50$, and $q_{0.9} - q_{0.1} = 109.5 - 87.5 = \$22$, respectively. For an ungrouped data set containing

n observations, the 75th and 25th percentiles are the values of the observations whose order numbers in the ordered sequence of observations correspond to $0.75n + 0.5$ and $0.25n + 0.5$, respectively. Similarly, the 90th and 10th percentiles are the values of the observations whose order numbers correspond to $0.9n + 0.5$ and $0.1n + 0.5$, respectively. For the data in Example 1.2, the 25th and 75th percentiles are the values of the 13th and 38th ordered observations, respectively. Thus, $q_{0.25} = \$4,973$, $q_{0.75} = \$10,207$, and the interquartile range is $5,234. Since for $n = 50$ $0.1n + 0.5 = 5.5$, the 10th percentile is the average of the values of the 5th and 6th ordered observations, or $q_{0.1} = 2,840.5$. Similarly, the 90th percentile is the average of the values of the 45th and 46th observations in the ordered sequence, or $q_{0.9} = 16,376.5$. Therefore, the interdecile range of the data in Example 1.2 is $13,536.

We have used Examples 1.1 and 1.2 throughout our discussion in this chapter to illustrate the various concepts. It is important to note that these examples present contrasting situations. The former symbolizes a data set in which the observations are fairly evenly distributed over the range of values, without any extreme observations. The latter illustrates a situation in which there is a highly dense cluster of observations and a few extremes, especially at the high end. The innate difference between these two examples is discernible through a general comparison of the numerical descriptive measures that have been computed for each, as in Table 1.11.

Note that for Example 1.1 the values for measures of central tendency are very close to each other, while those for Example 1.2 are considerably apart from one another. The same can be said of the standard, mean, and median deviations for the two examples. In Example 1.1 the values of the mean and median deviations are near the value of the standard deviation, whereas in Example 1.2 the mean and median deviations are approximately half the standard deviation. Furthermore, for Example 1.1 the interdecile range is a relatively large proportion of the range ($22/29 = 0.76$), while that of Example 1.2 is a relatively small proportion of the range ($13,536/63,825 = 0.21$).

This comparison makes it clear that numerical measures and frequency distributions do indeed uncover the inherent nature of a data set. However, the

TABLE 1.11   Summary of numerical descriptive measures for Examples 1.1 and 1.2

Numerical measure	Example 1.1 Ungrouped data	Grouped data	Example 1.2 Ungrouped data
Mean	97.90	97.75	9,811.34
Median	98.50	98.25	7,642.00
Mode	95.00	96.50	—
Variance	61.0154	61.2179	105,865,196.80
Standard deviation	7.81	7.82	10,289.08
Mean deviation	6.61	6.63	5,561.03
Median deviation	6.60	6.575	5,060.60
Range	29.00	—	63,825.00
Interquartile range	—	12.50	5,234.00
Interdecile range	—	22.00	13,536.00

user must still exercise some care in the choice and interpretation of such measures. Although the mean and the standard deviation have been used extensively as measures of central tendency and dispersion, respectively, and although they have very attractive theoretical properties, nevertheless there are problems — such as Example 1.2 — for which they may not be the most desirable measures. In general, therefore, for data sets dealing with physical measurements, such as instrument readings, parts specifications, weights, etc., the mean and the standard deviation or the mean deviation are the desirable measures. For data sets dealing with incomes and other economic and financial information, the median and the median deviation are the better choices for measures of central tendency and dispersion, respectively.

As a final note, many reporting services and government agencies provide information in frequency tables that not only have unequal class widths but also have open-end classes such as "annual income of $500,000 and over" to cover a wide range of data. The open-end classes occur at the extremes, with the extreme limits of the end classes not given. As a result, the midpoint for the open-end class is not defined, and approximations for some numerical measures, such as mean, variance, standard deviation, and mean deviation, cannot be computed unless either the individual observations contained in the open-end class are available or their arithmetic average is known.

Reference

1. N.L. Johnson and F.C. Leone, *Statistics and experimental design*, Vol. I, 2nd ed., Wiley, New York, 1977.

Exercises

1.1. Following are the lengths of time, in minutes, required by 50 customers in a large commercial bank to complete a banking transaction:

2.3	0.2	2.9	0.4	2.8
2.4	4.4	5.8	2.8	3.3
3.3	9.7	2.5	5.6	9.5
1.8	4.7	0.7	6.2	1.2
7.8	0.8	0.9	0.4	1.3
3.1	3.7	7.2	1.6	1.9
2.4	4.6	3.8	1.5	2.7
0.4	1.3	1.1	5.5	3.4
4.2	1.2	0.5	6.8	5.2
6.3	7.6	1.4	0.5	1.4

a. Construct a relative frequency distribution.
b. Construct a cumulative relative frequency distribution.
c. Using the results of part b, determine the interquartile and interdecile ranges.
d. Using the grouped data, compute the mean, median, mode, standard deviation, mean deviation, and median deviation.

e. Check your results in part d by computing the same measures for the ungrouped data.

1.2. The daily demand, in units of a product, for 30 working days is as follows:

38	35	76	58	48	59
67	63	33	69	53	51
28	25	36	32	61	57
49	78	48	42	72	52
47	66	58	44	44	56

a. Construct relative frequency and cumulative relative frequency distributions.
b. Using the cumulative distribution, determine the three quartiles.
c. Compute the mean, median, mode, standard deviation, mean deviation, and median deviation, using both the grouped and ungrouped data, and compare the two sets of results.
d. Comment on the nature of this frequency distribution as compared to the distribution in Exercise 1.1.

1.3. Here are three data sets:

$$1, 2, 3, 4, 5, 6;$$
$$1, 1, 1, 6, 6, 6;$$
$$-13, 2, 3, 4, 5, 20.$$

Compute the mean and the variance for each data set. What can you conclude?

1.4. The monthly sales volumes in thousands of dollars of a computer company's 20 salespersons are as follows:

40.2	29.3	35.6	88.2	42.9
26.9	28.7	99.8	35.6	37.8
44.2	32.3	55.2	50.6	25.4
31.7	36.8	45.2	25.1	39.7

a. Compute the mean, median, standard deviation, mean deviation, median deviation, interquartile range, and interdecile range.
b. Which measures of central tendency and dispersion would you choose and why?

1.5. Using the data from Exercise 1.2, let x_i be the ith daily demand for $i = 1, 2, ..., 30$. Transform the data by means of the relation

$$u_i = \frac{x_i - 51.5}{14.17}.$$

a. Construct a relative frequency distribution for the transformed data. Has there been any change in the nature of the frequency distribution when compared to that in Exercise 1.2?
b. Using the transformed data u_i, compute the mean and standard deviation and show that they are equal to zero and one, respectively.

1.6. The following grouped data represent earnings per share of stock for the top 50 retailers for the year 1979:

Class written limits	Frequency
1.10–1.86	4
1.87–2.63	14
2.64–3.40	11
3.41–4.17	9
4.18–4.94	7
4.95–5.71	1
5.72–6.48	2
6.49–7.25	2

a. Graph the cumulative relative frequency distribution.
b. Using the results of part a, determine the interdecile and interquartile ranges.
c. Compute the mean, median, and mode.
d. Compute the variance, standard deviation, mean deviation, and median deviation.

1.7. Grouped information about the number of points scored per team per game in the National Football League during the 1973 season is as follows:

Group	Frequency
0–3	27
4–10	66
11–17	91
18–24	70
25–31	57
32–38	34
39–45	16
46–52	3

a. Graph the relative frequency distribution.
b. Compute the mean and the mode.
c. Compute the variance, standard deviation, and mean deviation.

1.8. Twenty battery packs were randomly selected from a manufacturing process and subjected to a life test. The following data represent the lifetimes in hours of the 20 batteries:

52.5	62.7	58.9	65.7	49.3
58.9	57.3	60.4	59.6	58.1
62.3	64.4	52.7	54.9	48.8
56.8	53.1	58.7	61.6	63.3

a. Determine the mean and median.
b. Determine the standard deviation, mean deviation, and median deviation.
c. Determine the interquartile and interdecile ranges.

APPENDIX

Sum and Other Symbolic Notations

In statistics the use of symbolic notation is essential. For example, to distinguish among the values of n observations we use the symbolic notation $x_1, x_2, \ldots, x_n$. One of the most useful symbols is the Greek letter Σ (sigma), which is used, in large type, to express the sum of terms in a sequence. Thus the sum of x_1, $x_2, \ldots, x_n$ is designated by

$$\sum_{i=1}^{n} x_i = x_1 + x_2 + \cdots + x_n,$$

and is read "the summation of x_i, i going from 1 to n." The letter i is called the *summation index* and takes on successive integer values up to and including n, which is the upper limit, or the largest value for i. Examples of the use of Σ follow:

(a) $\displaystyle\sum_{i=1}^{n} x_i^2 = x_1^2 + x_2^2 + \cdots + x_n^2;$

(b) $\displaystyle\sum_{i=1}^{n} (x_i - a) = (x_1 - a) + (x_2 - a) + \cdots + (x_n - a);$

(c) $\displaystyle\sum_{i=1}^{n} (x_i - a)^2 = (x_1 - a)^2 + (x_2 - a)^2 + \cdots + (x_n - a)^2;$

(d) $\displaystyle\sum_{i=1}^{n} x_i y_i = x_1 y_1 + x_2 y_2 + \cdots + x_n y_n.$

In using the symbol Σ, the following three properties are important:
   Property 1. If c is any constant, then

$$\sum_{i=1}^{n} c x_i = c \sum_{i=1}^{n} x_i.$$

Property 2. If c is any constant, then

$$\sum_{i=1}^{n} c = nc.$$

Property 3. $\displaystyle\sum_{i=1}^{n} (x_i + y_i) = \sum_{i=1}^{n} x_i + \sum_{i=1}^{n} y_i.$

These properties are verified as follows:

(1) $\displaystyle\sum_{i=1}^{n} c x_i = c x_1 + c x_2 + \cdots + c x_n$

$$= c(x_1 + x_2 + \cdots + x_n)$$

$$= c \sum_{i=1}^{n} x_i.$$

(2) $\displaystyle\sum_{i=1}^{n} c = \underbrace{c + c + \cdots + c}_{n \text{ terms}}$

$\qquad\qquad = \underbrace{(1 + 1 + \cdots + 1)c}_{n \text{ terms}}$

$\qquad\qquad = nc.$

(3) $\displaystyle\sum_{i=1}^{n}(x_i + y_i) = (x_1 + y_1) + (x_2 + y_2) + \cdots + (x_n + y_n)$

$\qquad\qquad\qquad = (x_1 + x_2 + \cdots + x_n) + (y_1 + y_2 + \cdots + y_n)$

$\qquad\qquad\qquad = \displaystyle\sum_{i=1}^{n} x_i + \sum_{i=1}^{n} y_i.$

The symbol Σ is also used to designate summation over two distinct characteristics. For example, suppose we are given the function $p(x, y)$ of the variables x and y, which take on only integer values. In particular, say that x assumes the integer values 0 and 1, and y takes on the values 1, 2, and 3. Then the summation of $p(x, y)$ over all values of x and y is designated by

$$\sum_{x=0}^{1} \sum_{y=1}^{3} p(x, y) = p(0, 1) + p(0, 2) + p(0, 3) + p(1, 1) + p(1, 2) + p(1, 3).$$

Notice that we first set the summation index x to zero, then run the inside sum for each of the values of the summation index y. In turn, we raise x by one and repeat the process. This procedure also applies to situations in which double subscripts are used to distinguish between two characteristics. For example, consider the summation of the sequence x_{ij}, $i = 1, 2, \ldots, n$, $j = 1, 2, \ldots, m$ over all possible i and j. Such a summation may be designated by

$$\sum_{i=1}^{n} \sum_{j=1}^{m} x_{ij}.$$

In particular, if $n = 2$ and $m = 3$, then

$$\sum_{i=1}^{2} \sum_{j=1}^{3} x_{ij} = x_{11} + x_{12} + x_{13} + x_{21} + x_{22} + x_{23}.$$

Another useful symbol is the Greek letter Π (pi). This letter is used, again in large type, to indicate the product of successive terms in a sequence. For example, given the sequence of observations $x_1, x_2, \ldots, x_n$, the product of x_1, $x_2, \ldots, x_n$ is designated by

$$\prod_{i=1}^{n} x_i = x_1 x_2 \ldots x_n,$$

where the letter i serves the same purpose as in a summation.

CHAPTER TWO

Concepts in Probability

2.1 Introduction

Probability is a mechanism by which one may study random or chance occurrences as compared to deterministic phenomena. For example, no one is expected to predict with certainty the outcome of even so simple an experiment as the toss of a fair coin. However, any freshman in physics should be able to determine precisely how long it would take a falling object to hit the ground, given the height from which it was dropped.

Probability plays a crucial role in the application of statistical inference because a decision based on the information contained in a random sample may be wrong. Without an understanding of the basic laws of probability, it is difficult to utilize statistical methodology effectively.

To illustrate the use of probability in a decision-making environment, here is an example. A company produces a liquid detergent that it sells in 500-gram containers filled by a machine. Since overfilling means a loss for the company and underfilling results in a loss for the consumer — which may trigger punitive action against the company — the company makes every effort to maintain the mean net weight at the 500-gram level. In order to maintain proper control, the company has devised the following sampling scheme: At each of four distinct times during the production day, ten containers are selected at random from the filling process and their average net weight is determined. The process will be judged to be "in control" as long as the mean net weight of the sampled containers is between 498 and 502 grams, inclusive; otherwise, the process will be judged to be "out of control." In the latter case, the process will be stopped and an effort will be made to determine what, if anything, has caused the process to go out of control. Of course there are risks involved in either case. If the process is judged to be in control, it may in fact be out of control, and the company may be either losing product or subjecting itself to possible punitive action by the appropriate enforcement agencies. On the other hand, if the process is judged to be out of control, it may in reality be in control, and the company will be attempting to locate a nonexisting cause. The assessment of these risks can be done effectively only through the use of probability.

In the next three sections we will examine the *classical, relative frequency,* and *subjective* interpretations of probability. The first two are similar in that they are based on repeated experiments conducted under identical conditions, such as the toss of a fair coin. The subjective or personal interpretation of probability represents a measure of belief concerning a proposition such as that a new business venture will be successful. In Section 2.5, we will state some axioms and formally define probability based on these axioms. The axiomatic development encompasses all three interpretations of probability.

2.2 The Classical Definition of Probability

The initial development of probability was closely associated with games of chance. For example, consider a pair of balanced and distinguishable dice where we are interested in the two numbers that come up when the dice are rolled. The 36 possible pairs of numbers are given in Table 2.1.

A key feature of this example, as well as of many other examples involving games of chance, is the fact that the 36 outcomes are *mutually exclusive* since two or more pairs cannot turn up simultaneously. The 36 outcomes are also *equally likely* because their frequencies will be about the same in the long run if the dice are assumed to be balanced. Note that of the 36 outcomes, six yield a sum of 7, five yield a sum of 8, and so on. Intuitively, therefore, one may think of the probability of the sum 7 as the proportion of the number of outcomes that yield 7 to the total number of outcomes, or 6/36. It is important for the reader to understand that the proportion 6/36 is realized only in the long run; that is, for a very long sequence of rolls of a pair of balanced dice, we would find that about one-sixth of the rolls yielded a sum of 7. The proportion 6/36 does not mean that for every six rolls of the dice one roll is bound to yield a sum of 7. For situations of this type, the following classical definition of probability is appropriate:

Definition 2.1 If an experiment that is subject to chance can result in n mutually exclusive and equally likely ways, and if n_A of these outcomes have an attribute A, the probability of A is the proportion of n_A to n.

2.3 The Relative Frequency Definition of Probability

In many practical investigations the possible outcomes are not equally likely. For example, in a manufacturing environment the chance of observing a defective

TABLE 2.1 Possible outcomes of numbers that come up when two dice are rolled

1,1	1,2	1,3	1,4	1,5	1,6
2,1	2,2	2,3	2,4	2,5	2,6
3,1	3,2	3,3	3,4	3,5	3,6
4,1	4,2	4,3	4,4	4,5	4,6
5,1	5,2	5,3	5,4	5,5	5,6
6,1	6,2	6,3	6,4	6,5	6,6

item will normally be much smaller than that of observing a good item. It would therefore be inappropriate to utilize the classical definition of probability to assess the probability of observing a defective item. For many such cases the relative frequency interpretation of probability is used instead.

The relative frequency interpretation is based on the notion that an experiment can be conducted and repeated many times under very similar conditions. Each time the experiment is performed an outcome is observed. The outcome is unpredictable because of the chance nature of the experiment. Then the probability of the presence of a certain attribute is approximated by the relative frequency of the outcomes that possess this attribute. And as the number of times such an experiment is performed becomes very large, the relative frequency of the favorable outcomes to the attribute approaches the true probability of the attribute.

For example, say we want to determine the proportion defective for a manufacturing process. To do this we will sample a certain number of units and assume that each time an item is selected for observation constitutes an experiment. The results of these experiments may be classified into whether the item is or is not defective. If the manufacturing process is stable, assuring uniform conditions, as the number of units sampled increases the relative frequency of defective units to the total number of units sampled will approach the true process proportion defective.

To illustrate the relative frequency interpretation of probability, we simulated in a computer sampling a number of units n from a manufacturing process that is assumed to be producing 5% defective units. For each n we observed the number of defective units, and the results are given in Table 2.2 for values of n ranging from 20 to 10,000. It is reasonable to conclude from these results that the relative frequency of defective units appears to be heading for the true proportion of 0.05 as n becomes large. Thus the following definition of probability based on a relative frequency interpretation is suggested:

Definition 2.2   If an experiment is repeated n times under identical conditions and n_B of the outcomes favor an attribute B, the limit of n_B/n as n becomes large is defined as the probability of the attribute B.

TABLE 2.2   Results of a computer-simulated experiment

Number of units sampled (n)	Observed number of defectives	Relative frequency
20	2	0.10
50	3	0.06
100	4	0.04
200	12	0.06
500	28	0.056
1,000	54	0.054
2,000	97	0.0485
5,000	244	0.0488
10,000	504	0.0504

2.4 Subjective Interpretation of Probability

The repetition of an experiment under identical conditions is the basis for both the classical and the relative frequency interpretations of probability. However, many phenomena do not lend themselves to repetition but still require some notion of probability. For example, the firm that insured the 1980 Olympics had to determine a priori the risk that the games would not take place as planned. Or when a priceless painting or sculpture is insured against theft or damage, the insurer must have some notion of the risk involved to assess an appropriate premium. In none of these examples can one conceive a realistic repetitive experiment being performed under very similar conditions. Moreover, many times all of us have made statements that implied some sort of probability. For example, when one says "the package will probably arrive tomorrow," or when a stockbroker advises a client that a particular stock will probably go up in value, some notion of the probability of the occurrence of the propositions is being suggested.

The interpretation of probability for the preceding examples cannot be based on long-run frequencies. Rather, probability is interpreted as a degree of belief or conviction concerning the occurrence of a proposition. In this context, probability represents an individual's judgment about an unpredictable phenomenon. This interpretation of probability is therefore known as *subjective* or *personal*.

It is important to emphasize that the subjective interpretation of probability may also be applied to repetitive experiments. For example, a gambler who is playing blackjack may decide to take another card purely because she believes, without any thought of long-run frequencies, that this action will increase her chances of winning that particular hand. Or the captain of a football team may call "heads" when the coin is tossed because of his degree of belief about the outcome when that particular toss is made. Because of such applications, the subjective interpretation of probability is viewed by many to be more general than the previous two.

To illustrate the translation of a degree of belief into a probability, let us consider the following: Two petroleum engineers, say *A* and *B*, are asked for their assessment of the likelihood of oil discovery at a particular site. *A* responds by saying that he is 80% certain that oil will be discovered, while *B* says that he is 70% certain of oil discovery.* The percentage given is a measure of that engineer's degree of belief that oil will be discovered. Thus, different measures of belief may be assigned to the same proposition. But what do 80% and 70% really mean? The usual interpretation is as follows. Engineer *A* thinks it a fair bet to offer odds of 8 to 2 (i.e., bet \$8 against \$2 or any other dollar amounts with the same proportion) that oil will be discovered at the site. Similarly, *B* believes it a fair bet to offer odds of 7 to 3 (or bet \$7 against \$3) for the same occurrence. Then the subjective probabilities of *A* and *B* are defined to be the proportions $8/(8 + 2)$ and $7/(7 + 3)$, respectively. In general, therefore, if the

---

*By implication, *A* and *B* are also saying that they are 20% and 30% certain, respectively, that oil will not be discovered.

odds in favor of a proposition are *a* to *b*, the probability of the proposition is
$a/(a + b)$.

2.5   Axiomatic Development of Probability

We will formalize the definition of probability through a set of axioms by briefly
reviewing the basic concepts of set (or event) theory on which the formal definition
of probability is based. Such a definition of probability is general enough to
incorporate the various interpretations of probability that have been presented.

The collection of the possible outcomes of a chance experiment is important
in the definition of probability. To define this collection, consider experiments
involving the number of no-shows for a scheduled flight, the number of arrivals
at a service facility over a given length of time, or the life length of some
component. All of these are examples of unpredictable phenomena with a number
of possible outcomes. The number of no-shows may be any positive integer up
to the capacity of the airplane; the number of arrivals may be any positive integer
(theoretically) without limit; and the life length of a component may be any
positive real number. This prompts the following definition:

Definition 2.3   The set of all possible outcomes of a chance experiment is called
the *sample space*.

The set of all possible outcomes can be finite, countably infinite, or uncountably
infinite. For example, the number of no-shows constitutes a finite sample space
since the number does not exceed the finite seating capacity of the airplane. The
number of arrivals at a service facility constitutes a countably infinite sample
space because it is possible to place the outcomes in a one-to-one correspondence
with the positive integers, which are infinite in number, yet countable. The life
length of a component constitutes an uncountably infinite sample space because,
even though a life length may be measured, say, to the nearest minute, an actual
life length can be any positive real number, and thus any one of a continuum
of values. We now give the following definitions:

Definition 2.4   A sample space is said to be *discrete* if its outcomes can be put
in a one-to-one correspondence with a set of positive integers.

Definition 2.5   A sample space is said to be *continuous* if its outcomes consist
of an interval of real numbers.

Relative to the outcomes of a sample space, one may be particularly interested
in a subset of the outcomes. For example, an airline manager may wish to know
whether the number of no-shows is less than five, or a purchaser of an auto
battery may be interested in knowing whether the battery will survive 40 months
of normal operation. Thus, we have the following definition:

Definition 2.6   An *event* of the sample space is a group of outcomes of the
sample space whose members have some common characteristic.

By a common characteristic we mean that only a particular group of outcomes satisfy the characteristic, and the remaining outcomes of the sample space do not. An event is said to have occurred if the results of the chance experiment include any of the outcomes that define the event. In this context, the sample space is itself an event, and we may think of it as the *certain event* because an outcome of the sample space is certain to occur when the experiment is performed. For completeness, we also give the following definition:

Definition 2.7 The event that contains no outcomes of the sample space is the *null* or *empty event*.

We are now in a position to recall some definitions from the theory of events. Let E_1 and E_2 be any two events belonging to some sample space denoted by S.

Definition 2.8 The event that consists of all possible outcomes in E_1, in E_2, or in both is called the *union* of E_1 and E_2 and is indicated by $E_1 \cup E_2$.

Definition 2.9 The event that consists of all outcomes common to both E_1 and E_2 is called the *intersection* of E_1 and E_2 and is indicated by $E_1 \cap E_2$.

Definition 2.10 The events E_1 and E_2 are said to be *mutually exclusive* or *disjoint* if they have no outcomes in common; in other words, $E_1 \cap E_2 = \emptyset \equiv$ empty event.

Definition 2.11 If every outcome of E_2 is also an outcome of E_1, event E_2 is said to be *contained in* E_1, which is indicated by $E_2 \subset E_1$.

Definition 2.12 The *complement* of an event E with respect to the sample space S is the event containing the outcomes that are in S but not in E, and is indicated by $\overline{E}$.

These definitions may be illustrated pictorially by using Venn diagrams, as in Figure 2.1.

As a further example, let the experiment be the roll of a die; then the sample space $S = (1, 2, 3, 4, 5, 6)$. Define the events $E_1 = (2, 4, 6)$, $E_2 = (1, 3)$, and $E_3 = (2, 4)$. It is easy to see that $E_1 \cup E_2 = (1, 2, 3, 4, 6)$, $E_1 \cap E_3 = (2, 4)$, $E_1 \cap E_2 = \emptyset$, E_3 is entirely contained in E_1, and $\overline{E}_2 = (2, 4, 5, 6)$.

The probability of any outcome in the sample space is a real number that measures the likelihood of the outcome's occurrence when the experiment is performed. The probability of an event therefore is also a real number that measures the collective likelihood of occurrence for the outcomes of the event when the experiment is performed. We now give an axiomatic definition of probability.

FIGURE 2.1 Venn diagrams illustrating (a) union of two events; (b) intersection of two events; (c) mutually exclusive events; (d) containment of an event by another; and (e) an event and its complement

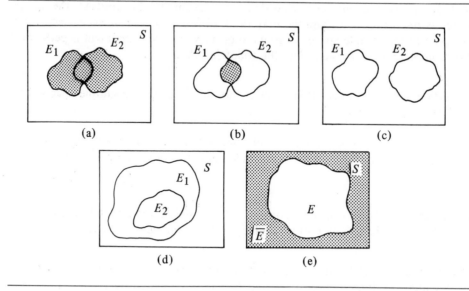

(a) (b) (c)

(d) (e)

Definition 2.13 Let S be any sample space and let E be any event of S. $P(E)$ will be called a *probability function* on the sample space S if the following axioms are satisfied:

1. $P(E) \geq 0$

2. $P(S) = 1$

3. If, for events $E_1, E_2, E_3, \ldots,$

   $E_i \cap E_j = \emptyset$ for all $i \neq j$, then

   $P(E_1 \cup E_2 \cup \cdots) = P(E_1) + P(E_2) + \cdots.$

The reason for these three axioms becomes apparent when one recalls, for instance, the relative frequency interpretation of probability. That is, the probability of an event reflects the proportion of times outcomes of that event will occur in repeated trials of an experiment. The axioms are also apparent for the subjective interpretation because a degree of belief is converted into a proportion. Thus, probabilities exhibit the essential characteristics of proportions in that any probability is a number between 0 and 1, and since an outcome is bound to occur when an experiment is performed, the probability of S is one. Moreover, if there are no common outcomes between two events E_1 and E_2, the probability of E_1 or E_2 occurring should be the same as the proportion of times E_1 occurs plus the proportion of times E_2 occurs.

Now let us prove a few consequences of the three axioms.

Theorem 2.1 $P(\emptyset) = 0$.

Proof:

$$S \cup \emptyset = S \quad \text{and} \quad S \cap \emptyset = \emptyset.$$

By Axiom 3,

$$P(S \cup \emptyset) = P(S) + P(\emptyset);$$

but by Axiom 2, $P(S) = 1$, and thus, $P(\emptyset) = 0$.

Theorem 2.2 For any event $E \subset S$, $0 \leq P(E) \leq 1$.

Proof: By Axiom 1, $P(E) \geq 0$; hence we only need to show that $P(E) \leq 1$.

$$E \cup \overline{E} = S \quad \text{and} \quad E \cap \overline{E} = \emptyset.$$

By Axioms 2 and 3,

$$P(E \cup \overline{E}) = P(E) + P(\overline{E}) = P(S) = 1;$$

since $P(\overline{E}) \geq 0$, $P(E) \leq 1$.

Axiom 3 identifies the probability of the union of two disjoint events. Alternatively, what if two events are not mutually exclusive? That is, what is the probability of the union of two events that are not necessarily disjoint? The following general result, which is often called the addition rule of probability, is now given.

Theorem 2.3 Let S be a sample space containing any two events A and B; then

$$P(A \cup B) = P(A) + P(B) - P(A \cap B).$$

Although no purpose is served by a formal proof, the theorem is intuitively quite reasonable. That is, $P(A)$ and $P(B)$ reflect the proportion of times the outcomes of A and B, respectively, will occur. However, with $P(A)$ and $P(B)$ the proportion of times the common outcomes will occur has been counted twice; thus, it is necessary to subtract that portion out once from the sum of $P(A)$ and $P(B)$. Of course the theorem reduces to Axiom 3 for disjoint events. The following example illustrates the addition rule of probability.

Example 2.1 A system containing two components A and B is wired in such a way that it will work if either component works. If it is known from previous experimentation that the probability of A working is $P(A) = 0.9$, that of B working is $P(B) = 0.8$, and the probability that both work is $P(A \cap B) = 0.72$, determine the probability that the system will work.

The probability that the system works is the same as the probability of the union between A and B; thus,

$$P(A \cup B) = P(A) + P(B) - P(A \cap B)$$
$$= 0.9 + 0.8 - 0.72 = 0.98.$$

2.6   Joint, Marginal, and Conditional Probabilities

We examine now the concept of joint, marginal, and conditional probabilities and develop the multiplicative law of probability. Consider an experiment in which we pick at random an adult person from a town consisting of n adults and note the characteristics of the person chosen with regard to smoking habits and sex. Let the sample space be the adult population of the town, which is partitioned into the disjoint events smoker A_1 and nonsmoker A_2, male B_1 and female B_2. The outcomes of S may be represented as in Table 2.3.

As an example, note that n_{11} of the n adults are smoking males, thus possessing both attributes A_1 and B_1. Suppose we want to determine the probability of the simultaneous occurrence of events A_1 and B_2. By using the relative frequency interpretation, we can argue that since exactly n_{12} of the n adults possess both attributes A_1 and B_2, the probability is n_{12}/n. Such a probability is called a *joint probability*, since we insist on the probability of the occurrence of outcomes that are common to both events A_1 and B_2. In general, therefore, the joint probability of events A_i and B_j is given by

$$P(A_i \cap B_j) = n_{ij}/n.$$

Suppose we are interested in the probability of event A_i without regard to any other events B_j of the sample space S. Specifically, say we need the probability of event A_2. Again by appealing to the relative frequency interpretation, the total number of nonsmokers (A_2) is $n_{21} + n_{22}$; thus

$$P(A_2) = (n_{21} + n_{22})/n.$$

This type of probability is referred to as *marginal* in the sense that one or more other criteria of the sample space are ignored. It follows, therefore, that

$$P(A_i) = \sum_{j=1}^{2} n_{ij}/n,$$

TABLE 2.3   Classification of n adults by smoking habits and sex

	B_1	B_2
A_1	n_{11}	n_{12}
A_2	n_{21}	n_{22}

but since

$$P(A_i \cap B_j) = n_{ij}/n,$$

$$P(A_i) = \sum_{j=1}^{2} P(A_i \cap B_j).$$

In other words, the marginal probability of an event A_i is equal to the sum of the joint probabilities of A_i and B_j, where the summation is taken over the events B_j. Similarly, the marginal probability of B_j is given by

$$P(B_j) = \sum_{i=1}^{2} P(A_i \cap B_j).$$

The extension to include more than two disjoint events should be obvious.

Finally, suppose we are interested in determining the probability of event A_i, given that event B_j has already occurred. For example, returning to Table 2.3, suppose an adult female (B_2) is chosen at random. Now what is the probability that the female chosen is a smoker (A_1)? Once more the argument rests on the relative frequency interpretation. However, since the event "female" has already occurred, that event replaces S as the sample space of interest. The probability of a smoker (A_1) is therefore the ratio of the number of females who smoke (n_{12}) to the total number of females ($n_{12} + n_{22}$). Hence

$$P(A_1|B_2) = n_{12}/(n_{12} + n_{22}),$$

where the vertical bar is read "given" and separates the event A_1, whose probability is conditioned on the prior occurrence of event B_2. This is called the *conditional probability* of A_1 given the occurrence of B_2. In general, therefore,

$$P(A_i|B_j) = n_{ij}/\sum_{i=1}^{2} n_{ij}, \tag{2.1}$$

and by symmetry,

$$P(B_j|A_i) = n_{ij}/\sum_{j=1}^{2} n_{ij}. \tag{2.2}$$

Suppose we divide both numerator and denominator on the right side of (2.1) by n. Thus

$$P(A_i|B_j) = \frac{n_{ij}/n}{\sum_{i=1}^{2} n_{ij}/n},$$

but

$$P(A_i \cap B_j) = n_{ij}/n$$

and

$$P(B_j) = \sum_{i=1}^{2} n_{ij}/n;$$

hence

$$P(A_i|B_j) = \frac{P(A_i \cap B_j)}{P(B_j)}, \quad P(B_j) > 0, \tag{2.3}$$

and equivalently,

$$P(B_j|A_i) = \frac{P(A_i \cap B_j)}{P(A_i)}, \quad P(A_i) > 0. \tag{2.4}$$

In defining joint, marginal, and conditional probabilities, we have used a specific example in which the sample space consisted of only a finite number of outcomes. However, the notion of joint, marginal, and conditional probabilities as defined here is quite general and can be extended to include any discrete or continuous sample space. Thus the following general definition is now given.

Definition 2.14 Let A and B be any two events belonging to a sample space S such that $P(B) > 0$. The conditional probability of A given that event B has occurred is the ratio of the joint probability of A and B to the marginal probability of B; thus

$$P(A|B) = \frac{P(A \cap B)}{P(B)}, \quad P(B) > 0. \tag{2.5}$$

The relation (2.5) can be written in a product form, which gives rise to the multiplication rule of probabilities, given by

$$P(A \cap B) = P(B)P(A|B). \tag{2.6}$$

By symmetry it is seen that the conditional probability of B given the occurrence of A is

$$P(B|A) = \frac{P(A \cap B)}{P(A)}, \quad P(A) > 0.$$

Thus,

$$P(A \cap B) = P(A)P(B|A)$$

is another version of the multiplication rule, implying that

$$P(A)P(B|A) = P(B)P(A|B). \tag{2.7}$$

Definition 2.14 can be extended to include any number of events belonging to a sample space. For example, it can be shown that for three events A, B, and C

$$P(A|B \cap C) = \frac{P(A \cap B \cap C)}{P(B \cap C)}, \quad P(B \cap C) > 0 \tag{2.8}$$

and

$$P(A \cap B|C) = \frac{P(A \cap B \cap C)}{P(C)}, \quad P(C) > 0. \tag{2.9}$$

The following three examples are provided for illustration.

Example 2.2   The residents of a large metropolitan area were surveyed to determine readership of *Time* and *Newsweek*. Based on the survey, it was determined that 20 percent of the residents read *Time*, 16 percent read *Newsweek*, and 1 percent read both. If a *Time* reader was selected at random, what is the probability that he or she is also a *Newsweek* reader?

Let A and B be the events representing *Time* and *Newsweek* readers, respectively; since $P(A) = 0.2$, $P(B) = 0.16$, and $P(A \cap B) = 0.01$,

$$P(B|A) = 0.01/0.2 = 0.05.$$

Moreover, we may also determine the probability of a *Time* reader if it were known that the one selected was a *Newsweek* reader; that is,

$$P(A|B) = 0.01/0.16 = 0.0625,$$

and the relation $P(A)P(B|A) = P(B)P(A|B)$, or $(0.2)(0.05) = (0.16)(0.0625)$, is ascertained.

Example 2.3   Many financial institutions use computerized credit-rating models to determine a rating score for loan applications. This score is used as an aid in deciding whether to grant a loan. Suppose that three percent of all loans default before maturity, and that the credit-rating models are 80 percent accurate in correctly predicting good loans. If 85 percent of all loan applications are given favorable scores by the computerized models and are granted a loan, determine the probability that an applicant receiving a loan as a result of a favorable rating will not default on the loan.

Let A be the event a loan defaults before maturity, and let B be the event the rating score is favorable. We are given that $P(A) = 0.03$, $P(B) = 0.85$, and $P(B|\overline{A}) = 0.8$, where $\overline{A}$ is the complement of A, or the event a loan does not default before maturity. What we seek is the conditional probability that the loan does not default before maturity, given a favorable rating score, or $P(\overline{A}|B)$. Using relation (2.7), we may write

$$P(B)P(\overline{A}|B) = P(\overline{A})P(B|\overline{A}),$$

or

$$P(\overline{A}|B) = \frac{P(\overline{A})P(B|\overline{A})}{P(B)},$$

and since $P(\overline{A}) = 0.97$, the desired probability works out to be $P(\overline{A}|B) = 0.9129$.

Example 2.4   A plant receives voltage regulators from two different suppliers B_1 and B_2, with 75 percent of the regulators coming from B_1 and the remainder from B_2. It is known that the percentage of defective regulators received from B_1 is 8 percent, and the percentage defective from B_2 is 10 percent. Determine the probability that a voltage regulator received by the plant will perform according to specifications (will be nondefective).

Let A be the event of a nondefective voltage regulator. Clearly, no one voltage regulator can be supplied by both B_1 and B_2; therefore, B_1 and B_2 are disjoint. As a result,

$$P(A) = P(A \cap B_1) + P(A \cap B_2),$$

but

$$P(A \cap B_1) = P(B_1)P(A|B_1)$$

and

$$P(A \cap B_2) = P(B_2)P(A|B_2),$$

where $P(B_1) = 0.75$, $P(B_2) = 0.25$, $P(A|B_1) = 0.92$, and $P(A|B_2) = 0.9$ are given; thus

$$P(A) = P(B_1)P(A|B_1) + P(B_2)P(A|B_2)$$

$$= (0.75)(0.92) + (0.25)(0.90) = 0.915.$$

Notice that in Example 2.4 there were only two suppliers, B_1 and B_2. In general, if there are n disjoint alternatives B_1, B_2, ..., B_n, the total probability of a final outcome, say event A, is given by

$$P(A) = \sum_{i=1}^{n} P(B_i)P(A|B_i). \tag{2.10}$$

2.7   Statistically Independent Events

In the consideration of the conditional probability of some event A, given the occurrence of another event B, the implication has been that A and B were somehow dependent on each other. In other words, information concerning the occurrence of B will subsequently affect the probability of A. Suppose, however, that the occurrence of B has no bearing on the probability of A in the sense that the conditional probability $P(A|B)$ is the same as the marginal probability $P(A)$, even though event B has occurred. Such a situation gives rise to an important concept known as *statistical independence*.

Definition 2.15   Let A and B be any two events belonging to a sample space S. The event A is said to be *statistically independent* of event B if $P(A|B) = P(A)$.

Some consequences of Definition 2.15 are now apparent. Since

$$P(A|B) = \frac{P(A \cap B)}{P(B)},$$

if A is independent of B,

$$P(A|B) = P(A) = \frac{P(A \cap B)}{P(B)}$$

or

$$P(A \cap B) = P(A)P(B).$$

Moreover, since

$$P(A \cap B) = P(A)P(B|A),$$

then

$$P(A)P(B) = P(A)P(B|A)$$

or

$$P(B) = P(B|A).$$

Therefore, we may conclude that if an event A is statistically independent of event B, then event B is independent of A and the following three relations hold:

1. $P(A|B) = P(A)$,

2. $P(B|A) = P(B)$, and

3. $P(A \cap B) = P(A)P(B)$.

We extend the concept of statistical independence with the following definition.

Definition 2.16 The events A_1, A_2, ..., A_k of a sample space S are statistically independent events if and only if the joint probability of any 2, 3, ..., or k of them equals the product of their respective marginal probabilities.

Thus the three events A, B, and C are statistically independent if and only if

1. $P(A \cap B) = P(A)P(B)$,

2. $P(A \cap C) = P(A)P(C)$,

3. $P(B \cap C) = P(B)P(C)$, and

4. $P(A \cap B \cap C) = P(A)P(B)P(C)$.

Example 2.5 A system containing five components is arranged in the manner shown in Figure 2.2, where the probabilities given indicate the chance that the component will work. If we assume that whether a component works or not is independent of whether any other component is working or not, what is the probability that the system will work?

Because of the assumption of independence, the system can work if components A, and B and/or C, and D and/or E work. Thus the probability that the system will work, say $P(F)$, may be expressed as

$$P(F) = P(A)P(B \cup C)P(D \cup E);$$

but notice that $P(B \cup C) = 1 - P(\overline{B})P(\overline{C})$ and $P(D \cup E) = 1 - P(\overline{D})P(\overline{E})$,

FIGURE 2.2   Configuration of a system with five components

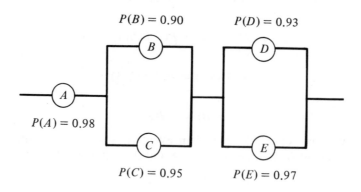

since, for example, $P(\overline{B})P(\overline{C})$ is the probability that neither component B nor component C is working. Therefore,

$$P(F) = (0.98)(0.995)(0.9979) = 0.973.$$

2.8   The Theorem of Bayes

Let us recall Example 2.4. Suppose we assume that when the voltage regulators are received, they are stored in such a way that they are indistinguishable with regard to supplier. Suppose further that we want to determine the probability that a particular voltage regulator came from supplier B_2 when it is known that it performs according to specifications. We seek the conditional probability of B_2, given the occurrence of event A. Hence

$$P(B_2|A) = \frac{P(B_2 \cap A)}{P(A)},$$

but

$$P(B_2 \cap A) = P(B_2)P(A|B_2)$$

and

$$P(B_2|A) = \frac{P(B_2)P(A|B_2)}{P(A)};$$

thus,

$$P(B_2|A) = \frac{(0.25)(0.9)}{0.915} = 0.2459.$$

The method used to solve this problem can be generalized to yield what is known as Bayes' theorem.

Theorem 2.4 If B_1, B_2, ..., B_n are n mutually exclusive events of which one must occur, that is, $\Sigma_{i=1}^{n} P(B_i) = 1$, then

$$P(B_j|A) = \frac{P(B_j)P(A|B_j)}{\displaystyle\sum_{i=1}^{n} P(B_i)P(A|B_i)}, \quad j = 1, 2, ..., n. \tag{2.11}$$

The expression given by (2.11) was developed by Reverend Thomas Bayes (1702–1761) and has been known as Bayes' theorem. On the surface, the expression is merely an application of conditional probabilities. However, it has been the key in the development of Bayesian statistical inference in which the subjective interpretation of probability is utilized. As we indicated in Chapter 1, we will not deal with Bayesian inference to a great extent in this book. We will consider some Bayesian questions from time to time, however, so that the reader may have a better perspective on statistical inference. Examples of Bayesian analysis follow.

Suppose a researcher is conducting an experiment in which he is aware that the result of interest will be affected by whichever one of n existing alternatives B_1, B_2, ..., B_n prevails. Although he is not certain as to which one of these alternatives will ultimately prevail, nevertheless he has some information on which he is willing to make a subjective judgment concerning the probabilities of the n alternatives. Thus he assigns probabilities $P(B_1)$, $P(B_2)$, ..., $P(B_n)$ to the n alternatives before obtaining the experimental evidence. Since these probabilities primarily reflect the researcher's judgment or degree of belief concerning the occurrences of B_1, B_2, ..., B_n, before an actual occurrence, they are known as *prior probabilities*. Now the researcher is in a position to obtain experimental evidence by collecting a set of data, denoted by A, observed under a specific alternative B_j. Hence, the conditional probabilities $P(A|B_j)$ may be computed. This will allow the determination of the probability of an alternative B_j given the experimental evidence A using Bayes' theorem. The conditional probabilities $P(B_j|A)$, $j = 1, 2, ..., n$ are known as *posterior probabilities* in the sense that they are determined after the experimental evidence has been obtained. Therefore, the probabilities $P(B_j|A)$ reflect the researcher's revised belief concerning the alternatives B_1, B_2, ..., B_n after the collection of the experimental data.

Example 2.6 In recent years much has been written about the possible link between cigarette smoking and lung cancer. Suppose that in a large medical center, of all the smokers who were suspected of having lung cancer, 90 percent of them did, while only 5 percent of the nonsmokers who were also suspected of having lung cancer actually did. If the proportion of smokers is 0.45, what is the probability that a lung cancer patient who is selected by chance is a smoker?

Let B_1 and B_2 be the events that a patient is a smoker or a nonsmoker, respectively, and let A be the event that a patient has lung cancer. B_1 and B_2 are the alternatives that may prevail. Their prior probabilities are assumed to be 0.45 and 0.55, respectively. Whether a patient has lung cancer or not may be affected by whichever of the two alternatives prevails and represents the experimental evidence. We are given that $P(A|B_1) = 0.9$ and $P(A|B_2) = 0.05$. What we wish to determine is the posterior probability of selecting a smoker, given that the patient has cancer, or $P(B_1|A)$.

By Bayes' theorem we have

$$P(B_1|A) = \frac{P(B_1)P(A|B_1)}{P(B_1)P(A|B_1) + P(B_2)P(A|B_2)}$$

$$= \frac{(0.45)(0.9)}{(0.45)(0.9) + (0.55)(0.05)}$$

$$= 0.9364.$$

The probability that a randomly selected lung cancer patient is a smoker is 0.9364.

Example 2.7 A corporation is contemplating marketing a new product. The corporation's executive officer wants the product to be superior to its closest competitor. Based on a preliminary evaluation by key personnel, it is decided to assign a 50 percent chance that the product is superior to its competitor, a 30 percent chance that it is about the same, and a 20 percent chance that it is inferior. A marketing survey on this product concludes that it is superior to its competitor. Based on the historical performance of such surveys, it is determined that if the product is really superior, the probability that the survey will reach the same conclusion is 0.7. If the product is about the same, the probability that the survey will conclude a superior product is 0.4. And if the product is inferior, the probability of the survey revealing a superior product is 0.2. Given the result of the marketing survey, what is the revised probability of a superior product?

This is an example of how an organization can update and revise initial probabilities as new information is made available. Let B_1, B_2, and B_3 be the events that the product is superior, about the same, or inferior to its competitor, respectively. The corresponding prior probabilities are 0.5, 0.3, and 0.2. Let A be the event that the marketing survey will reveal a superior product. The conditional probabilities involving the experimental evidence are $P(A|B_1) = 0.7$, $P(A|B_2) = 0.4$, and $P(A|B_3) = 0.2$. Then the desired posterior probability $P(B_1|A)$ is found to be

$$P(B_1|A) = \frac{P(B_1)P(A|B_1)}{P(B_1)P(A|B_1) + P(B_2)P(A|B_2) + P(B_3)P(A|B_3)}$$

$$= 0.6863.$$

2.9 Permutations and Combinations

In the process of computing probabilities of various events, it is necessary to enumerate the number of possible outcomes of an experiment, or to count the number of outcomes that are favorable to a given event. The enumeration process can be simplified by using two methods of enumeration called permutations and combinations.

A *permutation* is an arrangement of the objects of a set in a particular order. For example, consider the number of ways we can arrange the letters *a*, *b*, and *c*. For the first position we can choose any one of the three letters; we can select either of the two remaining letters for the second position; and for the third position we must select the unused letter. Thus there are a total of $3 \times 2 \times 1 = 6$ ways we can arrange the three letters. The six arrangements or permutations are

$$abc, \ acb, \ bac, \ bca, \ cab, \ cba.$$

By the same reasoning, the total number of ways we can arrange the four letters *a*, *b*, *c*, and *d* is $4 \times 3 \times 2 \times 1 = 24$. In general, therefore, the number of permutations of *n* different objects is

$$n(n - 1)(n - 2) \cdots (2)(1). \tag{2.12}$$

The product of a positive integer by all preceding positive integers is denoted by $n!$ and read "*n* factorial." For example, $2! = 2 \times 1 = 2$, $3! = 3 \times 2 \times 1 = 6$, $4! = 4 \times 3 \times 2 \times 1 = 24$, and so on. From (2.12) note that

$$n(n - 1)! = n!$$

or

$$(n - 1)! = n!/n.$$

Thus when $n = 1$, $0!$ is taken to be 1.

Let us now examine the number of permutations of *n* objects if only $r \leqslant n$ of these are used in any given arrangement. We use the same argument as before. For the first position we can select any one of the *n* objects, for the second position we can select one of the remaining $n - 1$ objects, and so on until we come to the *r*th position. At this point, we have already used $r - 1$ of the objects, and $n - (r - 1)$ remain, from which the selection is made. Therefore, the number of permutations of *n* objects taken *r* at a time is

$$P(n, r)^* = n(n - 1)(n - 2) \cdots (n - r + 1)$$

$$= \frac{n(n - 1)(n - 2) \cdots (n - r + 1)(n - r)!}{(n - r)!}$$

$$= \frac{n!}{(n - r)!}. \tag{2.13}$$

Note that if $r = n$, (2.13) yields the earlier result, $P(n, n) = n!$, or the number of permutations of *n* things taken *n* at a time is $n!$.

Example 2.8 Many states have auto license plates identified by three letters and three numbers. What is the total number of license plates possible, if no letter

---

*This is one of several ways to denote the number of permutations of *n* things taken *r* at a time. Other symbols that have been used are $_nP_r$, P_r^n, $P_{n,r}$, and $(n)_r$.

can be used more than once on the same plate? What is the total number without this restriction?

With the restriction, the number of permutations of the 26 letters of the alphabet taken three at a time is

$$P(26, 3) = \frac{26!}{23!} = \frac{26 \times 25 \times 24 \times 23!}{23!} = 15,600.$$

Since each of the 15,600 three-letter arrangements can be assigned 1,000 different three-digit numbers (000 to 999), the total number of distinct license plates is 15,600,000. Without the restriction, which is the usual practice, the six positions on a license plate can be filled as follows: Each of the first three positions can be filled in one of 26 ways, while each of the last three positions can be filled in one of ten ways, since there are 26 letters and ten numbers, respectively. Thus the total number of distinct license plates for this case is $26 \times 26 \times 26 \times 10 \times 10 \times 10 = 17,576,000$.

A *combination* of the objects of a set is a selection of those objects without regard to the order of appearance. By the number of combinations of r objects taken from a set of n objects we mean the total number of distinct selections, each selection containing r objects. The difference between permutations and combinations is that with the former we are interested in counting all possible selections and all arrangements of each selection, whereas with the latter we are only interested in counting the number of distinct selections. Thus, *abc* and *acd* are different three-letter combinations, while *acd* and *adc* are different permutations of the same combination. We can obtain the number of combinations of n things taken r at a time (denoted by $\binom{n}{r}$ and read "n combination r") by dividing the corresponding number of permutations by $r!$, since for each combination there are $r!$ permutations. Hence

$$\binom{n}{r}^* = P(n, r)/r!$$

$$= \frac{n!}{(n-r)!\, r!}. \tag{2.14}$$

From (2.14), note that

$$\binom{n}{n} = \frac{n!}{(n-n)!\, n!} = 1;$$

$$\binom{n}{0} = \frac{n!}{(n-0)!\, 0!} = 1;$$

$$\binom{n}{n-1} = \frac{n!}{[n-(n-1)]!(n-1)!} = n;$$

---

*Other commonly used symbols to denote the number of combinations of n things taken r at a time are $C(n,r)$, $_nC_r$, C_r^n, and $C_{n,r}$.

and

$$\binom{n}{n-r} = \frac{n!}{[n-(n-r)]!(n-r)!} = \binom{n}{r}.$$

For specific examples,

$$\binom{5}{2} = \frac{5!}{(5-2)!\,2!} = \frac{5 \times 4 \times 3!}{3!\,2!} = 10,$$

and

$$\binom{10}{8} = \binom{10}{2} = \frac{10!}{(10-2)!\,2!} = \frac{10 \times 9 \times 8!}{8!\,2!} = 45.$$

Example 2.9 Suppose five federal judgeships are to be filled in a certain state. The senior senator of the state submits to the president a list containing the names of ten men and four women. If the president decides that the five judgeships should go to three men and two women, in how many ways can this be done by using candidates on the list?

The number of distinct ways three men can be selected from ten is

$$\binom{10}{3} = \frac{10 \times 9 \times 8 \times 7!}{7!\,3!} = 120.$$

Similarly, the number of ways two women can be selected from four is

$$\binom{4}{2} = \frac{4 \times 3 \times 2!}{2!\,2!} = 6.$$

Since the number of ways we can select three men from ten is 120, and the number of ways we can select two women from four is 6, then the number of ways that both of these events can occur is

$$\binom{10}{3}\binom{4}{2} = 720.$$

References

1. P. G. Hoel, *Introduction to mathematical statistics*, 4th ed., Wiley, New York, 1971.
2. A. M. Mood and F. A. Graybill, *Introduction to the theory of statistics*, 2nd ed., McGraw-Hill, New York, 1963.

Exercises

2.1. The employees of New Horizons, Inc., are divided into three distinct divisions — administration, plant operation, and sales. The following table indicates the number of employees in each division classified by sex:

	Female (F)	Male (M)	Totals
Administration (A)	20	30	50
Plant Operation (O)	60	140	200
Sales (S)	100	50	150
Totals	180	220	400

a. Using a Venn diagram, illustrate the events O and F for all employees of New Horizons, Inc. Are they mutually exclusive?

b. If an employee is chosen at random,

   1. What is the probability that the person is female?
   2. What is the probability that the person works in sales?
   3. What is the probability that the person is a male working in the administration division?
   4. What is the probability that the person works in plant operation, if the person is a female?
   5. What is the probability that the person is female, if the person chosen works in the plant operation division?

c. Are the events S and M statistically independent?

d. Are the events A and F statistically independent?

e. Determine the following probabilities:

   1. $P(A \cup M)$
   2. $P(A \cup \overline{M})$
   3. $P(O \cap F)$
   4. $P(M|A)$

2.2. Use Definition 2.14 to show that for any two events A and B, $P(A|B) + P(\overline{A}|B) = 1$, so long as $P(B) \neq 0$.

2.3. Let A and B be any two nonempty events of S. If A and B are mutually exclusive, show that they cannot be independent. Deduce when two independent events are also mutually exclusive.

2.4. Let A and B be any two events of S. Use a Venn diagram to show that $P(A \cap \overline{B}) = P(A) - P(A \cap B)$.

2.5. A family has three children. Determine all permutations relative to the sexes of the children. Under suitable assumptions, what is the probability that exactly two of the children will be of the same sex? What is the probability of one boy and two girls? What is the probability that all three children are of the same sex?

2.6. Two cards are drawn without replacement from an ordinary deck of playing cards. What is the probability that both are aces?

2.7. A balanced coin is tossed ten times and all ten tosses yield heads. What is the probability of such an occurrence? If the coin is indeed balanced, what is the probability that the eleventh toss will be tails?

2.8. A local automobile retailer receives a shipment of 20 new automobiles from a manufacturer. Among the 20 automobiles, two contain major defects. The retailer decides to randomly select two of the 20 automobiles and to accept the shipment if neither automobile tested contains major defects. What is the probability that the shipment will be accepted?

2.9. You toss a coin with probability 2/3 for heads. If a head turns up, you pick a ball at random from an urn containing two red and three green balls. If a tail turns up, you pick a ball from another urn containing two red and two green balls. What is the probability of selecting a red ball?

2.10. Among 20 fuel cells manufactured for the space shuttle, three have serious defects. If four cells are selected at random,

a. What is the probability that all cells selected are free of serious defects?
b. What is the probability that one of the four will have serious defects?

2.11. The probability that a certain electrical component will work is 0.9. A machine contains two such components. The machine will operate as long as at least one of these components works.

a. Regarding whether these two components work or not, what are the possible outcomes and their respective probabilities? (You may assume independence of operation between these components.)
b. What is the probability that the machine will operate?

2.12. A system consists of three main components A, B, and C. These may be arranged in any one of the four configurations in Figure 2.3. If the three components operate independently, and if the probability of any one operating is 0.95, determine the probability of system operation for each of the four configurations.

2.13. A way to increase the probability of operation of a system — known as the reliability of the system — is to introduce backup components using a parallel configuration as illustrated in the second part of Figure 2.3. Suppose NASA desires a probability

FIGURE 2.3 Four configurations of three components

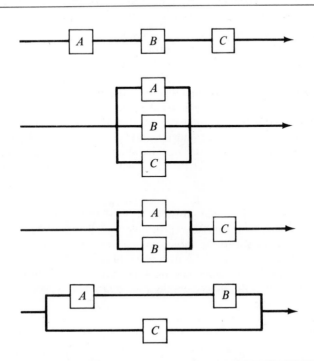

of successful earth orbit for the space shuttle of no less than 0.99999. How many rocket motors must be configured in parallel to achieve this reliability of operation if it is known that the probability of any one motor operating properly is 0.95? You may assume independence of operation of the rocket motors.

2.14. Suppose the probability that the Baltimore Colts will win the American Conference title is 0.25, and the probability that the San Diego Chargers will win it is 0.20. Moreover, the probability that the American Conference champion will win the Super Bowl is 0.45, 0.55, or 0.35, depending on whether the Colts, the Chargers, or some other team wins the American Conference title.

    a. What is the probability that an American Conference team will win the Super Bowl?

    b. Given that an American Conference team wins the Super Bowl, what is the probability that the Baltimore Colts win the American Conference title?

2.15. Five percent of the units produced by a manufacturing process are defective when the process is in control, i.e., running properly. When the process is out of control, 30 percent of the units produced are defective. The marginal probability that the process is in control is 0.92. If a unit chosen at random is found to be defective, what is the probability that the process is in control?

2.16. An assembly plant receives microcircuits from three different suppliers B_1, B_2, and B_3. Fifty percent are bought from B_1 and 25 percent from each of B_2 and B_3. The manufacturing percent defective for suppliers B_1, B_2, and B_3 are 5, 10, and 12 percent, respectively. If the circuits are stored in the plant without regard to supplier,

    a. Determine the probability that an assembled unit will contain a defective circuit.

    b. Determine the probability that the circuit in an assembled unit came from supplier B_2, if it is known that the circuit is good.

2.17. An investor is contemplating buying a substantial number of shares of common stock in some company. The performance of the stock over the next six months is of particular interest to the investor. Based on historical information, the stock's performance is related to the movement of the gross national product. If the GNP increases during the next six months, the probability that the stock will also increase in value is 0.8. If the GNP remains about the same, the probability that the stock will increase is 0.2. If the GNP decreases, the probability that the stock will increase is 0.1. If during the next six months the probabilities of 0.4, 0.3, and 0.3 are assigned to the events the GNP increases, remains about the same, or decreases, respectively, determine the probability that the stock will increase in value during the next six months.

2.18. Based on many geological surveys, an energy company has classified geological formations beneath potential oil wells as types 1, 2, and 3. For a particular site in which the company is considering drilling for oil, the probabilities of 0.35, 0.40, and 0.25 are assigned to the three types of formations, respectively. It is known from experience that oil is discovered in 40 percent of type 1 formations, in 20 percent of type 2 formations, and in 30 percent of type 3 formations. If oil is not discovered at this site, determine the probability that a type 2 formation exists.

CHAPTER THREE

Random Variables and Probability Distributions

3.1 The Concept of a Random Variable

In Chapter 2 we examined the basic concepts of probability with regard to events belonging to a sample space. Experiments may be devised in which the outcomes of the sample space are either quantitative or qualitative. As examples of qualitative outcomes, the toss of a fair coin will result in either "heads" or "tails," a product produced by a manufacturing process may be defective or nondefective, or an individual may prefer Brand X to Brand Y. It may be useful to quantify qualitative outcomes of a sample space and to study their random behavior using numerical measures. The concept of a random variable provides a means of relating any result of an experiment to a quantitative measure.

Definition 3.1 Let S be a sample space on which a probability function is defined. Let X be a real-valued function defined on S such that X transforms outcomes of S into points on the real line. Then X is said to be a *random variable*.

X is "random" because a probability regarding the outcomes of the sample space is involved, and X is a function defined on the sample space in such a way that it transforms the possible outcomes of the sample space to numerical quantities.

To illustrate the notion of a random variable, consider the single toss of a coin. This constitutes a sample space with two possible outcomes, "heads" and "tails." Now let $X(\text{tails}) = 0$ and $X(\text{heads}) = 1$; we have thus transformed the two possible outcomes of the sample space into points on the real line. By $P(X = 0)$ we mean the probability that the random variable X will assume the value zero or, equivalently, the probability that the toss will result in "tails." For further illustration, consider the roll of a pair of balanced and distinguishable dice and the 36 possible outcomes, as given in Table 2.1. Define as a random variable X the sum of the two faces. Table 3.1 relates the 36 outcomes to the

TABLE 3.1 Correspondence between outcomes of a pair of dice and a random variable representing the sum of the two faces

Outcome	Value of random variable	Number of occurrences	Probability
(1,1)	2	1	1/36
(1,2), (2,1)	3	2	2/36
(1,3), (2,2), (3,1)	4	3	3/36
(1,4), (2,3), (3,2), (4,1)	5	4	4/36
(1,5), (2,4), (3,3), (4,2), (5,1)	6	5	5/36
(1,6), (2,5), (3,4), (4,3), (5,2), (6,1)	7	6	6/36
(2,6), (3,5), (4,4), (5,3), (6,2)	8	5	5/36
(3,6), (4,5), (5,4), (6,3)	9	4	4/36
(4,6), (5,5), (6,4)	10	3	3/36
(5,6), (6,5)	11	2	2/36
(6,6)	12	1	1/36

corresponding values of the random variable X and their probabilities. The probabilistic nature of the random variable X, the sum of the two faces, can be seen in a line graph that plots each value of X against its probability, as in Figure 3.1.

Each of the preceding examples dealt with a random variable whose number of possible values was finite. However, we may define random variables whose sets of values are countable or uncountable. Since a random variable is a quantitative characterization of the outcomes of a sample space, a random variable inherits the discrete or continuous nature of the sample space.

Definition 3.2   A random variable X is said to be *discrete* if the number of values it can assume is countable (either finite or infinite), and if the values can be arranged in a sequence corresponding to the positive integers.

Definition 3.3   A random variable X is said to be *continuous* if its values consist of one or more intervals of the real line.

3.2   Probability Distributions of Discrete Random Variables

We now turn to the concept of the probability distribution of a discrete random variable. In Figure 3.1 the probabilities are plotted against the corresponding values of the random variable for the sum of the faces of a pair of dice. More generally, a discrete random variable X represents the outcomes of a sample space in such a way that by $P(X = x)$ we imply the probability that X will assume the value x. Thus, by considering all values of a random variable, it is possible to develop a mathematical function that assigns a probability to each *realization x* of the random variable X. Such a function is known as the *probability function** of the random variable X. The more general term *probability distribution*

---

*The complete name for such a function is the *probability mass function* of a discrete random variable.

FIGURE 3.1 Probabilities for the sums of two faces of a pair of dice

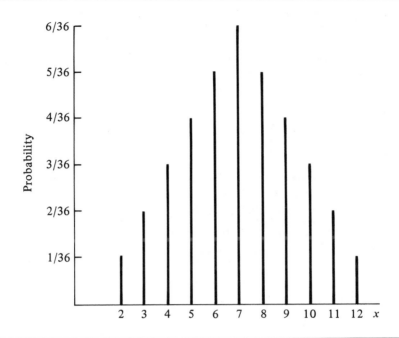

refers to the collection of values of a random variable and the distribution of probability among these values. However, reference to the probability distribution of X implies not only the existence of the probability function but also the existence of the *cumulative distribution function* of X.

Definition 3.4 Let X be a discrete random variable. The function $p(x) \equiv P(X = x)$ will be called a probability function of the random variable X if the following are satisfied:

1. $p(x) \geqslant 0$ for all values x of X;
2. $\Sigma_x \, p(x) = 1$.

Definition 3.5 The cumulative distribution function of the discrete random variable X is the probability that X is less than or equal to a specified value x and is given by

$$F(x) \equiv P(X \leqslant x) = \sum_{x_i \leqslant x} p(x_i).$$

In the discrete case, therefore, a random variable X is characterized by the probability function $p(x)$, which determines the *point probability* that $X = x$, and the cumulative distribution function $F(x)$, which represents the accumulated sum of point probabilities up to and including the value x of X. Notice that these definitions are consistent with the axioms of probability since the probability function is nonnegative for any value of the random variable, and the sum of the probabilities over the entire range of X is equal to one.

Example 3.1 Consider again the toss of a pair of balanced dice. If X is the random variable representing the sum of the two faces, the probability function of X is

$$p(x) = \begin{cases} \dfrac{6 - |7 - x|}{36} & x = 2, 3, ..., 12, \\ 0 & \text{elsewhere.} \end{cases} \tag{3.1}$$

Using (3.1), we can determine the probabilities for the various values of X as contained in Table 3.1 and graph these as in Figure 3.1. Moreover, we can evaluate the cumulative distribution function of X as follows:

$$F\ (1) \equiv P(X \leqslant\ 1) =\quad\ 0$$
$$F\ (2) \equiv P(X \leqslant\ 2) =\quad 1/36$$
$$F\ (3) \equiv P(X \leqslant\ 3) =\quad 3/36$$
$$F\ (4) \equiv P(X \leqslant\ 4) =\quad 6/36$$
$$F\ (5) \equiv P(X \leqslant\ 5) =\quad 10/36$$
$$F\ (6) \equiv P(X \leqslant\ 6) =\quad 15/36$$
$$F\ (7) \equiv P(X \leqslant\ 7) =\quad 21/36$$
$$F\ (8) \equiv P(X \leqslant\ 8) =\quad 26/36$$
$$F\ (9) \equiv P(X \leqslant\ 9) =\quad 30/36$$
$$F(10) \equiv P(X \leqslant 10) =\quad 33/36$$
$$F(11) \equiv P(X \leqslant 11) =\quad 35/36$$
$$F(12) \equiv P(X \leqslant 12) =\quad\ 1.$$

Notice that

$$P(X > 7) = 1 - P(X \leqslant 7) = 1 - F(7) = 15/36;$$
$$P(X = 7) = P(X \leqslant 7) - P(X \leqslant 6) = F(7) - F(6) = 6/36;$$
$$P(5 \leqslant X \leqslant 9) = P(X \leqslant 9) - P(X \leqslant 4) = F(9) - F(4) = 24/36.$$

In general, the cumulative distribution function $F(x)$ of a discrete random variable X is a nondecreasing function of the values x of X such that

1. $0 \leqslant F(x) \leqslant 1$ for any x;

2. $F(x_i) \geqslant F(x_j)$ if $x_i \geqslant x_j$;

3. $P(X > x) = 1 - F(x).$

FIGURE 3.2 Graphical representation of the cumulative distribution function of the sum of two faces when rolling a pair of dice

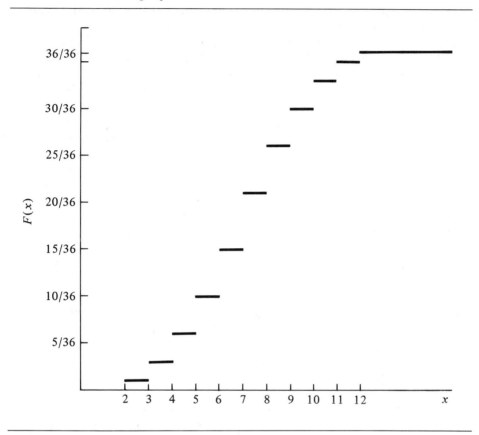

We may further state that for integer-valued random variables,

4. $P(X = x) = F(x) - F(x - 1)$;

5. $P(x_i \leq X \leq x_j) = F(x_j) - F(x_i - 1)$.

The graph of the cumulative distribution of Example 3.1 is given in Figure 3.2. As is apparent in this figure, the cumulative distribution function of a discrete random variable is a step function, which takes on the upper value at each jump.

3.3 Probability Distributions of Continuous Random Variables

In the last section we looked at probability distributions of discrete random variables. We now examine similar concepts for continuous random variables. In the discrete case positive probabilities are associated with point values of the random variable, but the sum of all probabilities equals one, even if the set of values is countably infinite. For continuous random variables this is not possible.

For this reason the probability that a continuous random variable X assumes a specific value x is taken to be zero.

The practicality of this result is illustrated by the following example. Suppose we are observing the length of time between successive arrivals at a service facility. If the measuring device can only measure time to within a tenth of a second, then an interarrival time of, say, 83.4 seconds can really be taken to mean that the true interarrival time is somewhere between 83.35 and 83.45 seconds. Therefore, in the continuous case it is more logical to seek probabilities of intervals rather than probabilities of individual points.

The probability distribution of a continuous random variable X is characterized by a function $f(x)$ known as the *probability density function*. The density function $f(x)$ is not the same as the probability function in the discrete case. Since the probability that X is equal to a specific value x is zero, the probability density function $f(x)$ does not represent the probability that $X = x$. Rather, it provides the means by which the probability of an interval $a \leq X \leq b$ can be determined.

To illustrate the notion of a probability density function, suppose we measured the interarrival times of 100 customers at a service facility and grouped the observations into ten one-minute intervals, as given in Table 3.2. Now we may plot the relative frequencies for each interval by using rectangles, as shown in Figure 3.3, to indicate that the frequency refers to the entire interval rather than any individual point of the interval. Notice that since the base is one, the area of each rectangle is the relative frequency of the corresponding interval, and therefore the sum of the areas of all the rectangles is one.

Instead of observing the interarrival times of 100 customers and grouping them into ten one-minute intervals, say we observed the times of 1000 customers and grouped them into 20 half-minute intervals; or we could observe the arrival times of 10,000 customers and group them into 40 quarter-minute intervals. Each succeeding histogram would be less and less irregular, but by and large the essence with regard to frequency would remain the same. By continuing this process of increasing the observed number of interarrival times while decreasing the width of the class intervals, we will eventually arrive at a limiting curve. That is, when the observed number of interarrival times is very large and the

TABLE 3.2 Grouped interarrival times of 100 customers at a service facility

Time interval	Number of arrivals	Relative frequency
$0 < x \leq 1$	22	0.22
$1 < x \leq 2$	18	0.18
$2 < x \leq 3$	17	0.17
$3 < x \leq 4$	13	0.13
$4 < x \leq 5$	14	0.14
$5 < x \leq 6$	8	0.08
$6 < x \leq 7$	6	0.06
$7 < x \leq 8$	7	0.07
$8 < x \leq 9$	3	0.03
$9 < x \leq 10$	2	0.02

FIGURE 3.3   Relative frequencies of grouped interarrival times for ten intervals

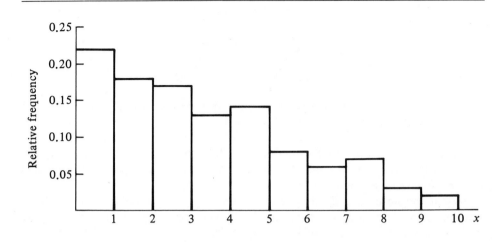

width of the class intervals is very small, the relative frequency would appear in essence as a smooth curve. Based on Figure 3.3, we may speculate that the limiting curve for this illustration would be as shown in Figure 3.4.

The function $f(x)$ whose graph is the limiting curve obtained for an extremely large number of observations and an extremely small interval width is the probability density function of the continuous random variable X, provided that the vertical scale is chosen so that the total area under the curve equals one. The probability density function of a continuous random variable X is formally defined as follows:

FIGURE 3.4   Limiting curve for the relative frequency of the interarrival times

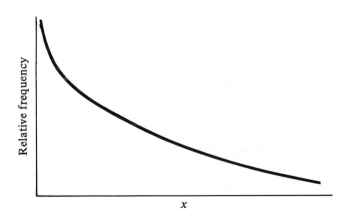

Definition 3.6   If there exists a function $f(x)$ such that

$$1.\ f(x) \geq 0,\ -\infty < x < \infty,$$

$$2.\ \int_{-\infty}^{\infty} f(x)dx = 1,\ \text{and}$$

$$3.\ P(a \leq X \leq b) = \int_{a}^{b} f(x)dx$$

for any a and b, then $f(x)$ is the probability density function of the continuous random variable X.

Since the total area under $f(x)$ is one, the probability of the interval $a \leq X \leq b$ is the area bounded by the density function and the points $X = a$ and $X = b$, as shown in Figure 3.5.

As in the case of a discrete random variable, the cumulative distribution function of a continuous random variable X is the probability that X will take on a value less than or equal to some specified x. That is,

$$P(X \leq x) = F(x) = \int_{-\infty}^{x} f(t)dt, \tag{3.2}$$

where t is a dummy variable of integration. Hence the cumulative distribution function $F(x)$ is the area bounded above by the density function and bounded to the right by the point $X = x$, as illustrated in Figure 3.6.

Since for any continuous random variable X,

$$P(X = x) = \int_{x}^{x} f(t)dt = 0,$$

FIGURE 3.5   A probability depicted as the area under the density curve

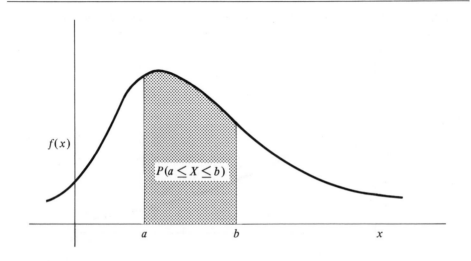

FIGURE 3.6 The cumulative distribution depicted as an area under the density curve

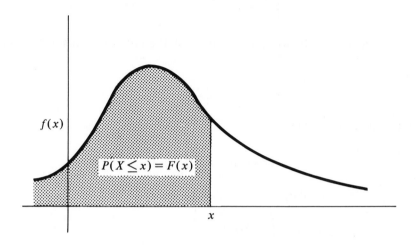

then

$$P(X \leq x) = P(X < x) = F(x).$$

The cumulative distribution $F(x)$ is a smooth nondecreasing function of the values of the random variable with the following properties:

1. $F(-\infty) = 0$;

2. $F(\infty) = 1$;

3. $P(a < X < b) = F(b) - F(a)$;

4. $dF(x)/dx = f(x)$.

The property that the derivative of the cumulative distribution function is the probability density function stems from the fundamental theorem of integral calculus.

Example 3.2 A random variable X representing the length of time in minutes between successive arrivals at a service facility has been found to have a probability density function given by

$$f(x) = \begin{cases} k \exp(-x/2),^* & x > 0, \\ 0 & \text{elsewhere} \end{cases}$$

for an appropriate constant k. Determine k, the cumulative distribution function, the probability that $2 < X < 6$, and the probability that $X \leq 8$.

*We will not hesitate to use "exp" rather than "e" whenever it appears to be less cumbersome.

We must insist that

$$\int_{-\infty}^{\infty} f(x)dx = 1;$$

therefore, since in this example $f(x) = 0$ if $x \leq 0$, then the value of k is determined by

$$k \int_{0}^{\infty} \exp(-x/2)dx = 1.$$

After integration we obtain

$$-2k \exp(-x/2) \Big|_{0}^{\infty} = 1,$$

and $k = 1/2$. The cumulative distribution function is

$$F(x) = \int_{-\infty}^{x} f(t)dt$$

$$= \int_{-\infty}^{0} 0\,dt + \frac{1}{2} \int_{0}^{x} \exp(-t/2)dt$$

$$= 1 - \exp(-x/2) \quad \text{for } x > 0,$$

and $F(x) = 0$ for $x \leq 0$. Moreover, $DF(x)/dx = 1/2 \exp(-x/2)$, as expected.

The probability that an interarrival length will be between 2 minutes and 6 minutes is

$$P(2 < X < 6) = \frac{1}{2} \int_{2}^{6} \exp(-x/2)dx = F(6) - F(2)$$

$$= [1 - \exp(-3)] - [1 - \exp(-1)] = 0.3181.$$

The probability that an interarrival length is less than 8 minutes is

$$P(X < 8) = F(8) = 1 - \exp(-4) = 0.9817.$$

Thus the probability that it exceeds 8 minutes is $1 - F(8) = \exp(-4) = 0.0183$.

Example 3.3   A random variable representing the proportion of fatal automobile accidents in the United States has the density function

$$f(x) = \begin{cases} 42x(1-x)^5 & 0 < x \leq 1 \\ 0 & \text{elsewhere.} \end{cases}$$

What is the probability that no more than 25 percent of the automobile accidents are fatal? In other words, what is $P[X \leq 0.25]$?

The function $f(x)$ is a probability density since

$$42 \int_{0}^{1} x(1-x)^5 dx = 42\left(\frac{x^2}{2} - \frac{5x^3}{3} + \frac{10x^4}{4} - \frac{10x^5}{5} + \frac{5x^6}{6} - \frac{x^7}{7}\right) \Big|_{0}^{1} = 1.$$

Notice that when the random variable X is, say, 1/4, the density function is $f(1/4) = 2.4917$. Thus in the continuous case it is quite possible to have the density function exceed unity for a specific value of the random variable even though the integral of the density function over the range of the random variable is one. Finally, the cumulative distribution function is

$$F(x) = 42 \int_0^x t(1 - t)^5 dt = 21x^2 - 70x^3 + 105x^4 - 84x^5 + 35x^6 - 6x^7.$$

Hence the probability that the proportion of fatal automobile accidents is less than 25 percent is

$$F(1/4) = 21(1/4)^2 - 70(1/4)^3 + 105(1/4)^4 - 84(1/4)^5 + 35(1/4)^6 - 6(1/4)^7$$

$$= 0.5551.$$

3.4   The Expected Value of a Random Variable

The *expected value* (or expectation) of a random variable is a very important concept in the study of probability distributions. The expectation of a random variable has its roots in games of chance because gamblers want to know what they "expect" to win over repeated play of a game. In this sense the expected value has meant the average amount one stands to win or lose per play over a very long series of plays. This meaning also holds with regard to a random variable. That is, the long-run average of a random variable is its expected value.

To illustrate the essence of expectation, we analyze the following game of chance. Suppose we are given a balanced coin with which we have three chances to toss "heads." The game ends as soon as we toss "heads," or after three attempts, whichever comes first. If the first, second, or third toss is "heads" we will receive \$2, \$4, and \$8, respectively. However, if we fail to toss "heads" in three attempts, we will lose \$20. To determine the long-run average gain or loss, let the random variable X be the amount won or lost each time the game is played. The possible values of X and their probabilities are given in Table 3.3. In the long run we expect to win \$2 about once out of every two tries, to win \$4 about once in every four tries, to win \$8 about once in every eight tries, and to lose \$20 about once in every eight attempts. The expected value, or the average amount won or lost per game if we were to play the game a very large number of times, is determined by multiplying each amount we stand to win or lose by the probability of its occurrence and adding the results. We therefore

TABLE 3.3 Probabilities of winning or losing in a game of chance

X	$P(X)$		
2	$P(X = 2) \equiv$	$P(H)$	$= 1/2$
4	$P(X = 4) \equiv$	$P(T \cap H)$	$= 1/4$
8	$P(X = 8) \equiv$	$P(T \cap T \cap H)$	$= 1/8$
-20	$P(X = -20) \equiv$	$P(T \cap T \cap T)$	$= 1/8$

expect to win

$$(\$2)(1/2) + (\$4)(1/4) + (\$8)(1/8) + (-\$20)(1/8) = \$0.50$$

per game. Note that the expected value of 50 cents is not one of the possible values of the random variable; it is entirely possible that a random variable never takes on its expected value.

This illustration suggests the following definition of the mathematical expectation of a random variable:

Definition 3.7 The expected value of a random variable X is the average or mean value of X and is given by

$$E(X) = \sum_x xp(x) \qquad \text{when } X \text{ is discrete, or}$$

$$E(X) = \int_{-\infty}^{\infty} xf(x)dx \quad \text{when } X \text{ is continuous,}$$

where $p(x)$ and $f(x)$ are the probability and density functions, respectively.

In general, the expected value of a function $g(x)$ of the random variable X is given by

$$E[g(X)] = \sum_x g(x)p(x) \qquad \text{if } X \text{ is discrete, or}$$

$$\tag{3.3}$$

$$E[g(X)] = \int_{-\infty}^{\infty} g(x)f(x)dx \quad \text{if } X \text{ is continuous.}$$

The expectation of a random variable X is not a function of X but a fixed number and a property of the probability distribution of X. Moreover, the expectation may not exist since the corresponding sum or integral in (3.3) may not converge to a finite value.

Example 3.4 If the random variable X is the sum of the two faces when rolling a pair of balanced and distinguishable dice, show that the expected value of X is 7.

Using the probability function of X given by (3.1) and Definition 3.7, we have

$$E(X) = \sum_{x=2}^{12} xp(x) = (2)(1/36) + (3)(2/36) + \cdots + (12)(1/36) = 7.$$

Example 3.5 Refer to Example 3.3 and determine the expected value of the proportion of fatal accidents in the United States.

Using Definition 3.7, the expected value of the proportion is

$$E(X) = 42 \int_0^1 xf(x)dx$$

$$= 42 \int_0^1 x^2(1 - x)^5 dx$$

$$= 42x^3 \left(\frac{1}{3} - \frac{5x}{4} + 2x^2 - \frac{5x^3}{3} + \frac{5x^4}{7} - \frac{x^5}{8} \right) \Big|_0^1$$

$$= 0.25.$$

Example 3.6 Assume that the time in hours required for repair of a piece of equipment in a manufacturing process is a random variable with probability density function

$$f(x) = \begin{cases} \dfrac{1}{5} \exp(-x/5) & x > 0, \\ 0 & \text{elsewhere.} \end{cases}$$

If the dollar penalty is equal to the square of the number of hours required for repair, determine the expected dollar value of the penalty per breakdown.

Here we need to compute the expected value of a function that relates the random variable (repair time) to the dollar penalty. This function is

$$g(x) = x^2;$$

therefore,

$$E[g(X)] = \int_{-\infty}^{\infty} g(x)f(x)dx = \frac{1}{5} \int_0^{\infty} x^2 \exp(-x/5)dx.$$

To evaluate integrals of this type in which the integrand is a product of a power term and a negative exponential integrated over the positive real line, it is best to use the mathematical function

$$\Gamma(n) = \int_0^{\infty} u^{n-1} \exp(-u)du, \qquad n > 0, \tag{3.4}$$

which is known as the *gamma function* of the argument n. Some properties of the gamma function are

1. $\Gamma(n + 1) = n!$ if n is a positive integer;
2. $\Gamma(n + 1) = n\Gamma(n)$, $n > 0$;
3. $\Gamma(1/2) = \sqrt{\pi}$.

Therefore, to evaluate the integral

$$E[g(X)] = \frac{1}{5} \int_0^{\infty} x^2 \exp(-x/5)dx,$$

in (3.4) let $u = x/5$; in other words, $x = 5u$ and $dx = 5du$. Then

$$E[g(X)] = \frac{1}{5} \int_0^\infty x^2 \exp(-x/5)dx = \frac{1}{5} \int_0^\infty (5u)^2 \exp(-u)5du$$

$$= 25 \int_0^\infty u^2 \exp(-u)du$$

$$= 25\Gamma(3)$$

$$= 50,$$

where 50 is the expected dollar value of the penalty per breakdown.

Example 3.7   An investor has $100,000 for a one-year investment. The investor is weighing two options: a money market fund that guarantees a fixed annual rate of return of 15% and an investment plan whose annual rate of return can be regarded as a random variable with values that depend on prevailing economic conditions. Based on the second plan's past history under a variety of economic conditions, a very reliable analyst has determined the possible values of return rate and their probabilities, listed in Table 3.4. Which investment plan should be selected if the choice is to be made based on the expected rate of return?

If the first plan, the money market fund, is selected, the return on an investment of $100,000 will be $15,000 since the rate is fixed at 15%. For the second plan, let the random variable X be the rate of return. Using Definition 3.7, we determine

$$E(X) = (0.3)(0.2) + (0.25)(0.2) + \cdots + (0.05)(0.05) = 0.205.$$

It follows, therefore, that the second plan is the better choice because it offers the investor an expected return of $20,500. The reader must be cautioned, however, that the return of $20,500 is only an expected value, and the investor has no guarantee of an actual return near this value.

Now we will state and show several important properties of the expectation of a random variable. We will use the continuous case, although these properties also apply for discrete random variables. Let X be a continuous random variable with probability density function $f(x)$.

1. The expected value of a constant c is the constant.

$$E(c) = \int_{-\infty}^\infty cf(x)dx = c \int_{-\infty}^\infty f(x)dx = c.$$

TABLE 3.4   Rates of return for Example 3.7

Rate of return (%)	Probability
30	0.20
25	0.20
20	0.30
15	0.15
10	0.10
5	0.05

2. The expected value of the quantity $aX + b$, where a and b are constants, is a times the expected value of X plus b.

$$E(aX + b) = \int_{-\infty}^{\infty} (ax + b)f(x)dx = a \int_{-\infty}^{\infty} xf(x)dx + b \int_{-\infty}^{\infty} f(x)dx$$

$$= aE(X) + b.$$

3. The expected value of the sum of two functions $g(X)$ and $h(X)$ of X is the sum of the expected values of $g(X)$ and $h(X)$.

$$E[g(X) + h(X)] = \int_{-\infty}^{\infty} [g(x) + h(x)]f(x)dx$$

$$= \int_{-\infty}^{\infty} g(x)f(x)dx + \int_{-\infty}^{\infty} h(x)f(x)dx$$

$$= E[g(X)] + E[h(X)].$$

3.5 Moments of a Random Variable

The *moments* of a random variable X* are the expected values of certain functions of X. They are a collection of descriptive measures that can be used to characterize the probability distribution of X and to completely specify it if all moments of X are known. Although one may define moments of X about any reference point, moments are usually defined about zero or about the expected value of X. The use of moments of a random variable to characterize the probability distribution is a worthwhile task. This is especially true in an environment in which the experimenter is not likely to know the probability distribution. All statements about moments are subject to the existence of the definitional sums or integrals.

Definition 3.8 Let X be a random variable. The rth moment of X about zero is defined by

$$\mu_r' = E(X^r) = \sum_{x} x^r p(x) \qquad \text{if } X \text{ is discrete, or}$$

$$\mu_r' = E(X^r) = \int_{-\infty}^{\infty} x^r f(x)dx \qquad \text{if } X \text{ is continuous.}$$

The first moment about zero is the *mean* or *expected value* of the random variable and is denoted by μ; thus $\mu_1' = \mu = E(X)$. Based on the material in Chapter 1, the mean of a random variable is thought of as a numerical quantity around which the values of the random variable tend to cluster. The mean is therefore a measure of central tendency.

---

*It is also appropriate to use the phrase *moments of the probability distribution of X*.

Definition 3.9   Let X be a random variable. The rth central moment of X or the rth moment about the mean of X is defined by

$$\mu_r = E(X - \mu)^r = \sum_x (x - \mu)^r p(x) \qquad \text{if } X \text{ is discrete, or}$$

$$\mu_r = E(X - \mu)^r = \int_{-\infty}^{\infty} (x - \mu)^r f(x) dx \qquad \text{if } X \text{ is continuous.}$$

The zeroth central moment of any random variable is one since

$$\mu_0 = E(X - \mu)^0 = E(1) = 1.$$

Similarly, the first central moment of any random variable is zero since

$$\mu_1 = E(X - \mu) = E(X) - \mu = 0.$$

The second central moment,

$$\mu_2 = E(X - \mu)^2,$$

is known as the *variance* of the random variable. Since

$$
\begin{aligned}
\mu_2 = Var(X) &= E(X - \mu)^2 \\
&= E(X^2 - 2X\mu + \mu^2) \\
&= E(X^2) - 2\mu^2 + \mu^2 \\
&= \mu_2' - \mu^2,
\end{aligned}
\tag{3.5}
$$

the variance of any random variable is the second moment about the origin minus the square of the mean. It is usually denoted by σ^2. The variance of a random variable is a measure of the spread or dispersion in the probability distribution of the random variable. In the continuous case, for example, if most of the area depicted by the density function lies close to the mean, the variance is small; if the area is spread out, the variance is large. The positive square root of the variance is known as the *standard deviation* and is denoted by σ. Although σ^2 and σ are the nearly universal symbols for the variance and standard deviation of a random variable, respectively, we will not hesitate to use the designations $\sigma^2(X)$ or $Var(X)$ for the variance and $\sigma(X)$ or $s.d.(X)$ for the standard deviation because of their explicit identification of the random variable involved. For the same reason, it will also be necessary at times to use the notation $\mu_r(X)$ to indicate the rth central moment of X.

It is useful to note that the variance of a random variable X is location invariant; that is, $Var(X + b) = Var(X)$ for any constant b. More generally, we show that $Var(aX + b) = a^2 Var(X)$ for any constants a and b. By definition,

$$
\begin{aligned}
Var(aX + b) &= E(aX + b)^2 - E^2(aX + b) \\
&= E(a^2X^2 + 2abX + b^2) - [aE(X) + b]^2 \\
&= a^2 E(X^2) + 2abE(X) + b^2 - a^2 E^2(X) - 2abE(X) - b^2 \\
&= a^2 E(X^2) - a^2 E^2(X) \\
&= a^2 [E(X^2) - E^2(X)] \\
&= a^2 Var(X).
\end{aligned}
$$

A measure that compares the relative dispersion of two probability distributions is the *coefficient of variation,* defined by

$$V = \sigma/\mu. \tag{3.6}$$

The coefficient of variation expresses the magnitude of dispersion of a random variable relative to its expected value. V is a standardized measure of variation relative to the mean, and it is especially useful in comparing two probability distributions when the scale of measurement differs appreciably. For example, given two random variables X and Y, assume that

$$E(X) = 120, \ Var(X) = 36; \ E(Y) = 40, \ Var(Y) = 16.$$

Although the dispersion of X as measured by the standard deviation is larger than that of Y in the absolute sense, the relative dispersion of X is less than the relative dispersion of Y because

$$V_X = 6/120 = 0.05,$$

but

$$V_Y = 4/40 = 0.10.$$

Therefore, the probability distribution of Y exhibits greater dispersion relative to the mean than does the distribution of X.

We will now examine the third and fourth central moments of a random variable X. These central moments provide useful information about the shape of the probability distribution of X. Although higher moments may be considered, their usefulness in characterizing a probability distribution is much less than that of the first four moments. The third central moment,

$$\mu_3 = E(X - \mu)^3, \tag{3.7}$$

is related to the *skewness* or *asymmetry* of the probability distribution of X. We showed above that the second central moment (the variance) can be expressed in terms of the first two moments about zero. In fact, any central moment of a random variable X can be expressed in terms of the moments of X about zero. By definition,

$$\mu_r = E(X - \mu)^r,$$

but the expansion of $(X - \mu)^r$ can be expressed as

$$(X - \mu)^r = \sum_{i=0}^{r} (-1)^i \frac{r!}{(r-i)!i!} \mu^i x^{r-i}.$$

Since the expectation of a sum is the sum of the expectations,

$$\mu_r = \sum_{i=0}^{r} (-1)^i \frac{r!}{(r-i)!i!} \mu^i E(X^{r-i})$$

$$= \sum_{i=0}^{r} (-1)^i \frac{r!}{(r-i)!i!} \mu^i \mu'_{r-i}.$$

FIGURE 3.7 Typical probability density functions of (a) positively skewed distributions, (b) negatively skewed distributions, and (c) symmetric distributions.

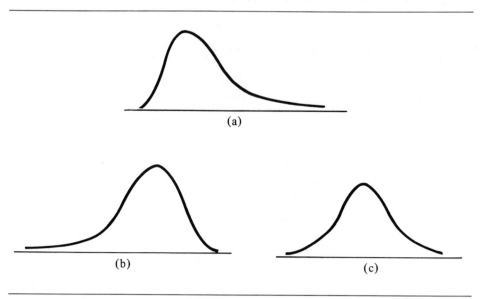

(a)

(b) (c)

In particular, therefore,

$$\mu_3 = \mu_3' - 3\mu\mu_2' + 2\mu^3. \tag{3.8}$$

For random variables whose probability distributions are single-peaked, if $\mu_3 < 0$, the distribution is said to be *negatively skewed;* if $\mu_3 > 0$, the distribution is called *positively skewed;* and if $\mu_3 = 0$, the distribution is called *symmetrical.* However, unless a probability distribution is single-peaked, we cannot entirely judge the shape of the distribution by simply knowing μ_3. And even then the third central moment by itself falls short as a measure of relative skewness because it depends on the units in which the random variable is measured. It turns out that the more appropriate measure of skewness is the standardized third moment, given by

$$\alpha_3^* = \mu_3/(\mu_2)^{3/2}, \tag{3.9}$$

which is known as the *coefficient of skewness.* The coefficient α_3 measures the skewness of a probability distribution relative to its dispersion. As Figure 3.7 illustrates, a probability distribution is positively skewed, negatively skewed, or symmetrical, respectively, if $\alpha_3 > 0$, $\alpha_3 < 0$, or $\alpha_3 = 0$. It should be noted that if the probability distribution of a random variable X is symmetrical, all odd-order central moments of X will be zero because each positive value of $(X - \mu)^r$ is canceled out by an equally probable and opposite negative value.

*On occasion it will be necessary to explicitly identify the random variable involved to remove ambiguity.

The fourth central moment,

$$\mu_4 = E(X - \mu)^4$$
$$= \mu_4' - 4\mu\mu_3' + 6\mu^2\mu_2' - 3\mu^4, \qquad (3.10)$$

reflects the *peakedness* or *kurtosis* of a probability distribution. Again it is preferable to use the standardized fourth moment,

$$\alpha_4 = \mu_4/\mu_2^2, \qquad (3.11)$$

as a relative measure of kurtosis. If $\alpha_4 > 3$, the probability distribution is relatively high-peaked and is called *leptokurtic*; if $\alpha_4 < 3$, the distribution is relatively flat-topped and is called *platykurtic*; and if $\alpha_4 = 3$, the distribution is neither very high-peaked nor very flat-topped and is called *mesokurtic*. These types of distributions are illustrated in Figure 3.8. The value 3 is used as a reference because in practice the standardized kurtosis of a probability distribution is often compared to that of a widely used distribution, known as the normal, whose value is 3. The normal distribution will be discussed in detail later.

The standardized third and fourth moments are also known, respectively, as the first and second shape factors of a probability distribution since, to a large extent, they dictate the shape of the probability distribution.

Example 3.8 Salespersons A and B, who sell life insurance, typically visit 8 and 12 potential clients per week, respectively. Let X and Y be two random

FIGURE 3.8   Typical probability density functions of (a) leptokurtic distributions, (b) platy-kurtic distributions, and (c) mesokurtic distributions

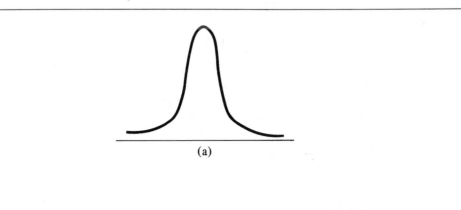
(a)

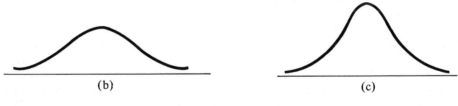
(b)   (c)

variables that represent, respectively, the number of insurance policies written by A and B as a result of these visits. Based on a substantial amount of historical information, the probabilities for the values of X and Y are as follows:

x	0	1	2	3	4	5	6	7	8
$p(x)$	0.02	0.09	0.21	0.28	0.23	0.12	0.04	0.01	0

y	0	1	2	3	4	5	6	7	8	9	10	11	12
$p(y)$	0.06	0.21	0.28	0.24	0.13	0.05	0.02	0.01	0	0	0	0	0

Compare and contrast the probability distributions of X and Y using their means, variances, and shape factors.

Based on Definition 3.8, the first four moments of X about zero are

$$\mu = (0)(0.2) + (1)(0.09) + \cdots + (8)(0) = 3.18$$

$$\mu_2' = (0)^2(0.02) + (1)^2(0.09) + \cdots + (8)^2(0) = 12.06$$

$$\mu_3' = (0)^3(0.02) + (1)^3(0.09) + \cdots + (8)^3(0) = 51.12$$

$$\mu_4' = (0)^4(0.02) + (1)^4(0.09) + \cdots + (8)^4(0) = 235.86.$$

Using expressions 3.5, 3.8, and 3.10, respectively, we determine that $Var(X) = 1.95$, $\mu_3(X) = 0.3825$, and $\mu_4(X) = 10.565$. The first two shape factors of the probability distribution of X are computed using (3.9) and (3.11), respectively, and are found to be $\alpha_3(X) = 0.1405$ and $\alpha_4(X) = 2.78$.

Following the same procedure, the first four moments of Y about zero work out to be $\mu = 2.45$, $\mu_2' = 8.03$, $\mu_3' = 31.25$, and $\mu_4' = 138.59$. Thus $Var(Y) = 2.03$, $\mu_3(Y) = 1.6418$, $\mu_4(Y) = 13.4504$, $\alpha_3(Y) = 0.5676$, and $\alpha_4(Y) = 3.26$.

There appears to be little difference between the distributions of X and Y relative to mean and variance, but the distribution of Y is much more positively skewed than that of X. Moreover, the distribution of X is a platykurtic ($\alpha_4 < 3$), while that of Y is leptokurtic ($\alpha_4 > 3$).

We now consider the concept of a *standardized random variable*. Let X be any random variable with mean μ and standard deviation σ. The quantity

$$Y = (X - \mu)/\sigma \tag{3.12}$$

defines a random variable Y with mean zero and standard deviation one. Such a random variable is called the standardized variable corresponding to X. In fact, for any particular value x of X the value $y = (x - \mu)/\sigma$ indicates the deviation of the particular value x from the expected value of X in terms of standard deviation units. For example, if X represents scores from an IQ test, and if $E(X) = 100$ and $Var(X) = 100$, then $Y = (X - 100)/10$ is the standardized variable corresponding to X. Moreover, if some individual's IQ is 120, then he or she is $y = 2$ standard deviation units above the mean IQ.

The expected value of Y is zero since

$$E\left(\frac{X - \mu}{\sigma}\right) = \frac{1}{\sigma} E(X - \mu) = 0.$$

In fact, since $E(Y) = 0$, the rth central moment of Y is

$$\mu_r(Y) = E(Y^r) = E\left(\frac{X - \mu}{\sigma}\right)^r$$

$$= \frac{1}{\sigma^r} E(X - \mu)^r$$

$$= \mu_r(X)/\sigma^r;$$

thus

$$\mu_r(Y) = \mu_r(X)/\{\mu_2(X)\}^{r/2}. \tag{3.13}$$

It is apparent from (3.13) that $Var(Y) = \mu_2(Y) = 1$. In particular, note that $\alpha_3(Y) = \alpha_3(X)$ and $\alpha_4(Y) = \alpha_4(X)$. The standardization of a random variable affects the mean and variance but not the shape factors.

Example 3.9 Consider the random variables X and Y with probability density functions

$$f(x) = \begin{cases} 1/30 & 80 \leq x \leq 110, \\ 0 & \text{elsewhere;} \end{cases}$$

and $f(y) = \begin{cases} \dfrac{1}{10,000} \exp(-y/10,000) & y > 0, \\ 0 & \text{elsewhere.} \end{cases}$

Determine and compare the mean, variance, standard deviation, and the third and fourth standardized moments of X and Y.

The primary objective here is to contrast the probability distributions of X and Y by comparing their first four moments, and, to some degree, provide a theoretical analogue to Examples 1.1 and 1.2. The reader may easily verify that the probability distributions of X and Y are distinctly different by graphing the density functions. As we will see, much of the apparent difference can also be uncovered through a comparison of the first four moments of X and Y.

For ease of computation, let $c_1 = 1/30$ and $c_2 = 1/10,000$. For the random variable X,

$$E(X) = c_1 \int_{80}^{110} x\,dx = \frac{c_1}{2} x^2 \Big|_{80}^{110} = 95$$

and

$$Var(X) = c_1 \int_{80}^{110} (x - 95)^2 dx = c_1 \int_{-15}^{15} u^2 du = 75,$$

where $u = x - 95$ and $dx = du$. It follows, therefore, that $s.d.(X) = 8.66$. For the higher moments we have

$$E(X - 95)^3 = c_1 \int_{80}^{110} (x - 95)^3 dx = c_1 \int_{-15}^{15} u^3 du = 0$$

and

$$E(X - 95)^4 = c_1 \int_{80}^{110} (x - 95)^4 dx = c_1 \int_{-15}^{15} u^4 du = 10,125.$$

Thus by (3.9) and (3.11), the first and second shape factors for the distribution of X are $\alpha_3(X) = 0/(75)^{3/2} = 0$ and $\alpha_4(X) = 10,125/5,625 = 1.8$, respectively. The probability distribution of X is symmetrical and is centered about the value 95, has a variance of 75 and a standard deviation of 8.66, and tends to be flat-topped.

For the random variable Y,

$$E(Y) = c_2 \int_0^\infty y \exp(-c_2 y) dy = c_2 \int_0^\infty \frac{1}{c_2} u \exp(-u) \frac{1}{c_2} du = \Gamma(2)/c_2 = 10,000$$

and

$$E(Y^2) = c_2 \int_0^\infty y^2 \exp(-c_2 y) dy = \Gamma(3)/c_2^2 = 2 \times 10^8,$$

where $u = c_2 y$ and $dy = du/c_2$. Thus $Var(Y) = 1 \times 10^8$, and $s.d.(Y) = 10,000$. Moreover,

$$E(Y^3) = c_2 \int_0^\infty y^3 \exp(-c_2 y) dy = \Gamma(4)/c_2^3 = 6 \times 10^{12}.$$

Then using (3.8) and (3.9), we determine that $E(Y - 10,000)^3 = 2 \times 10^{12}$, and $\alpha_3(Y) = 2$. Similarly,

$$E(Y^4) = c_2 \int_0^\infty y^4 \exp(-c_2 y) dy = \Gamma(5)/c_2^4 = 24 \times 10^{16}.$$

Using (3.10) and (3.11), respectively, we determine that $E(Y - 10,000)^4 = 9 \times 10^{16}$, and $\alpha_4(Y) = 9$. We conclude that the distribution of Y is positively skewed, is relatively high-peaked, has a mean of 10,000, a variance of 1×10^8, and a standard deviation of 10,000.

3.6   Some Other Measures of Central Tendency and Dispersion

Although the mean and variance of a random variable are the primary measures of central tendency and dispersion, other measures are commonly used. Recall from Chapter 1 that the median and mode are also useful measures of central tendency.

Definition 3.10   For any random variable X, the median is defined to be a value, say, $x_{0.5}$ of X such that

$$P(X < x_{0.5}) \leqslant 1/2 \quad \text{and} \quad P(X \leqslant x_{0.5}) \geqslant 1/2 \qquad \text{if } X \text{ is discrete, or}$$

$$P(X \leqslant x_{0.5}) = 1/2 \qquad\qquad\qquad\qquad \text{if } X \text{ is continuous.}$$

If there is only one such value of X, then $x_{0.5}$ is called the median of the distribution of X. The median is a measure of central tendency in the sense that it is the value which divides the probability distribution into two equal segments.

Definition 3.11   For any random variable X, the mode is defined to be a value x_m of X that maximizes the probability function if X is discrete, or the probability density function if X is continuous.

If there is only one such value of X, then x_m is called the mode of the distribution of X. If X is continuous, the mode is the solution of $df(x)/dx = 0$ as long as $d^2f(x)/dx^2 < 0$. If the second derivative is positive, the value is usually called the antimode; it is found in U-shaped distributions. If there are several maxima or minima, the probability distribution is referred to as multimodal.

As in the empirical discussion in Chapter 1, the mean of a random variable is generally the preferred measure of central tendency. However, in some situations the median, or to a lesser degree the mode, may be the more appropriate measure of central tendency. For example, in highly skewed unimodal distributions, the expected value of the random variable is strongly affected by the magnitude of the values in the tail of the distribution, whereas the median would not be so affected by these values. For negatively skewed unimodal distributions, the median is larger than the mean, while the opposite is true for positively skewed unimodal distributions. For symmetrical unimodal distributions the mean, median, and mode coincide.

Example 3.10   Let X be a random variable representing the lifetime of an electrical component in hours. If the probability density function of X is given by

$$f(x) = \begin{cases} \dfrac{1}{1000} \exp(-x/1000) & x > 0, \\[2mm] 0 & \text{elsewhere,} \end{cases}$$

determine and compare the mean and median.

The mean of X is

$$E(X) = \frac{1}{1000} \int_0^\infty x \exp(-x/1000)dx = 1000 \int_0^\infty u \exp(-u)du$$

$$= 1000\Gamma(2) = 1000 \text{ hours,}$$

where $x = 1000u$ and $dx = 1000du$. The median of X is

$$P(X \leqslant x_{0.5}) \equiv F(x_{0.5}) = \frac{1}{1000} \int_0^{x_{0.5}} \exp(-x/1000)dx = 0.5$$

$$= 1 - \exp(-x_{0.5}/1000) = 0.5.$$

Therefore,

$$x_{0.5} = -1000 \ln(0.5) = 693.15 \text{ hours.}$$

We can also show that this probability distribution is positively skewed since the coefficient of skewness $\alpha_3 = 2$. Thus the mean life of 1000 hours is affected by the values of random variable in the tail of the distribution. In fact, the probability that the life of any such component will exceed the average life is 0.3679 since

$$P(X > \mu) = 1 - F(\mu) = 1 - 0.6321 = 0.3679.$$

It would appear that the median life of 693.15 hours would be the more appropriate measure of central tendency in this case.

In addition to the variance, there are other measures of dispersion for random variables, such as the interdecile range, the interquartile range, and the mean deviation, as discussed in Chapter 1. The first two are functions of the quantiles of a probability distribution. The mean deviation conceptually parallels the standard deviation with the exception that the absolute difference between a random variable and its expected value is used rather than the square of the difference.

Definition 3.12 For any random variable X, the quantile value x_q of order q, $0 < q < 1$, is a value of X such that

$$P(X < x_q) \leqslant q \quad \text{and} \quad P(X \leqslant x_q) \geqslant q \quad \text{if } X \text{ is discrete, or}$$

$$P(X \leqslant x_q) = q \quad\quad\quad\quad\quad \text{if } X \text{ is continuous.}$$

Generally, the quantiles of a continuous random variable are relatively easy to determine. For discrete random variables, however, the quantiles are usually obtained by interpolation because exact solutions are not always possible.

Commonly used quantiles are the percentiles, deciles, and quartiles. The percentiles are the points of the random variable that divide the probability distribution into 100 intervals, each with probability 0.01; the deciles and quartiles are the points that divide the probability distribution into 10 and 4 intervals, each with probability 0.1 and 0.25, respectively. Notice that the median is also the 50th percentile, the 5th decile, and the 2nd quartile.

The interdecile range is the difference between the ninth and first deciles, and the interquartile range is the difference between the third and first quartiles. Thus the interdecile range measures the spread of the middle 80 percent of the probability distribution, and the interquartile range reflects the variation within the middle 50 percent of the distribution. In both cases, by excluding the effects

3.6 Some Other Measures of Central Tendency and Dispersion

of the values at the tails of a distribution, we are able to measure the variability of a random variable around the middle of its probability distribution.

The interdecile and interquartile ranges are two measures of dispersion used in many disciplines, including education, business, and economics as well as engineering. The interdecile range is often used in educational testing to measure variability in performance without regard to either the top 10 percent or the bottom 10 percent. The interquartile range has been used in business and economics to measure the variability of a random variable around the concentrated portion of its probability distribution.

Definition 3.13   The mean deviation of a random variable X is the expected value of the absolute difference between X and its mean and is given by

$$E|X - \mu| = \sum_{\text{all } x} |x - \mu| p(x) \qquad \text{if } X \text{ is discrete, or}$$

$$E|X - \mu| = \int_{-\infty}^{\infty} |x - \mu| f(x) dx \qquad \text{if } X \text{ is continuous.}$$

Although the mean deviation is a legitimate measure of dispersion, there are probability distributions for which it is not analytically tractable. Still, as was illustrated in Chapter 1, the mean deviation is a viable alternative to the standard deviation as a measure of dispersion for data sets based on empirical evidence. It should be noted that for long-tailed distributions the effect on the mean deviation of the values in the tails of the distribution is less than their effect on the standard deviation.

Example 3.11   Assume that in a certain filling process the deviation between the actual weight of a container and the specified weight is a random variable Z with probability density function

$$f(z) = \frac{1}{\sqrt{2\pi}} \exp(-z^2/2) \qquad -\infty < z < \infty.$$

Determine the mean, standard deviation, interdecile range, interquartile range, and mean deviation of Z.

As we shall see in Chapter 5, this density function is a special member of a very useful family of probability distributions known as the normal or Gaussian family. In fact, the cumulative distribution function of Z is well tabulated, as listed in Table D of the Appendix. Moreover, as we will see later,

$$E(Z) = 0, \ Var(Z) = 1, \text{ and } s.d.(Z) = 1.$$

To determine the interdecile range, the quantile values $z_{0.1}$ and $z_{0.9}$ defined by

$$\frac{1}{\sqrt{2\pi}} \int_{-\infty}^{z_{0.1}} \exp(-t^2/2) dt = 0.1 \quad \text{and} \quad \frac{1}{\sqrt{2\pi}} \int_{-\infty}^{z_{0.9}} \exp(-t^2/2) dt = 0.9$$

are obtained from Table D*; they are $z_{0.1} = -1.28$ and $z_{0.9} = 1.28$. The interdecile range is $z_{0.9} - z_{0.1} = 2.56$ units. In other words, the weight of 80 percent of all such containers will not deviate by more than 1.28 units in either direction from the specified weight. Similarly, the quantile values $z_{0.25}$ and $z_{0.75}$ are found in Table D to be $z_{0.25} = -0.675$ and $z_{0.75} = 0.675$. As a result, the interquartile range is $z_{0.75} - z_{0.25} = 1.35$ units.

For the mean deviation, since $E(Z) = 0$, we have

$$E|Z| = \frac{1}{\sqrt{2\pi}} \int_{-\infty}^{\infty} |z| \exp(-z^2/2) dz$$

$$= \frac{2}{\sqrt{2\pi}} \int_{0}^{\infty} z \exp(-z^2/2) dz$$

$$= -\frac{2}{\sqrt{2\pi}} \exp(-z^2/2) \Big|_{0}^{\infty}$$

$$= 2/\sqrt{2\pi}$$

$$= 0.7979 \text{ units.}$$

Notice that since the standard deviation is one, the interdecile range is approximately 2.56 standard deviation units, the interquartile range is about 1.35 standard deviation units, and the mean deviation is 0.7979 standard deviation units for this distribution. These results hold true for the entire family of normal distributions.

The following example is provided to illustrate a theoretical situation of a long-tailed distribution for which measures such as the median and interquartile and interdecile ranges are more appropriate for central tendency and dispersion than the mean and variance.

Example 3.12 Let X be a random variable with probability density function

$$f(x) = \begin{cases} \dfrac{1}{8} x^{-1/2} \exp(-x^{1/2}/4) & x > 0 \\ 0 & \text{elsewhere.} \end{cases}$$

Determine the mean, variance, standard deviation, median, interquartile range, and interdecile range of X.

It is left as an exercise to the reader to graph this probability density function and to verify that it integrates to one. The reader will no doubt notice that this density exhibits a fast decay toward the horizontal axis. As a result, it may be an appropriate distribution to represent, say, age at which death occurred as a result of childhood diseases, such as scarlet fever and diphtheria a generation ago, and to some extent, leukemia today.

---

*The use of Table D is fully explained in Chapter 5.

The expected value of X is

$$E(X) = \frac{1}{8} \int_0^\infty x^{1/2} \exp(-x^{1/2}/4)dx = \frac{1}{8} \int_0^\infty 4u \exp(-u)32u\,du = 16\Gamma(3) = 32,$$

where $u = x^{1/2}/4$, $x = 16u^2$, and $dx = 32u\,du$. Similarly,

$$E(X^2) = \frac{1}{8} \int_0^\infty x^{3/2} \exp(-x^{1/2}/4)dx = 256 \int_0^\infty u^4 \exp(-u)du = 256\Gamma(5) = 6{,}144.$$

So $Var(X) = 5{,}120$ and $s.d.(X) = 71.55$.

To determine the quantile values in this example, it would be easier to first determine the cumulative distribution function:

$$F(x) = \frac{1}{8} \int_0^x t^{-1/2} \exp(-t^{1/4}/4)dt = \int_0^{x^{1/2}/4} \exp(-u)du = 1 - \exp(-x^{1/2}/4),$$

where, as before, $u = t^{1/2}/4$ and $dt = 32u\,du$. By definition, the median is the value $x_{0.5}$ such that $F(x_{0.5}) = 0.5$. Then

$$1 - \exp(-x_{0.5}^{1/2}/4) = 0.5$$

$$\exp(-x_{0.5}^{1/2}/4) = 0.5$$

$$(-x_{0.5}^{1/2}/4) = \ln(0.5)$$

and

$$x_{0.5} = [-4 \ln(0.5)]^2 = 7.6872.$$

In other words, 50% of the values of X will be less than 7.6872, although the mean of X is 32, a sizable difference between the median and mean values. To show how inappropriate the mean of X would be as the sole measure of central tendency, consider the probability that X is less than its mean value:

$$P(X < 32) = F(32) = 1 - \exp(-32^{1/2}/4) = 0.7569.$$

The mean value of 32 can hardly be construed as a truly representative measure of central tendency if the probability of the random variable exceeding its mean value is less than 0.25.

The 10th, 25th, 75th, and 90th percentiles are determined by solving for x_q the equations $F(x_q) = 0.1$, 0.25, 0.75, and 0.90, respectively. Hence,

$$1 - \exp(-x_{0.1}^{1/2}/4) = 0.1$$

$$\exp(-x_{0.1}^{1/2}/4) = 0.9$$

$$x_{0.1} = [-4 \ln(0.9)]^2,$$

and $x_{0.1} = 0.1776$. Similarly, we determine that $x_{0.25} = [-4 \ln(0.75)]^2 = 1.3242$, $x_{0.75} = [-4 \ln(0.25)]^2 = 30.7490$, and $x_{0.9} = [-4 \ln(0.1)]^2 = 84.8304$. The interquartile range of X is $x_{0.75} - x_{0.25} = 30.7490 - 1.3242 = 29.4248$, and the interdecile range is $x_{0.9} - x_{0.1} = 84.8304 - 0.1776 = 84.6528$. Notice that the standard deviation of X is nearly 2.5 times the interquartile range and almost as large as the interdecile range. This result along with the facts that 25% of the values of X are less than 1.3242, 50% are less than 7.6872, and 75% are less than 30.749 point to the inadequacy of the variance, and thus the standard deviation, as the sole measure of variability in this situation.

3.7   Moment Generating Functions

We have already looked at direct ways of determining the moments of a random variable given its probability distribution. As an alternative method for determining the moments, we present the expectation of a certain function known as the *moment generating function*.

Definition 3.14   Let X be a random variable. The expected value of $\exp(tX)$ is called the moment generating function of X, denoted by $m_X(t)$, if the expected value exists for every value of t in some interval $-c < t < c$ where c is a positive number. In other words,

$$m_X(t) = E[\exp(tX)] = \sum_x \exp(tx)p(x) \qquad \text{if } X \text{ is discrete, or}$$

$$m_X(t) = E[\exp(tX)] = \int_{-\infty}^{\infty} \exp(tx)f(x)dx \qquad \text{if } X \text{ is continuous.}$$

Note that $m_X(t)$ is a function only of the argument t. If $t = 0$, then $m_X(0) = E(e^0) = 1$. If the moment generating function exists, it can be shown that it is unique and completely determines the probability distribution of X. In other words, if two random variables have the same moment generating function, they must have the same probability distribution. This fact will be used extensively in Chapter 7.

If the moment generating function exists for $-c < t < c$, then its derivatives of all orders will exist at $t = 0$. This assures that $m_X(t)$ will generate all moments of X about the origin. To show this, let us differentiate $m_X(t)$ with respect to t and evaluate the derivative at $t = 0$. Assuming we can interchange differentiation and expectation, we have

$$\frac{dm_X(t)}{dt}\bigg|_{t=0} = \frac{d}{dt} E\left[\exp(tX)\right]\bigg|_{t=0}$$

$$= E\left\{\frac{d}{dt}[\exp(tX)]\right\}$$

$$= E\left[X\exp(tX)\right]\big|_{t=0}$$

$$= E(X) = \mu.$$

Taking the second derivative and evaluating it at $t = 0$, we have

$$\frac{d^2 m_X(t)}{dt^2}\bigg|_{t=0} = \frac{d^2}{dt^2} E[\exp(tX)]\bigg|_{t=0}$$

$$= E\left\{\frac{d^2}{dt^2}[\exp(tX)]\right\}$$

$$= E\left\{\frac{d}{dt}[X\exp(tX)]\right\}$$

$$= E[X^2\exp(tX)]\big|_{t=0}$$

$$= E(X^2) = \mu_2'.$$

Continuing this process of differentiation, we can deduce that

$$\frac{d^r m_X(t)}{dt^r}\bigg|_{t=0} = \frac{d^r}{dt^r} E[\exp(tX)]\bigg|_{t=0}$$

$$= E\left\{\frac{d^r}{dt^r}[\exp(tX)]\right\}$$

$$= E[X^r\exp(tX)]\big|_{t=0}$$

$$= E(X^r) = \mu_r'.$$

The same result would be obtained if we were to replace the exponential function by its power series expansion

$$E[\exp(tX)] = E\left(1 + tX + \frac{t^2 X^2}{2!} + \cdots + \frac{t^r X^r}{r!} + \cdots\right)$$

and take derivatives with respect to t, each time evaluating the derivative at $t = 0$.

The notion of a moment generating function can be extended to other reference points besides the origin. In particular, we define a central moment generating function which, if it exists, will generate all central moments of a probability distribution.

Definition 3.15 Let X be a random variable. The expected value of $\exp[t(X - \mu)]$ is called the central moment generating function of X, denoted by $m_{X-\mu}(t)$, if the expected value exists for every value of t in some interval $-c < t < c$ where c is a positive number.

$$m_{X-\mu}(t) = E\{\exp[t(X - \mu)]\} = \sum_x \exp[t(x - \mu)]p(x) \qquad \text{if } X \text{ is discrete, or}$$

$$m_{X-\mu}(t) = E\{\exp[t(X - \mu)]\} = \int_{-\infty}^{\infty} \exp[t(x - \mu)]f(x)dx \qquad \text{if } X \text{ is continuous.}$$

The verification that $m_{X-\mu}(t)$ generates all central moments is left as an exercise to the reader.

Example 3.13   Let X be a random variable with probability density function

$$f(x) = \begin{cases} \dfrac{1}{\theta} \exp(-x/\theta) & x > 0, \\ 0 & \text{elsewhere,} \end{cases}$$

where θ is some number greater than zero. Determine the moment generating function of X.

By definition

$$m_X(t) = \frac{1}{\theta} \int_0^\infty \exp(tx) \exp(-x/\theta) dx$$

$$= \frac{1}{\theta} \int_0^\infty \exp\left[-x\left(\frac{1}{\theta} - t\right)\right] dx$$

$$= -\frac{\theta}{\theta(1 - \theta t)} \exp\left[-x\left(\frac{1}{\theta} - t\right)\right]\Bigg|_0^\infty$$

$$= (1 - \theta t)^{-1}.$$

Therefore,

$$\frac{dm_X(t)}{dt}\Bigg|_{t=0} = \theta(1 - \theta t)^{-2}\Bigg|_{t=0}$$

$$= \theta = E(X),$$

and

$$\frac{d^2 m_X(t)}{dt^2}\Bigg|_{t=0} = 2\theta^2(1 - \theta t)^{-3}\Bigg|_{t=0}$$

$$= 2\theta^2 = E(X^2).$$

As a result, $Var(X) = 2\theta^2 - \theta^2 = \theta^2$, and so on.

Example 3.14   Let X be a discrete random variable with probability function

$$p(x) = \frac{\exp(-\lambda)\lambda^x}{x!} \qquad x = 0, 1, 2, \ldots,$$

where λ is some number greater than zero. Determine the moment generating function of X.

Appealing to the definition, we have

$$m_X(t) = \sum_{x=0}^{\infty} \frac{\exp(tx)\exp(-\lambda)\,\lambda^x}{x!}$$

$$= \exp(-\lambda) \sum_{x=0}^{\infty} \frac{[\lambda \exp(t)]^x}{x!}.$$

Since

$$\sum_{x=0}^{\infty} \frac{[\lambda \exp(t)]^x}{x!} = 1 + \lambda e^t + \frac{\lambda^2 e^{2t}}{2!} + \cdots + \frac{\lambda^r e^{rt}}{r!} + \cdots$$

$$= \exp[\lambda \exp(t)],$$

then

$$m_X(t) = \exp(-\lambda)\,\exp[\lambda\exp(t)].$$

Hence

$$\left. \frac{dm_X(t)}{dt} \right|_{t=0} = \lambda\exp(-\lambda)\exp(t)\exp\left[\lambda \exp(t)\right] \Big|_{t=0}$$

$$= \lambda = E(X).$$

References

1. J. G. Freund, *Mathematical statistics,* 2nd ed., Prentice-Hall, Englewood Cliffs, N.J., 1971.
2. P. G. Hoel, *Introduction to mathematical statistics,* 4th ed., Wiley, New York, 1971.
3. W. Mendenhall and R. L. Schaeffer, *Mathematical statistics with applications,* Duxbury, North Scituate, Mass., 1973.

Exercises

3.1. Let the number of phone calls received by a switchboard during a five-minute interval be the random variable X with probability function $p(x) = e^{-3} (3)^x/x!$, $x = 0, 1, 2, \ldots$.

   a. Determine the probabilities that X equals 0, 1, 2, 3, 4, 5, 6, and 7.
   b. Graph the probability function for these values of X.
   c. Determine the cumulative distribution function for these values of X.
   d. Graph the cumulative distribution function.

3.2. Let X be a discrete random variable. Determine k such that the function $p(x) = k/x$, $x = 1, 2, 3, 4$, is the probability function of X. Then determine $P(1 \leq X \leq 3)$.

3.3. Let X be a continuous random variable.

a. Determine k such that the function

$$f(x) = \begin{cases} kx^2 & -1 \leqslant x \leqslant 1, \\ 0 & \text{elsewhere} \end{cases}$$

is the probability density function of X.

b. Determine the cumulative distribution function of X and graph $F(x)$.

c. Compute $P(X \geqslant 1/2)$ and $P(-1/2 \leqslant X \leqslant 1/2)$.

3.4. Let X be a continuous random variable.

a. Determine k such that the function

$$f(x) = \begin{cases} k \exp(-x/5) & x > 0, \\ 0 & \text{elsewhere} \end{cases}$$

is the probability density function of X.

b. Graph $f(x)$.

c. Compute $P(X \leqslant 5)$ and $P(0 \leqslant X \leqslant 8)$.

d. Determine $F(x)$ and graph it.

3.5. The life span in hours of an electrical component is a random variable with cumulative distribution function $F(x) = 1 - \exp(-x/100)$, $x > 0$.

a. Determine the probability density function of X.

b. Determine the probability that the life span of such a component will exceed 200 hours.

3.6. Let the cumulative distribution function of a random variable be given by

$$F(x) = \begin{cases} 0 & x < 0, \\ 2x - x^2 & 0 < x < 1, \\ 1 & x > 1. \end{cases}$$

a. Graph $F(x)$.

b. Determine $P(X < 1/2)$ and $P(X > 3/4)$.

c. Determine $f(x)$.

3.7. Let X be a random variable depicting the number of customer arrivals per hour at a retail store. Given the following information,

x	0	1	2	3	4	5	6	7	8
$p(x)$	0.05	0.10	0.10	0.10	0.20	0.25	0.10	0.05	0.05

determine $E(X)$ and $Var(X)$.

3.8. An insurance company must determine the annual premium to be charged for $50,000 one-year term life insurance for males in the 30–35 age bracket. Based on actuarial tables, the rate of death for this group is 5 per 1000 per year. If the random variable X is the monetary gain to the insurance company, determine the annual premium so that the company breaks even for a large number of such policies.

3.9. Let the probability density function of a random variable X be given by

$$f(x) = \begin{cases} 2(1 - x) & 0 < x < 1, \\ 0 & \text{elsewhere.} \end{cases}$$

Determine

a. $E(X)$ b. $Var(X)$

3.10. Let X be a random variable depicting the magnitude of the deviation from the prescribed net weight in grams of containers filled by a certain machine, and let the probability density function of X be given by

$$f(x) = \begin{cases} 1/10 & 0 < x < 10 \\ 0 & \text{elsewhere.} \end{cases}$$

Determine

a. $E(X)$ c. $\alpha_3(X)$
b. $Var(X)$ d. $\alpha_4(X)$

3.11. Assume the length in minutes of a business telephone conversation is a random variable with probability density function

$$f(x) = \begin{cases} \dfrac{1}{4}\exp(-x/4) & x > 0, \\ 0 & \text{elsewhere.} \end{cases}$$

Determine

a. $E(X)$
b. $Var(X)$
c. $\alpha_3(X)$
d. $\alpha_4(X)$
e. Referring to Exercise 3.10 and based on your answers to parts a through d of 3.11, compare the two probability distributions. Which one exhibits the larger relative dispersion?

3.12. The average grade on a statistics test is 62.5 with a standard deviation of 10. The professor suspects that the test may have been too difficult. As a result, she wishes to adjust the grades so that the average is now 70 with a standard deviation of 8. What adjustment of the type $aX + b$, where X is the current grade, should she use?

3.13. Let X be a random variable with mean μ and variance σ^2.

a. Evaluate $E(X - c)^2$ in terms of μ and σ^2 where c is any constant.
b. For what value of c is $E(X - c)^2$ a minimum?

3.14. Referring to Exercise 3.11, show that the random variable $Y = (X - 4)/4$ has mean zero and standard deviation one. Also show that the first and second shape factors of the distribution of Y are the same as those of the distribution of X.

3.15. Let the probability density function of X be as given in Exercise 3.9. Determine the mean deviation of X and compare it to the standard deviation of X.

3.16. Let the probability density function of X be as given in Exercise 3.10. Determine the mean deviation of X and compare it to the standard deviation.

3.17. Suppose the weekly income of professional consultants is a random variable with probability density function

$$f(x) = \begin{cases} \dfrac{1}{800}\exp(-x/800) & x > 0, \\ 0 & \text{elsewhere.} \end{cases}$$

   a. Determine the mean and median incomes.
   b. Determine the interquartile range.
   c. Determine the interdecile range.
   d. Determine the probability of a consultant's weekly income exceeding the average income.

3.18. Verify that the central moment generating function of a random variable X generates all central moments of X.

3.19. Let the probability density function of a random variable X be given by

$$
f(x) = \begin{cases} \dfrac{1}{16} x \exp(-x/4) & x > 0, \\ 0 & \text{elsewhere.} \end{cases}
$$

   a. Determine the moment generating function of X.
   b. Use the moment generating function to determine the mean and variance of X.

3.20. Consider the probability density function as given in Exercise 3.11. Determine the moment generating function and use it to verify that the mean and variance of X are as determined in Exercise 3.11.

3.21. Let X be a discrete random variable with probability function $p(x)$ for $x = 0,1,2,...,n$, and let a, b, and c be any constants. Show that $E(c) = c$, $E(aX + b) = aE(X) + b$, and $E[g(X) + h(X)] = E[g(X)] + E[h(X)]$, where $g(x)$ and $h(x)$ are any two functions of X.

3.22. Recall the discrete random variable X as defined in Exercise 3.21. Use Definitions 3.8 and 3.9 to show that $Var(X) = E(X^2) - E^2(X)$.

CHAPTER FOUR

Some Discrete Probability Distributions

4.1 Introduction

In Chapter 2 we established some basic principles of probability. In Chapter 3 we applied them to define random variables and probability distributions and to develop their general properties. In Chapters 4 and 5 we shall examine in detail some specific probability distributions that have proved themselves empirically to be useful probability models for many types of practical problems. Still, these are theoretical distributions in the sense that their probability functions or density functions have been derived mathematically based on certain assumptions that are assumed to hold for a random phenomenon. The choice of a probability distribution to represent a phenomenon of practical interest should be motivated by as much understanding of the nature of the phenomenon as is possible coupled with verification of the selected distribution through empirical evidence. The temptation to tacitly accept one of these probability distributions as being the appropriate probability model for a given practical problem should be resisted.

We will examine several distributions for both the discrete and continuous cases. In each instance we will discuss at length the distinguishing characteristics of the particular probability distribution and either derive or state means, variances, shape factors, and other numerical descriptive measures. As we suggested in Chapter 1, a probability distribution is usually characterized by one or more quantities called the parameters of the distribution. A parameter can take on any value from a range of possible values and, in that sense, defines a family of probability distributions that all have the same generic probability function or probability density function. We will be dealing with several types of parameters, such as count, proportion, rate, location, scale, and shape. We will adopt the convention of using the letters n and k for count parameters, p for proportion, λ for rate, μ for location, σ and θ for scale, and α and β for shape. When the discussion is of a general nature and no particular type of parameter has been identified, we shall use θ to designate a parameter.

Count and proportion parameters are self-explanatory. A rate parameter represents the rate with which random events occur over time or space. A location parameter relates the probability (density) function to the origin of the measurement scale and thus locates it on the x axis without having any effect on its appearance. The presence of a location parameter μ in the probability (density) function is always in the form of $(x - \mu)$. A scale parameter is a quantity that relates to the physical units of the values of a random variable and thus scales the random variable. A scale parameter influences the dispersion of the random variable, and as a result, it affects the appearance of the probability (density) function. The appearance of a scale parameter θ in the probability (density) function is in the form x/θ. A shape parameter affects the shape of the probability (density) function to a varying degree, depending on the particular model. Although many times a shape parameter is an exponent in the probability (density) function, there is no standard way that it can be associated to x with regard to its appearance in the probability (density) function.

We will examine in detail four families of discrete probability distributions and will comment on their application. These are the binomial, Poisson, hypergeometric, and negative binomial distributions.

4.2   The Binomial Distribution

The *binomial distribution* is one of the most useful discrete probability distributions. Its general areas of application include quality inspection, sales, marketing, medicine, opinion research, and others. It is motivated by the following scenario: Imagine a repetitive experiment in which the result is either the occurrence or nonoccurrence of an event. Without loss of generality, let the event's occurrence when the experiment is performed be labeled as "success" and its nonoccurrence be labeled as "failure." Further, let p be the probability of success at any time the experiment is performed and $1 - p$ be the probability of failure. Suppose the experiment is performed n independent times (called trials), and let the random variable X denote the number of successes observed in the n trials. We are interested in determining the probability of obtaining exactly $X = x$ successes during the n trials. The two key assumptions for the binomial distribution are:

1. The probability of success p remains constant from trial to trial.
2. The n trials are independent of each other.

Several practical problems appear to adhere reasonably well to these assumptions. For example, say a manufacturing process produces a given product in which some units will be defective. If the proportion of defective units produced by this process is constant over a reasonably long period of time and if, as a matter of routine quality inspection, we randomly select a number of these units, then statements of probability regarding the number of defective items can be made by using the binomial distribution. As another illustration, take a "solicitation to buy" campaign. If we assume the probability of purchase is constant for all individuals contacted, then the binomial distribution is the appropriate probability model since the individuals contacted are likely to be independent in their decisions to buy. As a final example, the Center for Disease Control has, among its various functions, the responsibility of monitoring communicable diseases. To meet that responsibility it must estimate the extent of a given communicable disease based on probability. It is doubtful indeed if the probability of contracting a given communicable disease is constant for all individuals of the general population. However, for a certain segment of the population, say those in a given age bracket, the probability of contracting the disease may very well be constant, so the binomial distribution would be an appropriate probability model.

To derive the probability function of the binomial distribution, let us first determine the probability that of the n trials we obtain x consecutive successes first, followed by $n - x$ consecutive failures. Since by assumption the n trials are independent, by Definition 2.15 the probability for this particular order is

$$\underbrace{p \cdot p \cdots p}_{x \text{ terms}} \cdot \underbrace{(1 - p)(1 - p) \cdots (1 - p)}_{(n - x) \text{ terms}} = p^x(1 - p)^{n-x}.$$

The probability of obtaining exactly x successes and $n - x$ failures in any other order remains the same since only the p's and $(1 - p)$'s are rearranged to suit the particular order. Therefore, the probability of exactly x successes and $n - x$ failures in any order is the product of $p^x(1 - p)^{n-x}$ times the number of distinct orders. The latter is the number of combinations of n things taken x at a time. We now have the following definition.

Definition 4.1 Let X be a random variable representing the number of successes out of n independent trials such that the probability of success at any one trial is p. Then X is said to have a binomial distribution with probability function*

$$p(x; n, p) = \begin{cases} \dfrac{n!}{(n - x)!x!} \, p^x(1 - p)^{n-x} & x = 0, 1, 2, \ldots, n, \\ 0 \quad \text{elsewhere.} & 0 \leq p \leq 1, \quad n \text{ integer.} \end{cases} \tag{4.1}$$

The parameters of the binomial distribution are n and p. These two parameters define a family of binomial distributions, each member of the family having the probability function as given by (4.1). To illustrate the effect of these parameters, graphs of the binomial probability function are provided in Figure 4.1. We will elaborate on this effect when we discuss moments and other descriptive measures.

The name "binomial distribution" is derived from the fact that the values of $p(x; n, p)$ for $x = 0, 1, 2, \ldots, n$ are the successive terms in the binomial expansion of $[(1 - p) + p]^n$; that is,

---

*To maintain consistency, we will use the notation $p(\ )$ throughout to indicate a probability mass function. We do not think the reader will be confused by the use of $p(x; n, p)$ for the binomial probability function and the use of the letter p for the proportion parameter.

FIGURE 4.1   Graphs of the binomial probability function

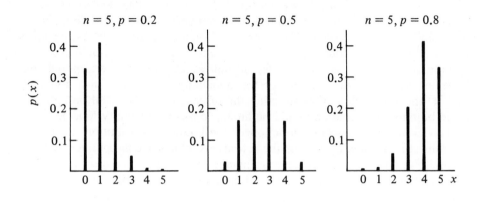

$$[(1 - p) + p]^n = (1 - p)^n + n(1 - p)^{n-1}p + \frac{n(n-1)}{2!}(1 - p)^{n-2}p^2 + \cdots + p^n$$

$$= \sum_{x=0}^{n} \frac{n!}{(n - x)!x!} p^x(1 - p)^{n-x}$$

$$= \sum_{x=0}^{n} p(x; n, p).$$

But since $[(1 - p) + p]^n = 1$ and $p(x; n, p) \geqslant 0$ for $x = 0, 1, 2, ..., n$, this also verifies that $p(x; n, p)$ is a probability function.

To illustrate the computation of probabilities using (4.1), let $n = 5$ and $p = 0.4$. Then

$$p(x; 5, 0.4) = \frac{5!}{(5 - x)!x!}(0.4)^x(0.6)^{5-x}, \quad x = 0, 1, 2, 3, 4, 5;$$

thus

$$p(0; 5, 0.4) = \frac{5!}{(5 - 0)!0!}(0.4)^0(0.6)^{5-0} = 0.0778,$$

$$p(1; 5, 0.4) = \frac{5!}{(5 - 1)!1!}(0.4)^1(0.6)^{5-1} = 0.2592,$$

$$p(2; 5, 0.4) = \frac{5!}{(5 - 2)!2!}(0.4)^2(0.6)^{5-2} = 0.3456,$$

$$p(3; 5, 0.4) = \frac{5!}{(5 - 3)!3!}(0.4)^3(0.6)^{5-3} = 0.2304,$$

$$p(4; 5, 0.4) = \frac{5!}{(5 - 4)!4!}(0.4)^4(0.6)^{5-4} = 0.0768,$$

$$p(5; 5, 0.4) = \frac{5!}{(5-5)!5!} (0.4)^5 (0.6)^{5-5} = 0.0102.$$

The probability that a binomial random variable X is less than or equal to some specified value x is given by the cumulative distribution function

$$P(X \leq x) = F(x; n, p) = \sum_{i=0}^{x} \binom{n}{i} p^i (1-p)^{n-i}. \tag{4.2}$$

The binomial distribution has been tabulated extensively for various values of n and p by using either (4.1) or (4.2) or both. In Table A in the Appendix we provide cumulative probabilities for selected values of x, n, and p. We can also determine individual probabilities using this table since the binomial random variable is integer-valued, and thus the property

$$p(x; n, p) = F(x; n, p) - F(x-1; n, p)$$

holds. To illustrate the use of Table A, let $n = 10$ and $p = 0.3$. The probability that X is at most 4 is

$$P(X \leq 4) = F(4; 10, 0.3) = 0.8497;$$

the probability that X is greater than 2 is

$$P(X > 2) = P(X \geq 3) = 1 - P(X \leq 2) = 1 - F(2; 10, 0.3) = 0.6172;$$

and the probability that X is exactly 5 is

$$p(5; 10, 0.3) = F(5; 10, 0.3) - F(4; 10, 0.3) = 0.1030.$$

It should be noted that if $n = 1$, the binomial probability function reduces to

$$p(x; p) = \begin{cases} p^x (1-p)^{1-x} & x = 0, 1, \\ 0 & \text{elsewhere,} \end{cases} \tag{4.3}$$

which is the probability function of the point binomial or Bernoulli distribution. The Bernoulli distribution is named after Jacques Bernoulli (1654–1705), the Swiss probabilist who developed the concept of independent trials.

Example 4.1 In a manufacturing process 15 units are randomly selected each day from the production line to check the percent defective of the process. Based on historical information, the probability of a defective unit is 0.05. Management has decided to stop the production line for inspection any time a sample of 15 units yields two or more defectives. What is the probability that on any given day the production process will be stopped?

If the binomial distribution is the appropriate model for this situation, we must assume that the 15 units randomly selected each day constitute a set of independent trials such that the probability of a defective unit is constant at 0.05 from trial to trial. Let X be the number of defective units found among the 15.

For $n = 15$ and $p = 0.05$, the probability that the production process will be stopped is the same as the probability that X is greater than or equal to 2. Thus

$$P(X \geqslant 2) = 1 - P(X \leqslant 1) = 1 - F(1; 15, 0.05) = 0.1709.$$

Example 4.2   Suppose that for individuals in a certain age bracket the probability of death as a result of a particular communicable disease is 0.001. How many individuals of this age group could be exposed to the disease such that the probability of no more than a single death occurring among this number is at least 0.95?

   To apply the binomial distribution to this situation, the crucial assumption is that the probability of death is constant for all individuals in this age group who contract the disease. Let X be the number of deaths occurring among n individuals in this age group who have contracted the disease. What is sought is the value of n such that the probability that X is less than or equal to 1 is greater than or equal to 0.95:

$$P(X \leqslant 1) = F(1; n, 0.001) \geqslant 0.95,$$

and for the equality

$$\sum_{x=0}^{1} \binom{n}{x} (0.001)^x (0.999)^{n-x} = 0.95$$

$$\binom{n}{0} (0.001)^0 (0.999)^n + \binom{n}{1} (0.001)^1 (0.999)^{n-1} = 0.95$$

$$(0.999)^{n-1}(0.999 + 0.001n) = 0.95.$$

This equation cannot be solved explicitly for n; however, by iterative techniques* we can determine that the integer value of n that comes closest to satisfying the equation is $n = 356$.

   We turn our attention now to the determination of the moments for the binomial distribution. We will illustrate both the direct method, based on Definition 3.8, and the indirect method, based on the moment generating function.

   By Definition 3.8 the first moment about zero of the binomial random variable X is the expected value of X

$$E(X) = \sum_{x=0}^{n} x \, \frac{n!}{(n-x)!x!} \, p^x (1-p)^{n-x}$$

$$= \sum_{x=1}^{n} x \, \frac{n!}{(n-x)!x!} \, p^x (1-p)^{n-x}$$

$$= \sum_{x=1}^{n} \frac{n!}{(n-x)!(x-1)!} \, p^x (1-p)^{n-x},$$

---

*An iterative technique is a numerical method of solving for the unknown in an equation by successively attempting updated values for the unknown until the value is found that comes closest to satisfying the equation.

where we have written the sum to range from 1 to n since, when $x = 0$, the first term is zero, and where we have canceled the x in the numerator with the x in $x!$. Factoring out n and p, we have

$$E(X) = np \sum_{x=1}^{n} \frac{(n-1)!}{(n-x)!(x-1)!} p^{x-1}(1-p)^{n-x}.$$

If we let $y = x - 1$ and $m = n - 1$, then

$$E(X) = np \sum_{y=0}^{m} \frac{m!}{(m-y)!y!} p^{y}(1-p)^{n-y}.$$

But $p(y; m, p) = [m!/(m-y)!y!]p^{y}(1-p)^{m-y}$ is the probability function of a binomial random variable Y with parameters $m = n - 1$ and p; thus $\sum_{y=0}^{m} p(y; m, p) = 1$, and the mean of a binomial random variable is

$$E(X) = \mu = np. \tag{4.4}$$

To obtain the variance, we need the second moment about zero, μ'_2, or

$$E(X^2) = \sum_{x=0}^{n} x^2 p(x; n, p);$$

but here, in the term $x^2/x!$ we will be able to cancel only one of the x's in the numerator, and the remaining x will prevent manipulation of the sum as was done in determining the mean. The alternative is to write x^2 as

$$x^2 = x(x-1) + x;$$

thus

$$E(X^2) = E[X(X-1)] + E(X). \tag{4.5}$$

Since $E(X)$ has already been determined, we use the same procedure to evaluate $E[X(X-1)]$:

$$E[X(X-1)] = \sum_{x=0}^{n} x(x-1) \frac{n!}{(n-x)!x!} p^x(1-p)^{n-x}$$

$$= \sum_{x=2}^{n} x(x-1) \frac{n!}{(n-x)!x!} p^x(1-p)^{n-x}$$

$$= \sum_{x=2}^{n} \frac{n!}{(n-x)!(x-2)!} p^x(1-p)^{n-x}$$

$$= n(n-1)p^2 \sum_{x=2}^{n} \frac{(n-2)!}{(n-x)!(x-2)!} p^{x-2}(1-p)^{n-x}.$$

Note that in the previous steps we have written the sum to range from 2 to n since the first two terms are zero, we have canceled $x(x-1)$, and we have factored out $n(n-1)p^2$. Now let $y = x - 2$ and $m = n - 2$; then

$$E[X(X - 1)] = n(n - 1)p^2 \sum_{y=0}^{m} \frac{m!}{(m - y)!y!} p^y(1 - p)^{m-y}$$

$$= n(n - 1)p^2 \sum_{y=0}^{m} p(y; m, p)$$

$$= n(n - 1)p^2.$$

From (4.5),

$$E(X^2) = \mu'_2 = n(n - 1)p^2 + np.$$

Thus the variance of a binomial random variable is

$$Var(X) = \mu'_2 - \mu^2$$

$$= n(n - 1)p^2 + np - n^2p^2$$

$$= np\,[(n - 1)p + 1 - np]$$

$$= np(1 - p). \tag{4.6}$$

This general method can be extended to determine higher moments. For example, to obtain the third moment about zero, we will determine $E[X(X - 1)(X - 2)]$ since

$$E[X(X - 1)(X - 2)]^* = \mu'_3 - 3\mu'_2 + 2\mu. \tag{4.7}$$

Similarly, for the fourth moment about zero, we will evaluate $E[X(X - 1)(X - 2)(X - 3)]$ since

$$E[X(X - 1)(X - 2)(X - 3)]^* = \mu'_4 - 6\mu'_3 + 11\mu'_2 - 6\mu. \tag{4.8}$$

For a binomial random variable,

$$E[X(X - 1)(X - 2)] = \sum_{x=0}^{n} x(x - 1)(x - 2)\frac{n!}{(n - x)!x!} p^x(1 - p)^{n-x}$$

$$= \sum_{x=3}^{n} \frac{n!}{(n - x)!(x - 3)!} p^x(1 - p)^{n-x}$$

$$= n(n - 1)(n - 2)p^3 \sum_{x=3}^{n} \frac{(n - 3)!}{(n - x)!(x - 3)!} p^{x-3}(1 - p)^{n-x}$$

$$= n(n - 1)(n - 2)p^3 \sum_{y=0}^{m} \frac{m!}{(m - y)!y!} p^y(1 - p)^{m-y}$$

$$= n(n - 1)(n - 2)p^3.$$

---

*Expressions such as these yield what are called factorial moments. In fact, the rth factorial moment of a random variable X is $E[X(X - 1)(X - 2) \cdots (X - r + 1)]$.

Using (4.7),

$$\mu_3' - 3\mu_2' + 2\mu = n(n-1)(n-2)p^3$$

$$\mu_3' = n(n-1)(n-2)p^3 + 3[n(n-1)p^2 + np] - 2np$$

$$= n(n-1)(n-2)p^3 + 3n(n-1)p^2 + np. \tag{4.9}$$

The third central moment μ_3 can be determined by using (3.8),

$$\mu_3 = n(n-1)(n-2)p^3 + 3n(n-1)p^2 + np - 3np[n(n-1)p^2 + np] + 2n^3p^3,$$

which, after some algebra, reduces to

$$\mu_3 = np(1-p)(1-2p). \tag{4.10}$$

Therefore, from (3.9) the standardized third moment for the binomial distribution is

$$\alpha_3 = \frac{np(1-p)(1-2p)}{[np(1-p)]^{3/2}}$$

$$= \frac{np(1-p)(1-2p)}{np(1-p)[np(1-p)]^{1/2}}$$

$$= \frac{1-2p}{[np(1-p)]^{1/2}}. \tag{4.11}$$

For the fourth moment about zero, we have

$$E[X(X-1)(X-2)(X-3)] = \sum_{x=0}^{n} x(x-1)(x-2)(x-3)$$

$$\cdot \frac{n!}{(n-x)!x!} p^x(1-p)^{n-x}$$

$$= \sum_{x=4}^{n} \frac{n!}{(n-x)!(x-4)!} p^x(1-p)^{n-x}$$

$$= n(n-1)(n-2)(n-3)p^4$$

$$\cdot \sum_{x=4}^{n} \frac{(n-4)!}{(n-x)!(x-4)!} p^{x-4}(1-p)^{n-x}$$

$$= n(n-1)(n-2)(n-3)p^4$$

$$\cdot \sum_{y=0}^{m} \frac{m!}{(m-y)!y!} p^y(1-p)^{m-y}$$

$$= n(n-1)(n-2)(n-3)p^4.$$

Substituting in (4.8) and solving for μ_4', we have

$$\mu_4' = n(n-1)(n-2)(n-3)p^4 + 6[n(n-1)(n-2)p^2$$
$$+ 3n(n-1)p^2 + np] - 11[n(n-1)p^2 + np] + 6np. \quad (4.12)$$

According to (3.10), the fourth central moment is

$$\mu_4 = \mu_4' - 4\mu\mu_3' + 6\mu^2\mu_2' - 3\mu^4,$$

which, after appropriate substitution and some algebra, works out to be

$$\mu_4 = np(1-p)\{3np(1-p) + [1 - 6p(1-p)]\}. \quad (4.13)$$

Then by (3.11) the standardized fourth moment for the binomial distribution is

$$\alpha_4 = \frac{np(1-p)\{3np(1-p) + [1 - 6p(1-p)]\}}{n^2p^2(1-p)^2} = 3 + \frac{[1 - 6p(1-p)]}{np(1-p)}. \quad (4.14)$$

The basic properties of the binomial distribution are summarized in Table 4.1. Notice that the mean of a binomial random variable is the product of the number of trials and the probability of success at each trial, and the variance is the product of the mean and the probability of failure. The variance of a binomial random variable is always less than the mean.

To obtain a better perspective on the binomial distribution and its shape factors, let us compute α_3 and α_4 for various values of the parameter p, as given in Table 4.2. We can conclude from the table that the binomial distribution is symmetric if $p = 1/2$, positively skewed if $p < 1/2$, and negatively skewed if $p > 1/2$. For the latter two cases, the skewness becomes less apparent as n becomes large. In addition, the binomial distribution is relatively flat-topped if $p = 1/2$. For any other value of p, the binomial distribution is relatively high-peaked. However, the point must be made that if n is substantially large, α_4 approaches 3 for any value of p, and the distribution is mesokurtic.

By Definition 3.14, the moment generating function for the binomial distribution is

$$m_X(t) = E(e^{tX}) = \sum_{x=0}^{n} e^{tx} \frac{n!}{(n-x)!x!} p^x(1-p)^{n-x}$$

TABLE 4.1   Basic properties of the binomial distribution

Probability function		Parameters
$p(x; n, p) = \dfrac{n!}{(n-x)!x!} p^x(1-p)^{n-x}$ $x = 0, 1, 2, ..., n$		n, positive integer $p, 0 \le p \le 1$

Mean	Variance	Coefficient of skewness	Relative kurtosis
np	$np(1-p)$	$\dfrac{1-2p}{[np(1-p)]^{1/2}}$	$3 + \dfrac{[1 - 6p(1-p)]}{np(1-p)}$

TABLE 4.2 Shape factors of the binomial distribution for various values of p

	$p = 1/10$	$p = 1/2$	$p = 9/10$
α_3	$\dfrac{8}{3\sqrt{n}}$	0	$-\dfrac{8}{3\sqrt{n}}$
α_4	$3 + \dfrac{46}{9n}$	$3 - \dfrac{2}{n}$	$3 + \dfrac{46}{9n}$

$$= \sum_{x=0}^{n} \frac{n!}{(n-x)!x!}(e^t p)^x (1-p)^{n-x}$$

$$= (1-p)^n + n(1-p)^{n-1}(e^t p)$$

$$+ \frac{n(n-1)}{2!}(1-p)^{n-2}(e^t p)^2 + \cdots + (e^t p)^n$$

$$= [(1-p) + e^t p]^n. \tag{4.15}$$

By taking the first two derivatives of (4.15) with respect to t we have

$$\frac{dm_X(t)}{dt} = ne^t p[(1-p) + e^t p]^{n-1}$$

and

$$\frac{d^2 m_X(t)}{dt^2} = n(n-1)(e^t p)^2[(1-p) + e^t p]^{n-2} + ne^t p[(1-p) + e^t p]^{n-1}.$$

By letting $t = 0$, we obtain the first and second moments about zero,

$$\left.\frac{dm_X(t)}{dt}\right|_{t=0} = np[(1-p) + p]^{n-1}$$

$$= np$$

and

$$\left.\frac{d^2 m_X(t)}{dt^2}\right|_{t=0} = n(n-1)p^2[(1-p) + p]^{n-2} + np[(1-p) + p]^{n-1}$$

$$= n(n-1)p^2 + np,$$

which are precisely the same as those determined by using the direct method. Higher moments can be determined by continuing this process of differentiating the moment generating function and evaluating the derivative for $t = 0$. Note that for this case the first two moments about zero were easier to obtain by using the moment generating function than by the direct method. However, this occurrence does not necessarily hold in general.

Example 4.3 A national motor club has begun a telephone drive to increase its membership. The club has determined from prior experience that about one out of 20 persons contacted joins the club. If on a given day 25 persons are contacted, what is the probability that at least two of them will subscribe for membership? What is the expected number?

Since in the long run one out of 20 persons contacted subscribes to membership, $p = 0.05$. Moreover, if we assume that the 25 persons contacted daily constitute a set of independent trials (a very reasonable assumption in this case) with constant probability for subscription of $p = 0.05$, and if we let the random variable X be the number among the $n = 25$ that end up subscribing, the desired probability is

$$P(X \geq 2) = 1 - P(X \leq 1) = 1 - F(1; 25, 0.05) = 0.3576.$$

Using (4.4), the expected value of X is $E(X) = (25)(0.05) = 1.25$.

4.3 The Poisson Distribution

The *Poisson distribution* (named after Siméon Denis Poisson, the nineteenth century French probabilist who described it) is another extremely useful discrete probability distribution in which the random variable represents the number of occurrences of independent events that take place at a constant rate. Many random events occur independently with a constant rate over time or space. Typical examples are the number of arrivals to a service facility in a given time span, the number of flaws in similar pieces of a given material, the number of similar units that fail in a specified time period, the number of bacteria in a given culture, the number of insurance claims processed by a large company over a given period of time, and so on. In fact, the Poisson distribution is the premier probability model used to analyze waiting-line problems. In addition, it offers excellent approximation to the binomial probability function when p is small and n is large. The Poisson probability function is derived in an appendix to this chapter.

Definition 4.2 Let X be a random variable representing the number of independent random events that occur at a constant rate over time or space. Then X is said to have a Poisson distribution with probability function

$$p(x; \lambda) = \begin{cases} \dfrac{e^{-\lambda}\lambda^x}{x!} & x = 0, 1, 2, \ldots; \quad \lambda > 0, \\ 0 & \text{elsewhere.} \end{cases} \quad (4.16)$$

The parameter of the Poisson distribution is λ, the average number of occurrences of the random event per unit of time. For values greater than zero, λ defines a family of distributions with probability function given by (4.16). Graphs of the Poisson probability function for various values of λ are provided in Figure 4.2.

FIGURE 4.2   Graphs of the Poisson probability function

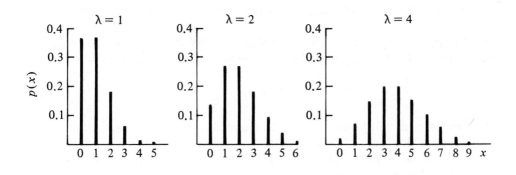

We can verify that (4.16) is a probability function since $p(x; \lambda) > 0$ for $x = 0, 1, 2, \ldots,$ and

$$\sum_{x=0}^{\infty} p(x; \lambda) = \sum_{x=0}^{\infty} \frac{e^{-\lambda}\lambda^x}{x!}$$

$$= e^{-\lambda} \sum_{x=0}^{\infty} \frac{\lambda^x}{x!}$$

$$= e^{-\lambda}\left(1 + \lambda + \frac{\lambda^2}{2!} + \cdots\right)$$

$$= e^{-\lambda}e^{\lambda}$$

$$= 1.$$

To illustrate, let $\lambda = 1.2$; then

$$p(x; 1.2) = \frac{e^{-1.2}1.2^x}{x!}, \quad x = 0, 1, 2, \ldots .$$

Thus

$$p(0; 1.2) = \frac{e^{-1.2}1.2^0}{0!} = 0.3012, \qquad p(4; 1.2) = \frac{e^{-1.2}1.2^4}{4!} = 0.0260,$$

$$p(1; 1.2) = \frac{e^{-1.2}1.2^1}{1!} = 0.3614, \qquad p(5; 1.2) = \frac{e^{-1.2}1.2^5}{5!} = 0.0062,$$

$$p(2; 1.2) = \frac{e^{-1.2}1.2^2}{2!} = 0.2169, \qquad p(6; 1.2) = \frac{e^{-1.2}1.2^6}{6!} = 0.0012,$$

$$p(3; 1.2) = \frac{e^{-1.2}1.2^3}{3!} = 0.0867, \qquad p(7; 1.2) = \frac{e^{-1.2}1.2^7}{7!} = 0.0002.$$

Although we can continue this process without end, we notice that the individual probabilities are becoming smaller and smaller as the random variable assumes larger and larger values. This is a general characteristic of the Poisson distribution.

The probability that a Poisson random variable X is less than or equal to some specified value x is given by the cumulative distribution function

$$P(X \leq x) = F(x; \lambda) = \sum_{i=0}^{x} \frac{e^{-\lambda}\lambda^i}{i!}. \tag{4.17}$$

In Table B of the Appendix, (4.17) is tabulated for selected values of x and λ. Notice again that since the Poisson random variable is integer-valued, we may use the cumulative probabilities of Table B to determine individual probabilities using the relation

$$p(x; \lambda) = F(x; \lambda) - F(x - 1; \lambda).$$

Several illustrations of the use of Table B now follow. Let $\lambda = 2.5$. The probability that X is less than 3 is

$$P(X < 3) = P(X \leq 2) = F(2; 2.5) = 0.5438;$$

the probability that X is no less than 4 is

$$P(X \geq 4) = 1 - P(X \leq 3) = 1 - F(3; 2.5) = 0.2424;$$

and the probability that X is exactly 2 is

$$p(2; 2.5) = F(2; 2.5) - F(1; 2.5) = 0.2565.$$

Example 4.4   After extensive lab testing of some electrical component, the manufacturer has determined that the average number of such components that fail prior to 1000 hours of operation is two. A buyer of a large number of these items has observed recently that five of them have failed inside 1000 hours. If the number of items that fail within 1000 hours is a Poisson random variable, is there sufficient evidence to doubt the manufacturer's conclusion?

Doubt in statistics can be supported in terms of probability. Whether or not an event should occur under certain conditions is decided on the probability of the event's occurrence given these conditions. If the probability of occurrence is small but the event has occurred anyway, then one may question, with some justification, the given conditions. At the same time, one must also keep in mind that however small the probability of occurrence really is, unless it is zero it does not preclude the event from ever occurring. Here we are given that $\lambda = 2$. We assume that the constant rate with which failures occur is two per 1000 hours, or an average of 1/500 units fail per hour. The probability of exactly five units failing in 1000 hours is

$$p(5; 2) = \frac{e^{-2}2^5}{5!} = 0.0361,$$

and the probability of at least five units failing in 1000 hours is

$$P(X \geq 5) = 1 - F(4; 2) = 0.0527.$$

Both of these probabilities are relatively small. That is, if the number of failures in 1000 hours is adequately described by the Poisson distribution with a constant rate of two, by chance alone there is only a 0.0361 probability of observing exactly five failures and a 0.0527 probability of observing at least five failures within 1000 hours of operation. However, before we are ready to take action against the manufacturer, some questions still need to be answered. For example, is the rate with which failures occur really constant at two per 1000 hours? And even if it were, is the environment under which the five failed components were operated the same as the environment that prevailed when the manufacturer was doing the testing? That is, is it possible that we may have inadvertently introduced extraneous factors that might have caused the unexpectedly high number of failures? Only an understanding of the particular situation can answer these questions.

Example 4.5 Consider the game of football as played by the 28 teams of the National Football League. Let the random variable of interest be the number of touchdowns (6 points) scored by each individual team per game. Given the actual number of touchdowns scored by each team in every game played during the 1979 regular season, is there reason to believe that the number of touchdowns is a Poisson random variable?

To answer the question, our approach at this time will be to compare the observed results with what would be expected if the number of touchdowns is a Poisson random variable, as in Table 4.3. The fourth column in the table indicates the theoretical probability for each of the values in the first column if the number of touchdowns is a Poisson random variable.

TABLE 4.3 Distribution of touchdowns scored per team per game during 1979 in the NFL

Number of touchdowns	Observed number of occurrences	Relative frequency	Theoretical probability	Expected number of occurrences
0	35	0.0781	0.0876	39.24
1	99	0.2210	0.2133	95.56
2	104	0.2321	0.2597	116.34
3	110	0.2455	0.2108	94.44
4	62	0.1384	0.1283	57.48
5	25	0.0558	0.0625	28.00
6	10	0.0223	0.0254	11.38
7*	3	0.0067	0.0124	5.56
Totals	448	0.9999	1.0000	448

*Actually this represents seven or more touchdowns, but this occurrence is definitely rare in the NFL.

The entries in the fourth column are found by first computing the value of the Poisson parameter λ and then evaluating the probability function (4.16) for the various values in column one. The value of λ is determined by forming the sum of the products of the corresponding entries of the first and third columns,

$$\lambda = (0)(0.0781) + (1)(0.2210) + \cdots + (7)(0.0067)$$

$$= 2.435,$$

which represents the average number of touchdowns scored per team per game. We compute the point probabilities using

$$p(x; 2.435) = \frac{e^{-2.435}(2.435)^x}{x!} \qquad x = 0, 1, 2, \dots .$$

These are the first seven entries in the fourth column of the table. The last entry in this column is the probability that X is greater than or equal to 7. The entries in the last column are found by multiplying each entry in column four by 448.

A comparison of columns two and five, or columns three and four, reveals a reasonably close agreement. Hence we would be inclined to conclude that the number of touchdowns is a Poisson random variable. Whether it truly is Poisson has to hinge on whether the number of touchdowns scored per team per game in the NFL constitutes a set of independent random events such that the rate of occurrence is constant during the 60 minutes of playing time. It should be noted that the rate of scoring touchdowns may indeed be constant in the NFL because the caliber of play and opposition appear to be much more uniform than, say, in collegiate football.

The Poisson distribution is also a limiting form of the binomial when $n \to \infty$ and $p \to 0$ in such a way that np remains constant. This result is obtained by stating the following theorem, which is due to Siméon Poisson.

Theorem 4.1   Let the random variable X be binomially distributed with probability function

$$p(x; n, p) = \frac{n!}{(n - x)!x!} p^x (1 - p)^{n-x} \qquad x = 0, 1, 2, \dots n.$$

If for $n = 1, 2, \dots$, the relation $p = \lambda/n$ holds for some constant $\lambda > 0$, then

$$\lim_{\substack{n \to \infty \\ p \to 0}} p(x; n, p) = \frac{e^{-\lambda}\lambda^x}{x!}, \qquad x = 0, 1, 2, \dots .$$

The proof of Theorem 4.1 is provided in an appendix to this chapter.

In the context of Theorem 4.1, the Poisson distribution is thought of as one in which the random variable can take on many different values — n is large — but with small probabilities — $p = \lambda/n$ is near zero. As a result, the Poisson probability function is used extensively to approximate the binomial probability function when n is relatively large and p is small, so that $\lambda = np$ is of moderate magnitude. In Table 4.4 we illustrate the improvement in the Poisson approximation

TABLE 4.4 Comparison of binomial and Poisson probabilities

	Binomial				Poisson
x	$p(x;\ 10,\ 0.2)$	$p(x;\ 20,\ 0.1)$	$p(x;\ 40,\ 0.05)$	$p(x;\ 100,\ 0.02)$	$p(x;\ 2)$
0	0.1074	0.1216	0.1285	0.1326	0.1353
1	0.2684	0.2702	0.2706	0.2707	0.2707
2	0.3020	0.2852	0.2777	0.2734	0.2707
3	0.2013	0.1901	0.1851	0.1823	0.1804
4	0.0881	0.0898	0.0901	0.0902	0.0902
5	0.0264	0.0319	0.0342	0.0353	0.0361
6	0.0055	0.0089	0.0105	0.0114	0.0120
7	0.0008	0.0020	0.0027	0.0031	0.0034
8	0.0001	0.0004	0.0006	0.0007	0.0009
9	0.0000	0.0001	0.0001	0.0002	0.0002

of the binomial probability function as n increases and p decreases such that $\lambda = np$ remains constant at 2.

Example 4.6 A buyer of large quantities of integrated circuits has adopted an acceptance plan that calls for the inspection of a sample of 100 chips randomly selected from a very large lot. If the buyer finds no more than two defective chips in the sample, the entire lot is accepted; otherwise the lot is rejected. If a lot containing 1 percent defectives is shipped to the buyer, what is the probability that it will be accepted?

Let the random variable X be the number of defective chips found in the sample of 100 and assume that X is binomially distributed. In other words, we assume that the 100 chips randomly selected from the large lot constitute 100 independent trials such that the probability of a defective chip is constant at 0.01. The probability of lot acceptance is the same as the probability that X is less than or equal to 2. Since $n = 100$ is relatively large and $p = 0.01$ is small, we can approximate the binomial probability by using the Poisson distribution, letting $\lambda = np = 1$:

$$P(\text{acceptance}) \equiv P(X \le 2) = F_P^*(2;\ 1) = 0.9197.$$

It should be noted for comparison that if the binomial distribution function were used,

$$P(X \le 2) = F_B^*(2;\ 100,\ 0.01) = 0.9206.$$

The moments of a Poisson random variable are determined along the same lines used to obtain the moments of a binomial random variable. If X is Poisson, its expected value is

---

*We are using the subscripts here to distinguish between the two distribution functions. We will use the same labeling to distinguish between probability functions, when necessary.

$$E(X) = \sum_{x=0}^{\infty} x \frac{e^{-\lambda}\lambda^x}{x!}$$

$$= e^{-\lambda} \sum_{x=1}^{\infty} \frac{\lambda^x}{(x-1)!}$$

$$= \lambda e^{-\lambda} \sum_{x=1}^{\infty} \frac{\lambda^{x-1}}{(x-1)!}$$

$$= \lambda e^{-\lambda} \sum_{y=0}^{\infty} \frac{\lambda^y}{y!}, \qquad y = x - 1$$

$$= \lambda. \tag{4.18}$$

For the variance of X,

$$E[X(X-1)] = \sum_{x=0}^{\infty} x(x-1) \frac{e^{-\lambda}\lambda^x}{x!}$$

$$= \lambda^2 e^{-\lambda} \sum_{x=2}^{\infty} \frac{\lambda^{x-2}}{(x-2)!}$$

$$= \lambda^2 e^{-\lambda} \sum_{y=0}^{\infty} \frac{\lambda^y}{y!}, \qquad y = x - 2$$

$$= \lambda^2. \tag{4.19}$$

Then, from (4.5),

$$E(X^2) = \mu_2' = \lambda^2 + \lambda,$$

and the variance of X is

$$Var(X) = \mu_2' - \mu^2$$

$$= \lambda^2 + \lambda - \lambda^2$$

$$= \lambda. \tag{4.20}$$

Thus a distinct characteristic of a Poisson random variable is that its mean is equal to its variance.

For the third moment, it is left as an exercise for the reader to show that

$$E[X(X-1)(X-2)] = \lambda^3. \tag{4.21}$$

By using (4.7),

$$\mu_3' = \lambda^3 + 3\lambda^2 + \lambda,$$

and the third central moment is

$$\mu_3 = \lambda.$$

As a result, the coefficient of skewness turns out to be

$$\alpha_3 = \mu_3/\mu_2'^{3/2} = 1/\sqrt{\lambda}. \tag{4.22}$$

For the fourth moment, one can use the same procedure as before to show that

$$E[X(X - 1)(X - 2)(X - 3)] = \lambda^4,\qquad(4.23)$$

and from (4.8),

$$\mu_4' = \lambda^4 + 6\lambda^3 + 7\lambda^2 + \lambda.\qquad(4.24)$$

Thus by using (3.10) the fourth central moment is

$$\mu_4 = 3\lambda^2 + \lambda,$$

and the standardized fourth moment for the Poisson distribution is

$$\alpha_4 = \mu_4/\mu_2^2 = 3 + \frac{1}{\lambda}.\qquad(4.25)$$

A summary of the Poisson distribution properties is provided in Table 4.5. The Poisson distribution is positively skewed for any value $\lambda > 0$, but the skewness diminishes for relatively large values of λ. In addition, the Poisson distribution is leptokurtic since α_4 is greater than 3 but tends to become mesokurtic for large λ.

The moment generating function for the Poisson distribution is

$$m_X(t) = \sum_{x=0}^{\infty} e^{tx} \frac{e^{-\lambda}\lambda^x}{x!}$$

$$= e^{-\lambda} \sum_{x=0}^{\infty} \frac{(\lambda e^t)^x}{x!}$$

$$= e^{-\lambda} e^{\lambda e^t}$$

$$= \exp[\lambda(e^t - 1)].\qquad(4.26)$$

Note that $m_X(0) = e^{\lambda(1-1)} = 1$, as it should. It is left as an exercise to the reader to show that (4.26) yields the moments of a Poisson random variable after appropriate differentiation.

In conclusion, the Poisson distribution is a positively skewed leptokurtic distribution that is used to model the number of independent random events that

TABLE 4.5 Basic properties of the Poisson distribution

Probability function			*Parameter*
$p(x; \lambda) = \dfrac{e^{-\lambda}\lambda^x}{x!}$ $x = 0, 1, 2, \ldots$			$\lambda > 0$

Mean	*Variance*	*Coefficient of skewness*	*Relative kurtosis*
λ	λ	$\dfrac{1}{\sqrt{\lambda}}$	$3 + \dfrac{1}{\lambda}$

occur at a constant rate over time or space. It has been used extensively to represent scenarios in the study of waiting lines, reliability, and quality control. It is also a limiting form of the binomial distribution and adequately approximates binomial probabilities for large n and small p. One should exercise care, however, in applying the Poisson distribution to situations in which the conditions of independence and constant rate of occurrence are doubtful.

Imagine, for example, the distribution of the number of speeding tickets received by drivers over, say, a ten-year period. One might be tempted to argue for the Poisson distribution since the probability of receiving a ticket on a given day is rather small and there are many days in ten years. However, it is unlikely that the conditions of independence and constant rate of occurrence would hold. Independence would be doubtful because if a particular driver receives a speeding ticket, it is reasonable to think that he or she would become more careful. The rates of occurrence for various age groups could be expected to vary since many insurance companies claim that older drivers are more obedient to speed limits than younger ones.

4.4   The Hypergeometric Distribution

To establish the basic conditions leading to another discrete probability distribution, known as the *hypergeometric,* consider the following problem: Let N be the number of delegates from a given state attending a national political convention, and let k of them be pledged to candidate A, while the remaining $N - k$ are pledged to candidate B. Suppose n of these delegates are randomly selected by a news organization to gauge delegate sentiment concerning an important rules issue on which the delegates are thought to be divided along candidate lines. If X is a random variable representing the number of delegates in the sample pledged to A, what is the probability function of X?

On the surface this situation may appear to be binomial since among the N delegates from this state there are two distinct groups with respective probabilities of k/N and $(N - k)/N$. However, look at the selection process for the sample of n delegates. It is reasonable to assume that once a delegate is selected and queried, that same delegate will not be selected again.* As a result, we will no longer have independence in the selection of one delegate to the next. For example, suppose the first delegate selected turns out to be pledged to candidate A. Now there are $N - 1$ delegates remaining of which $k - 1$ are pledged to A. Therefore, the conditional probability that the next delegate selected is also pledged to A is $(k - 1)/(N - 1)$ and not $k/N,$ and the conditional probability that the next delegate is pledged to B is $(N - k)/(N - 1)$ and not $(N - k)/N.$

To determine the probability that exactly x delegates pledged to A and $n - x$ delegates pledged to B are selected in the sample, we argue as follows: The number of distinct ways a sample of n delegates can be selected from a total of

---

*This is known as *sampling without replacement,* which is a key condition for the hypergeometric distribution. For the binomial it is assumed that sampling is done *with* replacement, thus assuring independence and constant probability.

N delegates is $\binom{N}{n}$; each particular sample of n delegates thus has a probability of $1/\binom{N}{n}$ of being selected. Similarly, the selection of exactly x delegates pledged to A is an event that can occur in $\binom{k}{x}$ different ways, and the selection of $(n - x)$ delegates pledged to B is an event that can occur in $\binom{N-k}{n-x}$ ways. The total number of ways both of these events can occur is $\binom{k}{x}\binom{N-k}{n-x}$. Thus the probability of selecting exactly x delegates pledged to candidate A is

$$p(x) = \frac{\binom{k}{x}\binom{N - k}{n - x}}{\binom{N}{n}}.$$

Definition 4.3 Let N be the total number of items in a finite population such that k of these are of one type and $N - k$ are of another. If a random sample* of n items is selected from this population, the probability that exactly x items in the sample will be of one type and $n - x$ will be of the other type is given by the hypergeometric probability function

$$p(x; N, n, k) = \begin{cases} \dfrac{\binom{k}{x}\binom{N - k}{n - x}}{\binom{N}{n}}, & x = 0, 1, 2, ..., n; \quad x \leqslant k, \quad n - x \leqslant N - k; \\ & N, n, k, \text{ positive integers,} \\ 0 & \text{elsewhere.} \end{cases} \qquad (4.27)$$

The parameters of the hypergeometric distribution are N, n, and k. These define a family of distributions with probability function given by (4.27). Graphs of (4.27) for various combinations of N, n, and k are provided in Figure 4.3.

The probability function (4.27) of the hypergeometric distribution and the cumulative distribution function, defined by

$$P(X \leqslant x) = F(x; N, n, k) = \sum_{i=0}^{x} \frac{\binom{k}{i}\binom{N - k}{n - i}}{\binom{N}{n}}, \qquad (4.28)$$

have been tabulated in [4] for values of N, n, and k ranging from $N = 2$, $n = 1$, to $N = 100$, $n = 50$. Part of this tabulation is provided in Table C in the Appendix. The calculation of hypergeometric probabilities can become tedious, especially if n is large. However, the work is simplified by using the following recursion formula,

$$p(x + 1; N, n, k) = \frac{(n - x)(k - x)}{(x + 1)(N - k - n + x + 1)} p(x; N, n, k), \qquad (4.29)$$

which can be derived directly from the hypergeometric probability function.

*For the definition of a random sample, see Chapter 7.

FIGURE 4.3 Graphs of the hypergeometric probability function

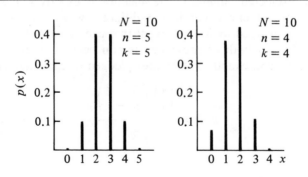

Example 4.7   Suppose there are 50 delegates from a given state to a national political convention of which 30 are pledged to candidate A and 20 are pledged to B. If five delegates are selected at random, what is the probability that among the five at least two are pledged to candidate A?

Let the random variable X be the number of delegates in the sample pledged to A. For $N = 50$, $n = 5$, and $k = 30$, the probability function of X is

$$p(x; 50, 5, 30) = \frac{\binom{30}{x}\binom{20}{5-x}}{\binom{50}{5}}, \quad x = 0, 1, ..., 5,$$

and the probability that $X \geq 2$ is

$$P(X \geq 2) = 1 - P(X \leq 1) = 1 - [p(0; 50, 5, 30) + p(1; 50, 5, 30)].$$

Since

$$p(0; 50, 5, 30) = \frac{\binom{30}{0}\binom{20}{5}}{\binom{50}{5}} = \frac{\binom{20}{5}}{\binom{50}{5}} = 0.007317,$$

and, from (4.29),

$$p(1; 50, 5, 30) = \frac{(5 - 0)(30 - 0)}{(0 + 1)(50 - 30 - 5 + 0 + 1)} p(0; 50, 5, 30) = 0.068597,$$

we find

$$P(X \geq 2) = 1 - (0.007317 + 0.068597) = 0.9241.$$

A fruitful area for application of the hypergeometric distribution has been in statistical quality control and acceptance sampling. In this context let N be the number of units in a lot of which k are defective. If a random sample of $n < N$ units is selected from the lot, the probability that the sample contains exactly x defective units is determined by using the hypergeometric probability function (4.27). In acceptance sampling the reason that only a sample of items is selected from the lot to be inspected is because of time and financial constraints. The decision whether to accept or reject the lot is usually based on the number of defective units found in the sample. These concepts will be discussed in greater detail in Chapter 11.

Example 4.8 A small automobile manufacturer specializes in custom-built automobiles. As a rule, the manufacturer buys the engines from Specific Motors, where they are built to stringent specifications. A lot of 40 engines has just been received by the manufacturer. His acceptance plan is to select eight engines at random and submit them to thorough testing. If none of the engines are found to have serious defects, the manufacturer will accept the lot; otherwise, the lot will be rejected. If the lot contains two engines with serious defects, what is the probability that the lot will be accepted?

Let X be the number of defective engines in the sample. For $N = 40$, $n = 8$, and $k = 2$, the probability of acceptance is

$$p(0; 40, 8, 2) = \frac{\binom{2}{0}\binom{38}{8}}{\binom{40}{8}} = 0.6359.$$

The lot of 40 engines thus has less than 2/3 of a chance of being accepted if it contains two defective engines. It should be noted that the essence of statistical quality control is the eventual improvement in the quality of the product. If a vendor knows that his or her product will undergo probability-based screening to gauge quality, the vendor may implement meaningful quality control on his own to minimize the number of rejected lots. It is reasonable to assume, therefore, that the ultimate result will be a better product.

What happens to the hypergeometric distribution if the sample size n is only a small fraction of a relatively large lot size N? Suppose a lot of 2000 units is submitted, 40 of which are defective. If a sample of 50 items is selected without replacement, the probability of, say, the first item selected being defective is $40/2000 = 0.02$. The conditional probability that the second item is defective, given that the first was defective, is $39/1999 = 0.0195$. Although these probabilities are not identical in value, from a practical point of view one could argue that the difference between these two values is insignificant. For this reason the binomial distribution is often used to approximate the hypergeometric distribution when the ratio n/N is small.

If the proportion of defective items in the lot is $p = k/N$, the hypergeometric probability function may be written as

$$p_H(x; N, n, p) = \frac{\binom{Np}{x}\binom{N - Np}{n - x}}{\binom{N}{n}}. \tag{4.30}$$

Then one can show that

$$\lim_{N\to\infty} p_H(x; N, n, p) = p_B(x; n, p),$$

where $p_B(x; n, p)$ is the binomial probability function. Thus the hypergeometric distribution approaches the binomial with parameters n and $p = k/N$ as the fraction n/N becomes small. Usually, the binomial probability function will adequately approximate (4.30) whenever $n < 0.1N$. Table 4.6 provides a comparison of binomial and hypergeometric probabilities as the ratio n/N decreases.

Example 4.9   A manufacturer claims that 1% of all units produced by his production process are defective. Suppose you order 1000 such units from the manufacturer and select 25 at random for inspection. If the manufacturer's claim is correct, what is the probability of observing two or more defective items in the sample of 25?

Let X be the number of defective units in the sample of 25. Then X is a hypergeometric random variable with parameters $N = 1000$, $n = 25$, and $k = Np = (1000)(.01) = 10$. Since the ratio n/N is considerably less than 0.1, we may use the binomial distribution to approximate the desired probability:

$$P(X \geq 2) = 1 - P(X \leq 1) = 1 - F_B(1; 25, 0.01) = 0.0258,$$

where $F_B(1; 25, 0.01)$ is the binomial cumulative distribution function. Let us attempt to analyze the decision process for this problem. The probability of two or more defective items in the sample of 25 is obviously small. Suppose we actually observe two or more defective items among 25; then our decision process relative to the lot should be based on probability. That is, if the assumed conditions are true, we have observed something that had only about a 2.5% chance of occurring. On the other hand, if the claim of 1% defective is not true and the

TABLE 4.6 Comparison of binomial and hypergeometric probabilities

x	Hypergeometric $p(x; 100, 20, 5)$	Binomial $p(x; 20, 0.05)$	Hypergeometric $p(x; 100, 10, 5)$	Binomial $p(x; 10, 0.05)$	Hypergeometric $p(x; 100, 5, 5)$	Binomial $p(x; 5, 0.05)$
0	0.3193	0.3585	0.5838	0.5987	0.7696	0.7738
1	0.4201	0.3774	0.3394	0.3151	0.2114	0.2036
2	0.2073	0.1887	0.0702	0.0746	0.0184	0.0214
3	0.0478	0.0596	0.0064	0.0105	0.0006	0.0011
4	0.0051	0.0133	0.0003	0.0010	0.0000	0.0000
5	0.0002	0.0022	0.0000	0.0001	0.0000	0.0000

proportion defective is actually, say, 3%, then the probability of observing two or more defective units is

$$P(X \geqslant 2) = 1 - F(1; 25, 0.03) = 0.1720,$$

which is more plausible in light of actual occurrence than 0.0258. Thus, if we actually observe two or more defective items among 25, we are likely to reject the lot.

We now determine the mean of the hypergeometric distribution in a procedure analogous to that used for the binomial distribution. If the probability function is as given by (4.27),

$$E(X) = \sum_{x=0}^{n} x \frac{\binom{k}{x}\binom{N-k}{n-x}}{\binom{N}{n}}$$

$$= \sum_{x=1}^{n} x \frac{\frac{k!}{(k-x)!x!}\binom{N-k}{n-x}}{\binom{N}{n}}$$

$$= k \sum_{x=1}^{n} \frac{\binom{k-1}{x-1}\binom{N-k}{n-x}}{\binom{N}{n}};$$

but one can show that

$$\binom{N}{n} = \frac{N}{n}\binom{N-1}{n-1},$$

or

$$\frac{N!}{(N-n)!n!} = \frac{N}{n}\left[\frac{(N-1)!}{(N-n)!(n-1)!}\right].$$

Then

$$E(X) = k \sum_{x=1}^{n} \frac{\binom{k-1}{x-1}\binom{N-k}{n-x}}{\frac{N}{n}\binom{N-1}{n-1}}$$

$$= \frac{nk}{N} \sum_{x=1}^{n} \frac{\binom{k-1}{x-1}\binom{N-k}{n-x}}{\binom{N-1}{n-1}}.$$

If we let $M = N - 1$, $r = k - 1$, $s = n - 1$, and $y = x - 1$,

$$E(X) = \frac{nk}{N} \sum_{y=0}^{s} \frac{\binom{r}{y}\binom{M - r}{s - y}}{\binom{M}{s}}$$

$$= \frac{nk}{N}; \tag{4.31}$$

the sum is one because it is the sum of a hypergeometric probability function with parameters M, s, and r. Notice that if $p = k/N$, the mean of a hypergeometric random variable is the same as that of a binomial random variable.

Following the same procedure, we can show that the variance of a hypergeometric distribution is

$$Var(X) = \frac{nk(N - k)}{N^2} \cdot \frac{(N - n)}{(N - 1)}. \tag{4.32}$$

If we let $p = k/N$ and $(1 - p) = (N - k)/N$,

$$Var(X) = np(1 - p)\left(\frac{N - n}{N - 1}\right).$$

As a result, the variance of a hypergeometric random variable is smaller than that of a corresponding binomial random variable by the factor $(N - n)/(N - 1)$. However, if N is large compared to n, this factor will be close to one, resulting in essentially the same variance as that of the binomial. The preceding result is expected since, if n is only a small fraction of the lot size N, the hypergeometric distribution approaches the binomial distribution.

The determination of the coefficient of skewness and the relative kurtosis for the hypergeometric distribution follows the same procedure as that for the binomial distribution. These quantities are given in Table 4.7. Notice that for $N > 2$, if $N < 2k$ or if $N < 2n$, the hypergeometric is negatively skewed. If $N = 2k$ or if $N = 2n$, it is symmetric. If $N > 2k$ and $N > 2n$, the distribution is positively skewed. For the moment generating function the reader is referred to [2]. It should be noted that the moment generating function of the hypergeometric distribution is rather tedious to work with in determining the moments. Table 4.7 provides summary information for this distribution.

4.5 The Negative Binomial Distribution

Imagine a binomial scenario in which a sequence of independent trials is observed and the probability of success at each trial is constant at p. Instead of fixing the number of trials at n and observing the number of successes, suppose we continue the independent trials until exactly k successes have occurred. Here the random variable is the number of trials necessary to observe exactly k

TABLE 4.7   Basic properties of the hypergeometric distribution

Probability function	*Parameters*
$$p(x; N, n, k) = \frac{\binom{k}{x}\binom{N-k}{n-x}}{\binom{N}{n}}$$ $$x = 0, 1, 2, ..., n$$ $$x \leq k, \quad n - x \leq N - k$$	N, n, k, positive integers $1 \leq n \leq N; \quad 1 \leq k \leq N$ $N = 1, 2, ...$

Mean	*Variance*	*Coefficient of skewness*	*Relative kurtosis*
$\dfrac{nk}{N}$	$\dfrac{nk(N-k)(N-n)}{N^2(N-1)}$	$\dfrac{(N-2k)(N-2n)(N-1)^{1/2}}{(N-2)[nk(N-k)(N-n)]^{1/2}}$	*

$$* \ \alpha_4 = \frac{N^2(N-1)}{(N-2)(N-3)nk(N-k)(N-n)}$$
$$\left\{N(N+1) - 6n(N-n) + 3\frac{k}{N^2}(N-k)\left[N^2(n-2) - Nn^2 + 6n(N-n)\right]\right\}.$$

successes. This situation leads to what is known as the *negative binomial distribution*.

The determination of the probability function follows the same type of reasoning used to obtain the probability functions of the binomial and hypergeometric distributions. We want to determine the probability that the nth trial results in the kth success. If the independent trials continue until we observe the kth success, then the last trial must have been a success. Prior to the last trial there must have been $k - 1$ successes in $n - 1$ trials. The number of distinct ways $k - 1$ successes can be observed in $n - 1$ trials is $\binom{n-1}{k-1}$. Therefore, the probability of k successes in n trials with the last trial being a success is

$$p(n; k, p) = \binom{n-1}{k-1} p^k(1-p)^{n-k} \qquad n = k, k+1, k+2, \dots . \quad (4.33)$$

Expression (4.33) is the probability function of what is known as the *Pascal distribution*. Using (4.33), we can obtain the probability function of the negative binomial distribution by substituting $n = x + k$ in (4.33), where x is a value of a random variable depicting the number of failures until exactly k successes are observed.

Definition 4.4   Let the number of independent trials required to achieve exactly k successes in a binomial experiment be $X + k$, where the probability of a success at each trial is p. Then X is said to be a negative binomial random variable with probability function

$$p(x; k, p) = \begin{cases} \binom{k + x - 1}{k - 1} p^k(1 - p)^x & \begin{array}{l} x = 0, 1, 2, \ldots \\ k = 1, 2, \ldots \\ 0 \leqslant p \leqslant 1, \end{array} \\ \\ 0 & \text{elsewhere.} \end{cases} \tag{4.34}$$

The distribution is called "negative binomial" because the probabilities as given by (4.34) correspond to the successive terms in the binomial expansion of

$$\left(\frac{1}{p} - \frac{1 - p}{p}\right)^{-k}.$$

The parameters of the negative binomial distribution are k and p, where k need not be an integer. If it is, the distribution is usually referred to as the Pascal distribution, which has also been interpreted as the distribution for the waiting time until the kth success. If k is not an integer, the probability function (4.34) is written in a form involving the gamma function,

$$p(x; k, p) = \frac{\Gamma(k + x)}{x!\,\Gamma(k)} p^k(1 - p)^x \qquad \begin{array}{l} x = 0, 1, 2, \ldots \\ k > 0, \quad 0 \leqslant p \leqslant 1. \end{array} \tag{4.35}$$

In this context the negative binomial is a particular kind of a compound Poisson distribution. A compound distribution of a random variable X is one that depends on a parameter that is also a random variable with a specified distribution. This problem will be discussed for the negative binomial distribution in Chapter 6.

It should be noted that if $k = 1$ in (4.34), a special case of the negative binomial arises, known as the *geometric distribution*, with probability function

$$p(x; p) = p(1 - p)^x, \qquad x = 0, 1, 2, \ldots, \quad 0 \leqslant p \leqslant 1. \tag{4.36}$$

The geometric random variable represents the number of failures before the first success. Graphs of the negative binomial probability function (4.34) for various values of k and p are given in Figure 4.4.

FIGURE 4.4 Graphs of the negative binomial probability function

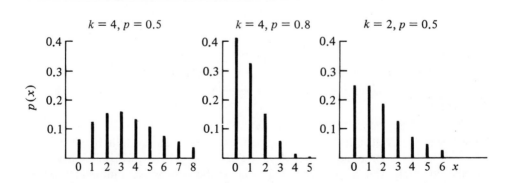

An extensive tabulation of individual and cumulative probabilities for the negative binomial distribution is available in [6]. It is also possible to use the binomial distribution to determine negative binomial probabilities. It can be shown that if X is negative binomial with probability function (4.34), then

$$P(X \leqslant x) = P(Y \geqslant k),$$

where Y is a binomial random variable with parameters $n = k + x$ and p. That is,

$$F_{NB}(x; k, p) = 1 - F_B(k - 1; k + x, p), \tag{4.37}$$

where $F_{NB}(x; k, p)$ is the cumulative negative binomial distribution and $F_B(k - 1; k + x, p)$ is the cumulative binomial distribution. Using (4.37), we can also determine individual negative binomial probabilities. For example,

$$P(X = x) = F_{NB}(x; k, p) - F_{NB}(x - 1; k, p)$$

$$= [1 - F_B(k - 1; k + x, p)] - [1 - F_B(k - 1; k + x - 1, p)]$$

$$= F_B(k - 1; k + x - 1, p) - F_B(k - 1; k + x, p). \tag{4.38}$$

To illustrate the use of (4.37) and (4.38), let $k = 2$ and $p = 0.5$ in (4.34):

$$p_{NB}(x; 2, 0.5) = (x + 1)(0.5)^2(0.5)^x, \quad x = 0, 1, 2, \dots.$$

The probability that $X \leqslant 3$ is

$$P(X \leqslant 3) = F_{NB}(3; 2, 0.5) = 1 - F_B(1; 5, 0.5) = 0.8125;$$

the probability that $X = 2$ is

$$P(X = 2) = F_B(1; 3, 0.5) - F_B(1; 4, 0.5) = 0.1875;$$

and the probability that $X > 1$ is

$$P(X > 1) = P(X \geqslant 2) = 1 - F_{NB}(1; 2, 0.5)$$

$$= 1 - [1 - F_B(1; 3, 0.5)]$$

$$= 0.5.$$

The primary application for the negative binomial distribution has been as an adequate alternative to the Poisson model when the rate of occurrence is not constant over time or space. It has frequently been used to model accident statistics, psychological data, consumer purchases, and other similar situations in which the rate of occurrence among groups or individuals is not expected to be the same. For example, auto accident statistics have consistently indicated that younger drivers have more accidents than older drivers, and that young male drivers have more accidents than young female drivers. In this context one does not view the negative binomial in terms of how many trials are needed to achieve a fixed number of successes. Rather one deals with the number of occurrences over time or space when the rate of occurrence is not constant. For a particular application along these lines, see [1].

The moments of a negative binomial random variable can be determined by first obtaining factorial moments, as was done for the binomial, Poisson, and hypergeometric distributions. It is also possible to obtain the negative binomial mean, variance, coefficient of skewness, and relative kurtosis from the binomial expressions given by (4.4), (4.6), (4.11), and (4.14), respectively. It can be shown that if in these expressions we replace the binomial parameters n, $(1 - p)$, and p with the quantities $-k$, $1/p$, and $-(1 - p)/p$, respectively, we will obtain the desired negative binomial moments. Accordingly, if X is negative binomial with probability function (4.34),

$$E(X) = \frac{k(1 - p)}{p}, \tag{4.39}$$

$$Var(X) = \frac{k(1 - p)}{p^2}, \tag{4.40}$$

$$\alpha_3 = \frac{2 - p}{[k(1 - p)]^{1/2}}, \quad \text{and} \tag{4.41}$$

$$\alpha_4 = 3 + \frac{(p^2 - 6p + 6)}{k(1 - p)}. \tag{4.42}$$

Useful information for the negative binomial distribution is provided in summary form in Table 4.8. Some basic properties of the negative binomial distribution are apparent from the table. The variance is always greater than the mean, the distribution is always positively skewed, and the distribution is leptokurtic since α_4 is always greater than 3, but $\alpha_4 \to 3$ as $k \to \infty$.

Example 4.10 In an article by R. Pollard (see [5]) the number of touchdowns scored by individual teams in collegiate football games is shown to be adequately described by a negative binomial distribution. Table 4.9 contains information for this data set analogous to that in Table 4.3. To determine the theoretical probability of occurrence if the number of touchdowns is negative binomial, it is necessary to obtain estimates of the parameters k and p. Since the mean and variance of

TABLE 4.8 Basic properties of the negative binomial distribution

Probability function			*Parameters*
$p(x; k, p) = \binom{k + x - 1}{k - 1} p^k (1 - p)^x$			$k, \quad k > 0$ (Pascal distribution if k is positive integer)
$x = 0, 1, 2, \ldots$			$p, \quad 0 \leq p \leq 1$

Mean	*Variance*	*Coefficient of skewness*	*Relative kurtosis*
$\dfrac{k(1 - p)}{p}$	$\dfrac{k(1 - p)}{p^2}$	$\dfrac{2 - p}{[k(1 - p)]^{1/2}}$	$3 + \dfrac{(p^2 - 6p + 6)}{k(1 - p)}$

TABLE 4.9 Distribution of the number of touchdowns scored per team per game in collegiate football, 1967

Number of touchdowns	Observed number of occurrences	Relative frequency	Theoretical probability	Expected number of occurrences
0	272	0.1174	0.1205	279
1	485	0.2094	0.2117	490
2	537	0.2319	0.2197	509
3	407	0.1757	0.1754	406
4	258	0.1114	0.1190	276
5	157	0.0678	0.0722	167
6	101	0.0436	0.0404	94
7	57	0.0246	0.0212	49
8	23	0.0099	0.0106	25
9	8	0.0035	0.0051	12
10	5	0.0022	0.0023	5
11 +	6	0.0026	0.0019	4
Totals	2316	1.0000	1.0000	2316

a negative binomial random variable are as given in expressions (4.39) and (4.40), respectively, by solving for k and p one obtains

$$p = \frac{E(X)}{Var(X)}, \quad \text{and} \quad k = \frac{E^2(X)}{Var(X) - E(X)}.$$

A method for estimating these parameters* is to assume that estimates of $E(X)$ and $Var(X)$ are the same as the sample mean and variance, $\bar{x}$ and s^2, which are computed to be 2.58 and 3.79, respectively. Accordingly, an estimate of p is determined to be 0.6807 and that of k is 5.5012. Since the latter is not an integer, the probability function as given by (4.35) is used to determine the theoretical probabilities.

The apparent difference in the distributions of the number of touchdowns scored by individual teams in the National Football League and in collegiate football may be explained to a large extent by the greater variability in the quality of opposition that appears to exist in college football as compared to the NFL. As a result, one would expect the rate at which touchdowns are scored in collegiate football to be more a function of the opposition than it is in the NFL. Thus, the negative binomial distribution is suggested.

By appealing directly to the definition, the moment generating function of the negative binomial distribution is determined as follows:

$$E(e^{tX}) = \sum_{x=0}^{\infty} e^{tx} \binom{k + x - 1}{k - 1} p^k (1 - p)^x$$

---

*For parameter estimation see Chapter 8, in particular Section 8.3.2.

$$= \sum_{x=0}^{\infty} \frac{(k + x - 1)!}{(k - 1)!x!} \, p^k [(1 - p)e^t]^x$$

$$= p^k + kp^k[(1 - p)e^t] + \frac{k(k + 1)}{2!} \, p^k[(1 - p)e^t]^2 + \cdots ,$$

but this is the binomial expansion of $\left[\dfrac{1}{p} - \dfrac{(1 - p)e^t}{p} \right]^{-k}$. Therefore, the moment generating function is given by

$$m_X(t) = \frac{p^k}{[1 - (1 - p)e^t]^k}. \tag{4.43}$$

With the binomial, Poisson, negative binomial, and hypergeometric distributions, we have attempted to provide the reader with discrete probability distributions that have been verified as adequate probability models for many interesting and practically useful random phenomena. Although these distributions are similar, each one of them possesses enough distinct characteristics to provide a user with the information necessary for proper selection. It should also be noted that if a particular random phenomenon does not appear to conform to all properties of a given probability distribution, that may be enough to rule out that distribution as an adequate model for that random phenomenon.

The binomial, Poisson, and negative binomial distributions all involve Bernoulli trials in which sampling is done with replacement. In the binomial, sampling is continued until a fixed number of trials have been conducted, with the probability of success or failure constant at each trial. In the Poisson the number of trials becomes infinitely large, so that the probability of occurrence or nonoccurrence of an event is constant over space and time. In the negative binomial, sampling is continued until a fixed number of successes are observed, so the number of trials may become infinite. The negative binomial is therefore a plausible alternative to the Poisson distribution when the rate of occurrence is not constant over time or space. In the hypergeometric distribution, the trials are not independent because sampling is performed without replacement. Not only is the sample size fixed, but the population size is assumed to be finite and, most often, relatively small.

References

1. A. G. Arbous and J. E. Kerrich, *Accident statistics and the concept of accident proneness,* Biometrics **7** (1951), 340–432.
2. N. L. Johnson and S. Kotz, *Discrete distributions,* Houghton Mifflin, Boston, 1969.
3. N. L. Johnson and F. C. Leone, *Statistics and experimental design,* Vol. I, Wiley, New York, 1977.
4. G. L. Lieberman and D. B. Owen, *Tables of the hypergeometric probability distribution,* Stanford Univ. Press, Stanford, Calif., 1961.
5. R. Pollard, *Collegiate football scores and the negative binomial distribution,* J. Amer. Statistical Assoc., **68** (1973), 351–352.
6. E. Williamson and M. H. Bretherton, *Tables of the negative binomial probability distribution,* Wiley, New York, 1963.

Exercises

4.1. Let X be binomially distributed with parameters n and p. Using the binomial probability function, verify that $p(n - x; n, 1 - p) = p(x; n, p)$.

4.2. In a binomial distribution, let X be the number of successes out of 10 independent trials where the probability of success at each trial is 0.8. Use the result of Exercise 4.1 to show that the probability of exactly six successes is the same as the probability of exactly four failures.

4.3. Using the binomial probability function, verify the recursion formula

$$p(x + 1; n, p) = \frac{(n - x)p}{(x + 1)(1 - p)} p(x; n, p).$$

4.4. Let the random variable X be binomially distributed with $n = 8$ and $p = 0.4$. Use the recursion formula from Exercise 4.3 to obtain point probabilities for the values of X. Graph the probability function.

4.5. Let X be binomially distributed with $n = 10$ and $p = 0.5$.

    a. Determine the probabilities that X is within one standard deviation of the mean and within two standard deviations of the mean.

    b. What would be your answers to part a if $n = 15$ and $p = 0.4$?

4.6. Suppose the probability of a defective unit coming off an assembly line is 0.05. If the number of units produced by this process constitutes a set of independent trials,

    a. what is the probability that among 20 such units, exactly two are defective?

    b. at most two are defective?

    c. at least one is defective?

4.7. An electronics firm claims that the proportion of defective units of a certain component it produces is 5%. A buyer of large quantities of these components inspects 15 units that were randomly selected from a large lot and finds four defectives. If the claim is correct and the assumptions for the binomial distribution prevail, what is the probability of such an occurrence? Would you be inclined to conclude that the claim is not correct?

4.8. The probability of successful operation of a communications satellite once placed in orbit is 0.9. Suppose five such satellites are placed in orbit. Assuming independence of operation,

    a. what is the probability that at least 80 percent will operate successfully?

    b. Would your answer to part a change if n were 10?

    c. Would your answer change if n were 20?

    d. Are these results unexpected? Comment.

4.9. It is known from past surveys that consumer preference for two competing brands, A and B, of a given product is evenly divided. If we assume independence of choice between these two brands, what is the probability that out of 25 randomly selected persons, no more than ten will indicate a preference for brand A?

4.10. Suppose a test containing 15 true or false questions is given. A passing grade consists of at least nine correct answers. If one tosses a balanced coin to decide between true and false for each question, what is the probability of a passing grade?

4.11. A life insurance salesperson knows that the more contacts with potential customers she makes, the better the chance of selling a policy. If the probability of anyone buying a policy from this salesperson as a result of a visit remains constant at 0.25, and if the visits constitute a set of independent trials, how many potential customers must the salesperson visit (say, per day) so that the probability of selling at least one policy is 0.80?

4.12. The management of a restaurant that operates on reservations only knows from experience that 15 percent of persons making table reservations will not show up. If the restaurant accepts 25 table reservations but has only 20 tables, what is the probability that all who show up will be accommodated? Comment on the assumptions of independence and constant probability for this problem.

4.13. Using the Poisson probability function, verify the recursion relation

$$p(x + 1; \lambda) = \frac{\lambda}{(x + 1)} p(x; \lambda).$$

4.14. Let X be Poisson distributed with parameter $\lambda = 2$. Using the result of Exercise 4.13, determine point probabilities for $X = 0, 1, 2, 3, 4, 5, 6, 7$, and 8, and graph the probability function.

4.15. The number of red blood cells for a fixed volume is a random variable that occurs with a constant rate. If the average number for this volume is nine red cells for normal persons, determine the probabilities that the number of red cells of a person will be within one standard deviation of the average and within two standard deviations of the average.

4.16. The number of customer arrivals at a bank is a Poisson random variable. If the average number of arrivals per hour is 120, what is the probability that in one minute at least three customers will arrive at this bank? Would you expect the arrival rate to be constant for a typical day?

4.17. Assume that accidents at a busy intersection occur randomly and independently at the average rate of two per week. Determine the joint probability that exactly one accident will occur this week, and exactly three accidents will occur the following week.

4.18. Let X be a binomial random variable. For $n = 20$, compute the binomial point probabilities and compare them with the corresponding Poisson probabilities for $p = 0.5, 0.3, 0.1$, and 0.01.

4.19. A company purchases large lots of electronic components. The decision to accept or reject these lots is based on a random sample of 100 units. Assuming a lot is rejected if three or more defective units are found in the random sample, what is the probability of rejecting a lot with 1 percent defective units? What is the probability of rejecting a lot with 8 percent defective units?

4.20. Let the number of units that fail in 100 hours of operation be Poisson distributed. If the average number of units that fail during this time is 8,

a. what is the probability of exactly one failure in 25 hours?
b. what is the probability of no more than two failures in 50 hours?
c. what is the probability of at least ten failures in 125 hours?

4.21. It has been determined that the probability of death due to a certain flu vaccination is 0.00002. If 100,000 people who received the vaccination can be thought of as a set of independent trials, what is the probability that no more than two will die as a result of the vaccination?

4.22. A manufacturer has assured a client company that the percent defective of the units produced by his process is only two. The company inspects 50 randomly selected units produced by this process and finds five defective units. How likely is this result if the manufacturing percent defective is as the manufacturer says it is?

4.23. The average number of serious accidents at a large industrial plant has been 10 per year, so management has instituted what it believes is an effective plan to reduce the number of serious accidents at the plant. In the year after the plan was implemented, four serious accidents occurred. How likely is the occurrence of four or fewer accidents per year if the average rate is still 10 per year? Thus, would one conclude that there might have been a reduction in the average number of accidents per year?

4.24. The Environmental Protection Agency has purchased 40 precision instruments to be used to measure air pollution at various locations. Eight of these are randomly selected and tested for defects. If four of the 40 instruments are defective, what is the probability that the random sample of eight will contain no more than one defective?

4.25. It is suspected that because of human error two (or possibly more) defective units have been included in a shipment of 50 units to an industrial firm. The seller acknowledges the error and charges the client company for only 48 of the units. Upon receipt of the shipment, the client company selects five units at random and finds one of these to be defective. Should the client company demand additional compensation?

4.26. Jurors for cases to be heard in a federal district court are supposedly selected at random from registered voters in that district. A list of 25 prospective jurors is compiled for a given month. The list contains the names of 20 males and five females.

   a. If the eligible voters in this district are evenly divided by sex, what is the probability that a list of 25 randomly selected individuals will contain 20 males and five females?
   b. Suppose that from this list of 25 a jury of twelve is chosen, and that it consists of eleven males and one female. What is the probability of such an occurrence if the individuals on the jury are randomly selected?
   c. If you were an attorney for the defense, how would you argue using the answers in part a and part b?

4.27. A lot of 1000 units is received. An acceptance sampling procedure calls for the random selection and inspection of ten units. If none of the ten units are defective, the lot is accepted; otherwise it is rejected. If the lot contains 5 percent defective units,

   a. determine the probability of acceptance using the hypergeometric distribution.
   b. Approximate your answer in part a by using the binomial distribution.
   c. Approximate your answer in part b by using the Poisson distribution.

4.28. In Exercise 4.27, how would your answers to parts a, b, and c change if the lot size were changed from 1000 to 40 units?

4.29. Let the binomial and negative binomial probability functions be as given by expressions 4.1 and 4.34, respectively. Show that

$$p_{NB}(x; k, p) = \frac{k}{x + k} \, p_B(k; x + k, p).$$

4.30. Let X be a negative binomial random variable with parameters $k = 3$ and $p =$

0.4. Use the result of Exercise 4.29 to compute point probabilities for the values 0, 1, 2, 3, 4, and 5 of X.

4.31. Greenwood and Yule* reported on the number of accidents among 414 machine operators for three successive months. In Table 4.10 the first column identifies the number of accidents experienced by the same operator, and the second column is the relative frequency for operators who had the indicated number of accidents during the three-month period.

TABLE 4.10

x	Relative frequency
0	0.715
1	0.179
2	0.063
3	0.019
4	0.010
5	0.010
6	0.002
7	0.000
8	0.002

Follow the procedure of Example 4.10 to compare the observed relative frequencies with the corresponding probabilities if the number of accidents is a negative binomial random variable.

4.32. A recent accounting graduate wishes to take the CPA test. If the number of times the test is taken constitutes a set of independent events with probability of passing at any one time equal to 0.6, what is the probability that no more than four attempts will be necessary to pass the test? Are the assumptions of independence and constant probability likely to prevail here? Comment.

4.33. Finished units are inspected in an inspection station as they come off the assembly line. The proportion defective for the assembly process is thought to be 0.05.

a. What is the probability that the 20th unit inspected will be the second defective unit found?

b. Suppose the 15th unit inspected is the second defective unit found. How likely is such an occurrence under the given conditions?

4.34. Which of the binomial, Poisson, hypergeometric, and negative binomial distributions would you not consider if someone told you that in a particular distribution

a. the mean is equal to the variance?

b. the mean is greater than the variance?

c. the mean is less than the variance?

d. the third moment about the mean is negative?

e. the random phenomenon of interest constitutes a set of independent trials?

f. sampling is with replacement?

g. sampling is without replacement?

---

*An inquiry into the nature of frequency distributions representative of multiple happenings with particular reference to the occurrence of multiple attacks of disease or of repeated accidents, J. of the Royal Statistical Soc. **83** (1920), 255.

APPENDIX

Derivation of the Poisson Probability Function

Let $p(x; t)$ be the probability of exactly x occurrences in a time interval of length t, and assume the following:

1. Events occur independently over the time period.
2. The probability of a single occurrence in a very small time interval of length dt is νdt, where ν is the constant rate of occurrence ($\nu > 0$).
3. The time interval dt is so small that the probability of more than a single occurrence in dt is negligible.

The event that by time $t + dt$ there have been exactly x occurrences can take place in two mutually exclusive ways:

1. There are x occurrences by time t, with probability $p(x; t)$, and no occurrences during dt, with probability $(1 - \nu dt)$. By the assumption of independence, the joint probability is $p(x; t)(1 - \nu dt)$.
2. There are $x - 1$ occurrences by time t, with probability $p(x - 1; t)$, and one occurrence during dt, with probability νdt. Again because of independence, the joint probability is $p(x - 1; t)\nu dt$.

That is,

$$p(x; t + dt) = p(x; t)(1 - \nu dt) + p(x - 1; t)\nu dt.$$

After multiplying, transposing $p(x; t)$ to the left, and dividing by dt, we have

$$\frac{p(x; t + dt) - p(x; t)}{dt} = \nu[p(x - 1; t) - p(x; t)].$$

If we take the limit as $dt \to 0$, by definition we have

$$\frac{dp(x; t)}{dt} = \nu[p(x - 1; t) - p(x; t)], \tag{4.44}$$

which is a linear differential equation with respect to t and a linear first-order difference equation with respect to x. If $x = 0$, (4.44) becomes

$$\frac{dp(0; t)}{dt} = \nu[p(-1; t) - p(0; t)]$$

$$= -\nu p(0; t),$$

since $p(-1; t)$ has to be zero. The general solution of the linear differential equation

$$\frac{dp(0; t)}{dt} = -\nu p(0; t)$$

is obtained by separating the variables and integrating both sides, which results in

$$\ln[p(0; t)] = \ln(c) - \nu t,$$

or

$$p(0; t) = ce^{-vt}.$$

Since the probability of zero occurrences during a time length $t = 0$ must be 1, $c = 1$, and

$$p(0; t) = e^{-vt}.$$

If $x = 1$, (4.44) becomes

$$\frac{dp(1; t)}{dt} = v[p(0; t) - p(1; t)],$$

or

$$\frac{dp(1; t)}{dt} + vp(1; t) = ve^{-vt}. \tag{4.45}$$

Equation (4.45) is a nonhomogeneous differential equation with the initial condition that $p(1; 0) = 0$ since the probability of exactly one occurrence during time $t = 0$ must be zero. The solution of (4.45) is

$$p(1; t) = (vt)e^{-vt}.$$

Similarly, for $x = 2$ and $p(2; 0) = 0$, (4.44) reduces to

$$\frac{dp(2; t)}{dt} + vp(2; t) = v^2 t e^{-vt},$$

whose solution is

$$p(2; t) = \frac{(vt)^2 e^{-vt}}{2!}.$$

By continuing this process, we can deduce that the probability of exactly x occurrences in t is

$$p(x; t) = \frac{(vt)^x e^{-vt}}{x!}, \qquad x = 0, 1, 2, \ldots \tag{4.46}$$

as long as $p(x; 0) = 0$. If we let $\lambda = vt$ in (4.46), the result is the Poisson probability function.

APPENDIX

Proof of Theorem 4.1

By multiplying numerator and denominator by n^x and substituting $n!/(n - x)! = n(n - 1)(n - 2) \cdots (n - x + 1)$, the binomial probability function is

$$p(x; n, p) = \frac{n(n - 1)(n - 2) \cdots (n - x + 1)}{n^x x!} (np)^x (1 - p)^{n-x}$$

$$= \frac{n(n-1)(n-2)\cdots(n-x+1)}{n^x}\frac{\lambda^x}{x!}(1-p)^{n-x}$$

$$= 1\left(1-\frac{1}{n}\right)\left(1-\frac{2}{n}\right)\cdots\left(1-\frac{x-1}{n}\right)\frac{\lambda^x}{x!}(1-p)^{n-x}$$

$$= \frac{\left(1-\dfrac{1}{n}\right)\left(1-\dfrac{2}{n}\right)\cdots\left(1-\dfrac{x-1}{n}\right)}{(1-p)^x}\frac{\lambda^x}{x!}(1-p)^{n}. \qquad (4.47)$$

Since

$$(1-p)^n = [(1-p)^{-1/p}]^{-np} = [(1-p)^{-1/p}]^{-\lambda},$$

and by definition

$$\lim_{z\to 0}(1+z)^{1/z} = e,$$

letting $z = -p$,

$$\lim_{p\to 0}[(1-p)^{-1/p}]^{-\lambda} = e^{-\lambda}.$$

Moreover,

$$\lim_{n\to\infty}\left(1-\frac{1}{n}\right)\left(1-\frac{2}{n}\right)\cdots\left(1-\frac{x-1}{n}\right) = 1$$

and

$$\lim_{p\to 0}(1-p)^x = 1.$$

Thus, in (4.47),

$$\lim_{\substack{n\to\infty \\ p\to 0}} p(x; n, p) = \frac{e^{-\lambda}\lambda^x}{x!}, \qquad x = 0, 1, 2, \dots .$$

CHAPTER FIVE

Some Continuous Probability Distributions

5.1 Introduction

In this chapter we examine several continuous probability models. These distributions have been used to study random phenomena in disciplines ranging from the applied sciences and engineering to business and economics. We will also develop a method for determining the probability distribution of a function of a random variable and introduce basic concepts for computer generation of random values.

More specifically, we will study the normal, uniform, beta, gamma, Weibull, and negative exponential probability models. The approach will be the same as in Chapter 4. We will discuss the properties of each model and indicate specific areas of application, thereby providing the reader with sufficient insight and understanding to use the models properly.

5.2 The Normal Distribution

The *normal* or *Gaussian distribution* is without a doubt the most important and most widely used continuous probability distribution. It is the cornerstone of the application of statistical inference in analysis of data because the distributions of several important sample statistics tend toward a normal distribution as the sample size increases. The graphical appearance of the normal distribution is a symmetrical bell-shaped curve that extends without bound in both positive and negative directions. A substantial number of empirical studies have indicated that the normal distribution provides an adequate representation of, or at least a first approximation to, the distributions of many physical variables. Some specific examples include meteorological data, such as temperature and rainfall, measurements on living organisms, scores on aptitude tests, physical measurements of manufactured parts, instrumentation errors and other deviations from established norms, and so on.

Yet one should exercise caution in assuming the normal distribution without some verification. If the normal distribution is the most widely used, it is also the most widely abused, partly because of the possible misinterpretation of the word "normal," especially if its literal meaning of "accepted standard or pattern" is applied. The erroneous assumption of the normal distribution can lead to some serious errors. It is possible for a normal distribution to provide a reasonably good approximation around the center of a random variable yet be inadequate for the extreme values in either direction. For example, if a certain material is designed with the strength to withstand a given amount of stress that is assumed to be normally distributed around some average value, the designed strength is a function of the assumption, and it may very well be compromised if an extreme stress is experienced.

The probability density function of the normal distribution, given in Definition 5.1, was discovered in 1733 by DeMoivre as a limiting form of the binomial probability function and was later studied by Laplace. It is also known as the Gaussian distribution because Gauss considered it in a paper published in 1809. Throughout the nineteenth century it was used extensively by scientists who frequently noted that errors in physical measurements followed a pattern that suggested the normal distribution.

Definition 5.1 A random variable X is said to be normally distributed if its probability density function is given by

$$f(x; \mu, \sigma) = \frac{1}{\sqrt{2\pi}\,\sigma} \exp\left[-\frac{1}{2}\left(\frac{x - \mu}{\sigma}\right)^2 \right], \qquad \begin{array}{l} -\infty < x < \infty \\ -\infty < \mu < \infty, \sigma > 0. \end{array} \quad (5.1)$$

The parameters of the normal distribution and the ones that completely specify the probability density function are μ and σ. These turn out to be, as we will see later, the mean and the standard deviation of X, respectively. Graphs of (5.1) for different values of μ and a fixed σ and vice versa are given in Figure 5.1.

It is apparent that for any pair of values for μ and σ, (5.1) would be bell-shaped and symmetric. If we take the first two derivatives of $f(x; \mu, \sigma)$ with respect to x and equate them to zero, we determine that the maximum of $f(x; \mu, \sigma)$ occurs when $x = \mu$, and the values $x = \mu \pm \sigma$ yield two points of inflection of the curve. The proof that (5.1) is a probability density function is provided in an appendix to this chapter.

The mean of a normally distributed random variable is defined by

$$E(X) = \frac{1}{\sqrt{2\pi}\,\sigma} \int_{-\infty}^{\infty} x \exp[-(x - \mu)^2/2\sigma^2] dx. \quad (5.2)$$

We want to show that $E(X) = \mu$. Suppose in (5.2) we add and subtract

$$\frac{\mu}{\sqrt{2\pi}\,\sigma} \int_{-\infty}^{\infty} \exp[-(x - \mu)^2/2\sigma^2] dx.$$

FIGURE 5.1   Graphs of the normal density function for various values of μ and σ

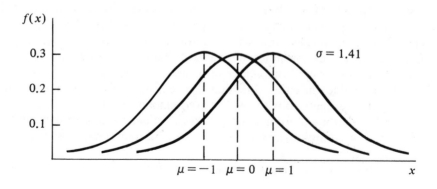

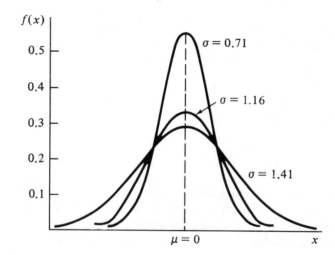

The identity is still maintained, but after rearranging the terms we have

$$E(X) = \frac{1}{\sqrt{2\pi}\,\sigma} \int_{-\infty}^{\infty} (x - \mu)\exp[-(x - \mu)^2/2\sigma^2]dx$$

$$+ \frac{\mu}{\sqrt{2\pi}\,\sigma} \int_{-\infty}^{\infty} \exp[-(x - \mu)^2/2\sigma^2]dx$$

$$= \frac{1}{\sqrt{2\pi}\,\sigma} \int_{-\infty}^{\infty} (x - \mu)\exp[-(x - \mu)^2/2\sigma^2]dx + \mu, \qquad (5.3)$$

since the value of the second integral is one. In (5.3), change the variable of integration such that $y = (x - \mu)/\sigma$, $x = \sigma y + \mu$, and $dx = \sigma dy$. Then

$$E(X) = \frac{\sigma}{\sqrt{2\pi}} \int_{-\infty}^{\infty} y \exp(-y^2/2)dy + \mu$$

$$= -\frac{\sigma}{\sqrt{2\pi}} \exp(-y^2/2) \Big|_{-\infty}^{\infty} + \mu = \mu. \tag{5.4}$$

The reader may recall from calculus that the last integral is zero because the integrand is an odd function* and the integration is performed over a symmetric interval around zero.

A normal distribution is symmetric around the mean μ. Since the maximum of the normal probability density occurs when $x = \mu$, μ is the mean, median, and mode of any normally distributed random variable X.

For other moments, we will determine the central moment generating function. By definition,

$$m_{X-\mu}(t) = E[e^{t(X-\mu)}] = \frac{1}{\sqrt{2\pi}\,\sigma} \int_{-\infty}^{\infty} \exp[t(x-\mu)]\exp[-(x-\mu)^2/2\sigma^2]dx$$

$$= \frac{1}{\sqrt{2\pi}\,\sigma} \int_{-\infty}^{\infty} \exp\left\{ -\frac{1}{2\sigma^2}[(x-\mu)^2 - 2\sigma^2 t(x-\mu)] \right\}dx.$$

Completing the square inside the bracket we have

$$(x-\mu)^2 - 2\sigma^2 t(x-\mu) = (x-\mu)^2 - 2\sigma^2 t(x-\mu) + \sigma^4 t^2 - \sigma^4 t^2$$

$$= (x-\mu-\sigma^2 t)^2 - \sigma^4 t^2$$

and

$$m_{X-\mu}(t) = \frac{1}{\sqrt{2\pi}\,\sigma} \int_{-\infty}^{\infty} \exp(\sigma^2 t^2/2)\exp\{-[x-(\mu+\sigma^2 t)]^2/2\sigma^2\}dx$$

$$= \exp(\sigma^2 t^2/2) \cdot \frac{1}{\sqrt{2\pi}\,\sigma} \int_{-\infty}^{\infty} \exp\{-[x-(\mu+\sigma^2 t)]^2/2\sigma^2\}dx$$

$$= \exp(\sigma^2 t^2/2), \tag{5.5}$$

since the integrand along with the factor $1/\sqrt{2\pi}\,\sigma$ is a normal probability density function with parameters $\mu + \sigma^2 t$ and σ.

Expanding (5.5) in a power series we have

$$m_{X-\mu}(t) = 1 + \frac{(\sigma t)^2}{2} + \frac{(\sigma t)^4}{4\cdot 2!} + \frac{(\sigma t)^6}{8\cdot 3!} + \frac{(\sigma t)^8}{16\cdot 4!} + \cdots .$$

Since the odd powers of t are not present, all odd-order central moments of X must be zero, and symmetry is assured.

The second derivative of $m_{X-\mu}(t)$ evaluated at $t = 0$ is the variance, which turns out to be

---

*A function $f(x)$ is said to be an odd function if $f(-x) = -f(x)$. Then $\int_{-a}^{a} f(x)dx = 0$. A function $f(x)$ is said to be an even function if $f(-x) = f(x)$. Then $\int_{-a}^{a} f(x)dx = 2\int_{0}^{a} f(x)dx$.

$$Var\ (X) = \left.\frac{d^2 m_{X-\mu}(t)}{dt^2}\right|_{t=0} = \sigma^2 + \frac{12t^2\sigma^4}{4\cdot2!} + \frac{30t^4\sigma^6}{8\cdot3!} + \cdots \left.\right|_{t=0} = \sigma^2;\quad (5.6)$$

thus the standard deviation is σ. Similarly, the fourth derivative of $m_{X-\mu}(t)$ evaluated at $t = 0$ is the fourth central moment, which is

$$\mu_4 = \left.\frac{d^4 m_{X-\mu}(t)}{dt^4}\right|_{t=0} = 3\sigma^4 + \frac{360t^2\sigma^6}{8\cdot3!} + \cdots \left.\right|_{t=0} = 3\sigma^4.\quad (5.7)$$

Accordingly, for any normal distribution the coefficient of skewness is $\alpha_3(X) = 0$, while the relative kurtosis is $\alpha_4(X) = 3\sigma^4/\sigma^4 = 3$.

For moments about zero, we can determine the moment generating function of X by appealing directly to the central moment generating function (or vice versa). Since

$$m_{X-\mu}(t) = E[e^{t(X-\mu)}]$$

$$= \exp(-\mu t)E[\exp(tX)]$$

$$= \exp(-\mu t)m_X(t),$$

for a normal distribution

$$\exp(-\mu t)m_X(t) = \exp(\sigma^2 t^2/2)$$

and

$$m_X(t) = \exp\left(\mu t + \frac{\sigma^2 t^2}{2}\right).\quad (5.8)$$

The probability that a normally distributed random variable X is less than or equal to some specified value x is given by the cumulative distribution function

$$P(X \le x) = F(x;\mu,\sigma) = \frac{1}{\sqrt{2\pi}\,\sigma}\int_{-\infty}^{x} \exp[-(t-\mu)^2/2\sigma^2]dt.\quad (5.9)$$

The integral in (5.9) cannot be integrated in closed form; however, $F(x;\mu,\sigma)$ can be tabulated as a function of μ and σ, which requires a separate table for each pair of values. Since there are an infinite number of values for μ and σ, this task is virtually impossible. Fortunately, the task is simplified by using the following transformation: Let the random variable Z be defined by the relation

$$Z = (X - \mu)/\sigma,\quad (5.10)$$

where μ and σ are the mean and standard deviation of X, respectively. Accordingly, Z^* is a standardized random variable with mean zero and standard deviation one, as discussed in Chapter 3.

If the transformation (5.10) is applied to (5.9), then

---

*We shall use Z to denote a standardized normal random variable.

$$P(X \le x) = P[Z \le (x - \mu)/\sigma] = \frac{1}{\sqrt{2\pi}\,\sigma} \int_{-\infty}^{(x-\mu)/\sigma} \exp(-z^2/2)(\sigma dz)$$

$$= \frac{1}{\sqrt{2\pi}} \int_{-\infty}^{(x-\mu)/\sigma} \exp(-z^2/2)dz. \qquad (5.11)$$

The integrand in (5.11) along with the factor $1/\sqrt{2\pi}$ is the probability density function of the standardized normal random variable Z. That is, if X is normally distributed with mean μ and standard deviation σ, then $Z = (X - \mu)/\sigma$ is also normally distributed with mean zero and standard deviation one. Thus for $z = (x - \mu)/\sigma$, $P(X \le x) = P(Z \le z)$ and

$$F_X(x; \mu, \sigma) = F_Z(z; 0, 1), \qquad (5.12)$$

where $F_Z(z; 0, 1)$ is the cumulative distribution function of the standardized normal. The graph of the distribution function for the standardized normal random variable is given in Figure 5.2.

The function $F_Z(z; 0, 1)$ is extensively tabulated and is given in Table D in the Appendix. For any specified value z, the entry in the table is the probability that the standard normal Z is less than or equal to z; that is,

$$P(Z \le z) = F_Z(z; 0, 1) = \frac{1}{\sqrt{2\pi}} \int_{-\infty}^{z} \exp(-t^2/2)dt. \qquad (5.13)$$

Let us introduce the convenient notation $X \sim N(\mu, \sigma)$ to mean that the random variable X is normally distributed with mean μ and standard deviation

FIGURE 5.2 The cumulative distribution function of the standard normal

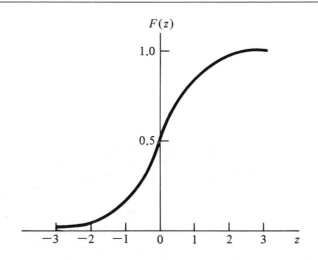

σ. If $X \sim N(\mu, \sigma)$, let us examine how we can determine the probability that a value of X will be between, say, a and b. By definition,

$$P(a \le X \le b) = \frac{1}{\sqrt{2\pi}\,\sigma} \int_a^b \exp[-(x - \mu)^2/2\sigma^2]dx,$$

but using (5.10) we have

$$P(a \le X \le b) = P\left(\frac{a - \mu}{\sigma} \le Z \le \frac{b - \mu}{\sigma}\right)$$

$$= \frac{1}{\sqrt{2\pi}} \int_{(a-\mu)/\sigma}^{(b-\mu)/\sigma} \exp(-z^2/2)dz$$

$$= F_Z\left(\frac{b - \mu}{\sigma}; 0, 1\right) - F_Z\left(\frac{a - \mu}{\sigma}; 0, 1\right). \qquad (5.14)$$

In other words, the probability that X is between a and b is exactly the same as the probability that Z is between $(a - \mu)/\sigma$ and $(b - \mu)/\sigma$, where Z is $N(0, 1)$. This correspondence of probabilities is illustrated in Figure 5.3.

We illustrate the use of Table D with the following examples.

Example 5.1   If X is $N(\mu, \sigma)$, what are the probabilities that a value of X will be within one, two, or three standard deviations of the mean?

$$P(\mu - \sigma \le X \le \mu + \sigma) = P\left(\frac{\mu - \sigma - \mu}{\sigma} \le Z \le \frac{\mu + \sigma - \mu}{\sigma}\right)$$

$$= P(-1 \le Z \le 1)$$

$$= F_Z(1; 0, 1) - F_Z(-1; 0, 1)$$

$$= 0.6826.$$

$$P(\mu - 2\sigma \le X \le \mu + 2\sigma) = P(-2 \le Z \le 2)$$

$$= F_Z(2; 0, 1) - F_Z(-2; 0, 1) = 0.9544.$$

$$P(\mu - 3\sigma \le X \le \mu + 3\sigma) = P(-3 \le Z \le 3)$$

$$= F_Z(3; 0, 1) - F_Z(-3; 0, 1) = 0.9974.$$

Thus for any normal random variable, the "one-sigma," "two-sigma," and "three-sigma" probabilities are 0.6826, 0.9544, and 0.9974, respectively. This result illustrates that for a normal distribution there is a high concentration of values around the mean.

Example 5.2   Let X be a random variable depicting human intelligence as measured by IQ tests. If X is $N(100, 10)$, determine the probabilities that X is greater than 100, less than 85, at most 112, at least 108, greater than 90, and between 95 and 120.

FIGURE 5.3 Correspondence between probabilities of X and probabilities of Z

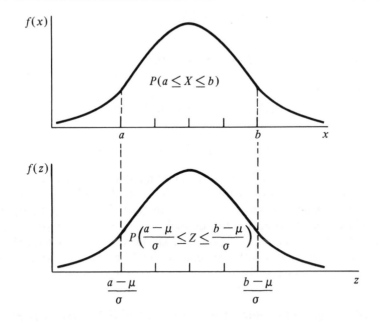

It should be noted that in working problems of this kind, the reader may find it advantageous to sketch corresponding areas under normal densities, as in Figure 5.3. Since the probability distribution of X is symmetric with the point of symmetry being the mean of X, then the probability that X exceeds its mean of 100 is 0.5, by definition. The other probabilities are determined as follows:

$$P(X < 85) = P\left(Z < \frac{85 - 100}{10}\right) = P(Z < -1.5)$$

$$= F_Z(-1.5; 0, 1) = 0.0668.$$

$$P(X \le 112) = P(Z \le 1.2) = F_Z(1.2; 0, 1) = 0.8849.$$

$$P(X \ge 108) = P(Z \ge 0.8) = 1 - F_Z(0.8; 0, 1) = 0.2119.$$

$$P(X > 90) = P(Z > -1) = 1 - F_Z(-1; 0, 1) = 0.8413.$$

$$P(95 \le X \le 120) = P(-0.5 \le Z \le 2) = F_Z(2; 0, 1) - F_Z(-0.5; 0, 1) = 0.6687.$$

Example 5.3 Suppose monthly demand for a product is closely approximated by a normal random variable with mean 200 units and standard deviation 40 units. How large an inventory must be available at the beginning of a month so that the probability of a stockout is no more than 0.05?

Let X be the monthly demand; then X is $N(200, 40)$. What we seek is the quantile value $x_{0.95}$ for the beginning inventory level such that the probability of an actual demand exceeding $x_{0.95}$ (stockout) is no more than 0.05. That is,

$$P(X > x_{0.95}) = 0.05$$

or

$$P(X \leq x_{0.95}) = 0.95.$$

It follows that

$$P[Z \leq (x_{0.95} - 200)/40] = 0.95$$

or

$$P(Z \leq z_{0.95}) = F_Z(z_{0.95}; 0, 1) = 0.95,$$

where $z_{0.95} = (x_{0.95} - 200)/40$ is the corresponding quantile value of the standard normal. To determine $z_{0.95}$ from Table D, we first scan the table for the probability nearest to 0.95. Once that value is found, we take the corresponding column and row values, interpolating for the desired $z_{0.95}$. For the example, $z_{0.95}$ is approximately 1.645, and since $z_{0.95} = (x_{0.95} - 200)/40$, $x_{0.95}$ is computed to be 265.8. This means the beginning monthly inventory should be no less than 266 units if the probability of a stockout is to be no more than 0.05.

Example 5.4   Suppose the outer diameter of certain ball bearings produced by a manufacturing process is approximately normally distributed with mean equal to 3.5 cm and standard deviation equal to 0.02 cm. If the diameter of this type of ball bearing must be no less than 3.47 cm and no more than 3.53 cm to be usable, what percentage of the bearings produced by this process must be scrapped?

Let X be the diameter of the bearing, where X is $N(3.5, 0.02)$. The probability of a usable bearing is the same as the probability that its diameter is between 3.47 cm and 3.53 cm. That is,

$$P(3.47 \leq X \leq 3.53) = P\left(\frac{3.47 - 3.5}{0.02} \leq Z \leq \frac{3.53 - 3.5}{0.02}\right)$$

$$= P(-1.5 \leq Z \leq 1.5)$$

$$= F_Z(1.5; 0, 1) - F_Z(-1.5; 0, 1)$$

$$= 0.8664.$$

Since 86.64% of the bearings produced are usable, it follows that $1 - 0.8664 = 0.1336$, or 13.36% must be scrapped.

In Example 3.11 we determined that for the standard normal distribution, the first and third quartile values are approximately equal to -0.675 and 0.675, while those for the first and ninth deciles are about -1.28 and 1.28, respectively. From (5.10) it follows that if X is $N(\mu, \sigma)$, the first and third quartile values of X are $x_{0.25} = -0.675\sigma + \mu$ and $x_{0.75} = 0.675\sigma + \mu$. Thus the interquartile range is $x_{0.75} - x_{0.25} = 1.35\sigma$. Similarly, the first and ninth decile values are

TABLE 5.1 Basic properties of the normal distribution

Probability density function				Parameters		
$$f(x; \mu, \sigma) = \frac{1}{\sqrt{2\pi}\,\sigma} \exp\left[-\frac{1}{2}\left(\frac{x-\mu}{\sigma}\right)^2 \right],$$ $$-\infty < x < \infty$$				$\mu, \qquad -\infty < \mu < \infty$ $\sigma, \qquad \sigma > 0$		

Mean	Variance	Mean deviation	Interquartile range	Interdecile range	Coefficient of skewness	Relative kurtosis
μ	σ^2	0.7979σ	1.35σ	2.56σ	0	3

$x_{0.10} = -1.28\sigma + \mu$ and $x_{0.90} = 1.28\sigma + \mu$, and the interdecile range is $x_{0.90} - x_{0.10} = 2.56\sigma$. From Example 3.11 we can also conclude that if $X \sim N(\mu,\sigma)$, then the mean deviation of X is

$$E|X - \mu| = 0.7979\sigma. \qquad (5.15)$$

Table 5.1 contains the basic properties of the normal distribution.

Example 5.5 The first column of Table 5.2 represents intervals of SAT math scores, and the second column contains the corresponding observed numbers of scores for 1979–80 college-bound seniors as reported in the College Board ATP Summary Report. The third column contains the relative frequencies, and the remaining columns contain corresponding information if the SAT math scores for males were normally distributed with mean 491* and standard deviation 120*.

While there appears to be some agreement between the observed and theoretical frequencies, it remains to be seen (Chapter 10) whether one can reject the notion that these SAT scores are normally distributed with mean 491 and standard deviation 120. As we have mentioned earlier, it is always important to check the tails of the observed distribution. For example, we know that for the SAT scores the events $X < 200$ and $X > 800$ are impossible. However, if $X \sim N(491, 120)$, $P(X < 200) = 0.0075$ and $P(X > 800) = 0.005$. The following example should illustrate more clearly the lack of agreement at the tails between the observed and assumed distributions.

Example 5.6 The number of units of a product sold daily by a retailer varies randomly with little, if any, day-of-the-week or seasonal effects. Based on historical information, it is believed that the daily demand is a normal random variable with mean and standard deviation of 100 and 12 units, respectively. To check this belief the retailer has noted the daily demands for the last 102 working days and has grouped these as in Table 5.3. Compare the observed relative frequencies with theoretical frequencies for a normal distribution with mean 100 and standard deviation 12.

*These quantities are provided in the College Board ATP Summary Report, 1979–80.

TABLE 5.2 SAT math scores for 1979–80 college-bound male high school seniors

Score	Actual number	Relative frequency	Standard normal interval	Probability of interval	Expected number
(200–249)	3,423	0.0072	(−2.425– −2.01)	0.0146	6,981.62
(250–299)	18,434	0.0385	(−2.01– −1.59)	0.0337	16,115.10
(300–349)	39,913	0.0835	(−1.59– −1.18)	0.0631	30,173.98
(350–399)	51,603	0.1079	(−1.18– −0.76)	0.1046	50,018.99
(400–449)	61,691	0.1290	(−0.76– −0.34)	0.1433	68,525.06
(450–499)	72,186	0.1510	(−0.34–0.075)	0.1630	77,945.46
(500–549)	72,804	0.1522	(0.075–0.49)	0.1580	75,554.49
(550–599)	58,304	0.1219	(0.49–0.91)	0.1307	62,499.83
(600–649)	46,910	0.0981	(0.91–1.325)	0.0888	42,463.54
(650–699)	30,265	0.0633	(1.325–1.74)	0.0517	24,722.58
(700–749)	16,246	0.0340	(1.74–2.16)	0.0255	12,193.92
(750–800)	6,414	0.0134	(2.16–2.575)	0.0104	4,973.21
Totals	478,193	1.0000		0.9874	472,167.78

As Figure 5.4 illustrates, the observed relative frequencies for the daily demands certainly suggest a bell-shaped curve. However, Table 5.4, in which the observed and theoretical relative frequencies are contrasted, shows a substantial discrepancy at the tails, even though there appears to be agreement around the middle. The assumption of a normal distribution for this type of situation can lead to a serious error when information concerning tail values is needed.

Recall that the binomial distribution is a limiting form of the Poisson when n is large and p is small. We want to show that the normal distribution is also a limiting form of the binomial when n is large and p is not too close to 0 or 1. The following theorem is known as the DeMoivre–Laplace limit theorem; it assures an adequate approximation by the normal distribution of binomial probabilities if n is sufficiently large.

Theorem 5.1 Let X be a binomial random variable with mean np and standard deviation $\sqrt{np(1-p)}$. The distribution of the random variable

$$Y = \frac{X - np}{\sqrt{np(1-p)}} \tag{5.16}$$

TABLE 5.3 Daily demands of a product

Daily demand	Frequency
(55–64)	6
(65–74)	4
(75–84)	6
(85–94)	20
(95–104)	32
(105–114)	18
(115–124)	6
(125–134)	6
(135–144)	4

FIGURE 5.4 Observed relative frequencies of daily demand for a product

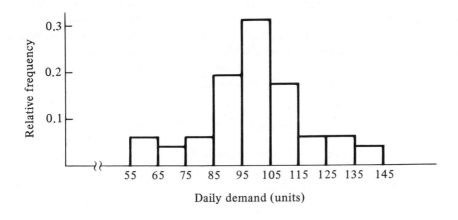

Daily demand (units)

approaches the standard normal as the number of independent trials $n \to \infty$. An outline of the proof is provided in an appendix to this chapter.

The essence of Theorem 5.1 is that if X is a binomial random variable for which the number of independent trials n is sufficiently large, then X is said to have an approximate normal distribution with mean np and standard deviation $\sqrt{np(1-p)}$. In fact, the approximation is adequate as long as $np > 5$ when $p \le 1/2$, or when $n(1-p) > 5$ for $p > 1/2$. That is,

$$P(a \le X_B \le b) \approx P\left(\frac{a - np}{\sqrt{np(1-p)}} \le Z_N \le \frac{b - np}{\sqrt{np(1-p)}}\right) \qquad (5.17)$$

where Z_N is $N(0, 1)$.

The approximation as given by (5.17) can be improved if we take into account that we are attempting to approximate probabilities for a discrete random variable

TABLE 5.4 Observed and theoretical relative frequencies of daily demands for a product

Daily demand	Relative frequency	Standard normal interval	Probability of interval
(55–64)	0.0588	(−3.75– −2.92)	0.0017
(65–74)	0.0392	(−2.92– −2.08)	0.0170
(75–84)	0.0588	(−2.08– −1.25)	0.0868
(85–94)	0.1961	(−1.25– −0.42)	0.2316
(95–104)	0.3137	(−0.42–0.42)	0.3256
(105–114)	0.1765	(0.42–1.25)	0.2316
(115–124)	0.0588	(1.25–2.08)	0.0868
(125–134)	0.0588	(2.08–2.92)	0.0170
(135–144)	0.0392	(2.92–3.75)	0.0017
Totals	0.9999		0.9998

from interval probabilities of a continuous random variable. For example, suppose we want to determine the probability that X is equal to x. We know that for any specified value x of a binomial random variable, the point probability is nonzero. However, if we used the normal approximation from Theorem 5.1, $P[Z = (x - np)/\sqrt{np(1 - p)}] = 0$. Instead we use the normal approximation for $P(X = x)$ by determining the probability of an interval of unit length — the same as the increment of a binomial random variable — such that the specified x is the midpoint of the interval. Therefore,

$$P(X_B = x) \approx P\left(\frac{x - np - 1/2}{\sqrt{np(1 - p)}} \leq Z_N \leq \frac{x - np + 1/2}{\sqrt{np(1 - p)}}\right).$$

As a result, expression (5.17) is modified to be

$$P(a \leq X_B \leq b) \approx P\left(\frac{a - np - 0.5}{\sqrt{np(1 - p)}} \leq Z_N \leq \frac{b - np + 0.5}{\sqrt{np(1 - p)}}\right). \qquad (5.18)$$

Example 5.7   A polling organization is planning a survey to gauge voter sentiment concerning two candidates, A and B, who are vying for public office. Suppose a random sample of 1000 citizens is taken. What is the probability that 550 or more of these will indicate a preference for candidate A if the population of voters is evenly divided between these candidates?

Let X be the random variable representing the number of citizens who will indicate a preference for candidate A. The random sample of 1000 citizens can be regarded as a set of independent trials with a 0.5 probability of success (candidate A) since by assumption the population of voters is evenly divided between the candidates. Thus X is a binomial random variable with mean $np = 500$ and standard deviation $\sqrt{np(1 - p)} = 15.81$. The probability that $X \geq 550$ can be adequately approximated by using the normal distribution since n is sufficiently large:

$$P(X \geq 550) \approx P[Z_N \geq (549.5 - 500)/15.81]$$

$$\approx P(Z_N \geq 3.13)$$

$$\approx 0.0009.$$

Since the probability of such an occurrence is extremely small if p indeed equals 0.5, we would be inclined to conclude that A is going to be the likely winner in the event that 550 or more of the 1000 polled indicate a preference for candidate A.

5.3   The Uniform Distribution

Suppose an event occurs in which a random variable assumes values from a finite interval in such a way that it is evenly distributed over the interval. That is, the probability of the random variable falling in each subinterval of equal length is the same. Such a random variable is said to be *uniformly distributed* over the interval.

Definition 5.2 A random variable X is said to be uniformly distributed over the interval (a, b) if the probability density function of X is given by

$$f(x; a, b) = \begin{cases} 1/(b-a) & a \le x \le b, \\ 0 & \text{elsewhere.} \end{cases} \tag{5.19}$$

The probability density function of a uniform distribution is constant in the interval (a, b), as illustrated in Figure 5.5. For this reason the uniform distribution is also referred to as the "rectangular" distribution.

The cumulative distribution function is easily determined to be

$$P(X \le x) = F(x; a, b) = (b-a)^{-1} \int_a^x dt$$

$$= \begin{cases} 0 & x < a, \\ (x-a)/(b-a) & a \le x \le b, \\ 1 & x > b. \end{cases} \tag{5.20}$$

It follows that for any subinterval (a_1, b_1) interior to (a, b),

$$P(a_1 \le X \le b_1) = F(b_1; a, b) - F(a_1; a, b)$$

$$= (b_1 - a_1)/(b-a). \tag{5.21}$$

This result illustrates that the probability of X taking on values from the subinterval (a_1, b_1) is $1/(b-a)$ times the length of the subinterval and, thus, equal to the probability that X falls in some other subinterval of the same length.

The uniform distribution is likely to provide adequate representation for

FIGURE 5.5 Graph of the uniform probability density function

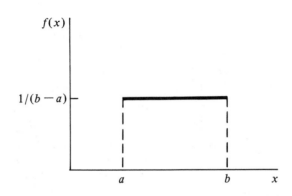

roundoff differences between recorded and true values of physical quantities. For example, if the weight of an individual is recorded to the nearest pound, then the difference between the recorded weight and the true weight would be some value between -0.5 and 0.5 pounds. The roundoff error is likely to be uniformly distributed in the interval $(-0.5, 0.5)$. Another use of the uniform distribution is to provide a fair approximation over a relatively narrow range for a random variable whose distribution is of some type other than the uniform.

Example 5.8   Recall the annual insurance premiums as given in Example 1.1. If we assume that the premiums are uniformly distributed in the interval ($81.5–$111.5), then the probability density function is

$$f(x; 81.5, 111.5) = 1/30, \qquad 81.5 \leq x \leq 111.5.$$

It follows from (5.21) that the probability of a premium falling on a subinterval of length $5 — the class width in Example 1.1 — is 5/30. Table 5.5 provides a comparison of the relative frequencies, as given in Table 1.1, and the corresponding theoretical probabilities based on the uniform distribution. Some agreement between the observed and theoretical frequencies is apparent.

The expected value of a uniformly distributed random variable is

$$E(X) = (b - a)^{-1} \int_a^b x\,dx$$

$$= (a + b)/2. \tag{5.22}$$

To obtain higher moments of X, it would be easier to work with the random variable $Y = X - [(a + b)]/2$, which shifts the mean to zero, since $E(Y) = E(X) - [(a + b)]/2$. Thus

$$f(y; \theta) = 1/\theta, \qquad -\theta/2 \leq y \leq \theta/2, \tag{5.23}$$

where $\theta = b - a$. Accordingly, the rth central moment of Y is the same as the rth moment about zero; that is,

$$\mu_r(Y) = \mu'_r(Y) = \theta^{-1} \int_{-\theta/2}^{\theta/2} y^r\,dy$$

TABLE 5.5   A comparison of observed and theoretical frequencies for a uniform distribution

Premium amount	Observed number	Relative frequency	Uniform interval	Probability of interval	Expected number
82– 86	3	0.075	81.5– 86.5	0.167	6.667
87– 91	7	0.175	86.5– 91.5	0.167	6.667
92– 96	8	0.200	91.5– 96.5	0.167	6.667
97–101	8	0.200	96.5–101.5	0.167	6.667
102–106	7	0.175	101.5–106.5	0.167	6.667
107–111	7	0.175	106.5–111.5	0.167	6.667
Totals	40	1.000		1.000	40.000

$$= \left(\frac{1}{\theta}\right) \cdot \frac{y^{r+1}}{r+1} \bigg|_{-\theta/2}^{\theta/2}$$

$$= \begin{cases} 0 & \text{if } r \text{ is odd,} \\ \theta^r/[(r+1)2^r] & \text{if } r \text{ is even.} \end{cases} \tag{5.24}$$

Since neither the variance nor the shape factors are affected by a location change, the variance, coefficient of skewness, and relative kurtosis of the uniformly distributed random variable X are determined from (5.24) to be

$$Var(X) = (b - a)^2/12, \tag{5.25}$$

$$\alpha_3(X) = 0, \text{ and} \tag{5.26}$$

$$\alpha_4(X) = \frac{(b-a)^4/80}{[(b-a)^2/12]^2} = \frac{9}{5}. \tag{5.27}$$

We can use (5.23) to determine the mean deviation as follows:

$$E|Y| = \theta^{-1} \int_{-\theta/2}^{\theta/2} |y| dy$$

$$= 2\theta^{-1} \int_0^{\theta/2} y dy$$

$$= \theta/4. \tag{5.28}$$

Thus the mean deviation of a uniformly distributed random variable is $(b - a)/4$.

A uniform distribution is symmetric and less peaked than a normal distribution. It has no mode, and its median is the same as its mean. The quantile value x_q, corresponding to a cumulative proportion q, is such that

$$F(x_q; a, b) = q,$$

which by (5.20) results in

$$x_q = a + (b - a)q. \tag{5.29}$$

The properties of a uniform distribution are summarized in Table 5.6.

TABLE 5.6 Basic properties of the uniform distribution

Probability density function			*Parameters*		
$f(x; a, b) = 1/(b - a), \quad a \le x \le b$			$a,$	$-\infty < a < \infty$	
			$b,$	$-\infty < b < \infty.$	

Mean	*Variance*	*Mean deviation*	*Quantile value*	*Coefficient of skewness*	*Relative kurtosis*
$(a + b)/2$	$(b - a)^2/12$	$(b - a)/4$	$x_q = a + (b - a)q$	0	9/5

Later we will examine the special case when $a = 0$ and $b = 1$. This is known as the uniform distribution on the unit interval $(0, 1)$ with probability density function

$$f(x; 0, 1) = 1, \qquad 0 \le x \le 1. \tag{5.30}$$

This distribution is especially important because it plays a key role in the computer simulation of values of a random variable with a specified distribution.

5.4   The Beta Distribution

A distribution that allows for a wide variety of shapes is the *beta distribution*. It has been used to represent physical variables whose values are restricted to an interval of finite length, and it has been used in finding quantities known as tolerance limits without requiring the assumption of the normal distribution. Moreover, the beta distribution plays a major role in Bayesian statistics. An example of this will be examined in Chapter 6.

Definition 5.3   A random variable X is said to be beta distributed if its probability density function is given by

$$f(x; \alpha, \beta) = \begin{cases} \dfrac{\Gamma(\alpha + \beta)}{\Gamma(\alpha)\Gamma(\beta)} x^{\alpha-1}(1 - x)^{\beta-1} & 0 < x < 1, \quad \alpha, \beta > 0, \\[2mm] 0 & \text{elsewhere.} \end{cases} \tag{5.31}$$

The quantities α and β of the the beta distribution are both shape parameters. Different values of α and β give rise to different shapes for the beta density. If both α and β are less than one, the beta distribution is U-shaped. If $\alpha < 1$ and $\beta \ge 1$, the distribution is reverse J-shaped, and if $\beta < 1$ and $\alpha \ge 1$, it is J-shaped. When α and β are both greater than one, the distribution is single-peaked with the peak at $x = (\alpha - 1)/(\alpha + \beta - 2)$. Finally, the beta distribution is symmetrical when $\alpha = \beta$. These different shapes of the beta distribution are illustrated in Figure 5.6 for specific values of α and β. Notice that if in (5.31) x is replaced by $1 - x$, the symmetry relation

$$f(1 - x; \beta, \alpha) = f(x; \alpha, \beta) \tag{5.32}$$

is obtained.

The name of the distribution is derived from its association with the beta function defined by

$$B(\alpha, \beta) = \int_0^1 x^{\alpha-1}(1 - x)^{\beta-1}dx. \tag{5.33}$$

It can be shown that the beta and gamma functions are related by the expression

$$B(\alpha, \beta) = \frac{\Gamma(\alpha)\Gamma(\beta)}{\Gamma(\alpha + \beta)}. \tag{5.34}$$

FIGURE 5.6 Graphs of the beta density function for various values of α and β

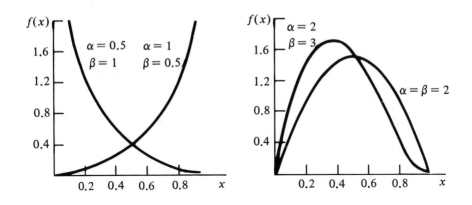

Using (5.33) and (5.34), it is obvious that (5.31) is a probability density function. That is,

$$\frac{\Gamma(\alpha + \beta)}{\Gamma(\alpha)\Gamma(\beta)} \int_0^1 x^{\alpha-1}(1 - x)^{\beta-1}dx = \frac{\Gamma(\alpha + \beta)}{\Gamma(\alpha)\Gamma(\beta)} B(\alpha, \beta) = 1,$$

and since $f(x; \alpha, \beta)$ is nonnegative, (5.31) is a probability density function.

The cumulative distribution function is defined by

$$P(X \le x) = F(x; \alpha, \beta) = \begin{cases} 0 & x \le 0, \\[2mm] \dfrac{\Gamma(\alpha + \beta)}{\Gamma(\alpha)\Gamma(\beta)} \displaystyle\int_0^x t^{\alpha-1}(1 - t)^{\beta-1}dt & 0 < x < 1, \quad (5.35) \\[2mm] 1 & x \ge 1. \end{cases}$$

The integral in (5.35) is the incomplete beta function

$$B_x(\alpha, \beta) = \int_0^x t^{\alpha-1}(1 - t)^{\beta-1}dt. \tag{5.36}$$

Thus the beta distribution function can be expressed as the incomplete beta function ratio given by

$$F(x; \alpha, \beta) = B_x(\alpha, \beta)/B(\alpha, \beta)$$
$$= I_x(\alpha, \beta) \qquad 0 < x < 1, \tag{5.37}$$

where $I_x(\alpha, \beta)$ is extensively tabulated (see [5,6]). In [5], quantile values x are given for which $I_x(\alpha, \beta)$ equals 0.0025, 0.005, 0.01, 0.025, 0.05, 0.1, 0.25, and 0.5 for various combinations of α and β. To find quantile values corresponding to higher percentage points, we examine the following:

$$P(X \le x) = P(1 - X \ge 1 - x)$$
$$= 1 - P(1 - X \le 1 - x);$$

then by the symmetry relation (5.32),

$$F(x; \alpha, \beta) = 1 - F(1 - x; \beta, \alpha)$$

or

$$I_x(\alpha, \beta) = 1 - I_{1-x}(\beta, \alpha). \tag{5.38}$$

Thus quantile values for upper percentage points are found by interchanging α and β and taking the percentage point to be $1 - x$. For illustration, let X be a beta random variable with $\alpha = 2$ and $\beta = 4$; the 90th, 95th, and 99th quantile values are 0.58389, 0.65741, and 0.77793, respectively. In Table 5.7 we provide the quartile values for combinations of α and β that give rise to distinct shapes for the beta distribution.

It is easier to determine the moments of the beta random variable directly than to use the moment generating function because the latter does not have a simple form. In particular, we shall determine a general expression for the rth moment about zero and use it to determine other moments:

$$\mu_r' = E(X^r) = \frac{\Gamma(\alpha + \beta)}{\Gamma(\alpha)\Gamma(\beta)} \int_0^1 x^{\alpha + r - 1}(1 - x)^{\beta - 1}dx$$

$$= \frac{\Gamma(\alpha + \beta)}{\Gamma(\alpha)\Gamma(\beta)} B(\alpha + r, \beta)$$

$$= \frac{\Gamma(\alpha + b)}{\Gamma(\alpha)\Gamma(\beta)} \cdot \frac{\Gamma(\alpha + r)\Gamma(\beta)}{\Gamma(\alpha + \beta + r)}$$

$$= \frac{\Gamma(\alpha + \beta)\Gamma(\alpha + r)}{\Gamma(\alpha)\Gamma(\alpha + \beta + r)}. \tag{5.39}$$

As a result,

$$E(X) = \frac{\Gamma(\alpha + \beta)\Gamma(\alpha + 1)}{\Gamma(\alpha)\Gamma(\alpha + \beta + 1)}$$

$$= \frac{\alpha}{\alpha + \beta}, \tag{5.40}$$

and

$$Var(X) = \frac{\alpha(\alpha + 1)}{(\alpha + \beta)(\alpha + \beta + 1)} - \frac{\alpha^2}{(\alpha + \beta)^2}$$

$$= \frac{\alpha\beta}{(\alpha + \beta)^2(\alpha + \beta + 1)}. \tag{5.41}$$

TABLE 5.7 Beta quartile values for various combinations of α and β

	$x_{0.25}$	$x_{0.50}$	$x_{0.75}$
$\alpha = \beta = 1/2$	0.14645	0.50000	0.85355
$\alpha = 1/2, \beta = 2$	0.02831	0.12061	0.31122
$\alpha = 2, \beta = 1/2$	0.68878	0.87939	0.97169
$\alpha = 4, \beta = 6$	0.29099	0.39308	0.50199

Following this procedure and after some algebra, one can determine that the coefficient of skewness and the relative kurtosis for the beta distribution are given by

$$\alpha_3(X) = \frac{2(\beta - \alpha)\sqrt{\alpha + \beta + 1}}{\sqrt{\alpha\beta}\,(\alpha + \beta + 2)}, \tag{5.42}$$

and

$$\alpha_4(X) = \frac{3(\alpha + \beta + 1)[2(\alpha + \beta)^2 + \alpha\beta(\alpha + \beta - 6)]}{\alpha\beta(\alpha + \beta + 2)(\alpha + \beta + 3)}. \tag{5.43}$$

By examining (5.42) we can see that the beta distribution is symmetrical only if $\alpha = \beta$, as we have already noted. If $\alpha < \beta$, the distribution is positively skewed, and if $\alpha > \beta$, the distribution is negatively skewed.

The basic properties of the beta distribution are summarized in Table 5.8.

Some areas in which the beta distribution has been used as a probability model include the distribution over a specified unit of time of the proportion of defective items produced by a manufacturing process; the distribution of the length of time to complete a project phase in PERT, Program Evaluation and Review Technique, (here one uses the generalized beta distribution; see [4]); and the distribution of the proportion of values that would fall between two relatively extreme observations.

The substance of the last area has to do with statistical tolerance limits. These limits are extremely important, especially in statistical quality control where assessment of product variability is essential. This assessment usually takes the form of measuring the quality of the particular batch being produced or of determining whether adjustments to the production process are necessary to improve quality. Statistical tolerance limits are not the same as physical tolerance or specification limits, which are sets of criteria designed in the manufacturing process to which all acceptable units are expected to conform. Statistical tolerance limits will be discussed in Chapter 8.

TABLE 5.8 Basic properties of the beta distribution

Probability density function		*Parameters*	
$f(x; \alpha, \beta) = \dfrac{\Gamma(\alpha + \beta)}{\Gamma(\alpha)\Gamma(\beta)} x^{\alpha - 1}(1 - x)^{\beta - 1}$ $0 < x < 1$		$\alpha,$ $\beta,$	$\alpha > 0$ $\beta > 0$

Mean	*Variance*	*Coefficient of skewness*	*Relative kurtosis*
$\dfrac{\alpha}{\alpha + \beta}$	$\dfrac{\alpha\beta}{(\alpha + \beta)^2(\alpha + \beta + 1)}$	$\dfrac{2(\beta - \alpha)\sqrt{\alpha + \beta + 1}}{\sqrt{\alpha\beta}\,(\alpha + \beta + 2)}$	*

$$*\frac{3(\alpha + \beta + 1)[2(\alpha + \beta)^2 + \alpha\beta(\alpha + \beta - 6)]}{\alpha\beta(\alpha + \beta + 2)(\alpha + \beta + 3)}$$

It can be shown that if the sum of the beta shape parameters is relatively large, the beta cumulative distribution function (5.35) can be adequately approximated by the difference of two standard normal distribution functions. That is,

$$F(x; \alpha, \beta) \approx F_N(z_u; 0, 1) - F_N(z_\ell; 0, 1),\tag{5.44}$$

where

$$z_u = \frac{[\beta] - 0.5 - (\alpha + \beta - 1)(1 - x)}{[(\alpha + \beta - 1)(x)(1 - x)]^{1/2}},$$

$$z_\ell = -\frac{(\alpha + \beta - 1)(1 - x) + 0.5}{[(\alpha + \beta - 1)(x)(1 - x)]^{1/2}},$$

and $[\beta]$ represents the largest integer not greater than β. Table 5.9 contains a comparison of the beta distribution function as given in (5.35) with that determined by (5.44). For each value x in the table the upper entry is the exact beta distribution value, and the lower entry is the one computed from (5.44). Other than for end values the agreement is adequate. Notice, however, that the discrepancy at the upper end diminishes as the sum of α and β becomes larger.

5.5   The Gamma Distribution

Another distribution with wide usage is the *gamma distribution*. Among the many uses of the gamma distribution is the following: Suppose a metal specimen is subjected to stress in such a way that it will break only if a certain number of stress cycles are applied. If the cycles occur independently and at a given average rate, then the length of time until the specimen breaks is a random variable that follows the gamma distribution.

Definition 5.4   The random variable X is said to be gamma distributed if its probability density function is

TABLE 5.9   A comparison of the beta and normal distribution functions

x	$\alpha = \beta = 5$	$\alpha = 10, \beta = 5$	$\alpha = 10, \beta = 15$
0.10	0.0008909	0.0000001	0.0000521
	0.0000317	0.0	0.0000007
0.25	0.04893	0.0003419	0.05466
	0.04182	0.0001078	0.04947
0.50	0.50	0.08978	0.8463
	0.4996	0.09009	0.8461
0.75	0.95107	0.74153	0.99989
	0.94118	0.72564	0.99886
0.90	0.9991091	0.99077	1.0
	0.9405883	0.95160	0.9756

$$f(x; \alpha, \theta) = \begin{cases} \dfrac{1}{\Gamma(\alpha)\theta^\alpha} x^{\alpha-1} \exp(-x/\theta) & x > 0, \quad \alpha, \theta > 0 \\ 0 & \text{elsewhere,} \end{cases} \tag{5.45}$$

where $\Gamma(\alpha)$ is the gamma function as defined in Chapter 3.

The gamma distribution is a versatile distribution that exhibits several shapes depending on the value of the parameter α. Figure 5.7 illustrates the shapes of the gamma density function for various values of α and θ. It can be seen that for $\alpha \le 1$, the gamma distribution is reverse J-shaped. For $\alpha > 1$, it exhibits a single peak occurring when $x = \theta(\alpha - 1)$. For a fixed α, the basic shape of the gamma distribution is not altered if θ is varied. As a result, the quantities α and θ are the shape and scale parameters, respectively, of the gamma distribution.

The gamma distribution has been used extensively in several diverse areas. For example, it has been used to represent random time to failure of a system that fails only if exactly α independent components fail and component failure occurs at a constant rate $\lambda = 1/\theta$ per unit of time. It has also been used extensively in waiting line problems to represent the total length of time to complete service if service is made up of exactly α substations and completions of service at each station occur independently at a constant rate $\lambda = 1/\theta$. Some additional instances that do not follow the above pattern, such as family incomes and age of male at first marriage, have also been adequately approximated by gamma distributions.

FIGURE 5.7 Graphs of the gamma density function for various values of α and θ

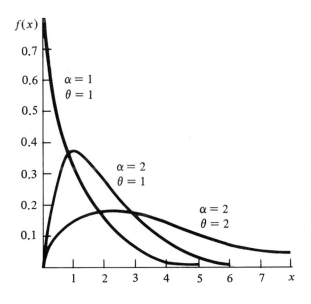

By using the gamma function as given by (3.5), we can show that (5.45) is a probability density function. That is, consider a change of variable of integration such that $u = x/\theta$, $x = \theta u$, and $dx = \theta du$; then

$$\frac{1}{\Gamma(\alpha)\theta^\alpha} \int_0^\infty x^{\alpha-1}\exp(-x/\theta)dx = \frac{1}{\Gamma(\alpha)\theta^\alpha} \int_0^\infty (\theta u)^{\alpha-1}\exp(-u)\theta du$$

$$= \frac{1}{\Gamma(\alpha)} \int_0^\infty u^{\alpha-1}\exp(-u)du = 1,$$

since $\Gamma(\alpha) = \int_0^\infty u^{\alpha-1}\exp(-u)du$.

Following a similar procedure, we show that the rth moment about zero is

$$\mu_r' = \frac{1}{\Gamma(\alpha)\theta^\alpha} \int_0^\infty x^{\alpha+r-1}\exp(-x/\theta)dx$$

$$= \frac{\theta^{\alpha+r}}{\Gamma(\alpha)\theta^\alpha} \int_0^\infty u^{\alpha+r-1}\exp(-u)du$$

$$= \frac{\theta^r\Gamma(\alpha+r)}{\Gamma(\alpha)}. \tag{5.46}$$

It follows, therefore, that

$$E(X) = \alpha\theta \tag{5.47}$$

and

$$Var(X) = \alpha\theta^2. \tag{5.48}$$

Moreover, after determining the appropriate central moments, we can show that the coefficient of skewness is

$$\alpha_3(X) = 2/\sqrt{\alpha}, \tag{5.49}$$

and the relative kurtosis is

$$\alpha_4(X) = 3\left(1 + \frac{2}{\alpha}\right). \tag{5.50}$$

From the shape factors $\alpha_3(X)$ and $\alpha_4(X)$, we notice that the gamma distribution is positively skewed and more peaked than a normal distribution since $\alpha_4(X) > 3$ for any $\alpha > 0$. However, also notice that as the shape parameter α of the gamma distribution becomes large, the positive skew is less pronounced and the relative kurtosis has the value 3 as its limit. In fact, for large α the gamma distribution is to some degree adequately approximated by a normal distribution. That is, the random variable

$$Z = (X - \alpha\theta)/\theta\sqrt{\alpha} \tag{5.51}$$

is approximately a standard normal for large α.

The moment generating function of the gamma random variable X is

$$E[\exp(tX)] = \frac{1}{\Gamma(\alpha)\theta^\alpha} \int_0^\infty x^{\alpha-1}\exp[-(1 - \theta t)x/\theta]dx.$$

Let $u = (1 - \theta t)x/\theta$, $x = u\theta/(1 - \theta t)$, and $dx = [\theta/(1 - \theta t)]du$. Then

$$E[\exp(tX)] = \frac{1}{\Gamma(\alpha)\theta^\alpha} \int_0^\infty \frac{u^{\alpha-1}\theta^{\alpha-1}}{(1 - \theta t)^{\alpha-1}} \exp(-u) \frac{\theta}{(1 - \theta t)} du$$

$$= \frac{1}{\Gamma(\alpha)(1 - \theta t)^\alpha} \int_0^\infty u^{\alpha-1}\exp(-u)du$$

$$= (1 - \theta t)^{-\alpha}, \qquad 0 \leq t < 1/\theta. \tag{5.52}$$

The cumulative distribution function is given by the expression

$$F(x; \alpha, \theta) = \frac{1}{\Gamma(\alpha)\theta^\alpha} \int_0^x t^{\alpha-1}\exp(-t/\theta)dt, \qquad x > 0. \tag{5.53}$$

Several variations of (5.53) have been extensively tabulated. For example, if we change the variable of integration to $u = t/\theta$ so that $t = \theta u$ and $dt = \theta du$, then (5.53) becomes

$$F(x; \alpha, \theta) = \frac{1}{\Gamma(\alpha)\theta^\alpha} \int_0^{x/\theta} (\theta u)^{\alpha-1}\exp(-u)\theta du$$

$$= \frac{1}{\Gamma(\alpha)} \int_0^{x/\theta} u^{\alpha-1}\exp(-u)du.$$

The integral $\int_0^{x/\theta} u^{\alpha-1}\exp(-u)du$ is known as the *incomplete gamma function* and is often denoted as $\gamma(x/\theta; \alpha)$. The ratio of $\gamma(x/\theta; \alpha)$ to the complete gamma function $\Gamma(\alpha)$ is called the *incomplete gamma function ratio* and is tabulated in [8] for various values of x/θ and α. Accordingly, the gamma cumulative distribution function is written as

$$P(X \leq x) = F(x; \alpha, \theta) = \gamma(x/\theta; \alpha)/\Gamma(\alpha). \tag{5.54}$$

In [7] is another extensive tabulation of a function equivalent to (5.53), given by

$$I(u, p) = F(x; \alpha, \theta), \tag{5.55}$$

where $u = x/\theta\sqrt{\alpha}$ and $p = \alpha - 1$. It should be noted that if the shape parameter α is a positive integer, (5.53) can be expressed in the closed form

$$F(x; \alpha, \theta) = 1 - \left[1 + \frac{x}{\theta} + \frac{1}{2!}\left(\frac{x}{\theta}\right)^2 + \cdots + \frac{1}{(\alpha - 1)!}\left(\frac{x}{\theta}\right)^{\alpha-1} \right]\exp(-x/\theta) \tag{5.56}$$

as a result of successive integrations by parts. Also, the quantile value x_q for which $F(x_q; \alpha, \theta) = q$ cannot be determined directly; it can be interpolated from the tables in either [7] or [8]. The basic properties of the gamma distribution are summarized in Table 5.10.

Example 5.9 Suppose a metal specimen will break after experiencing exactly two stress cycles. If stress cycles occur independently and at an average rate of two per 100 hours, determine the probability that the length of time until the

TABLE 5.10 Properties of the gamma distribution

Probability density function			Parameters	
$f(x; \alpha, \theta) = \dfrac{1}{\Gamma(\alpha)\theta^\alpha} x^{\alpha-1} \exp(-x/\theta)$			$\alpha,$	$\alpha > 0$
$x > 0$			$\theta,$	$\theta > 0$

Mean	Variance	Coefficient of skewness	Relative kurtosis
$\alpha\theta$	$\alpha\theta^2$	$2/\sqrt{\alpha}$	$3\left(1 + \dfrac{2}{\alpha}\right)$

second stress cycle is (a) within one standard deviation of the average time and (b) more than two standard deviation units above the mean.

Let X be the random variable representing the length of time until the second stress cycle is experienced. X is gamma distributed, with $\alpha = 2$ and $\theta = 50$ hours, since the average rate is 0.02 per hour. The probability density function is

$$f(x; 2, 50) = \frac{1}{\Gamma(2)50^2} x \exp(-x/50), \qquad x > 0,$$

and the cumulative distribution function, by (5.56), reduces to

$$F(x; \alpha, \theta) = 1 - \left(1 + \frac{x}{50}\right)\exp(-x/50), \qquad x > 0.$$

From (5.47) and (5.48), the mean and standard deviation of X are 100 and 70.71 hours, respectively. Thus

$$P(\mu - \sigma < X < \mu + \sigma) = P(29.29 < X < 170.71)$$
$$= F(170.71; 2, 50) - F(29.29; 2, 50)$$
$$= 0.7376.$$

Notice that the probability that a time length will be less than one standard deviation unit below the mean is 0.1172 and the probability that a time length will exceed the mean by one standard deviation unit is $1 - 0.8548 = 0.1452$. Finally,

$$P(X > \mu + 2\sigma) = P(X > 241.42)$$
$$= 1 - F(241.42; 2, 50)$$
$$= 0.0466.$$

Example 5.10 To show the extent of agreement between the normal and gamma distributions as a function of the shape parameter of the latter, we select the values of 3.5 and 7 for α, and for $\theta = 10$ we compute the cumulative distribution functions for various values of the respective random variables. This information is given in Table 5.11.

It is apparent from the information in Table 5.11 that the cumulative normal overestimates the cumulative gamma at the tails while it underestimates it around the middle. This holds for both values of α; however, for $\alpha = 7$, the agreement at the tails is considerably better than when $\alpha = 3.5$. As a result, one expects the extent of agreement to improve for values of α greater than 7.

When α is a positive integer, the gamma distribution is also known as the *Erlang probability model*, named after the Danish scientist who used it in the early 1900s to establish useful results for telephone traffic problems. There is a natural association between the Erlang and Poisson probability models. If we let the number of independent random events occurring in a specified time interval be a Poisson variable with a constant rate of occurrence $1/\theta$, then for a given α, the waiting time until the occurrence of the αth Poisson event is Erlang distributed. This result follows from a comparison of the cumulative distribution functions of the Poisson and Erlang models given by (4.17) and (5.56), respectively. That is, the probability of at most $\alpha - 1$ Poisson events in time x occurring at a constant rate $1/\theta$ follows from (4.17) and is

$$F_P(\alpha - 1; x/\theta) = \left[1 + \frac{x}{\theta} + \frac{1}{2!}\left(\frac{x}{\theta}\right)^2 + \cdots + \frac{1}{(\alpha - 1)!}\left(\frac{x}{\theta}\right)^{\alpha - 1} \right] \exp(-x/\theta).$$

TABLE 5.11 A comparison of the gamma and normal cumulative distribution functions

$\alpha = 3.5, \theta = 10, p = 2.5; \mu = 35, \sigma = 18.71$				$\alpha = 7, \theta = 10, p = 6; \mu = 70, \sigma = 26.46$			
X	u	Gamma $I(u, p)$	Normal $F(x; \mu, \sigma)$	X	u	Gamma $I(u, p)$	Normal $F(x; \mu, \sigma)$
0	0	0	0.0307	0	0	0	0.0041
5	0.27	0.0058	0.0516	10	0.38	0.000098	0.0116
10	0.53	0.0397	0.0902	20	0.76	0.004865	0.0294
15	0.80	0.1144	0.1423	30	1.13	0.0431	0.0655
20	1.07	0.2209	0.2119	40	1.51	0.1103	0.1292
25	1.34	0.3417	0.2981	50	1.89	0.2380	0.2236
30	1.60	0.4587	0.3936	60	2.27	0.3946	0.3520
35	1.87	0.5706	0.5000	70	2.65	0.5518	0.5000
40	2.14	0.6678	0.6064	80	3.02	0.6853	0.6480
45	2.41	0.7485	0.7019	90	3.40	0.7928	0.7764
50	2.67	0.8107	0.7881	100	3.78	0.8698	0.8708
55	2.94	0.8612	0.8577	110	4.16	0.9215	0.9345
60	3.21	0.8997	0.9098	120	4.54	0.9544	0.9706
65	3.47	0.9274	0.9485	130	4.91	0.9739	0.9884
70	3.74	0.9486	0.9693	140	5.29	0.9857	0.9959
75	4.01	0.9640	0.9838	150	5.67	0.9924	0.9987
80	4.28	0.9750	0.9920	160	6.05	0.9960	0.9997

On the other hand, if we assume that the waiting time is Erlang distributed, the probability that the time until the αth event will exceed a specified length x is given by

$$P(X > x) = 1 - F_E(x; \alpha, \theta)$$

$$= 1 - \left\{ 1 - \left[1 + \frac{x}{\theta} + \frac{1}{2!}\left(\frac{x}{\theta}\right)^2 + \cdots \right. \right.$$

$$\left. \left. + \frac{1}{(\alpha - 1)!}\left(\frac{x}{\theta}\right)^{\alpha - 1} \right] \exp(-x/\theta) \right\}$$

$$= \left[1 + \frac{x}{\theta} + \frac{1}{2!}\left(\frac{x}{\theta}\right)^2 + \cdots + \frac{1}{(\alpha - 1)!}\left(\frac{x}{\theta}\right)^{\alpha - 1} \right] \exp(-x/\theta)$$

$$= F_P(\alpha - 1; x/\theta). \tag{5.57}$$

In other words, the probability that the length of time until the αth event will exceed x is the same as the probability that the number of Poisson events observed in x is no more than $\alpha - 1$. Thus the Erlang distribution is the model for the waiting time until the αth Poisson event, and the Poisson distribution is the model for the number of independent events occurring in time x, the length of which is Erlang distributed. In this context $1/\theta$ is the constant rate of occurrence, and θ is the average time between two successive occurrences.

When the shape parameter α is equal to one, the Erlang (gamma) reduces to what is known as the *negative exponential distribution*. This distribution has been used extensively to represent random time lengths, and it will be discussed in greater detail in a subsequent section. Note here, however, that the random variable of a negative exponential distribution can be regarded as the length of time until the occurrence of the first Poisson event. Accordingly, the Erlang random variable is the sum of α independent, exponentially distributed random variables.

Another special case of the gamma model is the chi-square distribution. If in (5.45) we replace the shape parameter α with $\nu/2$ and the scale parameter θ with 2, the result is the probability density function of a chi-square random variable given by

$$f(x; \nu) = \begin{cases} \dfrac{1}{\Gamma(\nu/2)2^{\nu/2}} x^{\nu/2 - 1}\exp(-x/2) & x > 0, \\ 0 & \text{elsewhere.} \end{cases} \tag{5.58}$$

The chi-square distribution is characterized by a single parameter ν, which is called the *degrees of freedom*. As we shall see later, this distribution plays a significant role in statistical inference, especially with regard to inferences about variances. Usually the notation $X \sim \chi_\nu^2$ is used for brevity to denote that a random variable X is chi-square distributed with ν degrees of freedom.

The cumulative distribution function given by

$$P(X \le x) = \frac{1}{\Gamma(\nu/2)2^{\nu/2}} \int_0^x t^{\nu/2 - 1} \exp(-t/2)dt \qquad x > 0, \tag{5.59}$$

is extensively tabulated. In Table E of the Appendix are quantile values $x_{1-\alpha,\nu}$ such that

$$P(X \le x_{1-\alpha,\nu}) = \int_0^{x_{1-\alpha,\nu}} f(x;\nu)dx = 1 - \alpha$$

for selected cumulative proportions $1 - \alpha^*$ and various values of ν. For illustration if $\nu = 10$,

$$P(X \le x_{0.01,10}) = P(X \le 2.55) = 0.01,$$

$$P(X \le x_{0.05,10}) = P(X \le 3.94) = 0.05,$$

$$P(X \le x_{0.95,10}) = P(X \le 18.31) = 0.95,$$

$$P(X \le x_{0.99,10}) = P(X \le 23.19) = 0.99.$$

The chi-square moments are determined from (5.47)–(5.50) and are given by

$$E(X) = \nu,$$

$$Var(X) = 2\nu,$$

$$\alpha_3(X) = 4/\sqrt{2\nu},$$

$$\alpha_4(X) = 3\left(1 + \frac{4}{\nu}\right).$$

Similarly, from (5.52) the moment generating function of a chi-square distribution is

$$m_X(t) = (1 - 2t)^{-\nu/2} \qquad 0 \le t < \frac{1}{2}. \tag{5.60}$$

Notice that an interesting characteristic of a chi-square random variable is that its variance is twice its mean. In addition, since a chi-square distribution is a special case of the gamma, it is positively skewed and more peaked than a normal distribution but tends to a coefficient of skewness of zero and a relative kurtosis of 3 as ν tends to infinity.

5.6   The Weibull Distribution

The Weibull distribution was introduced by a Swedish physicist of the same name who showed, based on empirical evidence, that strength of materials is adequately modeled by this distribution [9]. In the last 25 years the Weibull distribution has been used extensively as a time-to-failure model for a wide variety of mechanical and electrical components.

Definition 5.5   A random variable X is said to be *Weibull distributed* if its probability density function is given by

---

*The introduction of the quantity α, $0 \le \alpha \le 1$, in this context is to facilitate a subsequent discussion of a concept known as "the probability of type I error," which is usually denoted by α.

$$f(x; \alpha, \theta) = \begin{cases} \dfrac{\alpha}{\theta^\alpha} x^{\alpha-1} \exp[-(x/\theta)^\alpha] & x > 0; \quad \alpha, \theta > 0, \\ 0 & \text{elsewhere.} \end{cases} \quad (5.61)$$

The Weibull distribution is a two-parameter family of distributions, the parameters being the shape parameter α and the scale parameter θ. An additional parameter may be introduced by replacing the Weibull random variable X by $X - a$, where a is a location parameter representing a threshold value or guarantee time. Graphs of (5.61) for various values of α and θ, as in Figure 5.8, show that the Weibull density exhibits several shapes, depending on the values of α. For example, if $\alpha < 1$, (5.61) is reverse J-shaped, and if $\alpha > 1$, the Weibull density is single-peaked.

The Weibull cumulative distribution function

$$F(x; \alpha, \theta) = \frac{\alpha}{\theta^\alpha} \int_0^x t^{\alpha-1} \exp[-(t/\theta)^\alpha] dt \quad (5.62)$$

can be determined in closed form by directly evaluating the integral in (5.62). That is,

$$F(x; \alpha, \theta) = \frac{\alpha}{\theta^\alpha} \left(-\frac{\theta^\alpha}{\alpha} \right) \exp[-(t/\theta)^\alpha] \Big|_0^x$$

$$= 1 - \exp[-(x/\theta)^\alpha], \quad x \geq 0. \quad (5.63)$$

From (5.63), the general quantile value x_q is

$$1 - \exp[-(x_q/\theta)^\alpha] = q$$

$$x_q = -\theta[\ln(1 - q)]^{1/\alpha}$$

$$= \theta \left[\ln\left(\frac{1}{1-q}\right) \right]^{1/\alpha}. \quad (5.64)$$

FIGURE 5.8   Graphs of the Weibull density function for various values of α and θ

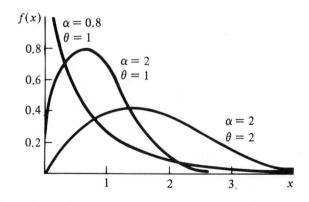

In particular, the median of a Weibull random variable X is

$$x_{0.5} = \theta[\ln(2)]^{1/\alpha}. \tag{5.65}$$

Moments and shape factors of a Weibull random variable are determined by first evaluating the rth moment about zero,

$$\mu_r' = E(X^r) = \int_0^\infty x^r f(x; \alpha, \theta)dx$$

$$= \frac{\alpha}{\theta^\alpha} \int_0^\infty x^{\alpha+r-1}\exp[-(x/\theta)^\alpha]dx. \tag{5.66}$$

In (5.66), let $u = (x/\theta)^\alpha$; then $x = \theta u^{1/\alpha}$ and $dx = (\theta/\alpha)u^{1/\alpha-1}\,du$. As a result,

$$\mu_r' = \frac{\alpha}{\theta^\alpha} \int_0^\infty (\theta u^{1/\alpha})^{\alpha+r-1} \exp(-u) \frac{\theta}{\alpha}u^{1/\alpha-1}du$$

$$= \theta^r \int_0^\infty u^{r/\alpha}\exp(-u)du$$

$$= \theta^r \Gamma\left(1 + \frac{r}{\alpha}\right). \tag{5.67}$$

From (5.67), the mean of X is

$$E(X) = \theta\Gamma\left(1 + \frac{1}{\alpha}\right), \tag{5.68}$$

and the variance of X is evaluated to be

$$Var(X) = \theta^2\left[\Gamma\left(1 + \frac{2}{\alpha}\right) - \Gamma^2\left(1 + \frac{1}{\alpha}\right)\right]. \tag{5.69}$$

Using the same procedure, we can also determine the coefficient of skewness and the relative kurtosis. These are given in Table 5.12. The shape factors can

TABLE 5.12   Basic properties of the Weibull distribution

Probability density function			*Parameters*	
$f(x; \alpha, \theta) = \dfrac{\alpha}{\theta^\alpha} x^{\alpha-1}\exp[-(x/\theta)^\alpha]$			$\alpha, \quad \alpha > 0$	
$x > 0$			$\theta, \quad \theta > 0$	

Mean	*Variance*	*Quantile value*	*Coefficient of skewness*	*Kurtosis*
$\theta\Gamma\left(1 + \dfrac{1}{\alpha}\right)$	$\theta^2\left[\Gamma\left(1 + \dfrac{2}{\alpha}\right) - \Gamma^2\left(1 + \dfrac{1}{\alpha}\right)\right]$	$x_q = \theta\left[\ln\left(\dfrac{1}{1-q}\right)\right]^{1/\alpha}$	*	**

$$*\alpha_3(X) = \frac{\Gamma(1 + 3/\alpha) - 3\Gamma(1 + 1/\alpha)\Gamma(1 + 2/\alpha) + 2\Gamma^3(1 + 1/\alpha)}{[\Gamma(1 + 2/\alpha) - \Gamma^2(1 + 1/\alpha)]^{3/2}}$$

$$**\alpha_4(X) = \frac{\Gamma(1 + 4/\alpha) - 4\Gamma(1 + 1/\alpha)\Gamma(1 + 3/\alpha)}{[\Gamma(1 + 2/\alpha) - \Gamma^2(1 + 1/\alpha)]^2} + \frac{6\Gamma^2(1 + 1/\alpha)\Gamma(1 + 2/\alpha) - 3\Gamma^4(1 + 1/\alpha)}{[\Gamma(1 + 2/\alpha) - \Gamma^2(1 + 1/\alpha)]^2}$$

be graphed as functions of the Weibull shape parameter (see [2]). Such graphs reveal the following: The Weibull distribution is symmetric only if $\alpha = 3.6$; if $\alpha > 3.6$, the Weibull is negatively skewed, and if $\alpha < 3.6$, it is positively skewed. The relative kurtosis is close to the normal distribution value of 3 when α is about 2.25 or about 5.83. In Table 5.13 we provide a comparison of the Weibull cumulative distribution function with the corresponding normal for $\alpha = 2.25$, 3.6, and 5.83, and scale parameter $\theta = 10$. The agreement appears to be relatively good at the tails as well as at the center, especially for $\alpha = 3.6$ and 5.83. Thus the Weibull distribution may be adequately approximated by a normal distribution as long as the shape parameter α is close to these values.

The properties of the Weibull distribution are summarized in Table 5.12.

Two special cases of the Weibull distribution family are worthy of mention. When the shape parameter α is equal to one, the Weibull — like the gamma — reduces to the negative exponential distribution. When $\alpha = 2$ and the Weibull scale parameter θ is replaced by $\sqrt{2}\,\sigma$, the Weibull density (5.61) reduces to

$$f(x; \sigma^2) = \frac{x}{\sigma^2} \exp(-x^2/2\sigma^2) \qquad x > 0, \tag{5.70}$$

which is the probability density function of what is known as the *Rayleigh distribution*.

Example 5.11   A manufacturer of clothes washers fully guarantees his product against breakdowns during the first twelve months of normal use. The manufacturer estimates a cost of \$75 to repair a washer during the warranty period. Based on

TABLE 5.13   A comparison of the Weibull and normal cumulative distribution functions

	$\alpha = 2.25; \theta = 10$		$\alpha = 3.6; \theta = 10$		$\alpha = 5.83; \theta = 10$	
X	Weibull	Normal (8.858, 4.128)*	Weibull	Normal (9.01, 2.788)*	Weibull	Normal (9.267, 1.828)*
0	0	0.01578	0	0.000619	0	0
1	0.005608	0.02872	0.000251	0.002052	0.000001	0.000003
2	0.026395	0.04746	0.003041	0.006037	0.000084	0.000034
3	0.0644	0.0778	0.013025	0.01539	0.000894	0.000302
4	0.1195	0.1190	0.036259	0.03593	0.004775	0.001988
5	0.1896	0.1762	0.0792	0.07493	0.017425	0.009903
6	0.2716	0.2420	0.1470	0.1401	0.049616	0.03673
7	0.3612	0.3264	0.2419	0.2358	0.1175	0.1075
8	0.4541	0.4150	0.3610	0.3594	0.2384	0.2451
9	0.5457	0.4880	0.4956	0.5000	0.4179	0.4404
10	0.6321	0.6064	0.6321	0.6368	0.6321	0.6554
11	0.7104	0.6985	0.7557	0.7611	0.8250	0.8289
12	0.7785	0.7747	0.8545	0.8599	0.9447	0.9332
13	0.8355	0.8413	0.9236	0.9236	0.9901	0.9793
14	0.8814	0.8925	0.9652	0.9641	0.999184	0.9952
15	0.9171	0.9319	0.9865	0.9842	0.999976	0.999155

*Mean and standard deviation

experimentation, the length of time until the first breakdown is determined to be a Weibull random variable with values of 2 and 40 for the shape and scale parameters, respectively. If the manufacturer expects to sell 100,000 units during the next model year and if multiple breakdowns of a unit during the warranty period are discounted, determine the expected warranty cost for the manufacturer.

Let the random variable X be the time length until a breakdown occurs. By assumption, the probability density function of X is

$$f(x; 2, 40) = \frac{2}{40^2} x \exp[-(x/40)^2], \qquad x > 0.$$

Then the probability that the first breakdown occurs during the warranty period is the same as the probability that X is less than or equal to 12. Using (5.63), we determine this probability to be

$$P(X \leq 12) = 1 - \exp[-(12/40)^2] = 0.0861.$$

It follows, therefore, that if we assume independence of operation, we can expect $(100,000)(0.0861) = 8610$ breakdowns to occur during the warranty period for a total cost of \$645,750.

5.7 The Negative Exponential Distribution

We have noted that the (negative) exponential distribution is a special case of the gamma and Weibull models. Since it is a special case of the gamma (Erlang), the exponential random variable is the length of time until the occurrence of the first Poisson event. That is, the exponential distribution can model the length of time between two successive Poisson events that occur independently and at a constant rate. The exponential distribution has been used extensively as a time-to-failure model in reliability problems, and as a model for random time lengths in waiting-line problems. We will show later that the exponential distribution exhibits a "memoryless" property. In other words, the probability of occurrence of present or future events does not depend on events that happened in the past. Thus the probability of a unit failing during a specified time interval depends only on the length of that interval and not on how long the unit has been in operation.

Definition 5.6 If the random variable X is exponentially distributed, its probability density function is given by

$$f(x; \theta) = \begin{cases} \dfrac{1}{\theta} \exp(-x/\theta) & x > 0, \quad \theta > 0, \\ 0 & \text{elsewhere.} \end{cases} \qquad (5.71)$$

The exponential density is characterized by a single parameter θ, which represents the average length of time between two independent Poisson events. In the context of reliability, θ is known as the mean time between failures, and

$1/\theta$ is the failure rate. The cumulative distribution follows directly from the Erlang or Weibull models and is given by

$$P(X \le x) = F(x; \theta) = 1 - \exp(-x/\theta). \qquad (5.72)$$

The general quantile value, moments, and shape factors for the exponentially distributed random variable X follow from corresponding expressions of the Weibull distribution with $\alpha = 1$. That is,

$$x_q = \theta \ln[1/(1 - q)],$$

$$E(X) = \theta,$$

$$Var(X) = \theta^2,$$

$$\alpha_3(X) = 2, \text{ and}$$

$$\alpha_4(X) = 9.$$

In reliability problems we are most often interested in the life length of a component or a system of components. The essential problem is to identify the probability distribution of the random variable that adequately models the unit time to failure. In this vein a very useful quantity is the reliability function.

Definition 5.7 Let T be a random variable representing the life length of a system and let $f(t)$ be the probability density function of T. The reliability function of the system at time t, $R(t)$, is the probability that the life length of the system will exceed the specified time t. Thus

$$R(t) = P(T > t) = 1 - F(t), \qquad t > 0. \qquad (5.73)$$

Another quantity that is extremely useful in selecting an appropriate probability density function for the life length of the unit (system) of interest is the failure rate or hazard function, defined as follows:

Definition 5.8 Let $f(t)$ be the probability density function, and let $R(t)$ be the reliability of a unit at a specified time t. The *failure rate* $h(t)$ is defined as the proportion of the units that fail during the interval $(t, t + dt)$ out of those that have survived to time t and is given by

$$h(t) = f(t)/R(t). \qquad (5.74)$$

If the failure rate is known, it is possible to determine the probability density function of the random variable T. Since $R(t) = 1 - F(t)$, by differentiating with respect to t we have that $R'(t) = -F'(t)$; but $F'(t) = f(t)$. As a result, the failure rate may be expressed as

$$h(t) = -R'(t)/R(t). \qquad (5.75)$$

Assuming the system is functioning at $t = 0$, $R(0) = 1$. Integrating both sides of (5.75) from 0 to t, we have

$$\int_0^t h(x)dx = -\int_0^t [R'(x)/R(x)]dx$$

$$= -\ln[R(t)] + \ln[R(0)]$$

$$= -\ln[R(t)],$$

where x is a dummy variable of integration. Since

$$-\ln[R(t)] = \int_0^t h(x)dx,$$

we have

$$R(t) = \exp\left[-\int_0^t h(x)dx\right].$$

Using (5.74), the probability density function is

$$f(t) = h(t)\exp\left[-\int_0^t h(x)dx\right]. \tag{5.76}$$

Many physical random phenomena exhibit failure rates that resemble a "bathtub curve," as illustrated in Figure 5.9. From time zero to time t_1, the failure rate is appreciable but decreases in value due to the "infant mortality syndrome," which suggests that early failures may be caused by manufacturing defects. During the time interval t_1 to t_2, $h(t)$ is nearly constant, but it begins to increase in value after t_2 due to wear-out failures. One can envision a constant failure rate if components are initially tested to weed out early failures and then replaced near time t_2 to avoid wear-out failures.

If the failure rate is constant, say $1/\theta$, the probability density function of the life length is the negative exponential. That is, if $h(t) = 1/\theta$, then from (5.76)

FIGURE 5.9 Typical failure rate function

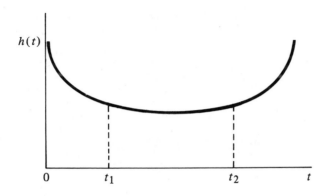

$$f(t) = \frac{1}{\theta}\exp\left[-\int_0^t \frac{1}{\theta}dx\right]$$
$$= \frac{1}{\theta}\exp(-t/\theta).$$

Notice that the converse is also true; if the life length is exponentially distributed, the failure rate is constant. Since the reliability function at time t for an exponentially distributed life length is

$$R(t) = \exp(-t/\theta), \qquad t > 0, \tag{5.77}$$

the failure rate is

$$h(t) = \frac{(1/\theta)\exp(-t/\theta)}{\exp(-t/\theta)}$$
$$= 1/\theta, \qquad t > 0.$$

A constant failure rate implies that the probability of failure in a specified time interval depends only on the length of that interval and not on how long a system has been in operation. This is the "memoryless" property. Although the life length of a component may not be exponential over the entire life of the unit, the life of a system containing such components can be adequately modeled by an exponential distribution by adhering to an initial screening and scheduled maintenance policy for the components.

Empirical justification for the exponential distribution in reliability problems has been provided by several researchers. The work of Davis [3], who showed that the life lengths for certain electrical components are adequately modeled by the exponential distribution, is typical. As an illustration of this work, Table 5.14 contains a comparison of observed and expected frequencies for grouped life lengths of a type V805 vacuum tube used in a transmitter. The average life length for this tube based on the observed data was 179 hours. Using this value for θ in (5.72), we are able to determine the theoretical probabilities for the exponential distribution.

TABLE 5.14 Observed and expected frequencies for V805 transmitter tube

Life length (hours)	Observed frequency	Relative frequency	Probability of interval	Expected frequency
0– 80	317	0.3511	0.3604	325.4
80–160	230	0.2547	0.2305	208.2
160–240	118	0.1307	0.1474	133.1
240–320	93	0.1030	0.0943	85.2
320–400	49	0.0543	0.0603	54.5
400–480	33	0.0365	0.0386	34.8
480–560	17	0.0188	0.0247	22.3
560–700	26	0.0288	0.0238	21.5
700 or more	20	0.0221	0.0200	18.1
Totals	903	1.0000	1.0000	903.1

The argument for using the exponential distribution to model random time lengths in waiting-line problems is entirely similar to that for life lengths. That is, if a service facility has been operating long enough for a near-equilibrium condition to exist, the probability of an arrival occurring or a service being completed in a time interval is likely to depend on the length of the interval and not on how long it has been since the occurrence of the last arrival or completion of service.

Although the exponential distribution has been used extensively to model random life lengths, it certainly is not the distribution for time to failure of all devices. Many electrical and mechanical devices exhibit increasing failure rates with increasing operating time over the total life of the device. There is reason to believe that the length of time such a component has been operating will affect its life length. In these cases the more appropriate models are likely to be the Weibull or Erlang distributions. These exhibit increasing, decreasing, or constant failure rates, depending on whether their shape parameters are greater than one, less than one, or equal to one, respectively. For example, for the Weibull distribution the reliability function at t is

$$R(t) = \exp[-(t/\theta)^{\alpha}] \qquad (5.78)$$

and the failure rate is

$$h(t) = \alpha t^{\alpha-1}/\theta^{\alpha}. \qquad (5.79)$$

The implication of a system with a decreasing failure rate is that the system undergoes "work-hardening" with time. An example of this phenomenon is the life span of a business. The longer a business has been operating, the less likely it is to fail in a specified interval of time.

5.8 The Distribution of a Function of a Random Variable

One of the key ingredients in statistical inference is the probability distribution of the "statistic" on which the inference will be based. Since statistics are functions of random variables, it is often possible to determine their distributions if we know the distributions of the random variables on which they are based.

To examine a technique for determining the distribution of a function of a random variable, consider the case of a single continuous random variable. Let X be a random variable with probability density function $f_X(x)$, and let $Y = g(X)$ define a function of X. Assume we are able to solve $y = g(x)$ for x, obtaining the inverse function $x = g^{-1}(y)$. If $g(x)$ and $g^{-1}(y)$ are single-valued functions of x and y, respectively, the transformation is said to be one-to-one. That is, to each point in the sample space of X there corresponds a unique point in the sample space of Y and vice versa. If we assume the existence of a one-to-one transformation and that $y = g(x)$ is a differentiable increasing function of x, the probability density function of Y may be determined as follows:

Because of the existence of a one-to-one transformation,

$$F_Y(y) = P(Y \le y)$$

$$= P[g(X) \le y]$$

$$= P[X \le g^{-1}(y)].$$

Then

$$F_Y(y) = F_X[g^{-1}(y)]. \tag{5.80}$$

By differentiating (5.80) with respect to y and using the chain rule, we have

$$f_Y(y) = \frac{dF_X[g^{-1}(y)]}{dx} \cdot \frac{dx}{dy}$$

$$= f_X[g^{-1}(y)] \frac{dx}{dy}. \tag{5.81}$$

If $g(x)$ is a decreasing function of x, the result will be the same as (5.81) except that the derivative of a decreasing function will be negative. Thus the following general statement can be made:

Theorem 5.2   Let X be a continuous random variable with probability density function $f_X(x)$ and define $Y = g(X)$. If $y = g(x)$ and $x = g^{-1}(y)$ are single-valued functions that are continuous and differentiable, and if $y = g(x)$ is either an increasing or a decreasing function in x, the probability density function of Y is given by

$$f_Y(y) = f_X[g^{-1}(y)] \left| \frac{dx}{dy} \right|, \tag{5.82}$$

where the quantity $J = |dx/dy|$ is known as the *Jacobian* of the transformation.

Theorem 5.2 follows from a change of variable technique in a definite integral, which we have illustrated on several occasions.

Let X be a continuous random variable with probability density function $f(x; \mu, \theta, \alpha)$ where μ, θ, and α are location, scale, and shape parameters, respectively. The effect of the shape parameter α can be made more clear by considering the distribution of the standardized random variable $Y = (X - \mu)/\theta$, which will not contain μ and θ. Using (5.82), the probability density function of Y is

$$f_Y(y) = \theta f_X(\theta y + \mu), \tag{5.83}$$

since the inverse relation is $x = \theta y + \mu$ and the Jacobian is $dx/dy = \theta$. In particular, let X be a gamma random variable with probability density function given by (5.45). The density function of $Y = X/\theta$ is

$$f_G(y; \alpha) = \frac{1}{\Gamma(\alpha)} y^{\alpha-1} \exp(-y), \qquad y > 0. \tag{5.84}$$

Similarly, if X is Weibull with probability density given by (5.61), the density of $Y = X/\theta$ is

$$f_W(y; \alpha) = \alpha y^{\alpha-1} \exp(-y^{\alpha}), \qquad y > 0. \tag{5.85}$$

If there is no shape parameter and if μ and θ are the mean and standard deviation of X, respectively, then (5.83) will give rise to a density function that is free of parameters and yields a mean of zero and a standard deviation of one. An example of this is the standardized normal probability density function.

Example 5.12   If the random variable X is uniformly distributed in the interval $(0, \pi)$, determine the probability density function of $Y = c \sin(X)$ for some positive constant c.

Notice here that the relation $y = c \sin(x)$ is a strictly increasing function of x in the interval $(0, \pi/2)$ and a strictly decreasing function of x in the interval $(\pi/2, \pi)$. When the functional relationship is increasing for some part of the range of the original random variable and decreasing for the remaining part, the probability density function of interest can be obtained by treating each part separately and adding the results. Thus the intervals $(0, \pi/2)$ and $(\pi/2, \pi)$ must be handled separately.

The inverse relation is

$$x = \sin^{-1}(y/c),$$

and the Jacobian of the transformation is

$$\left| \frac{dx}{dy} \right| = \frac{1}{c} \left[1 - \left(\frac{y}{c} \right)^2 \right]^{-1/2}$$

$$= (c^2 - y^2)^{-1/2}.$$

Since the density of X is

$$f(x) = 1/\pi \qquad 0 \le x \le \pi,$$

for the interval $(0, \pi/2)$,

$$f_1(y) = \frac{1}{\pi}(c^2 - y^2)^{-1/2} \qquad 0 \le y \le c,$$

and for the interval $(\pi/2, \pi)$,

$$f_2(y) = \frac{1}{\pi}(c^2 - y^2)^{-1/2} \qquad 0 \le y \le c.$$

As a result, the probability density function of Y is

$$f_Y(y) = f_1(y) + f_2(y)$$

$$= \frac{2}{\pi}(c^2 - y^2)^{-1/2}, \qquad 0 \le y \le c. \tag{5.86}$$

Example 5.13   Let X be a normally distributed random variable with mean μ and standard deviation σ. Determine the probability density function of $Y = \exp(X)$.

The relation $y = \exp(x)$ is an increasing and differentiable function of x. The inverse relation is $x = \ln(y)$, and the Jacobian is $dx/dy = 1/y$. Therefore, the density of Y is

$$f_Y(y; \mu, \sigma) = \frac{1}{\sqrt{2\pi}\,\sigma y} \exp\left\{ -\frac{1}{2}\left[\frac{\ln(y) - \mu}{\sigma}\right]^2 \right\}, \qquad y > 0. \qquad (5.87)$$

Expression (5.87) is the probability density function of what is known as the *log-normal model*. Although the quantities μ and σ are the parameters of the log-normal density, they are not location or scale parameters. Rather, they are the mean and standard deviation, respectively, of the related normal random variable. Whereas the normal random variable is often regarded as representing an additive effect of many small physical errors, the log-normal random variable is thought of as depicting a multiplicative effect of such errors. The log-normal distribution has been used in a variety of applications, including the problem of fatigue assessment of materials. See [1] for an in-depth examination of this distribution.

Another method for determining the distribution of a function of a random variable uses the moment generating function. Recall that a moment generating function, if it exists, uniquely determines a probability distribution. Thus if a function of a random variable is found to have a moment generating function that is a form of the moment generating function of a known distribution, that function of the random variable has the same distribution.

Example 5.14   Let Z be a normally distributed random variable with mean zero and standard deviation one. Show that the distribution of

$$Y = Z^2$$

is chi-square with one degree of freedom.

By definition, the moment generating function of Z^2 is

$$m_{Z^2}(t) = E[\exp(tZ^2)] = \int_{-\infty}^{\infty} \exp(tz^2) f(z)\,dz$$

$$= (2\pi)^{-1/2} \int_{-\infty}^{\infty} \exp(tz^2)\exp(-z^2/2)\,dz$$

$$= (2\pi)^{-1/2} \int_{-\infty}^{\infty} \exp[-(z^2/2)(1 - 2t)]\,dz$$

$$= (2\pi)^{-1/2} \int_{-\infty}^{\infty} \exp\left[-\frac{z^2}{2(1 - 2t)^{-1}} \right]dz.$$

Notice that other than the appropriate constant, the integrand of the last integral is the same as the probability density function of a normal random variable with mean zero and variance $(1 - 2t)^{-1}$. To make the integrand exactly like a normal density function with mean zero and variance $(1 - 2t)^{-1}$, we multiply both numerator and denominator by the standard deviation $(1 - 2t)^{-1/2}$, which in effect is multiplying the expression by 1. Thus

$$m_{Z^2}(t) = \frac{1}{(1 - 2t)^{1/2}} \int_{-\infty}^{\infty} \frac{1}{\sqrt{2\pi}\,(1 - 2t)^{-1/2}} \exp\left[- \frac{z^2}{2(1 - 2t)^{-1}} \right] dz$$

$$= (1 - 2t)^{-1/2},$$

since the integrand now is a normal probability density and by definition integrates to one from $-\infty$ to ∞. The moment generating function of $Y = Z^2$ is identical to that of a chi-square distribution with $\nu = 1$ degree of freedom (see (5.60)). Therefore, the square of a standard normal random variable is chi-square distributed with one degree of freedom.

5.9 Basic Concepts in the Computer Generation of Random Values

Since the advent of large-scale computer systems, computer simulation experiments have become extremely useful techniques for analyzing complex systems, which are often comprised of many interdependent components. In the simulation of such systems, the need arises to simulate random phenomena that are characteristic of the system. For example, if a large urban bank wishes to examine its current system of servicing customers, it must simulate customer traffic into the bank as well as service time required for each transaction. Both of these events are random occurrences.

What is usually done is to assume an appropriate probability distribution for each distinct phenomenon and to generate a sequence of values of the corresponding random variable within a computer. Since sequences of random values are generated by numerical algorithms that can be repeated exactly, such sequences are not truly random. However, these sequences exhibit enough random properties to be sufficient for most applications.

Our task here is not to examine the random properties of computer-generated random values, nor is it to determine the most efficient way of generating such quantities in a computer. Rather, our purpose is to familiarize the reader with possible ways of generating random values from some of the discrete and continuous probability distributions we have examined.

The uniform distribution on the interval $(0, 1)$ plays a key role in the generation of random values. To this end we state and prove the following theorem.

Theorem 5.3 For any continuous random variable X, the cumulative distribution function $F(x; \theta)$ with parameter θ may be represented by a random variable U, which is uniformly distributed on the unit interval.

Proof: Since by definition the cumulative distribution function of X is

$$F(x; \theta) = \int_{-\infty}^{x} f(t; \theta)dt,$$

to each value x there corresponds a value $F(x; \theta)$ that is necessarily in the interval $(0, 1)$. Moreover, $F(X; \theta)$ is also a random variable by virtue of the randomness of X. For each value u of the random variable U, the function $u = F(x; \theta)$ defines a one-to-one correspondence between U and X with the inverse relation being $x = F^{-1}(u)$. Since $du = dF(x; \theta) = f(x; \theta)dx$, the Jacobian of the transformation is

$$J = \left| \frac{dx}{du} \right| = [f(x; \theta)]^{-1} = [f(F^{-1}(u); \theta)]^{-1}.$$

The probability density function of the random variable U is by (5.82),

$$g(u) = f(F^{-1}(u); \theta)[f(F^{-1}(u); \theta)]^{-1}$$
$$= 1, \qquad 0 \le u \le 1.$$

The essence of Theorem 5.3 is that for many instances we are able to determine directly the value x corresponding to the value u of the random variables X and U, respectively, such that $F(x; \theta) = u$. For this reason practically all computer systems have a built-in capability of generating random values from a uniform distribution on the unit interval. In fact, most statistical computer packages, such as SAS, SPSS, and IMSL, provide the user with the opportunity of generating random values from a prescribed distribution. We illustrate the use of Theorem 5.3 in the generation of random values for some specific probability distributions.

5.9.1   Uniform Distribution on the Interval (a, b)

The probability density function is

$$f(x; a, b) = 1/(b - a), \qquad a \le x \le b.$$

To generate a random value x, $a \le x \le b$, we first generate a random value u from $(0, 1)$, equate it to the cumulative distribution function, integrate, and solve for the upper limit x. Thus

$$(b - a)^{-1} \int_a^x dt = u$$

$$\frac{x - a}{b - a} = u,$$

or

$$x = u(b - a) + a, \qquad a \le x \le b \tag{5.88}$$

5.9.2   The Weibull Distribution

The probability density function is

$$f(x; \alpha, \theta) = \frac{\alpha}{\theta^\alpha} x^{\alpha - 1} \exp[-(x/\theta)^\alpha], \qquad x > 0.$$

To generate Weibull random values $x > 0$, we solve the equation

$$\frac{\alpha}{\theta^\alpha} \int_0^x t^{\alpha-1} \exp[-(t/\theta)^\alpha] dt = u$$

$$\left(\frac{\alpha}{\theta^\alpha}\right)\left(-\frac{\theta^\alpha}{\alpha}\right) \exp[-(t/\theta)^\alpha]\Big|_0^x = u$$

or

$$1 - \exp[-(x/\theta)^\alpha] = u,$$

and

$$x = \theta\left[\ln\left(\frac{1}{1-u}\right)\right]^{1/\alpha}. \tag{5.89}$$

Since for $\alpha = 1$ the Weibull distribution reduces to the exponential, one may generate random values from an exponential distribution by using (5.89) with $\alpha = 1$.

5.9.3   The Erlang Distribution

The probability density function is

$$f(x; \alpha, \theta) = \frac{1}{\Gamma(\alpha)\theta^\alpha} x^{\alpha-1} \exp(-x/\theta), \qquad x > 0,$$

where α is a positive integer. Recall that the Erlang random variable is the sum of α independent exponentially distributed random variables. Therefore, an Erlang random value is the sum of α exponential random values, where each exponential value is generated by using (5.89).

5.9.4   The Normal Distribution

The normal cumulative distribution function

$$\frac{1}{\sqrt{2\pi}\,\sigma} \int_{-\infty}^x \exp\left[-\frac{1}{2}\left(\frac{t-\mu}{\sigma}\right)^2\right] dt = u$$

cannot be solved for x in closed form. Alternatively, it can be shown that if U_1 and U_2 are two independent random variables each uniformly distributed on the unit interval, then

$$Z_1 = (-2 \ln U_1)^{1/2} \sin(2\pi U_2) \quad \text{and}$$
$$Z_2 = (-2 \ln U_1)^{1/2} \cos(2\pi U_2) \tag{5.90}$$

are two independent standardized normal random variables.

5.9.5   The Binomial Distribution

To generate random values from a binomial distribution with probability function

$$p(x; n, p) = \frac{n!}{(n-x)!\,x!} p^x (1-p)^{n-x}, \qquad x = 0, 1, 2, \ldots, n$$

we consider the following: The binomial random variable is viewed as the sum of n draws from a Bernoulli process described by

$$Y = \begin{cases} 1 & \text{with probability } p \\ 0 & \text{with probability } (1 - p). \end{cases}$$

We can obtain a binomial random value by adding n such values of the random variable Y where each value is determined by

$$y = \begin{cases} 1 & \text{if } 0 \le u \le p \\ 0 & \text{if } p < u \le 1, \end{cases} \tag{5.91}$$

and where u is a uniform random value on the unit interval. That is, we generate n random values from the unit interval, convert these to a sequence of ones and zeros based on (5.91), and the sum of the ones in the sequence is a binomial random value.

5.9.6   The Poisson Distribution

Recall that the probability of exactly x occurrences in a time interval of length t is given by

$$p(x; t) = \frac{(vt)^x \exp(-vt)}{x!}, \qquad x = 0, 1, 2, \dots,$$

where v is the constant rate of occurrence, and $\lambda = vt$ is the average number of occurrences. Since the time difference between independent Poisson occurrences is exponentially distributed, one can generate a random Poisson value x by generating successive exponential random values using (5.89) for $\alpha = 1$. The process continues until the sum of $x + 1$ such values exceeds the prescribed time length t. The Poisson random value, therefore, is x.

References

1. A. Aitchison and J. A. C. Brown, *The log-normal distribution*, Cambridge Univ. Press, Cambridge, England, 1957.
2. K. V. Bury, *Statistical models in applied science*, Wiley, New York, 1975.
3. D. J. Davis, *An analysis of some failure data*, J. of the Amer. Statistical Assoc. **47** (1952), 113–150.
4. D. G. Malcolm, J. H. Roseboom, E. C. Clark, and W. Fazar, *Application of a technique for research and development program evaluation*, Operations Research **7** (1959), 646–658.
5. E. S. Pearson and H. O. Hartley, Eds., *Biometrika tables for statisticians*, Vol. I, 3rd ed., Cambridge Univ. Press, Cambridge, England, 1966.
6. K. Pearson, *Tables of the incomplete beta function*, Biometrika Office, University College, London, 1948.
7. K. Pearson, *Tables of the incomplete gamma function*, Biometrika Office, University College, London, 1957.
8. H. C. S. Thom, *Direct and inverse tables of the gamma distribution*, Environmental Data Service, Silver Spring, Md., 1968.

9. W. Weibull, *A statistical distribution function of wide applicability*, J. Appl. Mech. **18** (1951), 293–302.

Exercises

5.1. For the normal distributions $N(0,0.5)$ and $N(0,4)$, graph the probability density functions on the same graph.

5.2. Let $X \sim N(50, 10)$. Determine the following probabilities:

   a. $P(X < 40)$ d. $P(X > 35)$
   b. $P(X < 65)$ e. $P(40 < X < 45)$
   c. $P(X > 55)$ f. $P(38 < X < 62)$

5.3. Let $X \sim N(200, 20)$. Determine the following probabilities:

   a. $P(185 < X < 210)$ c. $P(X > 240)$
   b. $P(215 < X < 250)$ d. $P(X > 178)$

5.4. Let $X \sim N(-25, 10)$. Find the values x corresponding to the following probabilities:

   a. $P(X < x) = 0.1251$ c. $P(X > x) = 0.3859$
   b. $P(X < x) = 0.9382$ d. $P(X > x) = 0.8340$

5.5. Let $X \sim N(10, 5)$. Find the values x corresponding to the following probabilities:

   a. $P(X < x) = 0.05$ d. $P(X < x) = 0.01$
   b. $P(X < x) = 0.95$ e. $P(X < x) = 0.025$
   c. $P(X < x) = 0.99$ f. $P(X < x) = 0.975$

5.6. Let $X \sim N(\mu,\sigma)$. If the quantiles $x_{0.4} = 50$ and $x_{0.8} = 100$, determine the mean and variance of X.

5.7. A large university expects to receive 16,000 freshman student applications for the coming year. It can be safely assumed that the SAT scores of these applicants are adequately approximated by a normal distribution with mean 950 and standard deviation 100. If the university decides to admit the top 25 percent by SAT scores, what is the minimum SAT score that will be required for admission?

5.8. The diameters of pistons manufactured by a process are adequately approximated by a normal distribution with mean diameter 5 cm and standard deviation 0.001 cm. To be usable, the diameter of a piston has to be between 4.998 and 5.002 cm. If the diameter of a piston is less than 4.998, it must be scrapped; if it is greater than 5.002, the piston can be reworked. What percentage of pistons will be usable? What percentage will be scrapped? What percentage will be reworked?

5.9. The monthly demand for product A is normally distributed with mean 200 units and standard deviation 40 units. The demand for another product, B, is also normally distributed with mean 500 units and standard deviation 80 units. If a seller of these products stocks 280 units of A and 650 units of B at the beginning of a month, what is the probability that the seller will experience a stockout for both products during the month? You may assume independence.

5.10. The weight of cereal in a container is well approximated by a normal distribution with mean 600 grams. The filling process is designed so that the weight of no more than one container out of 100 will be outside the range 590–610 grams. What is the maximum value for the standard deviation necessary to meet this requirement?

5.11. The daily demand for automobile batteries at a large discount store is approximately normally distributed with mean 50 batteries and standard deviation 10 batteries. On two consecutive days 80 and 75 batteries are sold. If these days are typical, how likely is the sale of 80 or more and 75 or more batteries under the assumed conditions?

5.12. An aircraft manufacturer wishes to procure rivets to use in mounting aircraft engines. The required minimum tensile strength of each rivet is 25,000 lb. Three manufacturers of rivets (A, B, and C) are asked to provide pertinent information concerning the tensile strength of such rivets. The three manufacturers respond that the tensile strengths of their rivets are adequately described by normal distributions with mean tensile strengths of 28,000, 30,000, and 29,000 lb, respectively.

   a. Does the aircraft manufacturer have sufficient information to make a choice? Why?

   b. Suppose the standard deviations for A, B, and C are 1000, 1800, and 1200. What is the probability of a rivet produced by either A, B, or C not meeting the minimum requirements?

   c. If you were the aircraft manufacturer, would you choose among A, B, and C, based on your answer to part b? Why?

5.13. A manufacturer of automobile mufflers wishes to guarantee her mufflers for the life of the automobile. The manufacturer assumes the life of her mufflers is a normally distributed random variable with average life of 3 years and a standard deviation of 6 months. If the unit replacement cost is $10, what would be the total replacement cost for the first two years if 1,000,000 such mufflers are installed?

5.14. The time required to assemble a certain unit is a normally distributed random variable with mean 30 minutes and standard deviation 2 minutes. Determine the time such that the probability of a unit's assembly time exceeding this value is 0.02.

5.15. A newspaper polled 400 voting adults, randomly selected throughout a given state, concerning gun control. Of the 400 adults, 220 were in favor of tight gun control.

   a. How likely is the occurrence of 220 or greater if the voting public in this state is evenly divided on this issue?

   b. Suppose 2000 had been polled with the same proportion favoring gun control. How would this change your answer to part a?

   c. Suppose 10,000 are polled. Would the likelihood of the occurrence be substantially different than that in part b?

5.16. A multiple-choice test consists of 25 questions with 5 choices to each question. What is the probability that someone making random guesses on each question will miss more than half of the questions?

5.17. A national polling organization polled 1600 adults, randomly selected throughout the country, concerning the safety of nuclear power plants. Of the 1600 adults, 60 percent felt that the nuclear plants are unsafe. Based on these results, is there reason to doubt that the general adult population is neutral about this issue?

5.18. Let X be binomially distributed.

   a. For $n = 15$, $p = 0.25$, and $n = 15$, $p = 0.5$, compute the following probabilities: $P(X = 8)$, $P(X \leq 3)$, $P(X \leq 7)$, $P(X \geq 9)$, and $P(X \geq 12)$.

   b. Approximate these probabilities using the normal distribution.

   c. Repeat parts a and b with $n = 25$ and compare your results.

5.19. Let X be uniformly distributed on the interval (a,b).

    a. What is the probability that a value of X will be within one standard deviation of the mean?

    b. Can a value of X be as many as two standard deviations from the mean?

5.20. Let X be uniformly distributed on the interval (a,b). What is the greatest distance in standard deviation units that a value of X can be from the mean?

5.21. Let X be uniformly distributed on the interval (a,b). If $E(X) = 10$ and $Var(X) = 12$, determine a and b.

5.22. Suppose the concentration of a certain pollutant is uniformly distributed in the range 4 to 20 ppm (parts per million). If a concentration in excess of 15 ppm is considered toxic, what is the probability that a specimen will yield a toxic concentration level?

5.23. Let the random variable X be beta distributed with $\alpha = 3$ and $\beta = 1$.

    a. Graph the probability density function.

    b. Determine the mean, variance, mean deviation, coefficient of skewness, and relative kurtosis.

    c. What is the probability that a value of X will be within one standard deviation of the mean? Within two standard deviations of the mean?

    d. Determine the quartiles for this distribution.

5.24. If the parameters of the beta distribution are integers, it can be shown that the beta cumulative distribution is related to the binomial distribution as follows:

$$P(X < p) = I_p(\alpha, \beta) = \sum_{y=\alpha}^{n} \frac{n!}{(n-y)!y!} p^y (1-p)^{n-y},$$

where $n = \alpha + \beta - 1$ and $0 < p < 1$. If X is beta distributed with $\alpha = 2$ and $\beta = 3$, use this relation to determine $P(X < 0.1)$, $P(X < 0.25)$, and $P(X < 0.5)$.

5.25. For Exercise 5.24 determine the probabilities that a value of X will be within one standard deviation of the mean and within two standard deviations of the mean.

5.26. The proportion of defective units produced by a manufacturing process is a random variable that is adequately approximated by a beta distribution with $\alpha = 1$ and $\beta = 20$.

    a. What is the proportion mean and standard deviation?

    b. What is the probability that the proportion of defective units is greater than 10%? Greater than 15%?

5.27. Approximate your answer to part b of Exercise 5.26 using the normal approximation as given by expresion (5.44).

5.28. The market share of a large computer company varies randomly according to a beta distribution with $\alpha = 10$ and $\beta = 6$.

    a. Graph the probability density function.

    b. Determine the mean and standard deviation.

    c. Determine the probability that a market share will be less than the mean.

    d. Determine the probability that a market share will be within one standard deviation of the mean and within two standard deviations of the mean.

5.29. Let the random variable X be gamma distributed with $\alpha = 2$ and $\theta = 50$.

    a. What is the probability that a value of X will be less than the mean?

   b. What is the probability that a value of X will be more than two standard deviations from the mean?

   c. What is the probability that X will be less than its mode?

5.30. Let the random variable X be gamma distributed with $\alpha = 2$ and $\theta = 100$.

   a. Graph the probability density function.

   b. Determine the probability of a value of X being within one standard deviation of the mean and within two standard deviations of the mean.

   c. How would your answers to part b change if $\theta = 200$?

5.31. Let the age of a male at first marriage be a gamma random variable. If the average age is 30 years and the most likely age is 22 years, determine the parameters α and θ for this distribution.

5.32. The following is a partial tabulation of the incomplete gamma function as defined by (5.55) for $\alpha = 16$.

u	2	2.5	3.0	3.5	4.0	4.5
$I(u, 15)$	0.0082	0.0487	0.1556	0.3306	0.5333	0.7133

u	5.0	5.5	6.0	6.5	7.0
$I(u, 15)$	0.8435	0.9231	0.9656	0.9858	0.9946

For $\theta = 10$, compare these probabilities with those determined by using the normal approximation.

5.33. Use the moment generating function of the gamma distribution to determine the mean and variance.

5.34. Let the life of a component be gamma distributed with $\alpha = 2$.

   a. Determine the reliability function.

   b. For $\theta = 20$, determine the failure rate and graph it as a function of t.

   c. If $\theta = 20$, what is the reliability of the component at $t = 80$?

5.35. The assembly of a certain item consists of four distinct stages. If the total assembly time in hours of the item is a gamma random variable with scale parameter $\theta = 2$, what is the probability that an assembly time will be less than 15 hours?

5.36. Let X be a Weibull random variable with parameters $\alpha = 2$ and $\theta = 20$.

   a. Graph the probability density function.

   b. Determine the probability of realizing a value of X greater than the mean.

   c. Determine the probability that a value of X is within one standard deviation of the mean and within two standard deviations of the mean.

5.37. The lifetime of a system is adequately approximated by a Weibull distribution with $\alpha = 2$ and $\theta = 50$.

   a. Determine the mean and the deciles of this distribution.

   b. Determine the reliability of the system at $t = 75$.

5.38. A system consists of two independent components A and B. The system will operate as long as either one or both components operate. If the lifetime (in hours) of component A is a Weibull random variable with $\alpha = 1/2$ and $\theta = 10$, and if the lifetime of B is also Weibull distributed with $\alpha = 2$ and $\theta = 12$, what is the probability that the system will be operating beyond 20 hours?

5.39. Let X be exponentially distributed.

   a. What is the probability of a value of X exceeding the mean?

    b. What are the probabilities of a value of X being within one standard deviation of the mean and within two standard deviations of the mean?

5.40. If the failure rate of a component is constant and the reliability of the component at $t = 55$ is 0.4,

    a. determine the probability density function.
    b. determine the reliability of the component at $t = 100$.

5.41. A device has a constant failure rate $h(t) = 10^{-2}$ per hour.

    a. What is the reliability of the device at $t = 200$ hours?
    b. If 500 such devices fail independently, what is the expected number of failures among the 500 devices after 200 hours?

5.42. The compressor of an air conditioning unit has a failure rate function $h(t) = 2 \times 10^{-8}t$ per hour.

    a. What is the reliability function of the compressor?
    b. What is the reliability of the compressor at $t = 15{,}000$ hours?
    c. What is the mean life of the compressor?
    d. What is the median life?

5.43. Let the random variable X be uniformly distributed in the interval $(0, 1)$. Show that the random variable $Y = -2 \ln(X)$ will be chi-square distributed with two degrees of freedom.

5.44. If X is exponentially distributed with scale parameter θ, determine the distribution of $Y = (X - \theta)/\theta$.

5.45. If X is Weibull distributed with parameters α and θ, determine the distribution of $Y = X^{\alpha}$.

5.46. Select one discrete and one continuous probability distribution from Section 5.9 and generate two samples of 50 random values for each. Group the data for each case and determine the relative frequencies. Also compute the means and standard deviations and compare your results with those based on theory.

APPENDIX

Proof That Expression (5.1) Is a Probability Density Function

The first requirement that the function be nonnegative is satisfied since $f(x; \mu, \sigma) > 0$ for $-\infty < x < \infty$, $-\infty < \mu < \infty$ and $\sigma > 0$. To show that

$$\int_{-\infty}^{\infty} f(x; \mu, \sigma)\,dx = 1,$$

let

$$I = \frac{1}{\sqrt{2\pi}\,\sigma} \int_{-\infty}^{\infty} \exp\left[-(x - \mu)^2/2\sigma^2\right] dx$$

be the value of the integral and apply the linear transformation $y = (x - \mu)/\sigma$ so that $x = \sigma y + \mu$ and $dx = \sigma dy$. This yields

$$I = \frac{1}{\sqrt{2\pi}} \int_{-\infty}^{\infty} \exp(-y^2/2)\,dy.$$

If we can show that $I^2 = 1$, we can deduce that $I = 1$ since $f(x; \mu, \sigma)$ is positive. Accordingly,

$$I^2 = \frac{1}{\sqrt{2\pi}} \int_{-\infty}^{\infty} \exp(-y^2/2)dy \cdot \frac{1}{\sqrt{2\pi}} \int_{-\infty}^{\infty} \exp(-z^2/2)dz$$

$$= \frac{1}{2\pi} \int_{-\infty}^{\infty} \int_{-\infty}^{\infty} \exp\left[-(y^2 + z^2)/2\right]dydz,$$

where we have written the product of the two integrals as a double integral since functions of z are constant with respect to y and vice versa. Now let us change from rectangular coordinates as specified by y and z to polar coordinates involving r and θ, where $y = r\cos\theta$ and $z = r\sin\theta$. That is,

$$y^2 + z^2 = r^2\cos^2\theta + r^2\sin^2\theta = r^2,$$

and the element of area $dydz$ in rectangular coordinates is replaced by $rdrd\theta$ in polar coordinates. Since the limits $(-\infty, \infty)$ for both y and z cover the entire yz plane, the corresponding plane of r and θ is covered by using the limits $(0,2\pi)$ for θ and $(0,\infty)$ for r. Thus

$$I^2 = \frac{1}{2\pi} \int_0^{2\pi} \int_0^{\infty} \exp(-r^2/2)rdrd\theta$$

$$= \frac{1}{2\pi} \int_0^{2\pi} d\theta \int_0^{\infty} \exp(-r^2/2)rdr$$

$$= \frac{\theta}{2\pi}\Big|_0^{2\pi} \cdot [-\exp(-r^2/2)]\Big|_0^{\infty}$$

$$= 1,$$

and (5.1) is a probability density function.

APPENDIX

Proof of Theorem 5.1

Our approach is based on the fact that a moment generating function uniquely defines a distribution. We will show that the moment generating function of Y approaches that of a standard normal as $n \to \infty$. Since X is binomial,

$$m_X(t) = [(1 - p) + pe^t]^n.$$

Then

$$m_Y(t) = E(e^{tY}) = E\left\{\exp\left[t(X - np)/\sqrt{np(1 - p)}\right]\right\}$$

$$= \exp\left[-npt/\sqrt{np(1 - p)}\right] E\left\{\exp\left[tX/\sqrt{np(1 - p)}\right]\right\},$$

where $E\left\{\exp\left[tX/\sqrt{np(1-p)}\right]\right\}$ is the moment generating function of X with the argument being $t/\sqrt{np(1-p)}$. Thus

$$m_Y(t) = \exp\left[-npt/\sqrt{np(1-p)}\right]\left\{(1-p) + p\exp\left[t/\sqrt{np(1-p)}\right]\right\}^n ;$$

but

$$\exp\left[-npt/\sqrt{np(1-p)}\right] = \left\{\exp\left[-pt/\sqrt{np(1-p)}\right]\right\}^n$$

and

$$m_Y(t) = \left\{(1-p)\exp\left[-pt/\sqrt{np(1-p)}\right]\right.$$
$$\left. + p\exp\left[\frac{t}{\sqrt{np(1-p)}} - \frac{pt}{\sqrt{np(1-p)}}\right]\right\}^n$$

$$= \left\{(1-p)\exp\left[-pt/\sqrt{np(1-p)}\right]\right.$$
$$\left. + p\exp\left[(1-p)t/\sqrt{np(1-p)}\right]\right\}^n .$$

In the last expression, let us expand both exponential functions in a power series; we have

$$(1-p)\exp\left[-pt/\sqrt{np(1-p)}\right] = (1-p) - \frac{(1-p)pt}{\sqrt{np(1-p)}} + \frac{(1-p)p^2t^2}{2np(1-p)}$$

$$+ \text{ terms in } (-1)^k\left(\frac{1}{n}\right)^{k/2}, \qquad k = 3, 4, \ldots$$

$$= (1-p) - \frac{(1-p)pt}{\sqrt{np(1-p)}} + \frac{pt^2}{2n}$$

$$+ \text{ terms in } (-1)^k\left(\frac{1}{n}\right)^{k/2}, \qquad k = 3, 4, \ldots$$

and

$$p\exp\left[(1-p)t/\sqrt{np(1-p)}\right] = p + \frac{(1-p)pt}{\sqrt{np(1-p)}} + \frac{(1-p)^2pt^2}{2np(1-p)}$$

$$+ \text{ terms in } \left(\frac{1}{n}\right)^{k/2}, \qquad k = 3, 4, \ldots$$

$$= p + \frac{(1-p)pt}{\sqrt{np(1-p)}} + \frac{(1-p)t^2}{2n}$$

$$+ \text{ terms in } \left(\frac{1}{n}\right)^{k/2}, \qquad k = 3, 4, \ldots .$$

Substituting these expansions in $m_Y(t)$ and collecting terms, we have

$$m_Y(t) = \left[1 + \frac{t^2}{2n} + \text{terms in} \left(\frac{1}{n}\right)^{k/2}\right]^n, \qquad k = 3, 4, \ldots .$$

Since all terms containing $(1/n)^{k/2}$, $k = 3, 4, \ldots$, have exponents greater than one, $1/n$ can be factored out of each. Thus

$$m_Y(t) = \left\{1 + \frac{1}{n}\left[\frac{t^2}{2} + \text{terms in} \left(\frac{1}{n}\right)^{(k-2)/2}\right]\right\}^n, \qquad k = 3, 4, \ldots .$$

By definition

$$\lim_{n \to \infty}\left(1 + \frac{u}{n}\right)^n = e^u;$$

then as $n \to \infty$, the last expression for $m_Y(t)$ becomes identical to this form, with u representing everything inside the brackets of this expression. But as $n \to \infty$, all terms of u other than the first go to zero since they all contain positive powers of n in their denominators. Accordingly,

$$\lim_{n \to \infty} m_Y(t) = \exp(t^2/2),$$

which is the moment generating function of the standard normal distribution.

CHAPTER SIX

Joint Probability Distributions

6.1 Introduction

In the previous chapters we have considered probabilistic concepts with regard to a single random variable. Many times, however, one is able to measure more than a single distinct characteristic of a random phenomenon. For example, in a manufacturing process producing a number of units per time period, there is likely to be interest not only in the number of usable units, but also in the number of units that can be made usable after rework and the number of units that must be scrapped. In water pollution studies one is usually interested in measuring the concentration levels of several distinct pollutants in a body of water. A need therefore arises to study probability models containing more than a single random variable. Such models are known as *multivariate models*, whereas single variable models are termed *univariate*. In this chapter we will examine general concepts for discrete and continuous probability distributions involving two random variables. The extension to more than two variables should be apparent.

6.2 Bivariate Probability Distributions

We consider the definitions of joint probability distributions for the discrete and continuous cases with regard to two random variables.

Definition 6.1 Let X and Y be discrete random variables. The joint probability that $X = x$ and $Y = y$ is given by the bivariate probability function

$$p(x, y) = P(X = x, Y = y),$$

where $p(x, y) \geq 0$ for all x, y of X, Y, and $\Sigma_x \Sigma_y p(x, y) = 1$. The summation is over all possible x and y.

Based on Definition 6.1, the bivariate cumulative distribution function is the joint probability that $X \leq x$ and $Y \leq y$, given by

$$F(x, y) = P(X \leq x, Y \leq y) = \sum_{x_i \leq x} \sum_{y_i \leq y} p(x_i, y_i). \qquad (6.1)$$

173

This is an extension of the univariate case. The joint probability function for two discrete random variables gives rise to joint point probabilities, and the bivariate distribution function is an increasing step function for each nonzero point probability that $X = x$ and $Y = y$.

Example 6.1   Based on past experience, the proportion of usable units produced by a manufacturing process is p_1, and the proportions of rework and scrap units are p_2 and p_3, respectively. If we assume that the number of units n produced by this manufacturing process in a given time period constitutes a set of independent trials such that $p_1 + p_2 + p_3 = 1$, develop an expression for the probability of exactly x_1, x_2, and x_3 usable, rework, and scrap units, respectively.

This is an extension of the univariate binomial distribution. Even though there are three mutually exclusive outcomes (usable, rework, and scrap), it is necessary to define only two random variables since for any specified number of each, the sum of all three must add to n. Without loss of generality, let the random variables X and Y represent the number of usable and rework units, respectively, out of the total of n units. Thus for a given n, if $X = x$ and $Y = y$, then the number of scrap units must be $n - x - y$. Because of independence, the probability of a specified sequence of outcomes is

$$p_1^x p_2^y (1 - p_1 - p_2)^{n-x-y}.$$

Since there are $n!/[x!y!(n - x - y)!]$ equally likely ways that such a sequence can occur, the joint probability of exactly x, y, and $n - x - y$ usable, rework, and scrap units, respectively, is

$$p(x, y; n, p_1, p_2) = \frac{n!}{x!y!(n-x-y)!} \, p_1^x p_2^y (1 - p_1 - p_2)^{n-x-y},$$

$$x, y = 0, 1, 2, ..., n, \tag{6.2}$$

where $p_3 = 1 - p_1 - p_2$. Expression (6.2) is the joint probability function for what is known as the trinomial distribution. The parameters of this distribution are n, p_1, and p_2 since p_3 is exactly determined if p_1 and p_2 are known. The trinomial distribution has been applied extensively to situations consisting of three distinct outcomes, such as in consumer preference surveys in which there are three competing brands or in political surveys in which there are three competing candidates.

If there are k distinct mutually exclusive outcomes with probabilities p_1, p_2, ... p_k, respectively, then for n independent trials the trinomial generalizes to the multinomial distribution with probability function

$$p(x_1, x_2, ..., x_{k-1}; n, p_1, p_2, ..., p_{k-1}) = \frac{n!}{x_1!x_2! ... x_k!} \, p_1^{x_1} p_2^{x_2} ... p_k^{x_k}$$

$$x_i = 0, 1, 2, ..., n \quad \text{for } i = 1, 2, ..., k, \tag{6.3}$$

where $x_k = n - x_1 - x_2 - \cdots - x_{k-1}$ and $p_k = 1 - p_1 - p_2 - \cdots - p_{k-1}$.

Definition 6.2 Let X and Y be two continuous random variables. If there exists a function $f(x, y)$ such that the joint probability

$$P(a < X < b, c < Y < d) = \int_a^b \int_c^d f(x, y)dydx$$

for any a, b, c, and d where $f(x, y) \geq 0$, $-\infty < x, y < \infty$, and $\int_{-\infty}^{\infty}\int_{-\infty}^{\infty} f(x, y)dydx = 1$, then $f(x, y)$ is the bivariate probability density function of X and Y.

A joint probability density function of the two continuous random variables X and Y is a three-dimensional surface where the volume under the surface and above a rectangle specified by, say, $a < X < b$ and $c < Y < d$ is the same as the probability that the random variables will assume points within the rectangle.

The bivariate cumulative distribution function of X and Y is the joint probability that $X \leq x$ and $Y \leq y$, given by

$$P(X \leq x, Y \leq y) = F(x, y) = \int_{-\infty}^{x} \int_{-\infty}^{y} f(u, v)dvdu. \tag{6.4}$$

Hence the bivariate density function is found by differentiating $F(x, y)$ with respect to x and y; that is,

$$f(x, y) = \frac{\partial^2 F(x, y)}{\partial x \partial y}. \tag{6.5}$$

Example 6.2 Let X and Y be two random variables with joint probability density function given by

$$f(x, y) = \begin{cases} (x + y) & 0 \leq x, y \leq 1, \\ 0 & \text{elsewhere.} \end{cases}$$

Graph the joint probability density function, determine the joint cumulative distribution function, and thus determine the joint probability that $X \leq 1/2$ and $Y \leq 3/4$.

The graph of the joint density function is given in Figure 6.1. Notice that $f(x, y)$ is a joint probability density function since

$$\int_0^1 \int_0^1 (x + y)dydx = \int_0^1 \left(xy + \frac{y^2}{2}\right)\Big|_0^1 dx = \int_0^1 \left(x + \frac{1}{2}\right)dx = 1.$$

Then

$$F(x, y) = \int_0^x \int_0^y (u + v)dvdu = \int_0^x \left(uy + \frac{y^2}{2}\right)du = xy(x + y)/2, \qquad 0 \leq x, y \leq 1.$$

Thus

$$F(1/2, 3/4) = \left(\frac{1}{2}\right)\left(\frac{1}{2}\right)\left(\frac{3}{4}\right)\left(\frac{1}{2} + \frac{3}{4}\right) = 15/64.$$

FIGURE 6.1   Graph of the joint density function $f(x, y) = x + y$

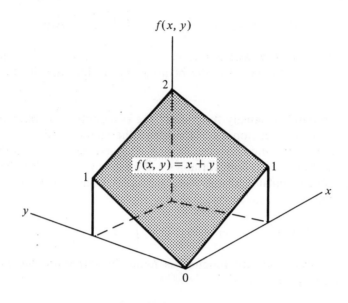

Moreover,

$$\frac{\partial F(x, y)}{\partial x} = xy + \frac{y^2}{2}$$

and

$$\frac{\partial^2 F(x, y)}{\partial x\, \partial y} = x + y = f(x, y).$$

6.3   Marginal Probability Distributions

For any probability distribution involving more than one random variable, we are able to determine a number of marginal distributions. For example, if X and Y are discrete random variables, the summation of the bivariate probability function over all possible values of, say, Y yields the univariate probability function of X. On the other hand, if X and Y are continuous, the integration of the bivariate probability density function over the entire range of Y produces the univariate probability density function of X. Accordingly, we give the following definitions:

Definition 6.3   Let X and Y be two discrete random variables with joint probability function $p(x, y)$. The marginal probability functions of X and Y are given by

$$p_X(x) = \sum_y p(x, y)$$

and

$$p_Y(y) = \sum_x p(x, y),$$

respectively.

Definition 6.4 Let X and Y be two continuous random variables with joint probability density function $f(x, y)$. The marginal probability density functions of X and Y are given by

$$f_X(x) = \int_{-\infty}^{\infty} f(x, y)dy$$

and

$$f_Y(y) = \int_{-\infty}^{\infty} f(x, y)dx,$$

respectively.

For jointly continuous random variables, if the cumulative distribution function $F(x, y)$ is known, the marginal cumulative distributions of X and Y are determined as follows:

$$P(X \leq x) = F_X(x) = \int_{-\infty}^{x} \int_{-\infty}^{\infty} f(t, y)dydt,$$

and

$$F_X(x) = \int_{-\infty}^{x} f_X(t)dt = F(x, \infty). \tag{6.6}$$

Similarly,

$$P(Y \leq y) = F_Y(y) = \int_{-\infty}^{y} \int_{-\infty}^{\infty} f(x, t)dxdt = \int_{-\infty}^{y} f_Y(t)dt = F(\infty, y). \tag{6.7}$$

Thus the marginal cumulative distribution of, say, X can be determined by letting Y assume its upper limit in the joint distribution function of X and Y.

Example 6.3 Let X and Y be two continuous random variables with joint probability density function

$$f(x, y) = \begin{cases} 3x(1 - xy) & 0 \leq x, y \leq 1, \\ 0 & \text{elsewhere.} \end{cases}$$

Determine the marginal densities and cumulative distributions of X and Y.

The marginal density of X is

$$f_X(x) = 3 \int_0^1 x(1 - xy)dy = 3 \left(xy - \frac{x^2 y^2}{2} \right) \Big|_0^1 = 3x \left(1 - \frac{x}{2} \right).$$

Similarly for Y,

$$f_Y(y) = 3 \int_0^1 x(1 - xy)dx = 3 \left(\frac{x^2}{2} - \frac{x^3 y}{3} \right) \Big|_0^1 = (3 - 2y)/2.$$

The joint cumulative distribution of X and Y is determined to be

$$F(x, y) = 3 \int_0^x \int_0^y u(1 - uv)\,dv\,du = 3 \int_0^x \left(uy - \frac{u^2y^2}{2} \right)\,du$$

$$= x^2y(3 - xy)/2, \qquad 0 \leq x, y \leq 1.$$

Therefore, the marginal cumulative distributions of X and of Y are given by

$$F_X(x) = F(x, 1) = x^2(3 - x)/2, \qquad 0 \leq x \leq 1,$$

and

$$F_Y(y) = F(1, y) = y(3 - y)/2, \qquad 0 \leq y \leq 1,$$

respectively.

6.4   Expectations and Moments for Bivariate Distributions

We now extend the concepts of expectations and moments to joint probability distributions.

Definition 6.5   Let X and Y be two jointly distributed random variables. The expected value of a function of X and Y, $g(x, y)$, is defined to be

$$E[g(X, Y)] = \sum_x \sum_y g(x, y)p(x, y)$$

if X and Y are discrete, or

$$E[g(X, Y)] = \int_{-\infty}^{\infty} \int_{-\infty}^{\infty} g(x, y)f(x, y)\,dy\,dx$$

if X and Y are continuous, where $p(x, y)$ and $f(x, y)$ are the joint probability and density functions, respectively.

Without loss of generality, let us restrict the discussion to the continuous case. As a consequence of Definition 6.5, the rth moment of, say, X about zero is

$$E(X^r) = \int_{-\infty}^{\infty} \int_{-\infty}^{\infty} x^r f(x, y)\,dy\,dx$$

$$= \int_{-\infty}^{\infty} x^r f_X(x)\,dx. \tag{6.8}$$

Similarly,

$$E(Y^r) = \int_{-\infty}^{\infty} y^r f_Y(y)\,dy. \tag{6.9}$$

The rth and sth *product moment* of X and Y about the origin is

$$E(X^r Y^s) = \int_{-\infty}^{\infty} \int_{-\infty}^{\infty} x^r y^s f(x, y)\,dy\,dx, \tag{6.10}$$

and that about the means is

$$E\{(X - \mu_X)^r (Y - \mu_Y)^s\} = \int_{-\infty}^{\infty}\int_{-\infty}^{\infty} (x - \mu_X)^r (y - \mu_Y)^s f(x, y)dydx, \quad (6.11)$$

where r and s are nonnegative integers. Notice that the rth moment of, say, X about zero is obtained from (6.10) by letting $s = 0$. Similarly the rth central moment of X can be determined from (6.11) when $s = 0$.

Of particular importance is the product moment about the means for $r = s = 1$. This product moment is known as the *covariance* of X and Y, and it is defined by

$$Cov(X, Y) = E\{(X - \mu_X)(Y - \mu_Y)\}. \quad (6.12)$$

Just as the variance is a measure of dispersion for a single random variable, the covariance measures the joint variability of X and Y. Thus the covariance is a measure of association between the values of X and Y relative to their dispersions. If, for example, there is a high probability that large values of X are associated with large values of Y, the covariance will be positive. On the other hand, if there is a high probability that large values of X are associated with small values of Y or vice versa, the covariance will be negative. As we will show later, the covariance is zero if X and Y are statistically independent.

By expanding the right side of (6.12), we are able to determine that

$$E\{(X - \mu_X)(Y - \mu_Y)\} = E[XY - X\mu_Y - Y\mu_X + \mu_X\mu_Y]$$

$$= E(XY) - \mu_X\mu_Y;$$

thus

$$Cov(X, Y) = E(XY) - E(X)E(Y). \quad (6.13)$$

If the covariance of X and Y is divided by the product of the standard deviations of X and of Y, the result is a dimensionless quantity known as the *correlation coefficient* and is denoted by $\rho(X, Y)$:*

$$\rho(X, Y) = Cov(X, Y)/\sigma_X\sigma_Y. \quad (6.14)$$

It can be shown that the correlation coefficient is contained in the interval $-1 \leqslant \rho \leqslant 1$. In fact, ρ is the covariance of two standardized random variables X' and Y' where $X' = (X - \mu_X)/\sigma_X$ and $Y' = (Y - \mu_Y)/\sigma_Y$. This means the correlation coefficient is only a standardized measure of linear association between the random variables X and Y relative to their dispersions. The value $\rho = 0$ indicates the absence of any linear association, and the values -1 and $+1$ indicate, respectively, perfect negative and perfect positive linear relationships. It is imperative that other interpretations of the word "correlation" be resisted. Additional discussion of the correlation coefficient will be given later when we discuss regression analysis.

---

*We will drop the identification of the random variables when not necessary.

Example 6.4   Let X and Y be two random variables with joint probability density function

$$f(x, y) = \begin{cases} \dfrac{2}{3}(x + y)\exp(-x) & x > 0, \quad 0 < y < 1, \\[2mm] 0 & \text{elsewhere.} \end{cases}$$

Determine the covariance and correlation coefficient for X and Y.

Taking appropriate expectations, we have

$$E(X) = \frac{2}{3} \int_0^\infty \int_0^1 (x^2 + xy)\exp(-x)\,dy\,dx$$

$$= \frac{2}{3} \int_0^\infty (x^2 + x/2)\exp(-x)\,dx$$

$$= \frac{2}{3} \int_0^\infty x^2 \exp(-x)\,dx + \frac{1}{3} \int_0^\infty x \exp(-x)\,dx$$

$$= \frac{2\Gamma(3)}{3} + \frac{\Gamma(2)}{3}$$

$$= 5/3;$$

$$E(X^2) = \frac{2}{3} \int_0^\infty \int_0^1 (x^3 + x^2 y)\exp(-x)\,dy\,dx$$

$$= \frac{2}{3} \int_0^\infty x^3 \exp(-x)\,dx + \frac{1}{3} \int_0^\infty x^2 \exp(-x)\,dx$$

$$= \frac{2\Gamma(4)}{3} + \frac{\Gamma(3)}{3}$$

$$= 14/3;$$

$$E(Y) = \frac{2}{3} \int_0^\infty \int_0^1 (xy + y^2)\exp(-x)\,dy\,dx$$

$$= \frac{1}{3} \int_0^\infty x \exp(-x)\,dx + \frac{2}{9} \int_0^\infty \exp(-x)\,dx$$

$$= \frac{\Gamma(2)}{3} + \frac{2}{9}$$

$$= 5/9;$$

$$E(Y^2) = \frac{2}{3} \int_0^\infty \int_0^1 (xy^2 + y^3)\exp(-x)\,dy\,dx$$

$$= \frac{2}{9} \int_0^\infty x \exp(-x)\,dx + \frac{1}{6} \int_0^\infty \exp(-x)\,dx$$

$$= \frac{2\Gamma(2)}{9} + \frac{1}{6}$$

$$= 7/18;$$

$$E(XY) = \frac{2}{3} \int_0^\infty \int_0^1 (x^2 y + xy^2) \exp(-x) dy dx$$

$$= \frac{1}{3} \int_0^\infty x^2 \exp(-x) dx + \frac{2}{9} \int_0^\infty x \exp(-x) dx$$

$$= \frac{\Gamma(3)}{3} + \frac{2\Gamma(2)}{9}$$

$$= 8/9.$$

Therefore,

$$Cov(X, Y) = E(XY) - E(X)E(Y) = 8/9 - (5/3)(5/9) = -1/27.$$

Since

$$Var(X) = E(X^2) - E^2(X) = 17/9$$

and

$$Var(Y) = E(Y^2) - E^2(Y) = 13/162,$$

the correlation coefficient is

$$\rho(X, Y) = \frac{-1/27}{\sqrt{(17/9)(13/162)}} = -0.0951.$$

6.5 Statistically Independent Random Variables

In Chapter 2 we stated that two events are statistically independent if their joint probability is equal to the product of their marginal probabilities. We shall now extend the notion of independence to random variables. To assure consistency of definition, we must insist that for statistically independent random variables the joint probability $P(a < X < b, c < Y < d)$ is equal to the product of the individual probabilities $P(a < X < b)$ and $P(c < Y < d)$. We give the following definition:

Definition 6.6 Let X and Y be two jointly distributed random variables. X and Y are said to be statistically independent if and only if

$$p(x, y) = p_X(x) p_Y(y) \qquad X \text{ and } Y \text{ discrete,}$$

or

$$f(x, y) = f_X(x) f_Y(y) \qquad X \text{ and } Y \text{ continuous,}$$

for all x and y, where $p(x, y)$ and $f(x, y)$ are the bivariate probability and density functions, respectively, and where $p_X(x)$, $p_Y(y)$, $f_X(x)$, and $f_Y(y)$ are the marginal probability or density functions as appropriate.

It follows from this definition that if X and Y are statistically independent, the joint probability

$$P(a < X < b, c < Y < d) = \int_a^b \int_c^d f(x, y)dydx$$

$$= \int_a^b \int_c^d f_X(x)f_Y(y)dydx$$

$$= \int_a^b f_X(x)dx \int_c^d f_Y(y)dy$$

$$= P(a < X < b)P(c < Y < d).$$

For the same condition,

$$E(XY) = \int_{-\infty}^\infty \int_{-\infty}^\infty xyf(x, y)dydx$$

$$= \int_{-\infty}^\infty \int_{-\infty}^\infty xyf_X(x)f_Y(y)dydx$$

$$= \int_{-\infty}^\infty xf_X(x)dx \int_{-\infty}^\infty yf_Y(y)dy$$

$$= E(X)E(Y).$$

Then if X and Y are statistically independent, $Cov(X, Y) = \rho(X, Y) = 0$. However, it must be emphasized that the converse is not true. That is, a covariance of zero is not a sufficient condition for independence. It should be noted that if X and Y are not statistically independent, they are statistically dependent.

We now state some useful results based primarily on Definitions 6.5 and 6.6. Let X and Y be two continuous random variables with joint probability density function $f(x, y)$.

The expected value of a linear function of X and Y is

$$E(aX + bY) = \int_{-\infty}^\infty \int_{-\infty}^\infty (ax + by) f(x, y)dydx$$

$$= a \int_{-\infty}^\infty \int_{-\infty}^\infty xf(x, y)dydx + b \int_{-\infty}^\infty \int_{-\infty}^\infty yf(x, y)dydx$$

$$= a E(X) + b E(Y) \qquad (6.15)$$

for any constants a and b.

The variance of a linear function of X and Y is

$$Var(aX + bY) = E(aX + bY)^2 - E^2(aX + bY)$$

$$= E(a^2X^2 + 2abXY + b^2Y^2) - [aE(X) + bE(Y)]^2$$

$$= a^2E(X^2) + 2abE(XY) + b^2E(Y^2)$$

$$\quad - a^2E^2(X) - 2abE(X)E(Y) - b^2E^2(Y)$$

$$= a^2Var(X) + b^2Var(Y) + 2abCov(X, Y). \qquad (6.16)$$

As a consequence of these results, the expected value of the sum of X and Y is the sum of their expected values, and the variance of the sum of X and Y is the sum of their variances plus twice the covariance of X and Y. Moreover, if X and Y are statistically independent,

$$Var(aX + bY) = a^2Var(X) + b^2Var(Y). \qquad (6.17)$$

Generalization of these results to n random variables follows by induction, and we state the following theorem:

Theorem 6.1 Let $X_1, X_2, \ldots, X_n$ be n random variables with a joint probability density function $f(x_1, x_2, \ldots, x_n)$. Then

$$E\left[\sum_{i=1}^{n} a_iX_i\right] = \sum_{i=1}^{n}\left[a_iE(X_i)\right]$$

$$Var\left[\sum_{i=1}^{n} a_iX_i\right] = \sum_{i=1}^{n} a_i^2Var(X_i) + \sum_{\substack{i=1 \\ i \neq j}}^{n}\sum_{j=1}^{n} a_ia_jCov(X_i, X_j)$$

for any constants a_i, $i = 1, 2, \ldots, n$.

Example 6.5 A salesman derives income by selling two distinct products A and B. From past experience he knows that the sales volume of A does not influence that of B. His monthly income is 10 percent of the dollar volume for product A and 15 percent of the volume for B. If on the average he sells $10,000 worth of product A per month, with a standard deviation of $2,000, while he sells $8,000 worth of B, with a standard deviation of $1,000, determine the expected value and the standard deviation of his monthly income.

Let X and Y be the monthly dollar volumes of products A and B, respectively. By assumption

$$E(X) = 10,000, \quad s.d.(X) = 2,000; \quad E(Y) = 8,000, \quad s.d.(Y) = 1,000.$$

Thus

$$E(0.1X + 0.15Y) = 0.1\,E(X) + 0.15\,E(Y) = \$2,200,$$

and

$$Var(0.1X + 0.15Y) = 0.01\,Var(X) + 0.0225\,Var(Y) = 62,500.$$

The standard deviation is $250.

6.6 Conditional Probability Distributions

Suppose a body of water contains two major pollutants. Let the random variables X and Y represent the concentration levels of these pollutants in a portion of the body of water represented by a rectangular surface area. Suppose the concentration level of Y is observed to be y, but that of X is not observed. If the joint probability density function $f(x, y)$ is known, we need to determine a function that will give the probability that the concentration level of X is contained in the interval (a, b) given the observed value y of Y. Consider the function

$$f(x, y)/f_Y(y),$$

where $f_Y(y)$ is the marginal density of Y. If the random variable Y is held fixed at the observed value y such that $f_Y(y) > 0$, then $f(x, y)/f_Y(y)$ defines a nonnegative function of X that integrates to one since by definition

$$\int_{-\infty}^{\infty} \frac{f(x, y)}{f_Y(y)} \, dx = \frac{1}{f_Y(y)} \int_{-\infty}^{\infty} f(x, y)dx = f_Y(y)/f_Y(y) = 1.$$

Thus $f(x, y)/f_Y(y)$ is a probability density function, and the probability that $a < X < b$, given the concentration level of Y is y, is

$$P(a < X < b \mid y) = \int_a^b \frac{f(x, y)}{f_Y(y)} \, dx. \tag{6.18}$$

Definition 6.7   Let X and Y be two random variables with joint probability density function $f(x, y)$. The conditional probability density function of the random variable X, denoted by $f(x \mid y)$, for a fixed value y of Y is defined by

$$f(x \mid y) = f(x, y)/f_Y(y),$$

where $f_Y(y)$ is the marginal probability density of Y such that $f_Y(y) > 0$.

By a similar definition the conditional probability density function of Y for a fixed value x of X is defined as

$$f(y \mid x) = f(x, y)/f_X(x) \qquad f_X(x) > 0, \tag{6.19}$$

where $f_X(x)$ is the marginal density of X. We can think of $f(x \mid y)$ as being the function that gives the probability density along the horizontal line in the (x, y) plane corresponding to the fixed value y of Y. Similarly, $f(y \mid x)$ is the function that gives the probability density along the vertical line in the (x, y) plane corresponding to the value x of X.

Notice that if the conditional density, say, $f(x \mid y)$ does not involve y, then X is statistically independent of Y. That is, if X and Y are statistically independent, then

$$f(x, y) = f_X(x)f_Y(y)$$

and

$$f(x \mid y) = f(x, y)/f_Y(y)$$
$$= f_X(x)f_Y(y)/f_Y(y)$$
$$= f_X(x).$$

Similarly, if

$$f(x, y) = f_X(x)f_Y(y),$$

then

$$f(y \mid x) = f_X(x)f_Y(y)/f_X(x)$$
$$= f_Y(y).$$

Conditional expectations are defined in a manner analogous to Definition 6.5. For example, the conditional expectations of X given $Y = y$ and of Y given $X = x$ are defined by

$$E(X \mid y) = \int_{-\infty}^{\infty} xf(x \mid y)dx$$

and (6.20)

$$E(Y \mid x) = \int_{-\infty}^{\infty} yf(y \mid x)dy,$$

respectively. The conditional expectation of X given y is a function of the fixed point y and represents the mean of X along the line corresponding to y. By symmetry the conditional expectation of Y given x is a function of x and represents the mean of Y along the line corresponding to x. Similarly,

$$Var(X \mid y) = E(X^2 \mid y) - E^2(X \mid y)$$

and (6.21)

$$Var(Y \mid x) = E(Y^2 \mid x) - E^2(Y \mid x),$$

where

$$E(X^2 \mid y) = \int_{-\infty}^{\infty} x^2 f(x \mid y)dx$$

and (6.22)

$$E(Y^2 \mid x) = \int_{-\infty}^{\infty} y^2 f(y \mid x)dy.$$

Example 6.6 Let X and Y be the concentration levels of two pollutants in parts per million (ppm) at a certain location of a body of water. If the joint probability density function is given by

$$f(x, y) = \begin{cases} (x + y)/8000 & 0 < x, y < 20, \\ 0 & \text{elsewhere,} \end{cases}$$

and if the concentration level of Y has been observed to be 10 ppm, determine the probability that the concentration level of X will be at most 14 ppm. Also determine the conditional mean and variance of X at $Y = 10$ ppm.

Since

$$f(x, y) = (x + y)/8000 \qquad 0 < x, y < 20,$$

we have

$$f_Y(y) = \frac{1}{8000} \int_0^{20} (x + y)dx = (y + 10)/400,$$

and the conditional probability density of X is

$$f(x \mid y) = (x + y)/20(y + 10),$$

which reduces to

$$f(x \mid Y = 10) = (x + 10)/400$$

for $Y = 10$. Therefore,

$$P(X \le 14 \mid Y = 10) = \int_0^{14} f(x \mid Y = 10)dx$$

$$= \frac{1}{400} \int_0^{14} (x + 10)dx$$

$$= 0.595.$$

For the conditional mean and variance of X at $Y = 10$ we have

$$E(X \mid Y = 10) = \int_0^{20} xf(x \mid Y = 10)dx$$

$$= \frac{1}{400} \int_0^{20} (x^2 + 10x)dx$$

$$= 11.67;$$

$$E(X^2 \mid Y = 10) = \int_0^{20} x^2 f(x \mid Y = 10)dx$$

$$= \frac{1}{400} \int_0^{20} (x^3 + 10x^2)dx$$

$$= 166.67;$$

$$Var(X \mid Y = 10) = 30.56.$$

6.7 Bayesian Analysis: The Prior and Posterior Distributions

In Section 2.8 Bayes' theorem was stated for conditional probabilities of discrete events. In this context we examined briefly how this theorem can be utilized to revise degrees of belief concerning the outcomes of a phenomenon as new information about the phenomenon becomes available. More important, however, is the representation of Bayes' theorem for the conditional distribution of either a discrete or a continuous random variable. Such a representation is important because, as we will see in Chapter 8, it provides the necessary mechanism for Bayesian inference. In this section we will examine the concepts of prior and posterior distributions and restate Bayes' theorem for these concepts.

Let Y be a random variable (discrete or continuous) defined in such a way that its values represent possible alternatives of a random phenomenon before experimentation. Let an investigator's degree of belief concerning these alternatives be expressed by a probability function $p_Y(y)$, called the *prior probability function* of Y, if Y is discrete, or a density function $f_Y(y)$, called the *prior probability density* of Y, if Y is continuous. The specification of the distributional form of $p_Y(y)$ or $f_Y(y)$ depends on the investigator's conviction concerning values of Y before current sample information is available. Such a conviction may be based on any other type of information that may be available to the investigator, including subjective judgment. Let $f(x \mid y)$ be the conditional probability density function of another random variable X^*, which depicts sample evidence as a function of a fixed alternative y of Y. The function $f(x \mid y)$ is called the *likelihood function* because it represents the likelihood of the sample result x, given the value y of Y.

When the prior information concerning the values of Y is combined with the sample information, the result is a revised or an updated set of information about the random variable Y. In other words, the combination of the prior distribution and the likelihood function yields a conditional distribution of Y, given the sample result, which is known as the *posterior distribution* of Y. The combination is according to Bayes' theorem, which we now state as follows:

Theorem 6.2 Let $p_Y(y)$ or $f_Y(y)$ be the prior probability or probability density function of Y, respectively, and let $f(x \mid y)$ be the likelihood function. Then the posterior probability or probability density function of Y given the sample evidence x is

$$p(y \mid x) = \frac{f(x \mid y)p_Y(y)}{\sum\limits_Y f(x \mid y)p_Y(y)} \qquad \text{if } Y \text{ is discrete,} \tag{6.23}$$

$$f(y \mid x) = \frac{f(x \mid y)f_Y(y)}{\int_Y f(x \mid y)f_Y(y)dy} \qquad \text{if } Y \text{ is continuous.} \tag{6.24}$$

The posterior probability function $p(y \mid x)$ or probability density function $f(y \mid x)$ reflects the investigator's *revised* degree of belief concerning the random variable Y after current sample information is gathered. Since information concerning a random variable can be periodically revised as additional sample evidence becomes available, a sequential approach is indeed possible here. In this context the current posterior distribution may actually become the future prior distribution when another revision concerning the random variable is necessary. The periodic revision of probabilities is made possible by successive applications of Theorem 6.2.

It is interesting to note that the denominator in (6.23) or (6.24) is the marginal or unconditional probability density function of X; that is,

$$f_X(x) = \sum_Y f(x \mid y)p_Y(y) \tag{6.25}$$

---

*The random variable X is assumed to be continuous here; it can also be discrete.

or

$$f_X(x) = \int_Y f(x \mid y) f_Y(y) dy, \tag{6.26}$$

depending on whether Y is discrete or continuous, respectively. Moreover, the numerator in (6.23) or (6.24) is the product of the likelihood function and the prior probability, and thus is the joint probability of X and Y expressed as

$$f(x, y) = f(x \mid y) p_Y(y) \qquad \text{if } Y \text{ is discrete,} \tag{6.27}$$

or

$$f(x, y) = f(x \mid y) f_Y(y) \qquad \text{if } Y \text{ is continuous.} \tag{6.28}$$

Notice that in (6.27) the function $f(x, y)$ is a bivariate mixture of a continuous and a discrete random variable.

Example 6.7 An appliance retailer has noticed that the proportion of customers who buy a particular brand of television varies randomly over time. The retailer concludes that the proportion is a discrete random variable that can assume the values of 0.3, 0.35, 0.4, and 0.45, depending on a variety of economic and other considerations. Based on some previous information, the retailer is willing to assign the prior probabilities of 0.4, 0.3, 0.2, and 0.1, respectively, to these values. Among the television sets currently being sold by the retailer, a sample of $n = 15$ reveals that eight of the sets sold are the brand of interest. If we assume that for a particular proportion, say p, the number of units of this brand sold for a fixed sample n is a binomial random variable, determine the posterior probabilities.

Let X be the random variable depicting the number of units of this brand sold out of a sample of n units. $X = 8$ for $n = 15$ represents the sample evidence conditioned on a particular proportion p of customer preference for this brand. By assumption X is binomial, and thus the likelihood function is

$$p(x; 15 \mid p) = \frac{15!}{(15 - x)! x!} p^x (1 - p)^{15 - x}, \qquad x = 0, 1, 2, \ldots, 15.$$

If $p = 0.3$, the likelihood of the sample result is

$$P(X = 8 \mid p = 0.3) = p(8; 15 \mid 0.3) = \frac{15!}{(15 - 8)! 8!} (0.3)^8 (0.7)^{15 - 8} = 0.0348.$$

For the other values of the proportion we determine

$$P(X = 8 \mid p = 0.35) = 0.071,$$

$$P(X = 8 \mid p = 0.4) = 0.1181,$$

$$P(X = 8 \mid p = 0.45) = 0.1647.$$

Notice here that both random variables are discrete. We can still use expression (6.23) of Bayes' theorem, though, to determine the posterior probabilities. Table 6.1 provides the computational details. Both the prior probabilities and the posterior

TABLE 6.1 Determination of posterior probabilities for Example 6.7

Proportion values	*Prior probability*	*Sample likelihood*	*Prior probability × likelihood*	*Posterior probability*
0.3	0.4	0.0348	0.01392	0.01392/0.07531 = 0.1848
0.35	0.3	0.071	0.02130	0.02130/0.07531 = 0.2828
0.4	0.2	0.1181	0.02362	0.02362/0.07531 = 0.3137
0.45	0.1	0.1647	0.01647	0.01647/0.07531 = 0.2187
Totals	1.0		0.07531	1.0000

probabilities must sum to one since each forms a probability distribution. Graphs of the prior and posterior probabilities are given in Figure 6.2, showing a very noticeable shift in the probabilities for the four possible values of the proportion. There has also been a shift in the expected value for the proportion of customer preference for this brand. The prior expected value is 0.35, and the posterior expected value is 0.3783.

In Section 4.5 we suggested that the negative binomial distribution is an adequate alternative to the Poisson model when the rate of occurrence is not constant over time or space. For example, in accident statistics it is unlikely for the rate of occurrence among various groups to be constant and independent over a fixed length of time. This may make a Bayesian approach more appropriate for such data.

Suppose we assume that all possible rates of occurrence can be regarded as values of the continuous random variable Λ, whose prior distribution is gamma with density

$$f(\lambda; k, \theta) = \frac{1}{\Gamma(k)\theta^k} \lambda^{k-1} \exp(-\lambda/\theta), \qquad \lambda > 0. \tag{6.29}$$

FIGURE 6.2 Prior and posterior probabilities for Example 6.7

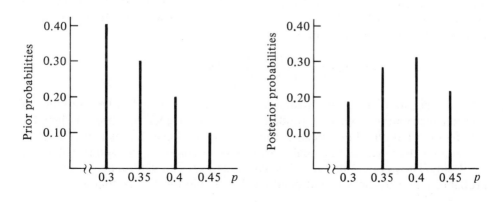

Let X be a discrete random variable representing the number of accidents observed for a specific group. Then we can argue that X is a Poisson random variable that depends on a specific λ of Λ, and the likelihood function is given by

$$p(x \mid \lambda) = \lambda^x \exp(-\lambda)/x! \qquad x = 0, 1, 2, \ldots . \tag{6.30}$$

Before we determine the posterior distribution of Λ, we wish to show that the marginal probability function of X is the negative binomial. That is, if for each value λ of Λ, X is Poisson distributed, then the unconditional distribution of X over all possible λ is the negative binomial.

It follows from (6.26) that the marginal probability function of X is

$$p_X(x) = \int_0^\infty p(x \mid \lambda) f_\Lambda(\lambda) d\lambda. \tag{6.31}$$

Notice that the integrand in (6.31) is the joint probability density function of X and Λ and thus is a bivariate mixture of a discrete and a continuous random variable.

Substitution of (6.29) and (6.30) in (6.31) leads to

$$p_X(x) = \frac{1}{\Gamma(k)\theta^k x!} \int_0^\infty \lambda^{x+k-1} \exp\left[-\lambda \left(\frac{\theta + 1}{\theta}\right)\right] d\lambda. \tag{6.32}$$

In the integrand of (6.32), let $u = \lambda [(\theta + 1)/\theta]$; thus $\lambda = [\theta/(\theta + 1)]u$ and $d\lambda = [\theta/(\theta + 1)]du$. Then

$$p_X(x) = \frac{1}{x!\Gamma(k)\theta^k} \int_0^\infty \theta/(\theta + 1)^{x+k} u^{x+k-1} \exp(-u) du$$

$$= \frac{\theta/(\theta + 1)^{x+k} \Gamma(x + k)}{x!\Gamma(k)\theta^k}$$

$$= \frac{\Gamma(x + k)}{x!\Gamma(k)} \left(\frac{1}{\theta + 1}\right)^k \left(\frac{\theta}{\theta + 1}\right)^x, \qquad \begin{array}{l} x = 0, 1, 2, \ldots, \\ k, \theta > 0. \end{array} \tag{6.33}$$

Expression (6.33) is seen to be identical to (4.35), the probability function of the negative binomial distribution for $k > 0$. Notice that in (6.33), $p = 1/(\theta + 1)$ and $1 - p = \theta/(\theta + 1)$, so that $0 < p < 1$ since $\theta > 0$. Moreover, from expression (4.39), the mean of X is

$$E(X) = \frac{k\theta/(\theta + 1)}{1/(\theta + 1)} = k\theta = E(\Lambda).$$

Thus the negative binomial distribution has been determined to be a mixture of Poisson distributions where a random rate of occurrence has been assigned a gamma distribution whose mean is the same as the Poisson mean. It is for this reason that the negative binomial is known as a compound Poisson distribution.

Using Theorem 6.2 and in particular (6.24), we can determine the posterior probability density of Λ conditioned on the sample result x as follows:

$$f(\lambda \mid x) = \frac{\lambda^{x+k-1}\exp\{-[(\theta + 1)/\theta]\lambda\}}{\Gamma(k)\theta^k x!} \bigg/ \frac{\Gamma(x + k)}{x!\Gamma(k)}\left(\frac{1}{\theta + 1}\right)^k\left(\frac{\theta}{\theta + 1}\right)^x$$

$$= \frac{\lambda^{x+k-1}\exp\{-[(\theta + 1)/\theta]\lambda\}}{\Gamma(k)x!\theta^k} \cdot \frac{\Gamma(k)x!(\theta + 1)^{x+k}}{\Gamma(x + k)\theta^x}$$

$$= \frac{[(\theta + 1)/\theta]^{x+k}\lambda^{x+k-1}\exp\{-[(\theta + 1)/\theta]\lambda\}}{\Gamma(x + k)}, \qquad \lambda > 0. \qquad (6.34)$$

A comparison of (6.34) with the density function of the gamma distribution, as given by (5.45), reveals that the posterior distribution of Λ is also gamma with shape parameter $x + k$ and scale parameter $\theta/(\theta + 1)$. It should be noted that if the prior and posterior distributions belong to the same family, as is the case here, the family is known as the *conjugate family* with respect to the distribution of the sample data. In this case, therefore, the gamma family is conjugate to the Poisson distribution.

Example 6.8   Suppose that for accident statistics we are willing to assign to the rate of occurrence a gamma prior distribution with shape parameter 2 and scale parameter 3. Suppose further that we observe two accidents for some particular rate. Determine the posterior density function of the rate, given the sample result, and compare it with the prior density.

Let Λ be the rate of occurrence. From (5.45) the prior density of Λ is

$$f_\Lambda(\lambda; 2, 3) = \frac{1}{9}\lambda\exp(-\lambda/3), \qquad \lambda > 0.$$

Given the sample result $X = 2$, the posterior density of Λ is determined from (6.34) to be

$$f(\lambda; 4, 3/4 \mid x) = \frac{1}{6}(4/3)^4\lambda^3\exp\left(-\frac{4}{3}\lambda\right), \qquad \lambda > 0.$$

Figure 6.3 provides a comparison of the prior and posterior density functions. It is apparent from the figure that the posterior density is considerably less skewed than the prior density. Notice also that the prior mean rate is 6, while the posterior mean rate is 3.

We stated in Section 5.4 that the beta distribution plays an important role in Bayesian statistics. To illustrate this we turn to a Bayesian analysis for the proportion parameter of a binomial distribution.

Example 6.9   For a manufacturing process, we are interested in the proportion defective. Since the process is likely to undergo minor changes from time to time, such as different shifts, variations in raw materials, and so on that may influence the proportion defective, it is reasonable to regard the proportion defective as a random variable with possible values from the interval $(0, 1)$. For a specified proportion defective, say p, it is known that the number of defective

FIGURE 6.3 Prior and posterior densities for Example 6.8

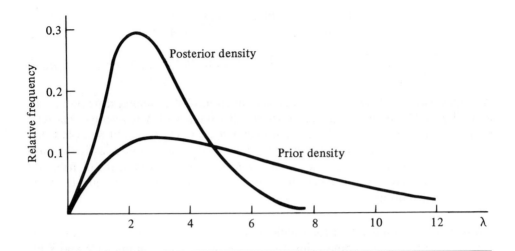

units x observed in a fixed random sample of n units is binomial. That is, the conditional probability function of X for a fixed n given p is

$$p(x; n \mid p) = \frac{n!}{(n - x)!x!}\, p^x(1 - p)^{n-x}, \qquad x = 0, 1, 2, \dots n.$$

If the prior distribution of the proportion defective is beta with probability density function

$$f_P(p; \alpha, \beta) = \frac{\Gamma(\alpha + \beta)}{\Gamma(\alpha)\,\Gamma(\beta)}\, p^{\alpha-1}(1 - p)^{\beta-1} \qquad 0 \leq p \leq 1, \tag{6.35}$$

show that the posterior distribution of the proportion defective, given the number of defectives x, is also beta.

From (6.24) the posterior probability density of the proportion defective is

$$
\begin{aligned}
f(p \mid x) &= \frac{p(x; n \mid p)f_P(p; \alpha, \beta)}{\displaystyle\int_0^1 p(x; n \mid p)f_P(p; \alpha, \beta)\,dp} \\[2ex]
&= \frac{\dfrac{n!}{(n - x)!x!}\, p^x(1 - p)^{n-x}\, \dfrac{\Gamma(\alpha + \beta)}{\Gamma(\alpha)\,\Gamma(\beta)}\, p^{\alpha-1}(1 - p)^{\beta-1}}{\dfrac{n!}{(n-x)!x!} \cdot \dfrac{\Gamma(\alpha + \beta)}{\Gamma(\alpha)\,\Gamma(\beta)} \displaystyle\int_0^1 p^{x+\alpha-1}(1 - p)^{n+\beta-x-1}\,dp} \\[2ex]
&= \frac{p^{x+\alpha-1}(1 - p)^{n+\beta-x-1}}{\displaystyle\int_0^1 p^{x+\alpha-1}(1 - p)^{n+\beta-x-1}\,dp};
\end{aligned}
$$

but from (5.33), the integral $\int_0^1 p^{x+\alpha-1}(1 - p)^{n+\beta-x-1}dp = B(x+\alpha, n+\beta-x)$. The posterior density is therefore

$$f(p \mid x) = \frac{p^{x+\alpha-1}(1 - p)^{n+\beta-x-1}}{B(x + \alpha, n + \beta - x)}$$

$$= \frac{\Gamma(n + \alpha + \beta)}{\Gamma(x + \alpha)\,\Gamma(n + \beta - x)}\, p^{x+\alpha-1}(1 - p)^{n+\beta-x-1} \qquad 0 \leqslant p \leqslant 1, \quad (6.36)$$

which is seen to be a beta density with parameters $(x + \alpha)$ and $(n + \beta - x)$. Therefore, the conjugate family for the binomial distribution is the beta family.

6.8 The Bivariate Normal Distribution

In Chapter 5 we considered the normal distribution for a single random variable. The concept of a normal distribution may be extended to include several random variables. In particular, the bivariate normal distribution has been used extensively to describe the joint probabilistic behavior of two random variables.

Definition 6.8   The random variables X and Y are said to have a *bivariate normal distribution* if their joint probability density function is given by

$$f(x, y) = \frac{1}{2\pi\,\sigma_X\sigma_Y\sqrt{1 - \rho^2}}\exp\left\{ -\frac{1}{2(1 - \rho^2)}\left[\left(\frac{x - \mu_X}{\sigma_X}\right)^2 \right.\right.$$

$$\left.\left. - 2\rho\left(\frac{x - \mu_X}{\sigma_X}\right)\left(\frac{y - \mu_Y}{\sigma_Y}\right) + \left(\frac{y - \mu_Y}{\sigma_Y}\right)^2\right]\right\} \qquad -\infty < x, y < \infty, \qquad (6.37)$$

where

$$\mu_X = E(X), \quad \mu_Y = E(Y), \quad \sigma_X^2 = Var(X), \quad \sigma_Y^2 = Var(Y),$$

and where ρ is the correlation coefficient of X and Y, as defined in Section 6.4.

As Figure 6.4 illustrates, the bivariate normal density is a three-dimensional surface that literally looks like a bell. Any vertical cut through the surface produces a curve of the univariate normal form, while planes parallel to the xy plane intersect the surface in ellipses that are called *contours of constant probability*.

It is of interest to note that although generally the condition $\rho = 0$ is only a necessary condition of independence, for the bivariate normal it is also a sufficient condition. That is, if $\rho = 0$, then

$$f(x, y) = \frac{1}{2\pi\sigma_X\sigma_Y}\exp\left[-\frac{1}{2}\left(\frac{x-\mu_X}{\sigma_X}\right)^2 - \frac{1}{2}\left(\frac{y-\mu_Y}{\sigma_Y}\right)^2\right]$$

$$= \frac{1}{\sqrt{2\pi}\,\sigma_X}\exp\left[-(x - \mu_X)^2/2\sigma_X^2\right] \cdot \frac{1}{\sqrt{2\pi}\,\sigma_Y}\exp\left[-(y - \mu_Y)^2/2\sigma_Y^2\right]$$

$$= f_X(x)f_Y(y),$$

where $f_X(x)$ and $f_Y(y)$ are the univariate normal densities of X and Y, respectively.

FIGURE 6.4 Bivariate normal density with $E(X) = E(Y) = 0$, $Var(X) = Var(Y) = 1$, and $\rho = 0$

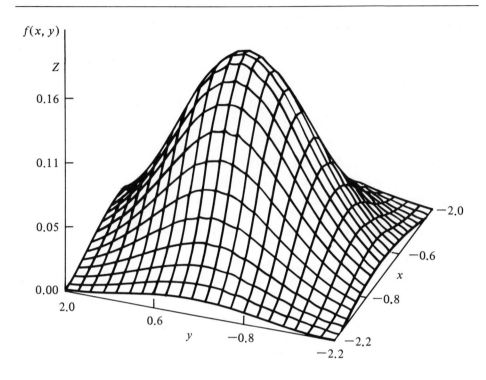

One can show that by using (6.37) and integrating out y, the marginal density of X is normal with mean μ_X and variance σ_X^2. Similarly, the marginal density of Y is normal with mean μ_Y and variance σ_Y^2. By Definition 6.7 the conditional probability density of X given the value y of Y works out to be

$$f(x \mid y) = \frac{1}{\sqrt{2\pi\,\sigma_X^2(1 - \rho^2)}}$$
$$\times \exp\left\{ -\frac{1}{2\sigma_X^2(1 - \rho^2)}\left[x - \mu_X - \frac{\rho\,\sigma_X}{\sigma_Y}(y - \mu_Y)\right]^2 \right\}. \quad (6.38)$$

Expression (6.38) is a normal probability density function with

$$E(X \mid y) = \mu_X + \frac{\rho\sigma_X}{\sigma_Y}(y - \mu_Y) \quad \text{and} \quad Var(X \mid y) = \sigma_X^2(1 - \rho^2).$$

A similar expression can be obtained for the conditional density of Y given the value x of X.

Example 6.10 Let X and Y be the horizontal and vertical deviations of a manned space vehicle from the prescribed landing point at the Sea of Tranquility. Assume that X and Y are independently distributed bivariate normal random variables with means $\mu_X = \mu_Y = 0$ and equal variances. What are the maximum allowable standard deviations of X and Y that will satisfy NASA's requirement of a probability of 0.99 that the vehicle will land within 500 ft of the prescribed landing point in both horizontal and vertical directions?

Because of independence and the assumption that $\sigma_X = \sigma_Y = \sigma$, the joint probability

$$P(-500 < X < 500, \; -500 < Y < 500) = P(-500 < X < 500)$$

$$\cdot P(-500 < Y < 500)$$

$$= P\left(-\frac{500}{\sigma} < Z < \frac{500}{\sigma}\right)$$

$$\cdot P\left(-\frac{500}{\sigma} < Z < \frac{500}{\sigma}\right)$$

$$= P^2\left(-\frac{500}{\sigma} < Z < \frac{500}{\sigma}\right).$$

Since by assumption

$$P^2\left(-\frac{500}{\sigma} < Z < \frac{500}{\sigma}\right) = 0.99,$$

$$P\left(-\frac{500}{\sigma} < Z < \frac{500}{\sigma}\right) = 0.99499$$

or

$$P\left(Z > \frac{500}{\sigma}\right) = 0.0025,$$

but

$$P(Z > 2.81) = 0.0025;$$

hence $500/\sigma = 2.81$, and $\sigma_X = \sigma_Y \leq 177.94$ ft.

References

1. P. G. Hoel, *Introduction to mathematical statistics*, 4th ed., Wiley, New York, 1971.
2. R. V. Hogg and A. T. Craig, *Introduction to mathematical statistics*, 4th ed., Macmillan, New York, 1978.
3. B. W. Lindgren, *Statistical theory*, 3rd ed., Macmillan, New York, 1976.

Exercises

6.1. Sixty persons were randomly selected and asked for their preferences among three competing brands, A, B, and C. The preferences were 27, 18, and 15, respectively. How likely is this result if there are no other brands and the market shares are all the same?

6.2. Suppose 25 units are randomly selected from a production process that usually produces 90 percent usable units and 7 percent reworkable units. What is the probability that 22 of the 25 units are usable and 2 are reworkable?

6.3. Let the joint probability density function of the random variables X and Y be

$$f(x, y) = \begin{cases} (3x - y)/5 & 1 < x < 2, \quad 1 < y < 3, \\ 0 & \text{elsewhere.} \end{cases}$$

   a. Determine the joint cumulative distribution function.
   b. What is the joint probability that $X < 3/2$ and $Y < 2$?
   c. Using your answer to part a, determine the marginal cumulative distributions of X and Y.
   d. Determine the marginal density functions of X and of Y.

6.4. Let the joint probability density function of the random variables X and Y be

$$f(x, y) = \begin{cases} x \exp[-x(y + 1)] & x, y > 0, \\ 0 & \text{elsewhere.} \end{cases}$$

   a. Verify that $f(x, y)$ is a joint probability density function.
   b. What is the joint probability that $X < 2$ and $Y < 1$?
   c. Determine the marginal density functions of X and of Y.
   d. Are X and Y statistically independent?

6.5. Let X and Y be discrete random variables where the possible values of X and Y are -1, 0, and 1. The following table gives the joint probabilities for all possible pairs of values of X and Y.

		X		
		-1	0	1
	-1	1/16	3/16	1/16
Y	0	3/16	0	3/16
	1	1/16	3/16	1/16

   a. Determine the marginal probability functions $p_X(x)$ and $p_Y(y)$.
   b. Are X and Y statistically independent random variables?
   c. Determine $Cov(X, Y)$.

6.6. For the joint probability density function given in Exercise 6.3, determine $Cov(X, Y)$ and $\rho(X, Y)$.

6.7. Depending on priority, a computer program waits a certain length of time in the input queue and then executes for another length of time in the central processor. Let the joint probability density function for the input and execution times (in minutes) be

$$f(t_1, t_2) = \begin{cases} 2 \exp\left[-\left(\dfrac{t_1}{5} + 10t_2 \right) \right] & t_1, t_2 > 0, \\ 0 & \text{elsewhere.} \end{cases}$$

Given the joint cumulative distribution

$$F(t_1, t_2) = \begin{cases} [1 - \exp(-t_1/5)][1 - \exp(-10t_2)] & t_1, t_2 > 0, \\ 0 & \text{elsewhere,} \end{cases}$$

a. determine the joint probability that the input queue time will not exceed 8 minutes and the execution time will not exceed 12 seconds;

b. determine the marginal density functions and deduce that these lengths of time are independent random variables.

6.8. Let the random variables X and Y represent the proportions of respective markets of two distinct products produced by the same firm, and let the joint probability density function of X and Y be given by

$$f(x, y) = \begin{cases} (x + y) & 0 \le x, y \le 1, \\ 0 & \text{elsewhere.} \end{cases}$$

a. Determine the marginal density functions of X and Y.

b. Are X and Y statistically independent?

c. If $X = 0.2$, determine the conditional probability density function of Y.

6.9. Let the random variables X and Y represent the length and width (in centimeters) of a sheet of steel. If X and Y are independent with probability density functions

$$f_X(x) = \begin{cases} 1, & 99 < x < 100, \\ 0 & \text{elsewhere,} \end{cases} \qquad f_Y(y) = \begin{cases} 1, & 49 < y < 50, \\ 0 & \text{elsewhere,} \end{cases}$$

use the definition of variance to determine the variance of the area XY of the sheet.

6.10. Let X be a continuous random variable, and let Y be discrete.

a. If $f(x, y) = x^y \exp(-2x)/y!$, $x > 0$, $y = 0, 1, 2, \ldots$, determine the marginal probability function of Y.

b. Determine the conditional probability function of X given that $Y = 2$.

c. Evaluate $E(X \mid 2)$ and $Var(X \mid 2)$.

6.11. Let X and Y be any two random variables. Show that $Var(aX - bY) = a^2 \, Var(X) + b^2 \, Var(Y) - 2ab \, Cov(X, Y)$, where a and b are any constants.

6.12. Let X and Y be any two random variables. Show that $Cov(aX, bY) = ab \, Cov(X, Y)$, where a and b are any constants.

6.13. If X and Y are independent, $Var(X + Y) = Var(X - Y) = Var(X) + Var(Y)$. Compare this result with $Var(X + Y)$ and $Var(X - Y)$ when $Cov(X, Y) > 0$ or $Cov(X, Y) < 0$. What conclusions can be drawn?

6.14. Suppose the rate Λ with which automobile accidents occur over a fixed length of time is a gamma random variable with both shape and scale parameters equal to 2. If for each value λ of Λ the conditional distribution of the number of accidents X is Poisson, determine the marginal probability function of X and evaluate the probabilities for $X = 0, 1, 2, \ldots, 10$. How do these probabilities compare with those determined under the assumption of a constant rate of $\lambda = 4$?

6.15. Suppose the incidence of lung cancer for a certain number of adults without regard to smoking habits, age, etc., is a gamma random variable with shape and scale parameters 2 and 2, respectively. For a specific group of adults, the number that will develop lung cancer is a Poisson random variable whose parameter depends on the incidence of cancer for that group. Determine the unconditional probability that no more than two adults will develop cancer in this group.

6.16. In Exercise 6.15, suppose $x = 5$ adults of a certain number develop cancer. Determine the posterior density of Λ given x and compute and compare the prior and posterior means and variances.

6.17. Suppose a plant manager realizes that the proportion of defective units in his production process is not constant but behaves as a random variable. Without any evidence he is willing to assume that the distribution of the proportion defective is beta with $\alpha = 1$ and $\beta = 24$.

   a. Graph the prior density function and determine its mean and variance.
   b. Suppose he takes a random sample of $n = 12$ units and finds one defective unit. Under suitable assumptions, determine and graph the posterior probability density function.
   c. Find the posterior mean and variance and compare them to the prior mean and variance.
   d. Use Exercise 5.24 to determine the posterior probability that the proportion defective is at most 0.05.

6.18. Suppose the proportion of successful launchings of communications satellites is a beta random variable with parameters $\alpha = 21$ and $\beta = 1$. If, of the last twelve launchings, one failed, determine the posterior probability density of the proportion of successful launchings and compute the posterior probability that the proportion successful exceeds 0.95. Use expression 5.44.

6.19. The joint probability density function of the monthly demand for two products is the bivariate normal

$$f(x, y) = \frac{1}{100\pi\sqrt{3}} \exp\left\{ -\frac{2}{3}\left[\left(\frac{x - 50}{10}\right)^2 - \left(\frac{x - 50}{10}\right)\left(\frac{y - 25}{10}\right) + \left(\frac{y - 25}{10}\right)^2 \right] \right\}.$$

   a. What is the correlation coefficient between X and Y?
   b. What is the covariance between X and Y?
   c. Determine the conditional probability density function $f(x \mid y)$.
   d. Suppose an actual demand for Y is 30. What is the conditional probability that X is less than 65?

6.20. Suppose IQ (X) and undergraduate grade point average (Y) are random variables that are jointly distributed as a bivariate normal with $\mu_X = 100$, $\sigma_X = 10$, $\mu_Y = 3$, $\sigma_Y = 0.3$, and $Cov(X, Y) = 2.25$.

   a. If someone's IQ is 120, what are the conditional mean and standard deviation of the grade point average?
   b. Given that IQ is 120, determine the probability that the grade point average will exceed 3.5.
   c. Suppose someone's grade point average is 2.8. What is the probability that the person's IQ exceeds 115?

CHAPTER SEVEN

Random Samples and Sampling Distributions

7.1 Introduction

It was suggested in Chapter 1 that to comprehend the essence of statistical inference, it is necessary to understand the essence of both a population and a sample. On one hand, a population represents the "state of nature," or the way things are, with regard to a particular random phenomenon as identified by a measurable characteristic X. The way things are relative to X is also defined by a probability model called the probability distribution of the population. On the other hand, a sample is the collection of data from repeated trials of an experiment conducted for the purpose of obtaining representative evidence from the population about the characteristic X. If the manner in which the sample is observed is impartial and technically sound, then one expects the sample to contain useful information about the state of nature, and inferences can be made about the state of nature based on the sample information. But such inferences are inductive and therefore subject to risk since they represent reasoning from the particular to the general.

In Chapters 4 through 6 we examined in some detail several probability distributions that may serve as candidate models for the distribution of a population of interest. In the remaining chapters our general objective is to examine many techniques by which the inductive process known as statistical inference can be applied to yield useful and reliable results. That is, statistical inference is defined as *the collection of techniques for making inductive inferences and for measuring the risk in such inferences*. In this chapter we will establish some basic theoretical concepts for sampling and statistical inference. The actual application of these concepts will be taken up in detail in later chapters.

7.2 Random Samples

Since statistical inference relies on only a sample of the items in the population of interest, the process by which a sample is produced must be one that ensures the selection of a good sample. We suggested in Chapter 1 that a good sample is produced when the sampling process gives each item in the population an equal and independent chance of being included in the sample. If the population consists of *N* objects from which a sample of size *n* is selected, the sampling process must also ensure that each sample of size *n* has the same probability of being selected. Such a procedure leads to what is commonly referred to as a *simple random sample*. In this context the word "random" suggests total impartiality in the selection of a sample.

The essence of inductive inference demands a random sample because a sample is selected primarily to provide the means by which an inference can be made about some feature of the underlying population. For example, inferences can be drawn about certain assumed conditions of a population based on whether the observed sample is within the sampling variation that is expected to prevail if these conditions were true. Thus the quality of randomness in a sample ensures the application of probability to evaluate the risk inherent in an inductive process.

At this point we should structure the broad concept of a simple random sample according to the concepts of probability that we discussed in Chapters 2 through 6. We do this by examining several frequently encountered sampling situations. The first situation arises in many experiments involving random phenomena in engineering and the physical sciences. Here the population of interest does not consist of tangible objects from which a number will be selected to form the sample. Rather, the population is thought of as a collection of an infinite number of possible results for some measurable characteristic. The characteristic is usually a physical measurement, such as the concentration level of a pollutant, the demand for a product, or the waiting time in a service facility. Let *X* be the measurable characteristic and let $f(x; \theta)$ be the probability density function of the population distribution. The following is a way of sampling from this type of population:

1. An experiment is devised and performed that yields the observation X_1 of the measurable characteristic *X*. The experiment is repeated under identical conditions, yielding the observation X_2. The process continues in this manner until *n* observations $X_1, X_2, ..., X_n$ have been made of the characteristic *X*.

In this sampling scenario, sample observations are collected through independent trials of an experiment repeated under conditions that are identical for all controllable factors. In this context we think of the observation of the *i*th performance of the experiment as being a selection from the same source that exists for the observation of any other trial for *X*. In essence, therefore, the taking of observations under identical conditions as a result of repeated and independent trials of an experiment constitutes what is called *random sampling with replacement*. Accordingly, each of the observations $X_1, X_2, ..., X_n$ is a random variable whose probability distribution is the same as that of the population.

A somewhat different situation calls for the selection of tangible objects from a population consisting of a finite number of objects, such as humans, animals, electrical or mechanical components, and so on. The measurable characteristic of interest may be an attribute, such as the state of a component (defective or nondefective), the opinion of an individual on some issue (in favor or opposed), or it may be a quantitative measurement, such as the IQ of an individual or the life length of a component. There are two ways of taking random samples from this type of population:

2. After suitable mixing of the objects in the population, the first object is drawn, and the measurable characteristic is observed. Let the observation be denoted by X_1. The first object drawn is then put back in the population, the objects in the population are once again thoroughly mixed, and the second object is drawn. Let the second observation be denoted by X_2. The process continues in this manner until n objects have been drawn for a sample of observations X_1, X_2, ..., X_n of the characteristic X.
3. After suitable mixing of the objects in the population, n objects are selected one after another without replacing the objects drawn before the next selection. This process also yields a sample of observations X_1, X_2, ..., X_n of the characteristic X.

Notice that sampling technique 2 constitutes sampling with replacement, and technique 3 is sampling without replacement. In the general context of a simple random sample, if objects are drawn in such a way as to ensure that every object currently in the population has an equal chance of being selected, the sampling technique will be called random. Sampling technique 2 is called random sampling with replacement, and technique 3 is called random sampling without replacement. In technique 2 each of the observations X_1, X_2, ..., X_n is a random variable whose probability distribution is the same as that of the population since, before each draw, the population has exactly its original form with all objects drawn earlier replaced. In sampling technique 3 the observations X_1, X_2, ..., X_n are also random variables with marginal distributions the same as that of the population. That is, it can be shown that even though drawn objects are not replaced, the unconditional distribution of X_i is the same as that of the population for all $i = 1, 2, ..., n$.

The basic difference between sampling techniques 2 and 3 is in the notion of independence. In technique 2 the observations X_1, X_2, ..., X_n constitute a set of independent and identically distributed (IID) random variables, since, with the replacement process, no observation is affected by any other. In sampling technique 3, although the observations X_1, X_2, ..., X_n are identically distributed, they are not independent.

Recall that sampling is with replacement in technique 1 even though the population is not made up of tangible objects. In fact, sampling technique 2 is a special case of 1 since the population remains unaffected by each draw. It is of interest to note, however, that random sampling without replacement may be preferred when the number of objects in the population is relatively small.* In such a case, if sampling is done with replacement, it is not unlikely that the same object will be selected more than once. It is for this reason that in legitimate

---

*The reader may recall that this is precisely what constitutes a hypergeometric distribution, as discussed in Section 4.4.

preference surveys, sampling is done without replacement. On the other hand, if the number of objects in a population is extremely large, it is immaterial whether sampling is done with or without replacement. As the population size increases, random sampling without replacement is for all intents and purposes the same as random sampling with replacement.

In our discussion of statistical inference we will assume the existence of a random sample as described by sampling technique 1 and formally defined as follows:

Definition 7.1   If the random variables X_1, X_2, ..., X_n have the same probability (density) function as that of the population distribution, and if their joint probability (density) function is equal to the product of the marginals, then X_1, X_2, ..., X_n are said to be n independent and identically distributed (IID) random variables that constitute a *random sample* from the population.

It is important to emphasize that if statistical inference is the ultimate goal, one must make an honest attempt to obtain a random sample to provide the necessary theoretical basis for the inference. From a practical point of view this is not always easy. For example, many times it is difficult to decide whether identical conditions are being maintained throughout the collection of a sample in scientific experiments. This is especially true when uncontrollable environmental factors may create heterogeneous conditions. However, it remains the responsibility of the experimenter to decide whether an observed sample of data is, by and large, random.

To illustrate sampling from a scientific experiment, suppose one is interested in the concentration level of a certain pollutant at a particular location in a body of water. To observe this, a buoy containing an instrument to measure the concentration level is placed at the location. The instrument is set to record the concentration level for each of n time periods. Thus the observations X_1, X_2, ..., X_n form a sample of the pollutant's concentration level at this location. Before the instrument actually records the concentration level during the ith time period, the observation X_1 is a random variable for $i = 1, 2, ..., n$. The recorded value x_i — the actual numerical value of the observation X_i — is a *realization* of the random variable. At the end of n time periods the actual measurements x_1, x_2, ..., x_n as recorded by the instrument are the realizations, or the sample data, of the corresponding random variables X_1, X_2, ..., X_n. One may ask, Is this truly a random sample? No one can provide a legitimate answer without the benefit of additional information. For example, is the experimenter aware of any events during the sampling period that might cause a significant change in the concentration level of the pollutant? Does the experimenter regard the chosen sampling period to be typical for the concentration level, or might there be some seasonal fluctuations that should be considered? Is instrument error likely to increase with time? Questions such as these should be answered before passing judgment on the randomness of a sample.

In the context of Definition 7.1, the joint probability (density) function of X_1, X_2, ..., X_n is the likelihood function of the sample given by

$$L(\underline{x}; \theta) = \prod_{i=1}^{n} f(x_i; \theta), \tag{7.1}$$

where $\underline{x} = \{x_1, x_2, ..., x_n\}$ denotes the sample data. When the realizations $\underline{x}$ are known, $L(\underline{x}; \theta)$ is a function of the unknown parameter θ. The usefulness of the likelihood function for parameter estimation will be examined in Chapter 8.

Example 7.1 We illustrate the concept of a random sample as given in Definition 7.1 by working the following: Let $X_1, X_2, ..., X_n$ constitute a random sample of n IID random variables from a population whose probability distribution is exponential with density

$$f(x; \theta) = \frac{1}{\theta} \exp(-x/\theta), \qquad 0 < x < \infty.$$

When X_1 is observed and its realization x_1 is recorded,

$$f(x_1; \theta) = \frac{1}{\theta} \exp(-x_1/\theta), \qquad 0 < x_1 < \infty.$$

Now X_2 is observed, and realization x_2 recorded. Because X_1 and X_2 are statistically independent and have the same marginal densities,

$$f(x_2|x_1) = f(x_2; \theta) = \frac{1}{\theta} \exp(-x_2/\theta), \qquad 0 < x_2 < \infty.$$

The joint density function of X_1 and X_2 is

$$f(x_1, x_2; \theta) = f(x_1; \theta) f(x_2; \theta) = \frac{1}{\theta^2} \exp[-(x_1 + x_2)/\theta], \qquad 0 < x_i < \infty, i = 1, 2.$$

It follows, therefore, that for a random sample of size n,

$$L(x_1, x_2, ..., x_n; \theta) = \frac{1}{\theta^n} \exp[-(x_1 + x_2 + \cdots + x_n)/\theta],$$
$$0 < x_i < \infty, i = 1, 2, ..., n.$$

7.3 Sampling Distributions of Statistics

In the introductory remarks of Chapter 1 we noted briefly that sample characteristics called "statistics" are used to make inferences about population characteristics called "parameters." Our objective here is to examine in detail the role that statistics play with regard to inference. In particular, we will develop the notion of a sampling distribution of a statistic, which is perhaps the most important concept in statistical inference.

To place statistics in better perspective we must formally define and discuss a population parameter.

Definition 7.2 A *parameter* is a numerical characterization of a population distribution such that it describes either partially or completely the probability density function of the characteristic of interest.

For example, when we specify the value of the exponential scale parameter θ, we completely describe the probability density function

$$f(x; \theta) = \frac{1}{\theta} \exp(-x/\theta).$$

"Complete description" suggests that any probability statement of interest for this distribution can be made once the value of θ is known. For illustration, if $\theta = 2$, then

$$P(X > 4) = \frac{1}{2} \int_4^\infty \exp(-x/2)dx = 0.1353.$$

On the other hand, if we specify a value for the gamma shape parameter α, the probability density function

$$f(x; \alpha, \theta) = \frac{1}{\Gamma(\alpha)\theta^\alpha} x^{\alpha-1} \exp(-x/\theta)$$

has not been completely described since no mention has been made of the value of the scale parameter θ.

The essence of this is that since parameters are inherent in practically all probability models, without knowledge of their values it is impossible to compute the desired probabilities. It is for this reason that the notion of a statistic and its sampling distribution is so important in statistical inference. That is, parameters or their functions are estimated based on statistics, which are determined from the information contained in a random sample.

Before proceeding with the definition of a statistic, we should note that from a classical (non-Bayesian) point of view, a parameter is always regarded as a fixed and usually unknown constant. From a Bayesian perspective a parameter is always assumed to be a random variable with some probability distribution. Our approach to parameters will be based primarily on the classical point of view, but the Bayesian approach will also be presented for proper balance.

Definition 7.3   A *statistic* is any function of the observable random variables in a sample such that the function does not contain any unknown quantities.

Let the sample $\underline{X} = \{X_1, X_2, ..., X_n\}$ consists of n IID random variables with probability density function $f(x; \theta)$ depending on an unknown parameter θ. Suppose we define functions, such as

$$T_1(\underline{X}) = (X_1 + X_2 + \cdots + X_n)/n,$$

$$T_2(\underline{X}) = (X_1^2 + X_2^2 + \cdots + X_n^2)/n,$$

$$T_3(\underline{X}) = X_1 + X_2,$$

and so on. All of these are statistics because they are completely determined by the random variables of the sample. Generally, let $T = u(\underline{X})$ denote a statistic. Since T is a function of random variables, it is itself a random variable, and its specific value $t = u(\underline{x})$ will be determined once the realizations $\underline{x}$ corresponding to $\underline{X}$ are known. If a statistic T is used to estimate an unknown parameter θ, then T is called an *estimator* of θ, and the specific value t that results from the sample data is called an *estimate* of θ. That is, an estimator is a statistic that identifies the functional mechanism by which an estimate is to be determined once the observations of the sample are realized.

A statistic is substantively different from a parameter. A parameter is a constant, but a statistic is a random variable. Moreover, a value of a parameter completely describes a probability model (assuming a single parameter distribution); no one value of a statistic can play such a role because each value depends on the observations of the particular sample selected. And since we must assume that samples are taken randomly, no one sample is more valid than any other sample that might have been selected.

To illustrate the notion of a statistic, let us solve the following problem: Suppose we are interested in the average life of a certain kind of miniature battery. We are assured that all of the batteries are produced by the same manufacturing process using identical materials. We decide to select at random five batteries from each day of production for 20 days. For each day's sample, the five batteries will be subjected to a life test, and the observed lifetimes will be recorded. The test will terminate when all batteries cease to function. Since the manufacturing process is assumed to be the same throughout the sampling period, this scheme will yield 20 distinct random samples, each containing five independent and identically distributed random variables. Let $\underline{X}_j = \{X_{1j}, X_{2j}, ..., X_{5j}\}$ denote the random variables of the jth sample for $j = 1, 2, ..., 20$, and let $\underline{x}_j = \{x_{1j}, x_{2j}, ..., x_{5j}\}$ be the corresponding observed lifetimes. Consider the statistic

$$T_j = (X_{1j} + X_{2j} + \cdots + X_{5j})/5$$

as an estimator of the average life of the batteries. If we assume that the observed lifetimes are as given in Table 7.1, then for the jth sample there is a realization t_j for the statistic T_j. That is, each day's sample will yield an estimate of the average life of the batteries.

Notice that the estimates in the table for the average life range from 140.8 to 157.2 hours. Thus an inherent variability exists among the estimates. A sample-to-sample variability of any statistic is expected since a statistic is a random variable. In fact, for any statistic there exists what is called its sampling (probability) distribution, which accounts for the inherent variability and provides the necessary means by which a statistic may be evaluated. We now define the sampling distribution of a statistic based on random samples according to Definition 7.1.

Definition 7.4. The *sampling distribution* of a statistic T is the probability distribution of T that would be determined as a result of an infinite number of independent random samples, each of size n, from an underlying population.

Since we are assuming random samples, the distribution of a statistic is a type of joint probability model of independent random variables, each variable

TABLE 7.1   Observed lifetimes (hours) of randomly selected miniature batteries

Sample number	1	2	3	4	5	6	7	8	9	10
	163	159	150	136	136	138	155	158	135	166
	132	144	125	157	146	145	145	150	144	142
	154	139	139	168	158	150	151	153	148	156
	152	146	134	158	154	138	154	151	150	154
	148	144	156	167	156	158	141	138	148	160
Sample average	149.8	146.4	140.8	157.2	150.0	145.8	149.2	150.0	145.0	155.6

Sample number	11	12	13	14	15	16	17	18	19	20
	150	154	148	149	150	147	158	164	153	135
	152	150	166	158	138	151	147	136	160	150
	163	141	148	139	153	161	141	143	156	164
	161	159	149	146	151	142	130	137	142	152
	139	153	154	136	161	149	147	152	156	144
Sample average	153.0	151.4	153.0	145.6	150.6	150.0	144.6	146.4	153.4	149.0

having identical probability density functions. Generally, the sampling distribution of a statistic is not of the same form as the probability density function of the population distribution.

We illustrate the sampling distribution of a statistic from the 20 sample averages given in Table 7.1. Utilizing the methods of Chapter 1, we group the twenty realizations into five classes and determine their relative frequencies, which are listed in Table 7.2.

It is apparent from the relative frequencies that the heaviest concentration of average lifetime is between 147.6 and 151 hours, with average lifetimes below 144 hours or above 154.6 having small likelihoods. It is this type of probability analysis that the sampling distribution of a statistic makes possible, and one that is essential in assessing the risk involved when making inferences.

We turn now to some basic theorems that will enable us to determine the sampling distributions of important statistics, such as the sample mean $\overline{X}$ and the sample variance S^2. The moment generating function will be used frequently because it uniquely determines a probability distribution.

TABLE 7.2   Grouping and relative frequencies for 20 sample means

Class limits	Class frequency	Relative frequency
140.6–144.0	1	0.05
144.1–147.5	6	0.30
147.6–151.0	7	0.35
151.1–154.5	4	0.20
154.6–158.0	2	0.10
Total	20	1.00

Theorem 7.1   Let $X_1, X_2, ..., X_n$ be n independent random variables with moment generating functions $m_{X_1}(t)$, $m_{X_2}(t)$, ..., $m_{X_n}(t)$. If

$$Y = a_1X_1 + a_2X_2 + \cdots + a_nX_n,$$

where $a_1, a_2, ..., a_n$ are constants, then

$$m_Y(t) = m_{X_1}(a_1t)m_{X_2}(a_2t) \cdots m_{X_n}(a_nt).$$

Proof: Using the definition and the assumption of independence, we have

$$m_Y(t) = E\{\exp[t(a_1X_1 + a_2X_2 + \cdots + a_nX_n)]\}$$

$$= E[\exp(ta_1X_1) \exp(ta_2X_2) \cdots \exp(ta_nX_n)]$$

$$= E[\exp(ta_1X_1)]E[\exp(ta_2X_2)] \cdots E[\exp(ta_nX_n)]$$

$$= m_{X_1}(a_1t)m_{X_2}(a_2t) \cdots m_{X_n}(a_nt).$$

Thus the moment generating function of a linear combination of n independent random variables is the product of the individual moment generating functions with arguments equal to the corresponding constant times t.

Theorem 7.2   Let $X_1, X_2, ..., X_n$ be independent normally distributed random variables with means $E(X_i) = \mu_i$ and variances $Var(X_i) = \sigma_i^2$ for $i = 1, 2, ..., n$. If

$$Y = a_1X_1 + a_2X_2 + \cdots + a_nX_n,$$

where $a_1, a_2, ..., a_n$ are constants, then Y is a normally distributed random variable with mean

$$E(Y) = a_1\mu_1 + a_2\mu_2 + \cdots + a_n\mu_n$$

and variance

$$Var(Y) = a_1^2\sigma_1^2 + a_2^2\sigma_2^2 + \cdots + a_n^2\sigma_n^2.$$

Proof: Since X_i is normally distributed, its moment generating function is

$$m_{X_i}(t) = \exp[\mu_i t + (\sigma_i^2 t^2)/2].$$

From Theorem 7.1 it follows that the moment generating function of Y is

$$m_Y(t) = m_{X_1}(a_1t)m_{X_2}(a_2t) \cdots m_{X_n}(a_nt)$$

$$= \exp[\mu_1 a_1 t + (a_1^2\sigma_1^2 t^2)/2] \cdots \exp[\mu_n a_n t + (a_n^2\sigma_n^2 t^2)/2]$$

$$= \exp\left[t \sum_{i=1}^{n} a_i\mu_i + \left(t^2 \sum_{i=1}^{n} a_i^2\sigma_i^2 \right) \bigg/ 2 \right].$$

Hence Y is normally distributed with mean $\sum_{i=1}^{n} a_i\mu_i$ and variance $\sum_{i=1}^{n} a_i^2\sigma_i^2$.

From Theorem 7.2 it is seen that if $a_i = 1$ for $i = 1, 2, \ldots n$, then the sum of independent normally distributed random variables is also normally distributed with mean equal to the sum of the individual means and variance equal to the sum of the individual variances. This result is often referred to as the *additive property* of the normal distribution. It should be noted that the assumption of normality is not necessary to obtain the formulas for the mean and variance of Y in Theorem 7.2. In fact, based on Theorem 6.1, if $X_1, X_2, \ldots, X_n$ are n IID random variables with means $E(X_i) = \mu_i$ and variances $Var(X_i) = \sigma_i^2$, $i = 1, 2, \ldots, n$, then for $Y = a_1X_1 + a_2X_2 + \cdots + a_nX_n$,

$$E(Y) = \sum_{i=1}^{n} a_i\mu_i$$

and (7.2)

$$Var(Y) = \sum_{i=1}^{n} a_i^2\sigma_i^2,$$

where once again $a_1, a_2, \ldots, a_n$ are any constants.

Some interesting practical applications of Theorem 7.2 arise. The following is a typical example.

Example 7.2   Assume for a shaft and a mating bearing that the external diameter of the shaft X_1 and the internal diameter of the bearing X_2 are independent normally distributed random variables with means $E(X_1) = 3.25$ cm, $E(X_2) = 3.3$ cm, and standard deviations $s.d.(X_1) = 0.005$ cm, $s.d.(X_2) = 0.006$ cm, respectively. Of interest is the difference between X_2 and X_1, the clearance between the internal diameter of the bearing and the external diameter of the shaft. Let the clearance be denoted by Y, where $Y = X_2 - X_1$. If during assembly there is a random pairing of shafts and bearings, determine the clearance value $y_{0.004}$ such that the probability of Y being less than this value is 0.004.

Since X_1 and X_2 are independent, Theorem 7.2 applies by letting $a_1 = -1$ and $a_2 = 1$. Thus

$$E(Y) = (1)E(X_2) + (-1)E(X_1) = 0.05,$$

and

$$s.d.(Y) = \sqrt{(1)^2(0.006)^2 + (-1)^2(0.005)^2} = 0.00781.$$

That is, $Y \sim N(0.05, 0.00781)$. Then

$$P(Y < y_{0.004}) = 0.004$$

or

$$P[Z < (y_{0.004} - 0.05)/0.00781] = 0.004,$$

but

$$P[Z < -2.65] = 0.004;$$

thus

$$(y_{0.004} - 0.05)/0.00781 = -2.65,$$

and $y_{0.004} = 0.0293$ cm. Accordingly a clearance of no less than 0.0293 cm is required for the given conditions.

7.4 The Sampling Distribution of $\overline{X}$

One of the most important statistics is the mean of a set of independent and identically distributed random variables. This statistic is important because it plays a premier role in decision-making problems for unknown population means. Let a random sample $X_1, X_2, ..., X_n$ consist of n IID random variables such that $E(X_i) = \mu$ and $Var(X_i) = \sigma^2$ for all $i = 1, 2, ..., n$. Then the statistic

$$\overline{X} = (X_1 + X_2 + \cdots + X_n)/n \tag{7.3}$$

is defined to be the mean of the n IID random variables, or simply the sample mean. Notice that once the realizations $x_1, x_2, ..., x_n$ of $X_1, X_2, ..., X_n$, respectively, are known, the realization $\bar{x}$ of $\overline{X}$ is determined by averaging the sample data. If we let $a_i = 1/n$, $i = 1, 2, ..., n$ in (7.2), then the expected value and variance of $\overline{X}$ are

$$E(\overline{X}) = \sum_{i=1}^{n} \frac{1}{n} \mu = n(\mu/n) = \mu \tag{7.4}$$

and

$$Var(\overline{X}) = \sum_{i=1}^{n} \frac{1}{n^2} \sigma^2 = n(\sigma^2/n^2) = \sigma^2/n, \tag{7.5}$$

respectively, where μ and σ^2 are the mean and variance of the population distribution from which the random sample was drawn. The important thing to remember about this result is that it holds regardless of the probability distribution of the underlying population as long as it has a finite variance. From (7.5) the standard deviation of $\overline{X}$ is seen to be

$$s.d.(\overline{X}) = \sigma/\sqrt{n}, \tag{7.6}$$

which is sometimes referred to as the *standard error of the mean*.

Notice that as the sample size increases, the standard deviation, and thus the variability, of $\overline{X}$ decreases. That is, as the sample size increases, the precision of the sample mean for estimating the population mean increases. For example, if a random sample of $n = 25$ is drawn, $\overline{X}$ would have $\sqrt{25} = 5$ times more precision in estimating the population mean than would a single observation. This is a highly advantageous property of the statistic $\overline{X}$ because it assures that for a relatively large sample size, the realization of $\overline{X}$ is expected to be very close to the population mean μ. As a further illustration, suppose we compute the standard deviation of $\overline{X}$ for various values of n by assuming that $\sigma = 10$ and then plot the points, as indicated in Figure 7.1. By the nature of (7.6), the drop in the standard deviation of $\overline{X}$ is rather substantial as n takes on larger values, but as n increases beyond 30 or 40, the drop tapers off. In essence, therefore, a very large sample size is not cost-effective in making inferences about μ based on $\overline{X}$.

FIGURE 7.1 Typical behavior of the standard deviation of $\overline{X}$ as a function of the sample size

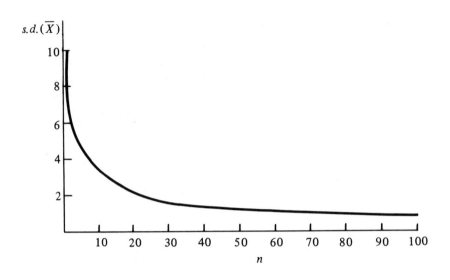

We now state and prove a theorem concerning the sampling distribution of $\overline{X}$ if a random sample consists of n independent normally distributed random variables.

Theorem 7.3   Let the random sample X_1, X_2, ..., X_n consist of n independent normally distributed random variables with means $E(X_i) = \mu$ and variances $Var(X_i) = \sigma^2$, $i = 1, 2, ..., n$. Then the distribution of the sample mean $\overline{X}$ is normal with mean μ and variance σ^2/n.

Proof: This theorem is really a corollary of Theorem 7.2. That is, let $a_i = 1/n$; since the means and variances are the same, the moment generating function of $\overline{X}$ is

$$m\overline{X}(t) = \exp\left[t \sum_{i=1}^{n} \frac{1}{n}\mu + \left(t^2 \sum_{i=1}^{n} \frac{1}{n^2}\sigma^2 \right) \bigg/ 2 \right]$$

$$= \exp[\mu t + (t^2\sigma^2)/2n],$$

which is seen to be the moment generating function of a normally distributed random variable with mean μ and variance σ^2/n. Thus the probability density function of $\overline{X}$ when sampling from a population whose distribution is normal is

$$f(\overline{x}; \mu, \sigma/\sqrt{n}) = \frac{\sqrt{n}}{\sqrt{2\pi}\,\sigma} \exp\left[-\frac{n(\overline{x} - \mu)^2}{2\sigma^2} \right], \qquad -\infty < \overline{x} < \infty. \qquad (7.7)$$

Example 7.3   A filling machine is set to pour 500 grams of cereal in a box container. Assume that the amount of cereal being poured in each box is a normally distributed random variable with mean 500 grams and standard deviation 20 grams. To check that the average weight of cereal poured is being maintained at 500 grams, a random sample of 25 boxes is selected periodically and the contents of each box are weighed. The plant manager has decided to stop the process and look for possible malfunction any time a sample average value is either greater than 510 grams or less than 490 grams. Determine the probability of stopping the process.

Let $X_1, X_2, ..., X_{25}$ be 25 independent normally distributed random variables representing the amount of cereal in the boxes of a given random sample. By assumption $X_i \sim N(500, 20)$, $i = 1, 2, ..., 25$. Then from Theorem 7.3 the sample average $\overline{X}$ is also normally distributed with mean 500 and standard deviation $20/\sqrt{25} = 4$. The desired probability is seen to be one minus the probability that $\overline{X}$ falls between 490 and 510 grams; thus

$$P(\text{Stopping the process}) = 1 - P(490 < \overline{X} < 510)$$

$$= 1 - P\left(\frac{490 - 500}{4} < Z < \frac{510 - 500}{4}\right)$$

$$= 1 - P(-2.5 < Z < 2.5)$$

$$= 0.0124.$$

Example 7.4   Show that if $X_1, X_2, ..., X_n$ are n independent exponentially distributed random variables with probability density function

$$f(x; \theta) = \frac{1}{\theta}\exp(-x/\theta) \qquad x > 0,$$

the distribution of $\overline{X}$ is gamma.

Recall that the moment generating function of an exponentially distributed random variable is $(1 - \theta t)^{-1}$. Thus, for each X_i of the sample,

$$m_{X_i}(t) = (1 - \theta t)^{-1}.$$

It follows from Theorem 7.1 with $a_i = 1/n$, $i = 1, 2, ..., n$, that the moment generating function of the sample mean $\overline{X}$ is

$$m_{\overline{X}}(t) = m_{X_1}(t/n)m_{X_2}(t/n) \cdots m_{X_n}(t/n)$$

$$= [1 - (\theta t/n)]^{-1}[1 - (\theta t/n)]^{-1} \cdots [1 - (\theta t/n)]^{-1}$$

$$= [1 - (\theta t/n)]^{-n}.$$

But this is the moment generating function of a gamma distribution with shape parameter n and scale parameter θ/n. Accordingly, the probability density of $\overline{X}$ when sampling from a population whose probability distribution is the exponential is

$$f(\bar{x}; n, \theta/n) = \frac{n^n}{\Gamma(n)\theta^n} \bar{x}^{n-1} \exp(-n\bar{x}/\theta), \qquad \bar{x} > 0. \tag{7.8}$$

Notice that if we replace α with n and θ with θ/n in expressions (5.47) and (5.48), we obtain

$$E(\bar{X}) = n\frac{\theta}{n} = \theta \tag{7.9}$$

and

$$Var(\bar{X}) = n\frac{\theta^2}{n^2} = \theta^2/n, \tag{7.10}$$

as we should since θ and θ^2 are the mean and variance, respectively, of an exponentially distributed random variable.

Recall from Section 5.5 that if the shape parameter of a gamma distribution is large, probabilities involving a gamma random variable are adequately approximated by a normal distribution. Since $\bar{X}$ is gamma distributed with mean θ and standard deviation $\theta/\sqrt{n}$ when sampling from an exponential distribution with parameter θ, then for large n,

$$Z = \frac{\bar{X} - \theta}{\theta/\sqrt{n}} \tag{7.11}$$

is approximately $N(0, 1)$.

Example 7.5   Based on past experiments, the life of an electrical component is exponentially distributed with mean life of 100 hours. If a random sample of 16 components is drawn from the process producing them, what is the probability that the sample mean life will be more than 120 hours?

From (7.9) and (7.10), the mean of $\bar{X}$ is 100 hours and the standard deviation is $100/\sqrt{16} = 25$ hours. Assuming the shape parameter $n = 16$ is sufficiently large to use the approximation given by (7.11), we have

$$P(\bar{X} > 120) = P\left(Z > \frac{120 - 100}{25}\right) = 0.2119.$$

For comparison, the probability that $\bar{X} > 120$ can be computed directly using the incomplete gamma function $I(u, p)$ as defined by (5.55); in this case $u = (16)(120)/100\sqrt{16}$ and $p = 16 - 1$. Thus

$$P(\bar{X} > 120) = 1 - I(4.8, 15) = 0.2021.$$

So far, we have established that the sampling distribution of $\bar{X}$ is normal when sampling from a normal population and gamma when sampling from an exponential population. What if we cannot specify the probability distribution from which we are sampling? That is, what is the (approximate) sampling distribution of $\bar{X}$, irrespective of the distribution of the random variables of the sample? To gain insight about the sampling distribution of $\bar{X}$ when the underlying probability model is not specified, consider a simulation study in which random values are generated using the procedures given in Section 5.9.

Suppose we generate 50 samples of size $n = 10$ each from a Poisson distribution with parameter $\lambda = 2$. For each sample we compute the sample mean, producing 50 realizations of the statistic $\overline{X}$. We group these values and determine their relative frequencies. We repeat the process but with a sample size of $n = 40$ rather than 10. Once again we repeat the process, but now, instead of generating values from a Poisson, we generate random values from a uniform distribution on the interval (0, 1). Figure 7.2 depicts the relative frequency distribution for each of the four cases. Notice that when $n = 10$, no typical pattern in the distribution of $\overline{X}$ emerges. However, when $n = 40$, the distribution of $\overline{X}$ definitely assumes a bell shape and thus resembles a normal distribution for both the Poisson and the uniform models.

Based on this limited simulation study, it appears that for relatively large n the distribution of $\overline{X}$ is approximately normal. In fact, no matter what type of

FIGURE 7.2 Relative frequency distributions of $\overline{X}$ when sampling from a Poisson or a uniform distribution for $n = 10$ and $n = 40$

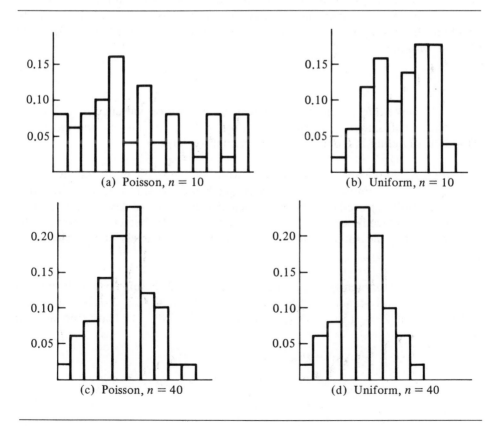

probability model we are sampling from, as long as its mean and variance exist, the sampling distribution of $\overline{X}$ will be approximately $N(\mu, \sigma/\sqrt{n})$ for large n.

This constitutes one of the most important theorems in statistical inference, known as the *Central Limit Theorem*.

Theorem 7.4   Let $X_1, X_2, ..., X_n$ be n IID random variables with an unspecified probability distribution, and having a finite mean μ and a finite variance σ^2. The sample average $\overline{X} = (X_1 + X_2 + \cdots + X_n)/n$ has a distribution with mean μ and variance σ^2/n that tends to normal as n tends to ∞. In other words, the random variable $(\overline{X} - \mu)/(\sigma/\sqrt{n})$ has a limiting standard normal distribution. (An outline of the proof of this theorem is given in an appendix to this chapter.)

The essence of the Central Limit Theorem is that for sufficiently large n, the distribution of $(\overline{X} - \mu)/(\sigma/\sqrt{n})$ is approximately normal with mean zero and standard deviation one, irrespective of the model from which the random sample is drawn. It should be noted that if the underlying model is nearly like a normal distribution — that is, if it is symmetrical and relatively concentrated around the point of symmetry — the normal approximation will be good even for rather small sample sizes. On the other hand, if the underlying model is unlike the normal — for example, if it is highly skewed — the normal approximation will be good only for relatively large values of n. In most instances it is safe to conclude that the approximation is adequate as long as $n > 30$. Therefore, the random variable

$$Z = \frac{\overline{X} - \mu}{\sigma/\sqrt{n}} \tag{7.12}$$

is used to make inferences about μ when the population variance σ^2 is known. Z is $N(0, 1)$ if sampling is from a normal distribution and is approximately $N(0, 1)$ if sampling is from some other model for large n.

Example 7.6   Suppose the number of barrels of crude oil produced by a well each day is a random variable with an unspecified distribution. If the production for 64 randomly selected days is observed and if the standard deviation in number of barrels produced per day is known to be $\sigma = 16$ barrels, determine the probability that the sample mean will be within four barrels of the true mean production per day.

Since n is sufficiently large, the distribution of $\overline{X}$ is approximately normal with mean μ and standard deviation $\sigma/\sqrt{n} = 16/\sqrt{64} = 2$. Equivalently, the distribution of $Z = (\overline{X} - \mu)/2$ is approximately $N(0, 1)$. Thus, the desired probability is

$$P(|\overline{X} - \mu| < 4) = P(\mu - 4 < \overline{X} < \mu + 4)$$
$$= P[(\mu - 4 - \mu)/2 < Z < (\mu + 4 - \mu)/2]$$
$$= P(-2 < Z < 2)$$
$$= 0.9544.$$

7.5   The Sampling Distribution of S^2

Another important statistic used for inferences concerning population variances is the sample variance, denoted by S^2. Recall that S^2 measures variability and indicates spread or dispersion among observations. Since dispersion is as important a consideration as central tendency, the importance of S^2 for inferences about σ^2 is comparable to that of $\overline{X}$ for inferences about μ.

We will develop the sampling distribution of S^2 when sampling from a normal population. Initially, it will be necessary to assume that μ is known and σ^2 is not. In this context S^2 is defined by

$$S^2 = \sum_{i=1}^{n} (X_i - \mu)^2/n, \tag{7.13}$$

where $X_1, X_2, \ldots, X_n$ constitute a random sample from a normal distribution with known mean μ and unknown variance σ^2. To determine a sampling distribution that will allow inferences to be made about σ^2 based on S^2 as defined by (7.13), we state and prove the following theorem.

Theorem 7.5   Let $X_1, X_2, \ldots, X_n$ constitute a random sample from a normal distribution with mean μ and variance σ^2. The distribution of the random variable

$$Y = \sum_{i=1}^{n} (X_i - \mu)^2/\sigma^2$$

is chi-square with n degrees of freedom.

Proof: Since $X_i \sim N(\mu, \sigma)$, $i = 1, 2, \ldots, n$, $Z_i = (X_i - \mu)/\sigma$ defines n independent standard normal random variables. Thus

$$Y = \sum_{i=1}^{n} Z_i^2.$$

From Theorem 7.1,

$$m_Y(t) = m_{Z_1^2}(t) m_{Z_2^2}(t) \cdots m_{Z_n^2}(t)$$

$$= (1 - 2t)^{-1/2}(1 - 2t)^{-1/2} \cdots (1 - 2t)^{-1/2},$$

since the square of a standard normal is chi-square distributed with one degree of freedom (see Example 5.14). Thus

$$m_Y(t) = (1 - 2t)^{-n/2},$$

which is the moment generating function of a chi-square distribution with n degrees of freedom. Accordingly, $Y \sim X_n^2$.

Example 7.7   Consider some physical measurement of a precision instrument whose variability is of interest. Assume that based on past experiences, the physical measurement is a normally distributed random variable with mean 10 units and standard deviation 0.1 units. If a random sample of size 25 is taken from the manufacturing process producing such instruments, what is the probability that the value of the sample variance will exceed 0.014 squared units?

Based on Theorem 7.5, the probability that $S^2 > 0.014$ when sampling from $N(10, 0.1)$ with $n = 25$ is the same as

$$P(Y > ns^2/\sigma^2) = P[Y > (25)(0.014)/0.01]$$

$$= P(Y > 35)$$

$$= 1 - P(Y \leq 35)$$

where $Y \sim X_{25}^2$. From Table E of the Appendix it is seen that $P(Y \leq 35)$ is approximately 0.9; thus

$$P(Y > 35) \approx 0.1,$$

and the probability that a sample variance value will exceed 0.014 squared units is about 0.1 for the stated conditions.

From a practical point of view the sample variance as defined by (7.13) is of little use since it is extremely rare to know the population mean μ. Accordingly, if we are sampling from a normal distribution with unknown mean μ and variance σ^2, the sample variance is defined to be

$$S^2 = \sum_{i=1}^{n} (X_i - \overline{X})^2/(n - 1). \tag{7.14}$$

In Chapter 8 we will see why the divisor $(n - 1)$ is used. The replacement of the unknown μ by the sample mean $\overline{X}$ gives rise to the presence of another statistic in the definition of S^2. Thus to determine the sampling distribution of S^2, as defined by (7.14) and based on a random sample from a normal distribution, we must also account for the sample average $\overline{X}$. As it turns out, the sampling distribution of $(n - 1)S^2/\sigma^2$ is also chi-square but with $n - 1$ degrees of freedom. We will show this by first proving a useful theorem involving the addition of two independent chi-square random variables and then by expressing (7.14) in an equivalent form to take advantage of this theorem.

Theorem 7.6   If X_1 and X_2 are two independent chi-square distributed random variables with ν_1 and ν_2 degrees of freedom, respectively, then

$$Y = X_1 + X_2$$

is also chi-square distributed with $\nu_1 + \nu_2$ degrees of freedom.

Proof: From Theorem 7.1, the moment generating function of Y is

$$m_Y(t) = m_{X_1}(t)m_{X_2}(t)$$

$$= (1 - 2t)^{-\nu_1/2}(1 - 2t)^{-\nu_2/2}$$

$$= (1 - 2t)^{-(\nu_1 + \nu_2)/2},$$

which is the moment generating function of a chi-square random variable with $\nu_1 + \nu_2$ degrees of freedom.

Now to deduce the sampling distribution of $(n - 1)S^2/\sigma^2$, it is seen from (7.14) that

$$(n - 1)S^2 = \sum_{i=1}^{n} (X_i - \overline{X})^2;$$

but

$$\sum_{i=1}^{n} (X_i - \overline{X})^2 = \sum_{i=1}^{n} (X_i - \mu - \overline{X} + \mu)^2$$

$$= \sum_{i=1}^{n} [(X_i - \mu) - (\overline{X} - \mu)]^2$$

$$= \sum_{i=1}^{n} [(X_i - \mu)^2 - 2(X_i - \mu)(\overline{X} - \mu) + (\overline{X} - \mu)^2]$$

$$= \sum_{i=1}^{n} (X_i - \mu)^2 - 2(\overline{X} - \mu) \sum_{i=1}^{n} (X_i - \mu) + n(\overline{X} - \mu)^2$$

$$= \sum_{i=1}^{n} (X_i - \mu)^2 - 2(\overline{X} - \mu)n(\overline{X} - \mu) + n(\overline{X} - \mu)^2$$

$$= \sum_{i=1}^{n} (X_i - \mu)^2 - n(\overline{X} - \mu)^2.$$

Thus

$$(n - 1)S^2 + n(\overline{X} - \mu)^2 = \sum_{i=1}^{n} (X_i - \mu)^2.$$

Dividing both sides by the population variance σ^2 we have

$$\frac{(n - 1)S^2}{\sigma^2} + \frac{n(\overline{X} - \mu)^2}{\sigma^2} = \frac{\sum_{i=1}^{n} (X_i - \mu)^2}{\sigma^2},$$

or

$$\frac{(n - 1)S^2}{\sigma^2} + \left(\frac{\overline{X} - \mu}{\sigma/\sqrt{n}}\right)^2 = \frac{\sum_{i=1}^{n} (X_i - \mu)^2}{\sigma^2}. \tag{7.15}$$

From Theorem 7.5, $\sum_{i=1}^{n} (X_i - \mu)^2/\sigma^2$ is chi-square distributed with n degrees of freedom. Similarly, $[(\overline{X} - \mu)/\sigma/\sqrt{n}]^2$ is chi-square distributed with one degree of freedom since $(\overline{X} - \mu)/(\sigma/\sqrt{n})$ is $N(0, 1)$. Therefore, if we assume that $(n - 1)S^2/\sigma^2$ and $[(\overline{X} - \mu)/\sigma/\sqrt{n}]^2$ are independent random variables, then from Theorem 7.6 the distribution of $(n - 1)S^2/\sigma^2$, when sampling from a population whose distribution is normal with unknown mean and variance, is chi-square with $n - 1$ degrees of freedom. For proof of independence the reader is referred to [3]. The probability density function of $Y = (n - 1)S^2/\sigma^2$ follows from (5.58) and is given by

$$f(y; n-1) = \begin{cases} \dfrac{1}{\Gamma[(n-1)/2]2^{(n-1)/2}}\, y^{[(n-1)/2]-1}\, \exp(-y/2) & y > 0, \\ \\ 0 & \text{elsewhere.} \end{cases}$$ (7.16)

Notice that since $Y \sim X^2_{n-1}$, $E(Y) = n - 1$ and $Var(Y) = 2(n - 1)$. In addition, since $Y = (n - 1)S^2/\sigma^2$, $S^2 = \sigma^2 Y/(n - 1)$. It follows, therefore, that

$$E(S^2) = E[\sigma^2 Y/(n - 1)] = \frac{\sigma^2}{(n - 1)} E(Y) = \sigma^2,$$ (7.17)

and

$$Var(S^2) = Var[\sigma^2 Y/(n - 1)] = \frac{\sigma^4}{(n - 1)^2} Var(Y) = \frac{2\sigma^4}{n - 1}.$$ (7.18)

7.6   The Student's *t* Distribution

Recall from Section 7.5 that when sampling from a normal distribution with known standard deviation σ, the distribution of $Z = (\overline{X} - \mu)/(\sigma/\sqrt{n})$ is $N(0, 1)$. From a practical point of view, the requirement that σ be known precludes making inferences about μ because usually the population standard deviation is not known. Given the availability of a random sample, the logical thing to do in such a case is to replace σ with an estimate such as s, a value of the sample standard deviation S. Unfortunately, when this is done, the distribution of $(\overline{X} - \mu)/(S/\sqrt{n})$ is not $N(0, 1)$, even when sampling from a normal distribution. However, it is possible to determine the exact sampling distribution of $(\overline{X} - \mu)/(S/\sqrt{n})$ when sampling from $N(\mu, \sigma)$, with both μ and σ^2 unknown. To this end we examine the theoretical aspects of what is known as the Student's *t* distribution.*

Let us assume that we are performing an experiment in which we observe two independent random variables X and Z; X is chi-square distributed with ν degrees of freedom, and Z is normally distributed with mean zero and standard deviation 1. Let another random variable T be a function of X and Z in such a way that

$$T = \frac{Z}{\sqrt{X/\nu}}.$$ (7.19)

That is, T is defined to be the ratio of a standard normal to the square root of a chi-square divided by its degrees of freedom. The set of all possible values of the random variable T is in the interval $(-\infty, \infty)$ since the values of Z are in this interval and the values of X are positive. The value

$$t = \frac{z}{\sqrt{x/\nu}}$$

---

*The *t* distribution was developed in 1908 by W. S. Gosset, who published his work under the pen name "Student."

is said to be a value of a Student's *t* random variable. This leads to the following theorem.

Theorem 7.7 Let Z be a standard normal random variable, and let X be a chi-square random variable with ν degrees of freedom. If Z and X are independent, then the random variable

$$T = \frac{Z}{\sqrt{X/\nu}}$$

has a Student's *t* distribution with ν degrees of freedom and a probability density given by

$$f(t; \nu) = \frac{\Gamma[(\nu + 1)/2]}{\sqrt{\pi\nu}\,\Gamma(\nu/2)}[1 + (t^2/\nu)]^{-(\nu+1)/2}, \qquad -\infty < t < \infty, \quad \nu > 0. \quad (7.20)$$

The derivation of the Student's *t* density function is given in an appendix to this chapter.

From (7.20) it is seen that the parameter of the *t* distribution is ν, which, as in the chi-square, is called the degrees of freedom. For any $\nu > 0$, the *t* distribution is symmetrical about zero, and the density function achieves its maximum value when $t = 0$. As is evident from Figure 7.3, the shape of the Student's *t* density is very similar to that of the standard normal, with the *t* density having wider tails. In fact, as the degrees of freedom become large, the Student's *t* distribution approaches the standard normal.

The expected value of T can be shown to be

$$E(T) = 0 \qquad \nu > 1, \tag{7.21}$$

and the variance is

$$Var(T) = \nu/(\nu - 2) \qquad \nu > 2. \tag{7.22}$$

FIGURE 7.3 Comparison of the standard normal and Student's *t* densities

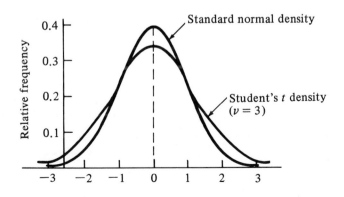

In Table F of the Appendix are found quantile values $t_{1-\alpha,\nu}$ such that

$$P(T \leq t_{1-\alpha,\nu}) = \int_{-\infty}^{t_{1-\alpha,\nu}} f(t; \nu)dt = 1 - \alpha, \qquad 0 \leq \alpha \leq 1, \qquad (7.23)$$

for selected cumulative proportions $1 - \alpha$ and values of ν. For example, if $\nu = 15$,

$$P(T \leq t_{0.90,15}) = P(T \leq 1.341) = 0.90,$$

$$P(T \leq t_{0.95,15}) = P(T \leq 1.753) = 0.95,$$

$$P(T \leq t_{0.99,15}) = P(T \leq 2.602) = 0.99.$$

Since the Student's t distribution is symmetrical around zero, for $\alpha > 0.5$ the quantile values $t_{1-\alpha,\nu}$ will be negative but with magnitudes identical to the corresponding values on the right side. Thus for $\nu = 15$,

$$P(T \leq t_{0.10,15}) = P(T \leq -1.341) = 0.10,$$

$$P(T \leq t_{0.05,15}) = P(T \leq -1.753) = 0.05,$$

$$P(T \leq t_{0.01,15}) = P(T \leq -2.602) = 0.01.$$

To illustrate the similarity of the Student's t distribution to the standard normal for relatively large values of ν, Table 7.3 compares right-side quantile t values to the corresponding standard normal values for increasing values of ν. For $\alpha = 0.1$ or 0.05, the agreement is within approximately 0.05 units, even for ν as low as 30. In fact, many authors suggest that from a practical point of view there is little to be gained by using the Student's t distribution instead of the standard normal as long as $\nu \geq 30$.

Recall that to make inferences about μ when sampling from a normal distribution with mean and variance unknown, we need to determine the distribution of $(\overline{X} - \mu)/(S/\sqrt{n})$. When sampling from $N(\mu, \sigma)$ we know from Theorem 7.3 that the distribution of $(\overline{X} - \mu)/(\sigma/\sqrt{n})$ is $N(0, 1)$. For the same condition, we know from (7.15) and Theorem 7.6 that the distribution of $(n - 1)S^2/\sigma^2$ is chi-square with $n - 1$ degrees of freedom. Since $\overline{X}$ and S^2 can be shown to be independent, it follows from Theorem 7.7 that the distribution of

$$\frac{\dfrac{\overline{X} - \mu}{\sigma/\sqrt{n}}}{\sqrt{\dfrac{(n - 1)S^2/\sigma^2}{(n - 1)}}} = \frac{\overline{X} - \mu}{\sigma/\sqrt{n}} \cdot \frac{\sigma}{\sqrt{S^2}},$$

TABLE 7.3 Comparison of quantile values of Student's t and standard normal distributions

α	$t_{1-\alpha,\,20}$	$t_{1-\alpha,\,30}$	$t_{1-\alpha,\,40}$	$t_{1-\alpha,\,50}$	$z_{1-\alpha}$
0.10	1.325	1.310	1.303	1.299	1.282
0.05	1.725	1.697	1.684	1.676	1.645
0.01	2.528	2.457	2.423	2.403	2.326

or

$$T = \frac{\overline{X} - \mu}{S/\sqrt{n}},$$ (7.24)

is Student's t with $n - 1$ degrees of freedom.

Example 7.8 The Environmental Protection Agency has given an average highway-miles-per-gallon rating of 45 to a particular subcompact car. An independent consumer organization has purchased one of these cars and has tested it to verify the EPA rating. The car was driven for a distance of 100 miles on each of 25 different occasions. Each time the actual miles per gallon achieved during the trip was recorded. For the 25 trials the average and standard deviation turned out to be 43.5 and 2.5 miles per gallon, respectively. If we assume that the actual highway miles per gallon for this car is a normal random variable, is there reason to doubt the EPA average rating based on this test?

This problem illustrates some of the practical difficulties one can encounter in implementing the notion of random sampling. Ideally, 25 cars of the same make, model, and engine configuration should have been selected at random from the assembly process so that the gasoline consumption for each would be regarded as a random variable. However, in this and many cases, a true random sample would be prohibitively expensive. At any rate, whether the observed information verifies the EPA rating must be determined based on probability. That is, if μ were really equal to 45 miles per gallon, what is the probability that by chance alone we would observe a value of $\overline{X}$ of no more than 43.5 miles per gallon based on a sample of size 25 and an estimate of σ of 2.5?
From (7.24), it is seen that

$$t = \frac{\overline{x} - \mu}{s/\sqrt{n}} = \frac{43.5 - 45}{2.5/\sqrt{25}}$$

$$= -3$$

is a value of a Student's t distribution with 24 degrees of freedom. In Table F of the Appendix we see that $P(T \leq -3) < 0.005$. That is, if the true mean is 45, the probability of observing a value of T of no more than -3 units is less than 0.005. Either we have observed something that has a chance of less than 5 in 1000 of occurring, or μ is really less than 45. In such a situation we are likely to choose the second explanation.

7.7 The Distribution of the Difference Between Two Sample Means

Often the need arises to compare the means of two distinct distributions. For example, suppose we are interested in comparing the average lifetimes of the Mears and Sawbuck and the J. C. Nickel "48-month" automobile batteries.

Presumably the batteries sold by the two retailers are produced by different companies and possibly manufactured to different specifications. For each make we assume that there is a distinct distribution that accounts for the lifetimes of the batteries.

Let X be a random variable representing the life of a 48-month battery from Mears and Sawbuck such that $X \sim N(\mu_X, \sigma)$. Similarly, let Y be the corresponding random variable for J. C. Nickel batteries such that $Y \sim N(\mu_Y, \sigma)$, and assume that X and Y are independent. Notice that the variances of X and Y are assumed to be the same. Now suppose a random sample of n_X batteries is selected from Mears and Sawbuck, and a random sample of n_Y batteries is chosen from J. C. Nickel. The batteries of the two samples are placed in identical life tests where all identifiable external factors are controlled. Differences in the observed lifetimes within each brand will be due only to the inherent variability of the manufacturing process that produced the batteries. Of interest is an inferential statement concerning the difference $\mu_X - \mu_Y$ between the two unknown means.

A viable approach to this problem is to base the inference on the difference between the sample means $\overline{X}$ and $\overline{Y}$. Accordingly, it is necessary to determine the distribution of $\overline{X} - \overline{Y}$ when sampling from two independent normal populations with equal variances. If we assume the common variance σ^2 is known, from Theorem 7.3 the distribution of $\overline{X}$ is normal with mean μ_X and variance σ^2/n_X. The distribution of $\overline{Y}$ is also normal but with mean μ_Y and variance σ^2/n_Y. Since $\overline{X}$ and $\overline{Y}$ are independent normally distributed random variables, by letting $a_1 = 1$ and $a_2 = -1$ in Theorem 7.2 the distribution of $\overline{X} - \overline{Y}$ is normal with mean $\mu_X - \mu_Y$ and variance $(\sigma^2/n_X) + (\sigma^2/n_Y) = \sigma^2(1/n_X + 1/n_Y)$. It follows, therefore, that if σ^2 is known, the distribution of

$$Z = \frac{\overline{X} - \overline{Y} - (\mu_X - \mu_Y)}{\sigma\sqrt{\dfrac{1}{n_X} + \dfrac{1}{n_Y}}} \tag{7.25}$$

is $N(0, 1)$. Expression (7.25) provides an appropriate means by which an inference can be made about the difference of two population means when sampling from two independent normal distributions with equal variances.

In the development of (7.25) we assumed that σ^2 was known. It is unlikely, however, for one to know σ^2 in a real environment. Thus once again we seek the distribution of $\overline{X} - \overline{Y}$ when sampling from two independent normal populations with equal but unknown variances. For each of the two random samples we can define the sample variances S_X^2 and S_Y^2 as given by (7.14). Since $(n_X - 1)S_X^2/\sigma^2$ and $(n_Y - 1)S_Y^2/\sigma^2$ are two independent chi-square random variables, with $n_X - 1$ and $n_Y - 1$ degrees of freedom, respectively, from Theorem 7.6 the distribution of

$$W = \frac{(n_X - 1)S_X^2}{\sigma^2} + \frac{(n_Y - 1)S_Y^2}{\sigma^2} \tag{7.26}$$

is also chi-square with $n_X + n_Y - 2$ degrees of freedom. It follows from (7.19) that the ratio of Z in (7.25) to the square root of W divided by its degrees of freedom has a Student's t distribution with $n_X + n_Y - 2$ degrees of freedom. That is,

$$\frac{[\overline{X} - \overline{Y} - (\mu_X - \mu_Y)]/\sigma\sqrt{\dfrac{1}{n_X} + \dfrac{1}{n_Y}}}{\sqrt{\dfrac{[(n_X - 1)S_X^2 + (n_Y - 1)S_Y^2]/\sigma^2}{n_X + n_Y - 2}}} = \frac{\overline{X} - \overline{Y} - (\mu_X - \mu_Y)}{\sqrt{\dfrac{(n_X - 1)S_X^2 + (n_Y - 1)S_Y^2}{n_X + n_Y - 2}\left(\dfrac{1}{n_X} + \dfrac{1}{n_Y}\right)}},$$

or

$$T = \frac{\overline{X} - \overline{Y} - (\mu_X - \mu_Y)}{S_p\sqrt{\dfrac{1}{n_X} + \dfrac{1}{n_Y}}}, \tag{7.27}$$

where

$$S_p^2 = [(n_X - 1)S_X^2 + (n_Y - 1)S_Y^2]/(n_X + n_Y - 2) \tag{7.28}$$

is usually called the "pooled" estimator of the common variance σ^2. Notice from (7.28) that S_p^2 is a weighted average of the two sample variances S_X^2 and S_Y^2 with the weights being the degrees of freedom. Accordingly, an inference about the difference between μ_X and μ_Y when sampling from two independent normal distributions with the same but unknown variance is based on (7.27).

At this point it is natural for the reader to inquire what happens if one cannot assume the same variance for both distributions. If the variances σ_X^2 and σ_Y^2 are not equal but are known, the problem is simple. The distribution of

$$Z = \frac{\overline{X} - \overline{Y} - (\mu_X - \mu_Y)}{\sqrt{\dfrac{\sigma_X^2}{n_X} + \dfrac{\sigma_Y^2}{n_Y}}} \tag{7.29}$$

is still $N(0, 1)$ for the same reasons as those that led to (7.25). On the other hand, if the two variances are not known and are not equal, (7.27) should not be used because the problem becomes much more complicated. In essence, such a situation constitutes the so-called Fisher–Behrens problem, which is beyond the scope of this text. Approximations to this problem exist, one of which may be found in [1].

7.8   The *F* Distribution

Recall from Section 7.5 that inferences about σ^2 when sampling from a normal distribution are based on the statistic $(n - 1)S^2/\sigma^2$, which has a chi-square distribution with $n - 1$ degrees of freedom. In this section we want to develop the appropriate statistic to use in making inferences about the variances of two independent normal distributions based on random samples from each. We analyze the theory of an extremely useful distribution, known as the F distribution.

Suppose we are conducting an experiment in which we observe two independent random variables X and Y, each having a chi-square distribution with ν_1 and ν_2

degrees of freedom, respectively. Let us define another random variable F that is a function of X and Y in such a way that

$$F = \frac{X/\nu_1}{Y/\nu_2}. \tag{7.30}$$

That is, the random variable F is the ratio of two independent chi-squares, each chi-square variable being divided by its degrees of freedom. This leads to the following theorem.

Theorem 7.8   Let X and Y be two independent chi-square random variables with ν_1 and ν_2 degrees of freedom, respectively. The random variable

$$F = \frac{X/\nu_1}{Y/\nu_2}$$

is said to have an F distribution with probability density function

$$g(f; \nu_1, \nu_2)^* = \begin{cases} \dfrac{\Gamma[(\nu_1 + \nu_2)/2]\nu_1^{\nu_1/2}\,\nu_2^{\nu_2/2}}{\Gamma(\nu_1/2)\Gamma(\nu_2/2)} f^{(\nu_1-2)/2}\,(\nu_2 + \nu_1 f)^{-(\nu_1+\nu_2)/2} & f > 0, \\ 0 & \text{elsewhere.} \end{cases} \tag{7.31}$$

(The derivation of the probability density function of F is similar to that of the Student's t and is left as an exercise to the reader.)

The F distribution is completely determined by the degrees of freedom ν_1 and ν_2. It can be shown that the expected value is

$$E(F) = \nu_2/(\nu_2 - 2) \qquad \nu_2 > 2, \tag{7.32}$$

and the variance is

$$Var(F) = \frac{\nu_2^2(2\nu_2 + 2\nu_1 - 4)}{\nu_1(\nu_2 - 2)^2(\nu_2 - 4)} \qquad \nu_2 > 4. \tag{7.33}$$

The F distribution is positively skewed for any values of ν_1 and ν_2, but becomes less skewed as ν_1 and ν_2 take on larger values.

Quantile values $f_{1-\alpha,\nu_1,\nu_2}$ can be found in Table G of the Appendix such that

$$P(F \le f_{1-\alpha,\nu_1,\nu_2}) = \int_0^{f_{1-\alpha,\nu_1,\nu_2}} g(f; \nu_1, \nu_2)df = 1 - \alpha, \qquad 0 \le \alpha \le 1 \tag{7.34}$$

for selected cumulative proportions $1 - \alpha$ and various combinations of the degrees of freedom of the numerator ν_1, as in ratio (7.30), and the degrees of freedom of the denominator ν_2. For example, if $\nu_1 = 5$ and $\nu_2 = 10$, then

$$P(F \le f_{0.90,5,10}) = P(F \le 2.52) = 0.90,$$

$$P(F \le f_{0.95,5,10}) = P(F \le 3.33) = 0.95,$$

$$P(F \le f_{0.99,5,10}) = P(F \le 5.64) = 0.99.$$

*Here we are using g to denote the density to avoid confusion with the argument f.

Notice that in Table G the quantile values $f_{1-\alpha,\nu_1,\nu_2}$ are given only for $\alpha < 0.5$. If left side quantile values are desired — that is, for $\alpha > 0.5$ — they can be found by the following method: If the random variable F has the F distribution with ν_1 and ν_2 degrees of freedom, then the variable $F' = 1/F$ is also F distributed but with degrees of freedom ν_2 and ν_1. This is seen to be true because, from (7.30),

$$F' = \frac{1}{\dfrac{X/\nu_1}{Y/\nu_2}} = \frac{Y/\nu_2}{X/\nu_1}. \tag{7.35}$$

Now if we desire quantile values $f_{1-\alpha,\nu_1,\nu_2}$ for $\alpha > 0.5$,

$$P(F \le f_{1-\alpha,\nu_1,\nu_2}) = P\left(\frac{1}{F} > \frac{1}{f_{1-\alpha,\nu_1,\nu_2}}\right) = 1 - \alpha,$$

or

$$P\left(\frac{1}{F} \le \frac{1}{f_{1-\alpha,\nu_1,\nu_2}}\right) = \alpha. \tag{7.36}$$

But $1/F = F' \sim F$ distributed with ν_2 and ν_1 degrees of freedom. Then the αth quantile value of F' is such that

$$P(F' \le f'_{\alpha,\nu_2,\nu_1}) = \alpha. \tag{7.37}$$

Since (7.36) and (7.37) are identical, it follows that

$$f'_{\alpha,\nu_2,\nu_1} = 1/f_{1-\alpha,\nu_1,\nu_2}$$

and

$$f_{1-\alpha,\nu_1,\nu_2} = 1/f'_{\alpha,\nu_2,\nu_1} \qquad \text{for } \alpha > 0.5. \tag{7.38}$$

To illustrate, let $\nu_1 = 8$ and $\nu_2 = 12$. Then

$$P(F \le f_{0.05,8,12}) = P(F \le 1/f'_{0.95,12,8}) = P(F \le 1/3.28) = P(F \le 0.305) = 0.05,$$

or

$$P(F \le f_{0.01,8,12}) = P(F \le 1/f'_{0.99,12,8}) = P(F \le 1/5.67) = P(F \le 0.176) = 0.01.$$

Now let us return to the problem of developing an appropriate statistic to use in making inferences about the variances of two independent normal distributions. Let $X_1, X_2, ..., X_{n_X}$ be a random sample of independent normally distributed random variables, each with mean μ_X and variance σ_X^2. Also let $Y_1, Y_2, ..., Y_{n_Y}$ be n_Y independent and normally distributed random variables, each with mean μ_Y and variance σ_Y^2. If we assume independence among the X's and Y's, the statistics

$$(n_X - 1)S_X^2/\sigma_X^2$$

and

$$(n_Y - 1)S_Y^2/\sigma_Y^2$$

are two independent chi-square random variables with $n_X - 1$ and $n_Y - 1$ degrees of freedom, respectively. Then it follows from Theorem 7.8 that the random variable

$$\frac{\dfrac{(n_X - 1)S_X^2}{\sigma_X^2} \Big/ (n_X - 1)}{\dfrac{(n_Y - 1)S_Y^2}{\sigma_Y^2} \Big/ (n_Y - 1)} = \frac{S_X^2/\sigma_X^2}{S_Y^2/\sigma_Y^2} \tag{7.39}$$

has an F distribution with $n_X - 1$ and $n_Y - 1$ degrees of freedom.

An application of (7.39) is apparent if we recall the general problem in Section 7.7. That is, for an inference about the difference between two population means, either we have to know the population variances or we must assume that we know at least their ratio. A plausible way to check the validity of that assumption is to use (7.39). If the assumption that $\sigma_X^2 = \sigma_Y^2$ is correct, the F statistic given by (7.39) reduces to

$$F = S_X^2/S_Y^2. \tag{7.40}$$

Once values of S_X^2 and S_Y^2 are determined from the samples and the ratio (7.40) is computed, we would be inclined to conclude that the assertion of equal variances is incorrect so long as this ratio is sufficiently different from unity. In other words, if the two variances are indeed equal, the probability of observing a value of F that is sufficiently different from unity is small.

Finally, it should be noted that in this section as well as in Sections 7.5 through 7.7, the material was developed under the assumption of random sampling from normal distributions. In reality, the normality assumption may or may not be justifiable. From a practical point of view, however, the reader should be aware that the more non-normal the underlying probability model is, the less dependable these techniques are for inference. This is especially true for inferences about variances using either the chi-square or the F distribution.

References

1. P. G. Hoel, *Introduction to mathematical statistics*, 4th ed., Wiley, New York, 1971.
2. R. V. Hogg and A. T. Craig, *Introduction to mathematical statistics*, 4th ed., MacMillan, New York, 1978.
3. B. W. Lindgren, *Statistical theory*, 3rd ed., MacMillan, New York, 1976.
4. A. M. Mood and F. A. Graybill, *Introduction to the theory of statistics*, 2nd ed., McGraw-Hill, New York, 1963.

Exercises

7.1. Suppose a marketing research firm mails out questionnaires to 1000 residents of a certain suburb in a large metropolitan area to find out about their purchasing habits. Of the 1000 residents, 80 respond to the questionnaire. Does this constitute a random sample? Discuss the merits of such an approach for obtaining a random sample.

7.2. In an automobile assembly plant, 50 of the first 1000 cars assembled for the new model year will be selected and thoroughly inspected for quality of assembly. The plant manager decides to inspect every 20th automobile assembled. Does this constitute a random sample? Comment.

7.3. Determine the likelihood functions if X_1, X_2, ..., X_n constitute a random sample from the following distributions:

a. Poisson, with parameter λ;
b. Geometric, with parameter p;
c. Uniform in the interval (a, b);
d. $N(\mu, \sigma)$.

7.4. Repeat Exercise 7.3 for the following distributions:

a. Gamma, with parameters α and θ,
b. Weibull, with parameters α and θ.

7.5. Let X_1, X_2, ..., X_n be a random sample from a population whose distribution is normal, with unknown mean μ and variance σ^2. Which of the following are statistics?

a. $\Sigma X_i - \mu$ d. $X_1^2 + X_2^2 - \exp(X_3)$
b. $\sigma X_1 + \sigma X_2$ e. $X_i/\sigma, i = 1, 2, ..., n$
c. $X_i, i = 1, 2, ..., n$ f. $\Sigma(X_i - \overline{X})^2$

7.6. Let X_1, X_2, ..., X_n be n independent Poisson random variables with parameters λ_1, λ_2, ..., λ_n, respectively. Use the moment generating function to show that the sum of these variables is also Poisson with parameter $\lambda_1 + \lambda_2 + \cdots + \lambda_n$.

7.7. Let X_1 and X_2 be two independent Poisson random variables with parameters λ_1 and λ_2, respectively. Show that the difference between X_1 and X_2 is not a Poisson random variable.

7.8. Let X_1 and X_2 be two independent binomial random variables with parameters n_1 and p and n_2 and p, respectively. Show that the sum of X_1 and X_2 is also a binomial random variable with parameters $n_1 + n_2$ and p.

7.9. Let X_1 and X_2 be two independent exponentially distributed random variables with the same parameter θ. Show that the sum of X_1 and X_2 is a gamma random variable with shape parameter 2 and scale parameter θ.

7.10. For a certain income level, the Internal Revenue Service knows that the amounts claimed for medical deductions (X_1), charitable contributions (X_2), and miscellaneous deductions (X_3), are independent normally distributed random variables with means \$400, \$800, and \$100 and standard deviations \$100, \$250, and \$40, respectively.

a. What is the probability that the total amount claimed for these three deductions is no more than \$1,600?
b. If someone from this income level reports on his return a total of \$2,100 for these deductions, how likely is this or a larger amount under the given conditions?

7.11. An appliance store carries three different makes of refrigerators. Let X_1, X_2, and X_3 be random variables representing monthly sales volumes for the three makes at this store. If X_1, X_2, and X_3 are independent normally distributed random variables with means \$8,000, \$15,000 and \$12,000 and standard deviations \$2,000, \$5,000, and \$3,000, respectively, determine the probability that for a particular month the total sales volume for all refrigerators at this store will exceed \$50,000.

7.12. In a service-providing facility, the total system time is made up of two independent components — the length of time that one must wait before service begins (X_1), and the length of time for the actual service (X_2). If X_1 and X_2 are independent exponentially distributed random variables with mean time 4 minutes each, what is the probability that the system time will exceed 15 minutes? (Hint: See Exercise 7.9.)

7.13. Let X_1, X_2, ..., X_n be a random sample from a population whose distribution is gamma with parameters α and θ. Use the moment generating function to show that the distribution of the sample mean $\overline{X}$ is also gamma, with shape parameter $n\alpha$ and scale parameter θ/n.

7.14. Use the material from Section 5.9 to generate random values from binomial and exponential distributions and demonstrate the Central Limit Theorem. Specifically, for $n = 10$ and $n = 40$, generate 50 samples from a binomial distribution with $p = 0.4$. Repeat the process by generating 50 samples from an exponential distribution with parameter $\theta = 100$. To a reasonable degree, have you demonstrated the Central Limit Theorem?

7.15. For a certain aptitude test, it is known from past experience that the average score is 1000 with standard deviation 125. If the test is administered to 100 randomly selected individuals, approximate the following probabilities involving the sample mean $\overline{X}$.

a. $P(985 < \overline{X} < 1015)$ c. $P(\overline{X} > 1020)$

b. $P(960 < \overline{X} < 1040)$ d. $P(\overline{X} < 975)$

7.16. A contractor for a large office building is considering buying a large quantity of high intensity light bulbs from a certain manufacturer. The manufacturer assures the contractor that the average life of the bulbs is 1000 hours with standard deviation 80 hours. The builder decides to buy bulbs from this manufacturer only if a random sample of 64 such bulbs yields an average life of at least 1010 hours. What is the probability of the contractor buying these bulbs from this manufacturer?

7.17. A federal inspector for weights and measures visits a packaging plant for the purpose of affirming that the net weight of the packages is as indicated on the package. The plant manager assures the inspector that the average weight is 750 grams with standard deviation 5 grams. The inspector selects 100 packages at random and determines their average weight to be 748 grams. Under these conditions, how likely is a result of 748 grams or less? What do you suggest the inspector do?

7.18. In the manufacture of a certain motor bearing, the mean diameter is known to be 5 cm with standard deviation 0.005 cm. The process is monitored by periodically selecting 64 bearings at random and measuring their diameters. The process is allowed to continue as long as the probability of a sample average falling between two specified limits is 0.95. Determine these limits.

7.19. In the production of a certain welded material, the standard deviation of the breaking strength of the material is known to be 25 pounds. What must be the process average breaking strength if, based on a random sample of 50 specimens, the probability of the sample mean exceeding 250 pounds is 0.95?

7.20. Generate 50 samples of size 25 each from a normal distribution with mean 60 and standard deviation 10. Compute the sample variance for each sample using equation (7.14).

a. Determine the mean and variance of S^2 using the 50 computed values. How do they compare with Equations (7.17) and (7.18)?

b. Group the 50 computed values of S^2 and graph the relative frequencies. Comment on your result.

7.21. Repeat Exercise 7.20, but instead of generating random values from a normal distribution, generate from an exponential distribution with scale parameter $\theta = 30$. Comment on your results.

7.22. Control of variation in the thickness of a plastic material is important to a plant manager. The distribution of the thickness for the production process is known to be normal with a standard deviation of 0.01 cm. A random sample of 25 pieces of this material yields a sample standard deviation of 0.015 cm. If the population variance is $(0.01)^2$ cm^2, what is the probability that a sample variance will be as large or larger than $(0.015)^2$ cm^2? What might you conclude, therefore, about the variation of this process?

7.23. If a random sample of $n = 16$ is drawn from a normal distribution with unknown mean and variance, determine $P(S^2/\sigma^2 \leq 2.041)$.

7.24. If a random sample of size $n = 21$ is drawn from a normal distribution with unknown mean and variance, determine $P(S^2/\sigma^2 \leq 1.421)$.

7.25. A cigarette manufacturer claims that one of her brands has an average nicotine content of 0.6 mg per cigarette. An independent testing organization has measured the nicotine content of 16 such cigarettes and has determined the sample average and standard deviation to be 0.75 and 0.175 mg. of nicotine. If we assume the amount of nicotine in these cigarettes is a normal random variable, how likely is the sample result given the manufacturer's claim?

7.26. For the past twelve months the average daily sales volume at a fast-food restaurant has been $2,000. Management feels that the next 25 days will be typical for the current sales volume. At the end of 25 days the average and standard deviation turn out to be $1,800 and 200, respectively. Assume that daily sales volume is a normally distributed random variable. If you were management, would you have reason to believe, based on this result, that there has been a drop in the average sales volume per day?

7.27. A gasoline refiner is thinking about modifying the current process for producing gasoline from crude oil. The refiner will adopt the modification only if the average gasoline yield (as a percentage of crude) is increased. Based on a laboratory experiment using random samples of size 12 for each method, the average gasoline yield for the current method is 24.6 with standard deviation 2.3, and the average for the proposed method is 28.2 with standard deviation 2.7. The refiner believes the yields of the two methods are independent normally distributed random variables with equal variances. Based on this evidence, should the proposed method be adopted?

7.28. An independent testing organization is interested in testing the braking distance at 50 mph for two makes of automobiles. For the first make, nine randomly selected cars were tested in a controlled environment. The sample mean and standard deviation were 145 ft and 8 ft, respectively. For the second make, twelve randomly selected cars had an average braking distance of 132 ft and a standard deviation of 10 ft. Based on this evidence, is there reason to believe that the average braking distances for these cars are the same? Assume independent normal distributions for the braking distances with equal variances.

7.29. The variation in the number of units of a product that two operators A and B are turning out daily should be the same. Based on sample sizes of $n_A = 16$ days and

$n_B = 21$ days, the sample standard deviations are computed to be $s_A = 8.2$ units and $s_B = 5.8$ units. If the number of units produced by these operators daily are two independent random variables that are adequately approximated by normal distributions, do you have reason to believe that the variances are the same?

7.30. Based on the information given in Exercise 7.27, is there reason to believe the variances of the two refining methods are the same?

APPENDIX

Proof of the Central Limit Theorem

Our purpose here is to provide an outline for the proof of the Central Limit Theorem rather than to present the most general and mathematically elegant proof. We want to show that the moment generating function of $(\overline{X} - \mu)/(\sigma/\sqrt{n})$ tends to that of the standard normal as n tends to infinity. Let

$$Z_i = (X_i - \mu)/\sigma \qquad i = 1, 2, ..., n,$$

and let

$$Y = \frac{\overline{X} - \mu}{\sigma/\sqrt{n}}.$$

Since

$$\frac{1}{n} \sum_{i=1}^{n} \left(\frac{X_i - \mu}{\sigma/\sqrt{n}} \right) = \frac{1}{n} \cdot \frac{1}{\sigma/\sqrt{n}} \sum_{i=1}^{n} (X_i - \mu) = \frac{1}{n} \cdot \frac{1}{\sigma/\sqrt{n}} (n\overline{X} - n\mu) = \frac{\overline{X} - \mu}{\sigma/\sqrt{n}},$$

then

$$Y = \frac{1}{\sqrt{n}} \sum_{i=1}^{n} Z_i.$$

As a result, the moment generating function of Y is the same as the moment generating function of $(1/\sqrt{n}) \sum_{i=1}^{n} Z_i$. From Theorem 7.1,

$$m_Y(t) = [m_{Z_i}(t/\sqrt{n})]^n$$

$$= \{E[\exp(tZ_i/\sqrt{n})]\}^n,$$

since the Z_i are independent random variables.

Now let us expand $\exp(tZ_i/\sqrt{n})$ in a Taylor series expansion:

$$\exp(tZ_i/\sqrt{n}) = 1 + \frac{t}{\sqrt{n}} Z_i + \frac{t^2}{2n} Z_i^2 + \frac{t^3}{3!n^{3/2}} Z_i^3 + \cdots .$$

Taking expectations and recalling that $E(Z_i) = 0$ and $Var(Z_i) = 1$, $i = 1, 2, ..., n$, we have

$$E[\exp(tZ_i/\sqrt{n})] = 1 + \frac{t^2}{2n} + \frac{t^3}{3!n^{3/2}} E(Z_i^3) + \cdots .$$

Accordingly,

$$
\begin{aligned}
m_Y(t) &= \left[1 + \frac{t^2}{2n} + \frac{t^3}{3!\,n^{3/2}} E(Z_i^3) + \cdots \right]^n \\
&= \left\{ 1 + \frac{1}{n}\left[\frac{t^2}{2} + \frac{t^3}{3!\sqrt{n}} E(Z_i^3) + \cdots \right] \right\}^n \\
&= \left(1 + \frac{u}{n} \right)^n
\end{aligned}
$$

where

$$
u = \frac{t^2}{2} + \frac{t^3}{3!\sqrt{n}} E(Z_i^3) + \cdots .
$$

Now

$$
\lim_{n\to\infty} m_Y(t) = \lim_{n\to\infty}\left(1 + \frac{u}{n} \right)^n,
$$

but by definition

$$
\lim_{n\to\infty}\left(1 + \frac{u}{n} \right)^n = e^u.
$$

This brings about a situation identical to that encountered in the proof of Theorem 5.1. That is, as $n\to\infty$, all terms of u except the first go to zero because they all contain positive powers of n in their denominators. Therefore, we can deduce that

$$
\lim_{n\to\infty} m_Y(t) = \exp(t^2/2),
$$

or the limiting distribution of $Y = (\overline{X} - \mu)/(\sigma/\sqrt{n})$ is standard normal for large n.

APPENDIX

Derivation of the Student's t Probability Density Function

Let T be as defined by (7.19). Consider the conditional probability density of T when X is held fixed at x. Since

$$
f_Z(z) = \frac{1}{\sqrt{2\pi}} \exp(-z^2/2),
$$

the conditional probability density of

$$
T = Z/(x/v)^{1/2}
$$

is obtained by considering the inverse relation

$$
Z = (x/v)^{1/2} T
$$

and substituting in $f_Z(z)$, where the Jacobian of the transformation is

$$\frac{dz}{dt} = (x/v)^{1/2}.$$

Thus

$$f(t|x) = \frac{(x/v)^{1/2}}{\sqrt{2\pi}}\exp(-xt^2/2v), \qquad -\infty < t < \infty, \quad x > 0.$$

From (6.19) it is known that the joint density of T and X is

$$f(t, x) = f(t|x)f_X(x).$$

Since $X \sim X_v^2$,

$$f_X(x) = \frac{1}{2^{v/2}\Gamma(v/2)}x^{(v-2)/2}\exp(-x/2), \qquad x > 0.$$

Thus

$$f(t, x) = \frac{1}{\sqrt{2\pi v}\,2^{v/2}\Gamma(v/2)}x^{(v-1)/2}\exp\left(-\frac{x}{2} - \frac{xt^2}{2v}\right)$$

$$= c_1 x^{(v-1)/2}\exp(-c_2 x/2),$$

where $c_1 = 1/[\sqrt{2\pi v}\,2^{v/2}\Gamma(v/2)]$ and $c_2 = [1 + (t^2/v)]$. Integrating $f(t, x)$ with respect to x gives the probability density function of the Student's t distribution. Accordingly,

$$f_T(t) = c_1 \int_0^\infty x^{(v-1)/2}\exp(-c_2 x/2)dx$$

$$= c_1 \int_0^\infty (2y/c_2)^{(v-1)/2}\exp(-y)(2/c_2)dy, \quad \text{where } y = c_2 x/2 \text{ and } dx = (2/c_2)dy$$

$$= c_1(2/c_2)^{(v+1)/2} \int_0^\infty y^{(v-1)/2}\exp(-y)dy$$

$$= c_1(2/c_2)^{(v+1)/2}\Gamma[(v + 1)/2]$$

$$= \frac{1}{\sqrt{2\pi v}\,2^{v/2}\Gamma(v/2)} \cdot \frac{2^{(v+1)/2}}{[1 + (t^2/v)]^{(v+1)/2}}\Gamma[(v + 1)/2]$$

$$= \frac{\Gamma[(v + 1)/2]}{\sqrt{\pi v}\,\Gamma(v/2)}\left[1 + (t^2/v)\right]^{-(v+1)/2}, \qquad -\infty < t < \infty.$$

CHAPTER EIGHT

Point and Interval Estimation

8.1 Introduction

In the last chapter we noted briefly that statistics are used to estimate unknown parameters or their functions. In this chapter we will examine the concept of *parameter estimation* in detail by specifying desirable properties of estimators (statistics) and by developing appropriate techniques to implement the process of estimation. Unless indicated otherwise in this or any subsequent chapter, the sampling-theory approach will be assumed in which a parameter is taken to be a fixed but unknown quantity.

Simply put, parameter estimation involves the use of sample data in conjunction with some statistic to estimate the value of an unknown parameter. There are two ways of doing this: *point estimation* and *interval estimation*. In the first, one seeks an estimator that, based on the sample data, will give rise to a single-valued estimate of an unknown parameter value, known as a *point estimate*. In interval estimation, one determines an interval that is likely to contain the unknown parameter value. Such an interval is called a *confidence interval estimate*.

As in other chapters, we will identify an arbitrary probability density function of the underlying population distribution by $f(x; \theta)$, where the function depends on some arbitrary parameter θ, which may take on any value in some domain.* Thus the focal point of this chapter is to discuss desirable criteria for the determination of estimators of θ.

8.2 Desirable Properties of Point Estimators

To illustrate the need for parameter estimation, consider the following. When a random sample is obtained from the population distribution of a characteristic X, even if we can identify the functional form of the density, it is highly unlikely

---

*The domain of a parameter is usually called the parameter space.

that we will be able to specify it completely with all parameter values. In essence, then, we know the family of distributions from which we are sampling, but we cannot identify the particular member of that family because we do not know the parameter value. The parameter value has to be estimated based on the sample data. For example, suppose the service time distribution at a particular facility is exponential with unknown parameter θ. Say we observe $n = 25$ random lengths of time from this facility and compute the sample mean to be 3.5 minutes. Since for the exponential $E(X) = \theta$, a point estimate of θ is 3.5. Apparently, therefore, we are sampling from an exponential distribution whose mean is estimated to be 3.5 minutes.

It is possible to define many statistics to estimate an unknown parameter θ. For example, in the last illustration we could have just as easily chosen the sample median to estimate the mean. Then how does one go about selecting "good" estimators of θ? That is, what are the criteria to judge whether an estimator of θ is "good" or "bad"? Intuitively, what do we mean by a good estimator? If we think in terms of "human estimators," such as those found in large construction firms, then perhaps a good estimator is an individual whose estimates are nearly always close to the winning bid. As a further illustration, suppose we are privy to the procurement and sales records of three similar retailers — A, B, and C — who compete for the same trade. Since inventory is always an important aspect of a business, each of these retailers predicts the monthly demand for a particular item and orders accordingly. Suppose we determine the difference between actual and predicted demands for several months, where the difference is taken to be actual minus predicted, and based on these differences, we determine smoothed frequency distributions, as given in Figure 8.1.

Our intuition suggests that retailer C is doing the best job not only because C's distribution of the difference between actual and predicted demands is concentrated around the perfect value of zero but also because the variability of that difference is relatively small. For retailer A, even though the distribution

FIGURE 8.1 Smoothed frequencies for the difference between actual and predicted demands

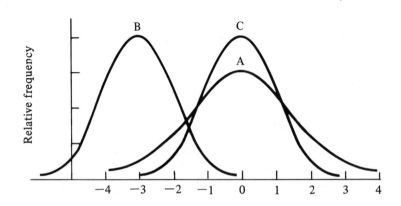

is also centered around zero, there is too much variability in the differences. The distribution of the differences for retailer B is concentrated around a negative value, which suggests that B overestimates the monthly demand most of the time.

If we accept the premise that the objective of parameter estimation is not unlike that of human estimators or predictors, then two desirable properties emerge from these illustrations: An estimator of a parameter θ should possess a sampling distribution concentrated around θ, and the variance of the estimator should be as small as possible.

We expand on these properties by considering the following. Let X_1, X_2, ..., X_n be a random sample of size n from a distribution with density function $f(x; \theta)$, and let $T = u(X_1, X_2, ..., X_n)$ be any statistic. The problem is to find the function u that is "best" at estimating θ. In seeking a best estimator of θ, we will be guided by an important quantity known as the mean squared error of an estimator.

Definition 8.1   Let T be any estimator of an unknown parameter θ. The *mean squared error of T* is defined to be the expectation of the squared difference between T and θ.

For any statistic T, we will denote the mean squared error of T by MSE(T); thus

$$\text{MSE}(T) = E(T - \theta)^2. \tag{8.1}$$

The reason why the mean squared error is an important quantity for judging possible estimators of θ can be seen by expanding (8.1); that is,

$$\begin{aligned}
\text{MSE}(T) &= E(T^2 - 2\theta T + \theta^2) \\
&= E(T^2) - 2\theta E(T) + \theta^2 \\
&= Var(T) + [E(T)]^2 - 2\theta E(T) + \theta^2 \\
&= Var(T) + [\theta - E(T)]^2. \tag{8.2}
\end{aligned}$$

The mean squared error of any estimator is the sum of two nonnegative quantities; one is the variance of the estimator, the other is the square of the so-called bias of the estimator. The reader will note that these two quantities relate directly to the desirable properties of an estimator that have been suggested so far. Specifically, the variance of an estimator should be as small as possible, and the sampling distribution of the estimator should be concentrated around the parameter. On the surface, therefore, the problem appears to be simple; that is, select as the best estimator of θ the statistic that has the smallest mean squared error among all possible estimators of θ. In reality, however, the problem is more complicated. Even if it were practical to determine the mean squared errors of a conceivably large number of estimators, one would find that for most densities $f(x; \theta)$ there does not exist one estimator that minimizes the mean squared error for all possible values of θ. That is, one estimator may have a minimum mean squared error for some values of θ, while another estimator may possess this property for other values of θ.

Example 8.1 Let X_1, X_2, ..., X_n be a random sample from some distribution such that $E(X_i) = \mu$ and $Var(X_i) = \sigma^2$, $i = 1, 2, ..., n$. Consider the statistics

$$T_1 = \overline{X}$$

and

$$T_2 = \sum_{i=1}^{n} X_i/(n + 1)$$

as possible estimators of μ. Determine the mean squared errors of T_1 and T_2 and show that $\text{MSE}(T_2) < \text{MSE}(T_1)$ for some values of μ while the converse is true for other values of μ.

The bias of T_1 is zero, since $E(T_1) = E(\overline{X}) = \mu$; thus

$$\text{MSE}(T_1) = Var(T_1) = \sigma^2/n.$$

For T_2,

$$E(T_2) = (n + 1)^{-1} E\left(\sum_{i=1}^{n} X_i \right)$$

$$= (n + 1)^{-1} \sum_{i=1}^{n} E(X_i)$$

$$= n\mu/(n + 1).$$

Similarly,

$$Var(T_2) = Var\left[(n + 1)^{-1} \sum_{i=1}^{n} X_i \right]$$

$$= (n + 1)^{-2} \sum_{i=1}^{n} Var(X_i)$$

$$= n\sigma^2/(n + 1)^2.$$

Thus

$$\text{MSE}(T_2) = \frac{n\sigma^2}{(n + 1)^2} + \left[\mu - \frac{n\mu}{(n + 1)} \right]^2$$

$$= \frac{n\sigma^2 + \mu^2}{(n + 1)^2}.$$

Say $n = 10$ and $\sigma^2 = 100$; then

$$\text{MSE}(T_1) = 10,$$

and

$$\text{MSE}(T_2) = (1000 + \mu^2)/121.$$

Equating these two quantities and solving for μ, we obtain that as long as $\mu < \sqrt{210}$, $\mathrm{MSE}(T_2) < \mathrm{MSE}(T_1)$; but if $\mu > \sqrt{210}$, then $\mathrm{MSE}(T_1) < \mathrm{MSE}(T_2)$.

For this reason we must examine additional criteria for selecting estimators of θ, even though the mean squared error will remain a most important concept. Specifically, we will examine *unbiased, consistent, minimum variance unbiased,* and *efficient* estimators. Then we will discuss an important concept in point estimation known as *sufficient statistics*. Throughout the discussion we will assume the existence of a single unknown parameter. It should be noted, however, that under fairly general conditions the concepts can be extended to include more than one unknown parameter.

8.2.1 Unbiased Estimators

Recall that the term $[\theta - E(T)]$ in the mean squared error of an estimator T is called the bias of the estimator. The bias of T can be positive, negative, or zero. Since the square of the bias is a component of the mean squared error, it would seem reasonable to insist that the bias of an estimator be as small as possible in absolute value. In other words it is desirable for an estimator to have its mean equal to the parameter the estimator is trying to estimate. This gives rise to the following definition.

Definition 8.2 The statistic $T = u(X_1, X_2, ..., X_n)$ is said to be an *unbiased estimator* of the parameter θ if $E(T) = \theta$ for all possible values of θ. Thus for any unbiased estimator T of θ, the sampling distribution of T is centered around θ and $\mathrm{MSE}(T) = Var(T)$.

In Section 7.4 we showed that $E(\overline{X}) = \mu$ regardless of the underlying population distribution. Therefore, the sample mean is an unbiased estimator of the population mean μ for all values of μ. In fact, if $X_1, X_2, ..., X_n$ is a random sample from the distribution of X with mean μ, then any X_i of the random sample is an unbiased estimator of μ since $E(X_i) = \mu$ for all $i = 1, 2, ..., n$. Moreover, if a statistic T is any linear combination of the random variables in the sample such that

$$T = a_1 X_1 + a_2 X_2 + \cdots + a_n X_n$$

where $\Sigma_{i=1}^{n} a_i = 1$, then T is an unbiased estimator of μ since

$$E(T) = E(a_1 X_1 + a_2 X_2 + \cdots + a_n X_n)$$

$$= a_1 \mu + a_2 \mu + \cdots + a_n \mu$$

$$= \mu.$$

In Section 7.5 we showed that if the sample variance S^2 is as given in (7.14), then $E(S^2) = \sigma^2$ when sampling from a normal distribution. In fact, we will now show that S^2, as defined in (7.14), is an unbiased estimator of σ^2 regardless of the underlying population distribution. Let $X_1, X_2, ..., X_n$ be a random sample from some distribution with unspecified density function such that $E(X_i) = \mu$ and $Var(X_i) = \sigma^2$ for all $i = 1, 2, ..., n$.

Then

$$E(S^2) = E\left[\sum_{i=1}^{n} (X_i - \overline{X})^2/(n-1)\right]$$

$$= (n-1)^{-1} E\left\{\sum_{i=1}^{n} [(X_i - \mu) - (\overline{X} - \mu)]^2\right\}$$

$$= (n-1)^{-1} E\left\{\sum_{i=1}^{n} [(X_i - \mu)^2 - n(\overline{X} - \mu)^2]\right\}^*$$

$$= (n-1)^{-1} \left[\sum_{i=1}^{n} E(X_i - \mu)^2 - nE(\overline{X} - \mu)^2\right];$$

but by definition $E(X_i - \mu)^2 = Var(X_i) = \sigma^2$ and $E(\overline{X} - \mu)^2 = Var(\overline{X}) = \sigma^2/n$. It follows that

$$E(S^2) = (n-1)^{-1} [n\sigma^2 - (n\sigma^2)/n]$$

$$= \frac{\sigma^2(n-1)}{n-1}$$

$$= \sigma^2.$$

In other words, S^2 is an unbiased estimator of σ^2 only when the divisor is $n-1$. This is the reason why in determining the sample variance we divide by $n-1$ rather than by n. The reader should be aware that this result does not make S unbiased for σ (see Section 11.2.2).

8.2.2   Consistent Estimators

It is reasonable to expect a good estimator of a parameter θ to become better as the sample size increases. That is, as the information based on a single random sample becomes more complete, the sampling distribution of a good estimator should become more closely concentrated around the parameter θ. We should have a better estimator of θ when it is based, say, on thirty observations than when it is based on five observations. Such a notion leads to what is known as a consistent estimator.

Definition 8.3   Let T be an estimator for a parameter θ, and let $T_1, T_2, ..., T_n$ be a sequence of estimators representing T based on sample sizes 1, 2, ..., n, respectively. Then T is said to be a (simple)** *consistent estimator* for θ if

$$\lim_{n\to\infty} P(|T_n - \theta| \leq \varepsilon) = 1$$

for all values of θ and $\varepsilon > 0$.

---

*See the material leading up to expression (7.15).
**One can also define a squared-error consistent estimator such that

$$\lim_{n\to\infty} E(T_n - \theta)^2 = 0, \qquad \text{for all } \theta,$$

but the notion of simple consistency is a more basic property.

The requirement that $\lim_{n \to \infty} P(|T_n - \theta| \leqslant \varepsilon) = 1$ for all θ constitutes what is termed *convergence in probability*. That is, if an estimator is consistent, it converges in probability to the parameter it is attempting to estimate as the sample size increases. This implies that the variance of a consistent estimator T_n decreases with increasing n, and that the mean of the sampling distribution of T_n approaches θ as n increases. Thus the conditions that T_n be an unbiased estimator of θ and that $Var(T_n) \to 0$ as $n \to \infty$ are sufficient (but not necessary) for consistency. For example, the sample mean $\overline{X}$ and the sample variance S^2 are consistent estimators of μ and σ^2, respectively. To show that $\overline{X}$ is a consistent estimator of μ, we will first state an important theorem known as Tchebysheff's inequality.

Theorem 8.1 Let X be a random variable with probability (density) function $f(x)$ such that both $E(X) = \mu$ and $Var(X) = \sigma^2$ are finite. Then

$$P(|X - \mu| \leqslant k\sigma) \geqslant 1 - \frac{1}{k^2}$$

or

$$P(|X - \mu| > k\sigma) \leqslant \frac{1}{k^2}$$

for any constant $k \geqslant 1$. (For the proof of this theorem, see [3].)

Tchebysheff's inequality is extremely important because it allows us to determine bounds on probabilities involving discrete or continuous random variables without having to specify their probability (density) functions. Simply put, Tchebysheff's theorem states that the probability of any random variable deviating by more than k standard deviations from its mean is less than or equal to $1/k^2$ for some $k \geqslant 1$. For example,

$$P(|X - \mu| \leqslant 2\sigma) \geqslant 1 - \frac{1}{4}$$

and

$$P(|X - \mu| \leqslant 3\sigma) \geqslant 1 - \frac{1}{9}$$

for any random variable X with finite mean μ and variance σ^2.

Now we want to use Theorem 8.1 to show that the sample mean $\overline{X}_n$, as a function of a random sample of size n, is a consistent estimator of μ.

Theorem 8.2 Let $X_1, X_2, ..., X_n$ be n IID random variables, such that $E(X_i) = \mu$ and $Var(X_i) = \sigma^2$ are finite for $i = 1, 2, ..., n$. Then $\overline{X}_n = \Sigma_{i=1}^{n} X_i/n$ is a consistent estimator of μ.

Proof: We want to show that

$$\lim_{n \to \infty} P(|\overline{X}_n - \mu| \leqslant \varepsilon) = 1.$$

Since $\overline{X}_n$ is a random variable such that $E(\overline{X}_n) = \mu$ and $Var(\overline{X}_n) = \sigma^2/n$, it follows from Tchebysheff's theorem that

$$P(|\overline{X}_n - \mu| > k\sigma/\sqrt{n}) \leq 1/k^2.$$

Let the positive constant k be equal to $\varepsilon\sqrt{n}/\sigma$, where ε is another positive real number. Then

$$P(|\overline{X}_n - \mu| > \varepsilon) \leq \frac{\sigma^2}{n\varepsilon^2}.$$

Since σ^2 is finite, taking the limit of this expression as n tends to infinity we have

$$\lim_{n\to\infty} P(|\overline{X}_n - \mu| > \varepsilon) = 0.$$

It follows, therefore, that

$$\lim_{n\to\infty} P(|\overline{X}_n - \mu| \leq \varepsilon) = 1,$$

and $\overline{X}_n$ is a consistent estimator of μ.

Theorem 8.2 is also known as the *law of large numbers*. It provides the theoretical foundation to estimate the mean of the population distribution based on the average of a finite number of observations so that the reliability of that average is better than that of any of the observations. This permits the determination of the sample size needed to assure with given probability that the ensuing sample mean will not deviate by more than a specified quantity from the population mean.

Example 8.2   Consider the selection of a random sample from some distribution that has a known variance $\sigma^2 = 10$ but an unknown mean μ. How large a sample must be taken so that the sample mean $\overline{X}_n$ will be within two units of the population mean with probability at least 0.9?

We will first develop a general expression for n. From Theorem 8.1 we know that

$$P(|\overline{X}_n - \mu| \leq k\sigma/\sqrt{n}) \geq 1 - \frac{1}{k^2}. \tag{8.3}$$

Let us choose a positive number α such that $\alpha = 1/k^2$, or $k = 1/\sqrt{\alpha}$, where necessarily $0 < \alpha < 1$. Then

$$P(|\overline{X}_n - \mu| \leq \sigma/\sqrt{n\alpha}) \geq 1 - \alpha. \tag{8.4}$$

Now let $\varepsilon > 0$ be the magnitude of the maximum allowable error between $\overline{X}_n$ and μ based on a random sample of size n. Then

$$\varepsilon = \sigma/\sqrt{n\alpha}. \tag{8.5}$$

Solving for n, we have

$$n = \frac{\sigma^2}{\alpha \varepsilon^2}. \tag{8.6}$$

To determine n for the given values, it is seen that $\alpha = 0.1$ and $\varepsilon = 2$. Substituting in (8.6), we obtain

$$n = 10/(0.1)(4)$$

$$= 25;$$

thus if we select a random sample of at least 25 observations from this distribution, the mean of the sample will be within two units of the population mean with probability of no less than 0.9. The probability of 0.9 associated with this statement is the measure of the reliability with which the inference about μ is being made based on $\overline{X}$.

8.2.3 Minimum Variance Unbiased Estimators

It is difficult to determine one estimator for a parameter that possesses minimum mean squared error for all possible values of the parameter. However, we may analyze a certain class of estimators and attempt to determine which one within that class has minimum mean squared error. For example, take the class of unbiased estimators for the parameter θ. If a statistic T belongs to that class, $E(T) = \theta$ and $MSE(T) = Var(T)$. Since it is desirable that the variance of an estimator be as small as possible, it follows that in the class of unbiased estimators we should look for the one, if it exists, that has minimum variance for all possible values of θ. Such an estimator is called a *uniformly minimum variance unbiased* (MVU) estimator of θ. The formal definition of an MVU estimator follows.

Definition 8.4 Let X_1, X_2, ..., X_n be a random sample from a distribution with probability (density) function $f(x; \theta)$. Let the statistic $T = u(X_1, X_2, ..., X_n)$ be an estimator of θ such that $E(T) = \theta$ and $Var(T)$ is less than the variance of any other unbiased estimator of θ for all possible values of θ. Then T is said to be the *minimum variance unbiased* estimator of θ.

The variance of an unbiased estimator is the most important quantity in deciding how good the unbiased estimator is for estimating a parameter θ. For example, let T_1 and T_2 be any two unbiased estimators of θ. T_1 is said to be a more efficient estimator of θ than T_2 if $Var(T_1) \leq Var(T_2)$, with strict inequality for some value of θ. It is common to use the ratio $Var(T_1)/Var(T_2)$ to determine the relative efficiency of T_2 with respect to T_1. If estimators are biased, their mean squared errors are used to determine relative efficiencies.

How does one go about determining an MVU estimator, if it exists? In most cases it would be prohibitive to determine the variances of all unbiased estimators of θ and then select the estimator with the smallest variance. The search for an MVU estimator is greatly aided by a concept known as the *Cramér–Rao lower bound,* which is presented in the following theorem. For proof and other details, including some regularity conditions, the reader is referred to [2].

Theorem 8.3   Let $X_1, X_2, ..., X_n$ be a random sample from a distribution with probability (density) function $f(x; \theta)$. If T is an unbiased estimator of θ, the variance of T must satisfy the inequality

$$Var(T) \geq \frac{1}{nE\left[\left(\frac{\partial \ln f(X; \theta)}{\partial \theta}\right)^2\right]}. \tag{8.7}$$

Theorem 8.3 establishes a lower bound for the variance of an unbiased estimator of θ. However, it does not necessarily imply that the variance of the MVU estimator of θ has to be equal to the Cramér–Rao lower bound. In other words it is possible to find an unbiased estimator of θ that has the smallest variance among all other unbiased estimators of θ, but whose variance exceeds the Cramér–Rao lower bound. Such an estimator is still an MVU estimator of θ. For an unbiased estimator whose variance attains the Cramér–Rao lower bound, we have the following definition.

Definition 8.5   If T is any unbiased estimator of a parameter θ such that

$$Var(T) = \frac{1}{nE\left[\left(\frac{\partial \ln f(X; \theta)}{\partial \theta}\right)^2\right]},$$

then T is said to be the *efficient* estimator of θ.

Thus, the efficient estimator of θ is the MVU estimator whose variance attains the Cramér–Rao lower bound. The efficient estimator of θ, if it can be found, is the best estimator of θ in the context of classical statistical inference.

Example 8.3   Let $X_1, X_2, ..., X_n$ be a random sample from a Poisson distribution with probability function $p(x; \lambda) = e^{-\lambda}\lambda^x/x!$. Determine the efficient estimator of λ.

Since $p(x; \lambda) = \lambda^x \exp(-\lambda)/x!$,

$$\ln p(x; \lambda) = x \ln(\lambda) - \lambda - \ln(x!)$$

and

$$\frac{\partial \ln p(x; \lambda)}{\partial \lambda} = \frac{x}{\lambda} - 1$$

$$= (x - \lambda)/\lambda.$$

Then

$$E\left[\left(\frac{\partial \ln p(X; \lambda)}{\partial \lambda}\right)^2\right] = E[(X - \lambda)/\lambda]^2$$

$$= \frac{1}{\lambda^2} E(X - \lambda)^2$$

$$= \frac{Var(X)}{\lambda^2};$$

but if X is Poisson, $Var(X) = \lambda$. As a result,

$$E\left[\left(\frac{\partial \ln p(X; \lambda)}{\partial \lambda}\right)^2\right] = \frac{1}{\lambda},$$

and by Definition 8.5 the variance of the efficient estimator of λ is

$$Var(T) = \frac{1}{n/\lambda} = \lambda/n = \sigma^2/n,$$

where $\sigma^2 = \lambda$ is the population variance. It follows, therefore, that the efficient estimator of the Poisson parameter λ is the sample mean $\overline{X}$.

We conclude this section on desirable properties of estimators by turning to the important concept of sufficient statistics. This concept is important because if an efficient estimator exists, it will be found to be a sufficient statistic.

8.2.4   Sufficient Statistics

Intuitively, a *sufficient statistic* for a parameter θ is one that utilizes all the information about θ that is contained in a random sample. For example, suppose $X_1, X_2, \ldots, X_{50}$ is a random sample of 50 observations from a gamma distribution with density function

$$f(x; 2, \theta) = \frac{1}{\theta^2} x \exp(-x/\theta) \qquad x > 0,$$

where the scale parameter θ, $\theta > 0$, is unknown. With a sufficient statistic for θ, what we have is a way of summarizing all measurements of the sample data in terms of a single value such that all sample information about θ is contained in that value. For this example, would the estimator

$$T = (X_1 + X_3 + \cdots + X_{49})/25$$

contain all information about θ? Even though the estimator T will yield a single value, it cannot possibly contain all sample information about θ, since half of the observations have been excluded. What about the sample mean $\overline{X}$? Surely $\overline{X}$ includes all observations in the random sample. Does that necessarily mean that all sample information about θ is exhausted by considering $\overline{X}$? We will say that a statistic $T = u(X_1, X_2, \ldots, X_n)$ is sufficient for a parameter θ if the joint distribution of $X_1, X_2, \ldots, X_n$, given T, is free of θ; that is, if T is given, then $X_1, X_2, \ldots, X_n$ has nothing further to say about θ.

The usefulness of a sufficient statistic is that if an unbiased estimator of a parameter θ is a function of a sufficient statistic, it will have a smaller variance than that of another unbiased estimator of θ that is not based on a sufficient statistic. In fact, if the efficient estimator of θ exists, it will be found to be a sufficient statistic. The criterion for determining a sufficient statistic is given by the following theorem, which is known as *Neyman's factorization theorem*.

Theorem 8.4   Let $X_1, X_2, \ldots, X_n$ be a random sample from a distribution with probability density function $f(x; \theta)$. The statistic $T = u(X_1, X_2, \ldots, X_n)$ is said to be a sufficient statistic for θ if and only if the likelihood function factors as

$$L(x_1, x_2, \ldots, x_n; \theta) = h(t; \theta)\, g(x_1, x_2, \ldots, x_n)$$

for every value $t = u(x_1, x_2, \ldots, x_n)$ of T, where $g(x_1, x_2, \ldots, x_n)$ does not involve the parameter θ.

Example 8.4   Let $X_1, X_2, \ldots, X_n$ be a random sample from a gamma distribution with probability density

$$f(x; \theta) = \frac{1}{\Gamma(\alpha)\theta^\alpha}\, x^{\alpha-1} \exp(-x/\theta) \qquad x > 0,$$

where the value of the shape parameter α is known. Determine a sufficient statistic for the scale parameter θ.

The likelihood function is

$$L(x_1, x_2, \ldots, x_n; \theta) = f(x_1; \theta) f(x_2; \theta) \cdots f(x_n; \theta)$$

$$= \frac{1}{\Gamma(\alpha)\theta^\alpha}\, x_1^{\alpha-1} \exp(-x_1/\theta) \cdot \frac{1}{\Gamma(\alpha)\theta^\alpha}\, x_2^{\alpha-1} \exp(-x_2/\theta)$$

$$\cdots \frac{1}{\Gamma(\alpha)\theta^\alpha}\, x_n^{\alpha-1} \exp(-x_n/\theta)$$

$$= \frac{1}{\Gamma^n(\alpha)\theta^{n\alpha}} \prod_{i=1}^{n} x_i^{\alpha-1} \exp\left(-\sum_{i=1}^{n} x_i/\theta\right)$$

$$= \frac{1}{\theta^{n\alpha}} \exp\left(-\sum x_i/\theta\right) \cdot \frac{\Pi x_i^{\alpha-1}}{\Gamma^n(\alpha)}$$

$$= h\left(\sum x_i; \theta\right) g(x_1, x_2, \ldots, x_n).$$

By Theorem 8.4, $\Sigma_{i=1}^{n} X_i$ is a sufficient statistic for θ.

In Example 8.4, suppose we consider an estimator of θ to be

$$T = \frac{1}{n\alpha} \sum_{i=1}^{n} X_i. \tag{8.8}$$

T is seen to be a function of the sufficient statistic ΣX_i. *T* is also a sufficient statistic for θ since the likelihood function in Example 8.4 can be factored as

$$L(x_1, x_2, \ldots, x_n) = h(t; \theta)\, g(x_1, x_2, \ldots, x_n).$$

where $\Sigma X_i = n\alpha T$ and

$$h(t; \theta) = \frac{1}{\theta^{n\alpha}} \exp(-n\alpha t/\theta). \tag{8.9}$$

As a result, the conditions of the factorization theorem are satisfied. In fact, one can show that any one-to-one function of a sufficient statistic is also sufficient.

Example 8.5 Let $X_1, X_2, \ldots, X_n$ be a random sample from a Poisson distribution with probability function

$$p(x; \lambda) = \lambda^x \exp(-\lambda)/x! \qquad x = 0, 1, 2, \ldots .$$

Show that the efficient estimator of λ is a sufficient statistic.

Recall from Example 8.3 that the efficient estimator of λ is the sample mean $\overline{X}$. We need to show that $\overline{X}$ is a one-to-one function of a sufficient statistic for λ. The likelihood function is

$$L(x_1, x_2, \ldots, x_n; \lambda) = p(x_1; \lambda)\, p(x_2; \lambda) \cdots p(x_n; \lambda)$$

$$= \frac{\lambda^{x_1}\exp(-\lambda)}{x_1!} \cdot \frac{\lambda^{x_2}\exp(-\lambda)}{x_2!} \cdots \frac{\lambda^{x_n}\exp(-\lambda)}{x_n!}$$

$$= \lambda^{\sum_{i=1}^{n} x_i} \exp(-n\lambda) \Big/ \prod_{i=1}^{n} x_i!$$

$$= h(\Sigma x_i; \lambda)\, g(x_1, x_2, \ldots, x_n)$$

where

$$h(\Sigma x_i; \lambda) = \lambda^{\Sigma x_i} \exp(-n\lambda).$$

By Theorem 8.4, the statistic $\sum_{i=1}^{n} X_i$ is sufficient for λ. Since the efficient estimator $\overline{X}$ is a one-to-one function of this statistic, $\overline{X}$ is also sufficient for λ.

8.3   Methods of Point Estimation

In the last section we talked about desirable properties for a good estimator. Now we want to examine how one obtains estimators that generally have good properties. Specifically, we will consider the method of maximum likelihood and the method of moments. In Chapter 13 we will also encounter the method of least squares in the context of fitting equations.

8.3.1   Maximum Likelihood Estimation

To introduce the concept of maximum likelihood estimation, think about the following. The flooding of rivers and streams is a natural phenomenon that at times has devastating consequences. Suppose in a given year, two serious floods occurred at a particular geographic location. If we assume that the number of floods per year at that location is a Poisson random variable with unknown parameter value λ, how should we proceed to estimate λ based on the single observation of $x = 2$? One possible method is to select the value of λ for which the probability of the observed value is maximized. For the observed value $x = 2$, it is possible that λ could be any positive number. For the sake of discussion, let us assume that the possible values of λ are 1, 3/2, 2, 5/2, and 3. Then the probabilities of the observed value $x = 2$ for each of these values of λ are as follows:

λ	1	3/2	2	5/2	3
$p(2; \lambda)$	0.1839	0.2510	0.2707	0.2565	0.2240

Apparently $p(2; \lambda)$ increases to a maximum of 0.2707 for $\lambda = 2$, then decreases for $\lambda > 2$. The value 2 for λ is the one for which the probability of the observed value is maximized. In other words the observation $x = 2$ is more likely to arise from a Poisson distribution with $\lambda = 2$ than, say, from a Poisson distribution with $\lambda = 1$ or 3, and so on. We can show that the value $\lambda = 2$ is the one for which $p(2; \lambda)$ is maximum by taking the derivative of $p(2; \lambda)$ with respect to λ and equating it to zero. Since

$$p(2; \lambda) = \lambda^2 \exp(-\lambda)/2!,$$

we have

$$\frac{dp(2; \lambda)}{d\lambda} = \frac{1}{2}[-\lambda^2 \exp(-\lambda) + 2\lambda \exp(-\lambda)]$$

$$= \frac{\lambda \exp(-\lambda)}{2}(2 - \lambda).$$

By equating the derivative to zero, it is seen that either $\lambda = 0$ or $\lambda = 2$. The second derivative with respect to λ yields $\exp(-\lambda)[1 - 2\lambda + (\lambda^2)/2]$, and the value of the second derivative at $\lambda = 2$ is $-\exp(-2) < 0$. Thus the estimate $x = 2$ is the value for which the probability of the observation is maximized. This is a *maximum likelihood estimate*.

In essence, the method of maximum likelihood selects as an estimate that value of a parameter that maximizes the probability of the observed random sample. In other words the method of maximum likelihood consists of finding as an estimate the value of a parameter that maximizes the likelihood function.

Definition 8.6   Let $X_1, X_2, ..., X_n$ be a random sample from a distribution with probability (density) function $f(x; \theta)$, and let $L(x_1, x_2, ..., x_n; \theta)$ be the likelihood of the sample as a function of θ. If $t = u(x_1, x_2, ..., x_n)$ is the value of θ that maximizes the likelihood function, then $T = u(X_1, X_2, ..., X_n)$ is the maximum likelihood estimator of θ, and t is the maximum likelihood estimate.

The method of maximum likelihood (ML) has the desirable property of yielding estimators that are functions of sufficient statistics, provided that the ML estimate is unique. Further, the ML method will yield the efficient estimator if one exists. However, ML estimators are not generally unbiased, as we will see. The process of obtaining ML estimators is relatively straightforward. Because of the nature of the likelihood function, we usually choose to maximize the natural logarithm of $L(\theta)$. That is, for many cases it is easier to determine an ML estimate by maximizing $\ln L(\theta)$ rather than maximizing $L(\theta)$. We illustrate the method with the following examples.

Example 8.6   In a binomial experiment we observe exactly $X = x$ successes in n trials. Determine the maximum likelihood estimator of the binomial parameter p.

In this case the likelihood function is the same as the probability that $X = x$; thus

$$L(x; p) = \frac{n!}{(n - x)!x!} p^x (1 - p)^{n-x}, \qquad 0 \le p \le 1.$$

Then

$$\ln L(x; p) = \ln(n!) - \ln[(n - x)!] - \ln(x!) + x \ln(p) + (n - x)\ln(1 - p).$$

To find the value of p for which $\ln L(x; p)$ is maximized, we take the derivative with respect to p and equate it to zero:

$$\frac{d[\ln L(x; p)]}{dp} = \frac{x}{p} - \frac{(n - x)}{(1 - p)} = 0.$$

Upon solving for p, we determine that the ML estimator of p is the so-called sample proportion X/n, and the ML estimate is x/n. To confirm that this value maximizes $\ln L(x; p)$, we take the second derivative with respect to p and evaluate it at x/n:

$$\frac{d^2[\ln L(x; p)]}{dp^2} = - \frac{np(1 - p) + (x - np)(1 - 2p)}{[p(1 - p)]^2}$$

and

$$\frac{d^2[\ln L(x; p)]}{dp^2}\bigg|_{x/n} = - \frac{x}{(x/n)^2[1 - (x/n)]} \qquad x/n < 1,$$

which confirms the result since the second derivative is negative. For a specific example, if we observe $x = 5$ based on $n = 25$ independent trials, the ML estimate of p is $5/25 = 0.2$.

Example 8.7   Let $X_1, X_2, ..., X_n$ be a random sample from a normal distribution with probability density function

$$f(x; \mu, \sigma^2) = \frac{1}{\sqrt{2\pi}\sigma} \exp[-(x - \mu)^2/2\sigma^2].$$

Determine the ML estimators of μ and σ^2.

Here we will proceed as in the case involving a single parameter. Since the likelihood function is a function of both μ and σ^2, the ML estimates of μ and σ^2 are the values for which the likelihood function attains a maximum value. Accordingly,

$$L(x_1, x_2, ..., x_n; \mu, \sigma^2) = \frac{1}{\sqrt{2\pi}\sigma} \exp[-(x_1 - \mu)^2/2\sigma^2] \cdots \frac{1}{\sqrt{2\pi}\sigma}$$

$$\times \exp[-(x_n - \mu)^2/2\sigma^2]$$

$$= (2\pi\sigma^2)^{-n/2} \exp\left[-\frac{1}{2\sigma^2} \sum_{i=1}^{n} (x_i - \mu)^2\right],$$

and

$$\ln L(x_1, x_2, ..., x_n; \mu, \sigma^2) = -\frac{n}{2}\ln(2\pi) - \frac{n}{2}\ln(\sigma^2) - \frac{1}{2\sigma^2} \sum_{i=1}^{n} (x_i - \mu)^2.$$

Upon taking the partial derivatives with respect to μ and with respect to σ^2 and equating them to zero, we have

$$\frac{\partial[\ln L(\mu, \sigma^2)]}{\partial \mu} = -\frac{2}{2\sigma^2} \sum_{i=1}^{n} (x_i - \mu) = 0$$

and

$$\frac{\partial[\ln L(\mu, \sigma^2)]}{\partial(\sigma^2)} = -\frac{n}{2\sigma^2} + \frac{1}{2\sigma^4} \sum_{i=1}^{n} (x_i - \mu)^2 = 0.$$

Solving the first equation for μ, then substituting this value for μ and solving the second equation for σ^2, we obtain

$$\hat{\mu} = \sum_{i=1}^{n} x_i/n = \bar{x}$$

and

$$\hat{\sigma}^2 = \sum_{i=1}^{n} (x_i - \bar{x})^2/n.$$

Although we will not confirm that these values maximize the likelihood function, they are indeed the ML estimates of μ and σ^2, respectively. Second derivatives should be taken if there is doubt. However, since a likelihood function is the product of either probabilities or densities, it is usually bounded above and is continuous in the parameters. Consequently, the usual result is that the solution of the first derivative yields a maximum.

Notice that we have introduced the customary "hat" notation $\hat{}$ to designate an ML estimate. We will use this notation throughout the balance of the text when necessary. Also notice that the ML estimator of σ^2 is biased, confirming our earlier remark that ML estimators are not necessarily unbiased.

The method of maximum likelihood possesses another desirable property known as the invariance property. Let $\hat{\theta} = u(X_1, X_2, ..., X_n)$ be the maximum likelihood estimator of θ. If $g(\theta)$ is a single-valued function of θ, then the maximum likelihood estimator of $g(\theta)$ is $g(\hat{\theta})$. For example, since the ML estimator of σ^2 when sampling from a normal distribution is

$$\hat{\sigma}^2 = \frac{1}{n} \sum_{i=1}^{n} (x_i - \bar{x})^2,$$

by the invariance property the ML estimator of the standard deviation σ is

$$\hat{\sigma} = \left[\frac{1}{n} \sum_{i=1}^{n} (x_i - \bar{x})^2 \right]^{1/2}$$

As a further illustration of the invariance property, the ML estimator of the Weibull reliability function is

$$\hat{R}(t) = \exp[-(t/\hat{\theta})^{\alpha}],$$

where $\hat{\theta}$ is the ML estimator of the scale parameter θ.

8.3.2 Method of Moments

Perhaps the oldest method of parameter estimation is the method of moments. This method consists of equating appropriate moments of the population distribution with the corresponding sample moments to estimate an unknown parameter of the distribution.

Definition 8.7 Let $X_1, X_2, \dots, X_n$ be a random sample from a distribution with probability (density) function $f(x; \theta)$. The rth sample moment about zero is defined to be

$$M_r' = \frac{1}{n} \sum_{i=1}^{n} X_i^r.$$

The method of moments provides a reasonable alternative when maximum likelihood estimators cannot be determined. Recall that parameters are usually functions of theoretical moments. For example, if the random variable X is gamma distributed (see Section 5.5), then

$$\mu = \alpha\theta \tag{8.10}$$

and

$$\mu_2' = \alpha(\alpha + 1)\theta^2. \tag{8.11}$$

Solving (8.10) for α and substituting in (8.11), we have

$$\alpha = \mu/\theta \tag{8.12}$$

and

$$\mu_2' = \frac{\mu}{\theta} \left(\frac{\mu}{\theta} + 1 \right) \theta^2$$

$$= \mu^2 + \mu\theta,$$

or

$$\theta = (\mu_2' - \mu^2)/\mu. \tag{8.13}$$

Substituting (8.13) for θ in (8.12) yields

$$\alpha = \mu^2/(\mu_2' - \mu^2). \tag{8.14}$$

Thus, both parameters of the gamma distribution are functions of the first two moments about zero.

In essence, the method of moments is implemented by equating as many sample moments to corresponding theoretical moments as are necessary to determine a moment estimator of an unknown parameter. For example, by (8.13) and (8.14), the moment estimators of the gamma parameters θ and α are

$$\widetilde{\theta} = (M_2' - \overline{X}^2)/\overline{X} \tag{8.15}$$

and

$$\widetilde{\alpha} = \overline{X}^2/(M_2' - \overline{X}^2), \tag{8.16}$$

respectively, where the tilde notation ($\widetilde{}$) is used to denote a moment estimator. As a further illustration, recall Example 4.10. We showed that the parameters p and k of a negative binomial distribution are also functions of the first two moments about zero since

$$p = \mu/(\mu_2' - \mu^2)$$

and

$$k = \mu^2/(\mu_2' - \mu^2 - \mu).$$

It follows, therefore, that moment estimators of p and k are given by

$$\widetilde{p} = \overline{X}/(M_2' - \overline{X}^2) \tag{8.17}$$

and

$$\widetilde{k} = \overline{X}^2/(M_2' - \overline{X}^2 - \overline{X}), \tag{8.18}$$

respectively.

8.3.3 Maximum Likelihood Estimation for Censored Samples

In some sampling situations, especially those involving life tests, the testing procedure may be terminated before it yields a complete random sample. In this section we will consider the principle of maximum likelihood for estimating unknown parameters based on such samples, which are called *censored* or *truncated* samples. In this context, we will concentrate exclusively on the notion of a life test.

A typical life test consists of n like units — such as electrical or mechanical components — randomly selected from some process and operated in a carefully controlled environment until each unit fails. The measurement of interest is the time to failure for each unit. If the life test is terminated only when all units of the sample have failed, the random sample of times to failure is said to be complete. However, because of time and financial constraints, a life test is usually terminated either after a predetermined amount of time x_0 has elapsed, or after a predetermined number $m \leq n$ of units have failed. Both of these conditions produce censored samples. If x_0 is a fixed length of time, the number of units out of n that fail from the start of the test to time x_0 is a random variable; this constitutes a type I censored sample. If m is fixed and the termination time X_m is the random variable, censoring is said to be of type II. With regard to inference, there is little substantive difference between these two types. Accordingly, we will restrict our discussion to type II censored sampling.

The sample data from a life test are the times at which failures occur. For example, say the first unit failure occurs at time x_1 from start, the second occurs at time x_2 from start, and so on until the mth failure occurs at time x_m, where $m \leq n$ is the predetermined number of failures required to terminate the life test. The recorded times of failure x_1, x_2, ..., x_m is an ordered sequence since $x_1 \leq x_2 \leq \cdots \leq x_m$. Notice that at the termination of the life test, $n - m$ units will not have failed; these $n - m$ units have survived time x_m. It should be clear that the complete sample is realized if $m = n$.

Suppose the lifetimes of the units are independent exponentially distributed random variables X_1, X_2, ..., X_n with density function

$$f(x; \theta) = \frac{1}{\theta} \exp(-x/\theta), \qquad x > 0, \quad \theta > 0.$$

Of interest is the maximum likelihood estimator of the parameter θ. The likelihood function for type II censored sampling is the joint probability that m units fail at ordered times x_1, x_2, ..., x_m and $n - m$ units survive time x_m. The portion of the likelihood function for the m units that fail at ordered times x_1, x_2, ..., x_m is $f(x_1; \theta)f(x_2; \theta) \cdots f(x_m; \theta)$. But this is only one of the possible ways in which exactly m out of n units fail. The total number of ways m units out of n units can fail is $n!/(n - m)!$. The probability of $n - m$ units surviving time x_m is the reliability function at time x_m; thus, for the exponential distribution,

$$P(X > x_m) = \exp(-x_m/\theta).$$

The likelihood function is therefore

$$L(x_1, x_2, ..., x_m; \theta) = \frac{n!}{(n-m)!} \left\{ \underbrace{\frac{1}{\theta}\exp(-x_1/\theta) \cdots \frac{1}{\theta}\exp(-x_m/\theta)}_{m \text{ terms}} \right.$$

$$\left. \cdot \underbrace{\exp(-x_m/\theta) \cdots \exp(-x_m/\theta)}_{(n-m) \text{ terms}} \right\}$$

$$= \frac{n!}{(n-m)!} \left\{ \frac{1}{\theta^m} \exp\left(-\frac{1}{\theta}\sum_{i=1}^{m} x_i \right) \cdot \exp\left[-\frac{(n-m)}{\theta} x_m \right] \right\}$$

$$= \frac{n!}{(n-m)!} \left[\frac{1}{\theta^m} \exp\left(-\frac{1}{\theta} T_m \right) \right], \qquad (8.19)$$

where

$$T_m = \sum_{i=1}^{m} x_i + (n - m)x_m. \qquad (8.20)$$

Taking the natural logarithm of L, we have

$$\ln L(x_1, x_2, \ldots, x_m; \theta) = \ln(n!) - \ln[(n - m)!] - m\ln\theta - \frac{1}{\theta} T_m.$$

Then

$$\frac{d[\ln L(x_1, x_2, \ldots, x_m; \theta)]}{d\theta} = -\frac{m}{\theta} + \frac{1}{\theta^2} T_m,$$

and by equating the derivative to zero, the maximum likelihood estimate of θ is

$$\hat{\theta} = \left[\sum_{i=1}^{m} x_i + (n - m)x_m \right] \Big/ m. \qquad (8.21)$$

Example 8.8   The scientific pocket calculators currently available usually contain battery packs that have to be replaced after a certain amount of usage. Suppose 50 such battery packs are randomly selected from a production process and submitted to a life test. It is decided to terminate the test when 15 out of the 50 cease to function properly. The recorded ordered times to failure in hours are 115, 119, 131, 138, 142, 147, 148, 155, 158, 159, 163, 166, 167, 170, and 172. If these are realizations of independent exponentially distributed random variables, determine the maximum likelihood estimate of θ.

Here

$$n = 50, m = 15, \sum_{i=1}^{15} x_i = 115 + 119 + \cdots + 172 = 2250, \text{ and } x_{15} = 172.$$

Therefore, by (8.21),

$$\hat{\theta} = \frac{2250 + (50 - 15)172}{15} = 551.33 \text{ hours.}$$

8.4   Interval Estimation

To introduce the notion of interval estimation, suppose a retail establishment has kept fairly good records of the number of units of a product it sold on a monthly basis. The average demand is of special interest to the company because it is used as a basis for inventory maintenance. Assume that the demand for the product is not influenced by seasonal fluctuations.

Suppose the company decides that the last 36 months are typical of the demand activity for this product, and based on this sample data computes the sample mean to be $\bar{x} = 200$ units. In other words, $\bar{x} = 200$ is a point estimate of an unknown parameter that represents the average demand for this product at this establishment. Does this estimate imply that the unknown mean demand is not likely to be as large as 250 or as small as 150? At this point we do not know because we have no indication of the possible error in the point estimate. The error in the point estimate is measured in terms of the sampling variation of the corresponding estimator.

For example, suppose the standard deviation of the sample mean $\overline{X}$ is 60 units. We may argue that according to the Central Limit Theorem, $\overline{X} \rightarrow N(\mu, 60)$ as $n \rightarrow \infty$. Thus the probability that $\overline{X}$ will be within, say, two standard deviations of μ is about 0.95. In other words, for large n,

$$P(|\overline{X} - \mu| < 120) = 0.95,$$

or

$$P(-120 < \overline{X} - \mu < 120) = 0.95. \tag{8.22}$$

Subtracting $\overline{X}$ and multiplying through by -1 inside the parentheses, we have

$$P(\overline{X} - 120 < \mu < \overline{X} + 120) = 0.95. \tag{8.23}$$

If we substitute the estimate $\bar{x} = 200$ for $\overline{X}$, we have

$$P(80 < \mu < 320) = 0.95, \tag{8.24}$$

which suggests that it is entirely possible for the true mean demand to be as large as 250 units or as small as 150 units so long as $s.d.(\overline{X}) = 60$. On the other hand, suppose the standard deviation of $\overline{X}$ were equal to 10. Then corresponding to (8.23), we would have

$$P(\overline{X} - 20 < \mu < \overline{X} + 20) = 0.95,$$

and for $\bar{x} = 200$,

$$P(180 < \mu < 220) = 0.95.$$

Now it is unlikely that μ is as large as 250 or as small as 150.

In both of these instances, the key has been the standard deviation of the point estimator. In essence, for interval estimation we consider both a point estimator of a parameter θ and its sampling distribution in order to determine an interval that will provide us with some assurance that θ is contained within the interval.

For more insight into interval estimation, we need to interpret the meaning of (8.23) and (8.24). Since $\overline{X}$ is a random variable, the interval $\overline{X} - 120$ to $\overline{X} + 120$ is a random interval, and the probability that this interval contains the true mean μ is 0.95. In other words, if we were to repeatedly draw samples of the same size from this population, and each time a sample is selected we were to compute specific values for the random interval $(\overline{X} - 120, \overline{X} + 120)$, then we would expect 95 percent of those computed intervals to contain the unknown mean μ. On the other hand, the specific interval 80 to 320 is but a realization of the random interval $(\overline{X} - 120, \overline{X} + 120)$ based on the data of a single sample in which the estimate $\bar{x} = 200$. Since the probability of 0.95 is with reference only to the random interval $(\overline{X} - 120, \overline{X} + 120)$, it would indeed be incorrect to say that the probability of μ being contained in the interval $(80, 320)$ is 0.95. That is, no probability can ever be directly attached to the statement $80 < \mu < 320$, because it contains nothing but constants. However, the 0.95 probability of the random interval does suggest that our confidence in the interval (80, 320) for containing the unknown mean μ is high. It is only in this sense that we are willing to assign a degree of confidence in the statement $80 < \mu < 320$ to be the same as the probability of the random interval $(\overline{X} - 120, \overline{X} + 120)$. Thus when we write

$$P(80 < \mu < 320) = 0.95,$$

we are not making a probability statement in the classical sense but rather are expressing this degree of confidence. Accordingly, the interval (80, 320) is called a 95 percent confidence interval for μ.

In general terms, the construction of a confidence interval for an unknown parameter θ consists of finding a sufficient statistic T and relating it to another random variable $X^* = f(T; \theta)$, where X involves θ but the distribution of X is free of θ, as well as any other unknown parameters. Then one selects two values x_1 and x_2 such that

$$P(x_1 < X < x_2) = 1 - \alpha,$$

where $1 - \alpha$ is called the *confidence coefficient*. By algebraically manipulating the two inequalities, we can alter the expression in the parentheses and express it as

$$P[h_1(T) < \theta < h_2(T)] = 1 - \alpha,$$

where $h_1(T)$ and $h_2(T)$ are functions of the statistic T and thus are random variables. The confidence interval for θ is then determined by substituting in $h_1(T)$ and $h_2(T)$ estimates computed from sample data, giving rise to what is called a two-sided confidence interval. Following the same procedure, we can also develop one-sided confidence intervals of the form

$$P[g_1(T) < \theta] = 1 - \alpha$$

or

$$P[\theta < g_2(T)] = 1 - \alpha.$$

The first is a lower one-sided confidence interval for θ, and the second is an upper one-sided confidence interval.

At this time we examine several situations involving the construction of confidence intervals for population means and variances. We will primarily be concerned with two-sided confidence intervals. As will become apparent, our discussion will have strong ties to the material of Sections 7.4 through 7.8.

8.4.1   Confidence Intervals for μ When Sampling from a Normal Distribution with Known Variance

Let X_1, X_2, ..., X_n be a random sample from a normal distribution with an unknown mean μ but a known variance σ^2. Of interest is the construction of a $100(1 - \alpha)\%$ confidence interval on μ where α is some small number such that $0 < \alpha < 1$. The construction of the confidence interval will be based on the best estimator of μ, namely the sample mean $\overline{X}$.

---

*This method is generally called the *pivotal method*, and X is known as the *pivotal random variable*.

To illustrate the fundamental approach to the construction of confidence intervals, consider the probability statement as given by (8.22). Adding μ inside the parentheses, we have

$$P(\mu - 120 < \overline{X} < \mu + 120) = 0.95.$$

Thus the limits $\mu - 120$ and $\mu + 120$ are seen to be functions of possible values of μ. In general, therefore, we may write

$$P[g_1(\mu) < \overline{X} < g_2(\mu)] = 1 - \alpha, \tag{8.25}$$

such that

$$\int_{-\infty}^{g_1(\mu)} f(\overline{x}; \mu)d\overline{x} = \alpha/2$$

and

$$\int_{g_2(\mu)}^{\infty} f(\overline{x}; \mu)d\overline{x} = \alpha/2,$$

where $f(\overline{x}; \mu)$ is the density function of the sampling distribution of $\overline{X}$, and $g_1(\mu)$ and $g_2(\mu)$ are some functions of μ that do not contain any other unknown parameters.

Of immediate concern is the determination of $g_1(\mu)$ and $g_2(\mu)$. Since $\overline{X} \sim N(\mu, \sigma/\sqrt{n})$, the standard normal $Z = (\overline{X} - \mu)/(\sigma/\sqrt{n})$, and

$$P[g_1(\mu) < \overline{X} < g_2(\mu)] = P\left[\frac{g_1(\mu) - \mu}{\sigma/\sqrt{n}} < Z < \frac{g_2(\mu) - \mu}{\sigma/\sqrt{n}}\right] = 1 - \alpha. \tag{8.26}$$

But since $P(z_{\alpha/2} < Z < z_{1-\alpha/2}) = 1 - \alpha$, where the quantile values $z_{\alpha/2}$ and $z_{1-\alpha/2}$ are such that $P(Z < z_{\alpha/2}) = \alpha/2$ and $P(Z < z_{1-\alpha/2}) = 1 - \alpha/2$, respectively, it follows that

$$\frac{g_1(\mu) - \mu}{\sigma/\sqrt{n}} = z_{\alpha/2} \tag{8.27}$$

and

$$\frac{g_2(\mu) - \mu}{\sigma/\sqrt{n}} = z_{1-\alpha/2}. \tag{8.28}$$

Solving (8.27) and (8.28) in terms of $g_1(\mu)$ and $g_2(\mu)$, respectively, we obtain

$$g_1(\mu) = \mu + z_{\alpha/2}\frac{\sigma}{\sqrt{n}} \tag{8.29}$$

and

$$g_2(\mu) = \mu + z_{1-\alpha/2}\frac{\sigma}{\sqrt{n}}. \tag{8.30}$$

Since for the standard normal $z_{\alpha/2} = -z_{1-\alpha/2}$, we can substitute $-z_{1-\alpha/2}$ for $z_{\alpha/2}$

in (8.29). Accordingly, we may substitute expressions (8.29) and (8.30) for $g_1(\mu)$ and $g_2(\mu)$, respectively, in (8.25) to obtain

$$P\left(\mu - z_{1-\alpha/2}\frac{\sigma}{\sqrt{n}} < \overline{X} < \mu + z_{1-\alpha/2}\frac{\sigma}{\sqrt{n}}\right) = 1 - \alpha. \tag{8.31}$$

Manipulating the inequalities inside the parentheses in (8.31), we have

$$P\left(\overline{X} - z_{1-\alpha/2}\frac{\sigma}{\sqrt{n}} < \mu < \overline{X} + z_{1-\alpha/2}\frac{\sigma}{\sqrt{n}}\right) = 1 - \alpha, \tag{8.32}$$

which is a generalization of the probability statement (8.23). In other words, the probability of the random interval $\overline{X} - z_{1-\alpha/2}(\sigma/\sqrt{n})$ to $\overline{X} + z_{1-\alpha/2}(\sigma/\sqrt{n})$ containing the true mean μ is $1 - \alpha$. If we replace the random variable $\overline{X}$ in (8.32) with the estimate $\bar{x}$ computed from the data of a single sample of size n, a $100(1 - \alpha)\%$ confidence interval for μ is

$$\bar{x} \pm z_{1-\alpha/2}\frac{\sigma}{\sqrt{n}}, \tag{8.33}$$

where $\bar{x} - z_{1-\alpha/2}(\sigma/\sqrt{n})$ and $\bar{x} + z_{1-\alpha/2}(\sigma/\sqrt{n})$ are called the lower and upper confidence limits for μ, respectively. That is, the confidence interval (8.33) is an interval estimate for μ.

By examining the confidence interval for μ as given by (8.33), it is relatively easy to see that the larger the sample size, the smaller the width of the interval; or the larger the confidence coefficient $1 - \alpha$, the wider the interval. Both of these results are logical since a large sample size will decrease the variance of the estimator, and a large confidence coefficient will increase the quantile value and make the interval wider.

Example 8.9   The following are the recorded weights in grams of the contents of 16 boxes of cereal that were randomly selected from a filling process to check the average weight: 506, 508, 499, 503, 504, 510, 497, 512, 514, 505, 493, 496, 506, 502, 509, 496. If the weight of each box is a normal random variable with standard deviation $\sigma = 5$ gm, determine 90%, 95%, and 99% confidence interval estimates for the mean fill of this process.

For a 90% confidence coefficient, $\alpha = 0.1$. The value $z_{0.95}$ is determined from Table D of the Appendix to be 1.645 since $P(Z > 1.645) = 0.05$. From the sample data we compute $\bar{x}$ to be 503.75 gm. Then by (8.33), a 90% confidence interval for the process mean fill is

$$503.75 \pm 1.645\frac{5}{\sqrt{16}},$$

or 501.69 to 505.81. The other desired confidence intervals may be determined following this same procedure. For comparison, the results are summarized in Table 8.1.

TABLE 8.1   Confidence intervals for Example 8.9

Confidence	$z_{1-\alpha/2}$	Lower limit	Upper limit
90%	1.645	501.69	505.81
95%	1.96	501.30	506.20
99%	2.575	500.53	506.97

Let us now consider a problem that is entirely similar to that in Example 8.2. Suppose here we are willing to specify that we are sampling from a normal distribution with unknown mean μ but a known variance σ^2. We would like to estimate the sample size required so that with probability $1 - \alpha$ the sample mean $\overline{X}$ will be within ε units of the population mean μ. To this end, recall (8.31). We may rewrite this expression as

$$P\left(-z_{1-\alpha/2}\frac{\sigma}{\sqrt{n}} < \overline{X} - \mu < z_{1-\alpha/2}\frac{\sigma}{\sqrt{n}} \right) = 1 - \alpha, \tag{8.34}$$

which yields

$$P(|\overline{X} - \mu| < \varepsilon) = 1 - \alpha$$

where

$$\varepsilon = z_{1-\alpha/2}\frac{\sigma}{\sqrt{n}}. \tag{8.35}$$

Solving for n in (8.35) yields the desired result,

$$n = \left(\frac{z_{1-\alpha/2}\sigma}{\varepsilon} \right)^2. \tag{8.36}$$

The only difference between expressions (8.6) and (8.36) is that (8.6) is determined without specifying the population distribution, whereas (8.36) assumes sampling from a normal distribution. It is reasonable to expect, therefore, that everything else being equal, an n determined by (8.36) will be much smaller than that determined by (8.6) simply because more is assumed. For comparison, if we are willing to assume sampling from a normal distribution, the sample size corresponding to the conditions of Example 8.2 would be

$$n = \frac{(1.645)^2\,10}{4} \approx 7,$$

as compared to $n = 25$ from (8.6).

From an application point of view, the fact that both expressions (8.6) and (8.36) assume knowledge of the population variance σ^2 constitutes a stringent requirement. If σ^2 is not known, one should use an estimate of σ^2 that perhaps may exist from a previous sample. If such an estimate is not available but the approximate range of the measurements is known, a rough estimate of the standard deviation is about 1/6 of the range since for most unimodal distributions the overwhelming majority of the observations will fall within three standard deviations on either side of the mean.

8.4.2 Confidence Intervals for μ When Sampling from a Normal Distribution with Unknown Variance

Let us turn now to the problem of finding a confidence interval for μ when sampling from a normal distribution for which we do not know the variance. Recall from Section 7.6 that when sampling from $N(\mu, \sigma)$, where μ and σ^2 are unknown, the random variable

$$T = \frac{\overline{X} - \mu}{S/\sqrt{n}} \tag{8.37}$$

has a Student's t distribution with $n - 1$ degrees of freedom. Then it is possible to determine the quantile value $t_{1-\alpha/2,\, n-1}$ of T for which

$$P(-t_{1-\alpha/2,\, n-1} < T < t_{1-\alpha/2,\, n-1}) = 1 - \alpha, \tag{8.38}$$

where the quantile value is such that $P(T < -t_{1-\alpha/2,\, n-1}) = \alpha/2$ and $P(T < t_{1-\alpha/2,\, n-1}) = 1 - \alpha/2$. Substituting for T in (8.38), we have

$$P\left(-t_{1-\alpha/2,\, n-1} < \frac{\overline{X} - \mu}{S/\sqrt{n}} < t_{1-\alpha/2,\, n-1}\right) = 1 - \alpha$$

or

$$P\left(-t_{1-\alpha/2,\, n-1}\frac{S}{\sqrt{n}} < \overline{X} - \mu < t_{1-\alpha/2,\, n-1}\frac{S}{\sqrt{n}}\right) = 1 - \alpha$$

and

$$P\left(\overline{X} - t_{1-\alpha/2,\, n-1}\frac{S}{\sqrt{n}} < \mu < \overline{X} + t_{1-\alpha/2,\, n-1}\frac{S}{\sqrt{n}}\right) = 1 - \alpha. \tag{8.39}$$

It follows that the interval $\overline{X} \pm t_{1-\alpha/2,\, n-1}(S/\sqrt{n})$ is a random interval, and the probability that it contains the true mean μ is $1 - \alpha$. Thus, given the data of a random sample of size n from which the estimates $\bar{x}$ and s^2 are computed, a $100(1 - \alpha)\%$ confidence interval for μ is

$$\bar{x} \pm t_{1-\alpha/2,\, n-1}\frac{s}{\sqrt{n}}. \tag{8.40}$$

For illustration and comparison, Table 8.2 lists 90%, 95%, and 99% confidence intervals for μ based on (8.40) and using the data of Example 8.9, where $\bar{x} = 503.75$ and $s = 6.20$. Notice that in the case involving the Student's t distribution, the intervals are wider.

TABLE 8.2 Confidence intervals for Example 8.9

Confidence	$t_{1-\alpha/2,\, n-1}$	Lower limit	Upper limit
90%	1.753	501.03	506.47
95%	2.131	500.45	507.05
99%	2.947	499.18	508.32

8.4.3 Confidence Intervals for Difference of Means When Sampling from Two Independent Normal Distributions

Let $X_1, X_2, \ldots, X_{n_X}$ and $Y_1, Y_2, \ldots, Y_{n_Y}$ be two random samples from independent normal distributions with means μ_X and μ_Y and variances σ_X^2 and σ_Y^2, respectively. We want to construct a confidence interval for the difference $\mu_X - \mu_Y$. Suppose we assume that the variances are known. Then from Section 7.7, the random variable

$$Z = \frac{\overline{X} - \overline{Y} - (\mu_X - \mu_Y)}{\sqrt{\dfrac{\sigma_X^2}{n_X} + \dfrac{\sigma_Y^2}{n_Y}}} \tag{8.41}$$

is $N(0, 1)$. Thus it is possible to find the quantile value $z_{1-\alpha/2}$ such that

$$P(-z_{1-\alpha/2} < Z < z_{1-\alpha/2}) = 1 - \alpha. \tag{8.42}$$

Substituting (8.41) in (8.42) and algebraically manipulating the inequalities, we have

$$P\Bigg(\overline{X} - \overline{Y} - z_{1-\alpha/2}\sqrt{\frac{\sigma_X^2}{n_X} + \frac{\sigma_Y^2}{n_Y}} < \mu_X - \mu_Y$$

$$< \overline{X} - \overline{Y} + z_{1-\alpha/2}\sqrt{\frac{\sigma_X^2}{n_X} + \frac{\sigma_Y^2}{n_Y}}\Bigg) = 1 - \alpha, \tag{8.43}$$

which is a random interval containing no unknown parameters. As was the case in Section 8.4.1, the pivotal random variable is the standard normal Z. Accordingly, a $100(1 - \alpha)\%$ confidence interval for $\mu_X - \mu_Y$ is

$$\overline{x} - \overline{y} \pm z_{1-\alpha/2}\sqrt{\frac{\sigma_X^2}{n_X} + \frac{\sigma_Y^2}{n_Y}}, \tag{8.44}$$

where the quantile value $z_{1-\alpha/2}$ is such that $P(Z < z_{1-\alpha/2}) = 1 - \alpha/2$.

If the variances σ_X^2 and σ_Y^2 are unknown but are assumed equal, then the random variable

$$T = \frac{\overline{X} - \overline{Y} - (\mu_X - \mu_Y)}{S_p\sqrt{\dfrac{1}{n_X} + \dfrac{1}{n_Y}}}$$

has a Student's t distribution with $k = n_X + n_Y - 2$ degrees of freedom. By following the same procedure as before, we determine that a $100(1 - \alpha)\%$ confidence interval for $\mu_X - \mu_Y$ is

$$\overline{x} - \overline{y} \pm t_{1-\alpha/2,k}S_p\sqrt{\frac{1}{n_X} + \frac{1}{n_Y}}, \tag{8.45}$$

where the pooled estimate of the common variance is

$$s_p^2 = \frac{(n_X - 1)s_X^2 + (n_Y - 1)s_Y^2}{n_X + n_Y - 2}.$$

Example 8.10   It is believed that accounting majors can expect a higher average starting salary than management majors. Random samples of both groups were recently obtained from a relatively homogeneous geographical area, yielding the data in Table 8.3. Determine a lower one-sided 90% confidence interval for the difference between the average salaries for accounting and management majors, denoted by $\mu_A - \mu_M$ (assume the variances σ_A^2 and σ_M^2 are equal).

From the sample data given, we can compute the following quantities:

$$n_A = 10 \qquad\qquad n_M = 14$$

$$\bar{x}_A = 16{,}250 \qquad\qquad \bar{x}_M = 15{,}400$$

$$s_A^2 = 1{,}187{,}222.22 \qquad s_M^2 = 1{,}352{,}307.69$$

$$s_p^2 = 1{,}284{,}772.73$$

$$s_p = 1133.48.$$

Then a lower one-sided 90% confidence interval is given by

$$\bar{x}_A - \bar{x}_M - t_{0.9,\,22}\, s_p \sqrt{\frac{1}{n_A} + \frac{1}{n_M}},$$

where the value $t_{0.9,\,22} = 1.321$, since for the Student's t, $P(T < 1.321) = 0.9$. Substituting the numerical results, we have

$$16{,}250 - 15{,}400 - (1.321)(1133.48)\sqrt{\frac{1}{10} + \frac{1}{14}} = 230.05.$$

TABLE 8.3   Starting annual salaries for recent graduates

Accounting majors	Management majors
$16,300	$13,200
18,200	15,100
17,500	13,900
16,100	14,700
15,900	15,600
15,400	15,800
15,800	14,900
17,300	18,100
14,900	15,600
15,100	15,300
	16,200
	15,200
	15,400
	16,600

So a lower one-sided 90% confidence interval for the true difference between average salaries for accounting and management majors is $230.05.

8.4.4 Confidence Intervals for σ^2 When Sampling from a Normal Distribution with Unknown Mean

Let us examine the problem of constructing a confidence interval for the population variance σ^2 when sampling from $N(\mu, \sigma)$. Recall from Section 7.5 that under these conditions, the sampling distribution of $(n - 1)S^2/\sigma^2$ is chi-square with $n - 1$ degrees of freedom. Then it is possible to determine quantile values $\chi^2_{\alpha/2, n-1}$ and $\chi^2_{1-\alpha/2, n-1}$ such that

$$P\left[\chi^2_{\alpha/2, n-1} < \frac{(n - 1) S^2}{\sigma^2} < \chi^2_{1-\alpha/2, n-1}\right] = 1 - \alpha. \tag{8.46}$$

We can express (8.46) as

$$P\left[\frac{1}{\chi^2_{\alpha/2, n-1}} > \frac{\sigma^2}{(n - 1)S^2} > \frac{1}{\chi^2_{1-\alpha/2, n-1}}\right] = 1 - \alpha.$$

Then it follows that the interval

$$\left[\frac{(n - 1)S^2}{\chi^2_{1-\alpha/2, n-1}}, \frac{(n - 1)S^2}{\chi^2_{\alpha/2, n-1}}\right]$$

is a random interval that contains no unknown parameters and contains σ^2 with probability $1 - \alpha$. Thus, based on the data of a random sample of size n, the estimate s^2 is computed and a $100(1 - \alpha)\%$ confidence interval for σ^2 is $(n - 1)s^2/\chi^2_{1-\alpha/2, n-1}$ to $(n - 1)s^2/\chi^2_{\alpha/2, n-1}$. It is of interest to note that the pivotal random variable here is $(n - 1)S^2/\sigma^2$ since its density function, given by (7.16), does not contain any unknown parameters.

Example 8.11 A process produces a certain kind of ball bearing whose inside diameter is set to be 3 centimeters. Twelve such bearings are randomly selected from this process and their inside diameters are measured to be 3.01, 3.05, 2.99, 2.99, 3.00, 3.02, 2.98, 2.99, 2.97, 2.97, 3.02, and 3.01. Assuming the diameter is a normally distributed random variable, determine a 99% confidence interval for the variance σ^2.

Since the desired confidence is 99%, $\alpha = 0.01$. From Table E of the Appendix, we determine that the quantiles $\chi^2_{0.005, 11}$ and $\chi^2_{0.995, 11}$ are 2.60 and 26.71, respectively. Finally the computed value of the sample variance is $s^2 = 0.0005455$. As a result, a 99% confidence interval for σ^2 is

$$\left[\frac{(12 - 1)(0.0005455)}{26.71}, \frac{(12 - 1)(0.0005455)}{2.60}\right],$$

or

$$(0.0002246, 0.0023079).$$

As this example illustrates, the midpoint of a confidence interval for a variance does not coincide with the point estimate. However, when an interval is constructed symmetrically, as is that for a mean when sampling from a normal distribution, the midpoint of the confidence interval is the point estimate.

8.4.5   Confidence Intervals for the Ratio of Two Variances When Sampling from Two Independent Normal Distributions

In industrial environments the need often arises to measure and compare the variabilities of two distinct processes. Suppose we have random samples from two independent normal distributions with unknown means and variances. Let the sample sizes be n_X and n_Y, and let the sample variances be S_X^2 and S_Y^2. Of interest is the construction of a confidence interval for the ratio σ_Y^2/σ_X^2 of the two population variances. Recall from Section 7.8 that the random variable $(S_X^2/\sigma_X^2)/(S_Y^2/\sigma_Y^2)$ has an F distribution with $n_X - 1$ and $n_Y - 1$ degrees of freedom. Then we may write

$$P\left(a < \frac{S_X^2/\sigma_X^2}{S_Y^2/\sigma_Y^2} < b\right) = 1 - \alpha, \tag{8.47}$$

where a and b are lower and upper quantile values of an F distribution such that

$$a = 1/f_{1-\alpha/2,\, n_Y-1,\, n_X-1} \quad \text{and} \quad b = f_{1-\alpha/2,\, n_X-1,\, n_Y-1}.$$

The probability statement given by (8.47) can be expressed as

$$P\left(a < \frac{S_X^2}{S_Y^2} \cdot \frac{\sigma_Y^2}{\sigma_X^2} < b\right) = 1 - \alpha$$

or

$$P\left(\frac{aS_Y^2}{S_X^2} < \frac{\sigma_Y^2}{\sigma_X^2} < \frac{bS_Y^2}{S_X^2}\right) = 1 - \alpha. \tag{8.48}$$

Thus a $100(1 - \alpha)\%$ confidence interval for σ_Y^2/σ_X^2 is given by

$$(as_Y^2/s_X^2,\ bs_Y^2/s_X^2).$$

To illustrate, recall Example 8.10. Suppose we desire a 90% confidence interval for σ_M^2/σ_A^2. Using Table G of the Appendix, the quantile values are

$$a = 1/f_{0.95,\, 13,\, 9} = 1/3.05^* = 0.328,$$

$$b = f_{0.95,\, 9,\, 13} = 2.71.$$

Since $s_A^2 = 1,187,222.22$ and $s_M^2 = 1,352,307.69$, a 90% confidence interval for the ratio σ_M^2/σ_A^2 of the two unknown variances is

$$[(0.328)(1,352,307.69)/1,187,222.22,\quad (2.71)(1,352,307.69)/1,187,222.22]$$

*By interpolation.

or

$$(0.3736, 3.0868).$$

8.4.6 Confidence Intervals for the Proportion Parameter p When Sampling from a Binomial Distribution

The product percent defective of a manufacturing process is the most important barometer of the quality of the process for producing a given product. Since a manufactured unit is either defective or nondefective, the number of defective units produced by the process is a binomial random variable, if we assume independence and constant probability. In a random sample of size n from a process, the parameter p, representing the proportion defective, is unknown. We would like to determine a confidence interval for p. Although it is possible to determine exact confidence intervals for p (see [2]), we will opt for an approximate confidence interval based on a large sample size. The reason for this decision stems from Theorem 5.1, which states that the distribution of a binomial random variable tends to normal as n tends to infinity.

In Example 8.6 we showed that the maximum likelihood estimator of p, denoted by $\hat{P}$, is

$$\hat{P} = X/n, \tag{8.49}$$

where X is binomial with parameters n and p. Notice that $\hat{P}$ is an unbiased estimator of p since

$$E(\hat{P}) = \frac{1}{n} E(X) = np/n = p.$$

The variance of $\hat{P}$ may be obtained as follows:

$$Var(\hat{P}) = Var(X/n)$$

$$= \frac{1}{n^2} [np(1 - p)]$$

$$= p(1 - p)/n. \tag{8.50}$$

Recall that the random variable $(X - np)/\sqrt{np(1 - p)}$ is approximately $N(0, 1)$ for large n. Then it can be shown that the distribution of

$$\frac{\hat{P} - p}{\sqrt{\dfrac{\hat{P}(1 - \hat{P})}{n}}} \tag{8.51}$$

also tends to $N(0, 1)$ for large n. Thus the probability of the random interval

$$\left[\hat{P} - z_{1-\alpha/2} \sqrt{\frac{\hat{P}(1 - \hat{P})}{n}}, \quad \hat{P} + z_{1-\alpha/2} \sqrt{\frac{\hat{P}(1 - \hat{P})}{n}} \right] \tag{8.52}$$

is approximately $1 - \alpha$ for large n. Accordingly, an approximate $100(1 - \alpha)\%$ confidence interval for the proportion parameter p is

$$\left[\hat{p} - z_{1-\alpha/2}\sqrt{\frac{\hat{p}(1 - \hat{p})}{n}}, \quad \hat{p} + z_{1-\alpha/2}\sqrt{\frac{\hat{p}(1 - \hat{p})}{n}}\right], \tag{8.53}$$

where the maximum likelihood estimate $\hat{p} = x/n$ is determined from the random sample of size n.

Example 8.12   A manufacturer has assured a client company, which purchases a particular product on a regular basis, that the product percent defective is no more than 5 percent. The company decides to substantiate the claim by selecting 200 units of this product at random from its inventory and testing them. Should the company suspect the manufacturer's claim if it uncovers 19 defective units out of the 200?

We will argue here that suspicion is warranted if a high confidence interval for the true proportion p is entirely to the right of the claimed 0.05 value. Say we select a 95% confidence. Since the realization of the binomial X is $x = 19$ and $n = 200$, the estimate of p is $19/200 = 0.095$. Substituting in (8.53), we have

$$\left[0.095 - 1.96\sqrt{\frac{0.095(1-0.095)}{200}}, \quad 0.095 + 1.96\sqrt{\frac{0.095(1-0.095)}{200}}\right],$$

which computes to be (0.05436, 0.1356). Apparently there is reason to suspect the manufacturer's claim, since the confidence interval is entirely to the right of the claimed value.

With regard to sampling from a binomial distribution, a frequently occurring problem is to estimate the sample size required so that with approximately $100(1 - \alpha)\%$ confidence the estimate of the proportion parameter will be within ε units of p. Given the maximum likelihood estimator X/n and following the same procedure as in Section 8.4.1, we can express (8.52) as

$$P\left(\left|\frac{X}{n} - p\right| < \varepsilon\right) \simeq 1 - \alpha,$$

where

$$\varepsilon = z_{1-\alpha/2}\sqrt{\frac{p(1 - p)}{n}}.$$

Solving for n, we obtain

$$n = [z_{1-\alpha/2}^2 \, p(1 - p)]/\varepsilon^2. \tag{8.54}$$

Notice in (8.54) that n is a function of the desired p. Since p is unknown and, in fact, is the quantity we are attempting to estimate, what is usually done here is to determine the most conservative value for n. This occurs whenever the quantity $p(1 - p)$ is a maximum. But we can show that for $0 \leq p \leq 1$, $p(1 - p)$ is a maximum when $p = 1/2$. In other words, $p = 1/2$ is the value we should use to determine the desired sample size based on (8.54).

As a reminder, the methods in this section should be used only when the sample size is sufficiently large. Otherwise, exact confidence intervals for the binomial parameter p exist, and they should be used instead. Along these lines, we should again emphasize that we have nearly always assumed sampling from a normal distribution throughout the discussion on interval estimation. The construction of confidence intervals for variances is especially sensitive to this assumption. Any substantive deviation from this assumption will significantly cloud the validity of the inference with regard to variances. On the other hand, the methods for confidence intervals involving means are relatively immune to modest departures from the assumption of normality as long as the sample sizes are large. Thus the methods in Sections 8.4.1 through 8.4.3 are to a large extent valid for large sample sizes even if we are not sampling from a normal distribution.

To illustrate that the use of the Student's t distribution remains valid for inferences about means, even if sampling is not from a normal distribution, we simulated the following experiment using the IMSL package. For sample sizes 15, 30, and 50, one thousand random samples were generated from an exponential distribution with parameter $\theta = 10$. Since θ is the mean of an exponentially distributed random variable, we used (8.40) to compute a 95% confidence interval for θ for each random sample and counted the number of intervals that did not contain the imposed value of 10. For $n = 15$ we found 86 such intervals, for $n = 30$ we found 68, and for $n = 50$ we found 55.

If sampling were from a normal distribution, we would expect $(0.05)(1000) = 50$ such intervals out of the 1000 not to contain the parameter value. It appears that the results approach those that are expected under normal sampling as the sample size increases, even though we are sampling from an exponential distribution. Accordingly, the effect of the violation of the normal assumption when using the Student's t distribution appears to be small, even for a relatively modest size for n.

8.5   Bayesian Estimation

So far we have approached statistical inference from the sampling theory point of view, which is based on the relative frequency interpretation of probability. Now we turn to the Bayesian approach to statistical inference and, in particular, to parameter estimation. Recall that the Bayesian approach is based on the subjective interpretation of probability, which views probability as a degree of belief concerning an uncertainty. The Bayesian view regards an unknown parameter as an uncertainty on which a degree of belief can be expressed and then revised based on sample information. An inference concerning the parameter is based on the revised degree of belief. In other words a parameter is viewed as a random variable that, prior to sample evidence, is assigned a (prior) distribution based on one's degree of belief regarding the behavior of the random parameter. When the sample evidence is obtained, the prior distribution is revised, and a posterior distribution of the parameter emerges. The posterior distribution is then used to make inferences about the parameter.

The Bayesian approach has been favored by many for parameter estimation, especially in situations where an unknown parameter cannot realistically be a fixed quantity. For example, the true proportion defective in a manufacturing process is likely to fluctuate, however slightly, depending on a number of factors, as was shown in Example 6.9. The true proportion of foreclosures on residential properties is likely to vary depending primarily on economic conditions. And the mean weekly demand for, say, automobiles will fluctuate as a function of several factors including the weather.

8.5.1 Bayesian Point Estimation

We consider now the determination of Bayesian point estimators. Since an unknown parameter is considered a random variable, let it be denoted by Θ and let θ denote a realization of Θ. Assume that Θ is a continuous random variable* with unconditional (prior) density function $f_\Theta(\theta)$, which reflects one's prior beliefs about the uncertainty of Θ. Let the sample information be represented by n IID random variables $X_1, X_2, ..., X_n$ with common density $f(x \mid \theta)$ conditional on the realization θ of Θ. From Chapter 7 it follows that the likelihood function, conditional on the particular value θ, is

$$L(x_1, x_2, ..., x_n \mid \theta) = f(x_1 \mid \theta)f(x_2 \mid \theta) \cdots f(x_n \mid \theta). \qquad (8.55)$$

It is important to emphasize here that even though Θ is a random variable, what we wish to do is estimate the particular value θ on which the sample evidence, as represented by the likelihood function, is conditioned. That is, Θ is an unobservable random variable that can assume various values, such as θ, that drive the sample result.

Using Theorem 6.2 and in particular (6.24), the posterior density of Θ given the sample result $\underline{x} = \{x_1, x_2, ..., x_n\}$ is

$$f(\theta \mid \underline{x}) = \frac{L(\underline{x} \mid \theta)f_\Theta(\theta)}{\displaystyle\int_\Theta L(\underline{x} \mid \theta)f_\Theta(\theta)d\theta}. \qquad (8.56)$$

From previous discussion, we know that the posterior density $f(\theta \mid \underline{x})$ represents the revised degree of belief concerning the uncertainty of Θ. But how should the posterior density be used to determine a point estimate of the realization θ? For this purpose, the Bayesian approach** considers a *loss function,* which represents the economic consequence of choosing, say, $t = u(\underline{x})$ as the estimate when the true value is θ. That is, the loss function assesses the economic loss when we say the value of θ is t when it is actually θ. A loss function, denoted by $l(t, \theta)$, is a nonnegative function of t and θ such that it is zero only if t is the same as θ. Notice that since a loss function is a function of the random

---

*An unknown parameter is more likely to be continuous than discrete, but the discrete case can also be handled in a similar manner.

**For a thorough discussion of the Bayesian approach, the reader is referred to [6].

parameter Θ, then the loss is also a random variable. We are now in a position to define a Bayes estimator.

Definition 8.8 Let $f_\Theta(\theta)$ be the prior density of a random parameter Θ, and let $L(x_1, x_2, ..., x_n \mid \theta)$ be the likelihood function of a random sample of n IID random variables conditioned on the realization θ of Θ. Moreover, let $f(\theta \mid \underline{x})$ be the posterior density of Θ, and let $l(t, \Theta)$ be the loss function. The *Bayes estimator* of θ, say, $T = u(X_1, X_2, ..., X_n)$, is one for which the expectation of the loss function given by

$$E[l(t, \Theta)] = \int_\Theta l(t, \theta)f(\theta \mid \underline{x})d\theta$$

is a minimum.

From Definition 8.8 it is clear that to determine a Bayes estimator, one must specify a loss function. The specification of a particular loss function is a difficult task because economic consequences are not easily measurable. For many applied problems a reasonable argument can be made for using a loss function of the form

$$l(t, \theta) = (t - \theta)^2, \tag{8.57}$$

which is known as a *squared error* or *quadratic* loss function. For a quadratic loss function, it can be shown that the Bayes estimator of θ is the posterior expectation, $E(\Theta \mid \underline{x})$, of Θ. In other words, the mean of the posterior distribution of Θ is the Bayes estimate of θ for a squared error loss function. Notice that this is a reasonable choice to estimate the realization θ since the mean of a random variable is a measure of central tendency and represents the center of gravity of the probability distribution of the random variable.

Example 8.13 A retailer deals in high-quality stereo systems, which she guarantees for two years. From previous information the retailer believes that the proportion of units returned for service or replacement during the two-year period is very close to 0.04 but does vary slightly from this value. The retailer is willing to assign a beta prior distribution to the proportion with parameters $\alpha = 1$ and $\beta = 24$. Based on a random sample of 25 units, the retailer observed that two units required service or replacement during the two-year period. Assuming that the number of units requiring service or replacement in a fixed sample of n units is a binomial random variable, determine the Bayes estimate of the proportion.

In Example 6.9, we showed that for the conditions of this problem the posterior distribution of the proportion is also beta with density given by (6.36). Let the random proportion be denoted by P. Since the parameters of the posterior density of P are $x + \alpha$ and $n + \beta - x$, using (5.40) the posterior mean

$$E(P \mid x) = \frac{x + \alpha}{n + \alpha + \beta} \tag{8.58}$$

is the Bayes estimate of the realization p. Before we compute the estimate, it is worthwhile to compare the Bayes estimate with the maximum likelihood estimate x/n, as determined in Example 8.6. Notice that the Bayes estimate coincides with the maximum likelihood estimate only if $\alpha = \beta = 0$. For this problem the sample result for $n = 25$ is $x = 2$, and the prior parameter values are $\alpha = 1$ and $\beta = 24$. Thus the Bayes estimate is $(2 + 1)/(25 + 1 + 24) = 0.06$, and for comparison, the ML estimate is $2/25 = 0.08$.

It is apparent, therefore, that a Bayes estimate is influenced by both the sample result and the prior distribution. In fact, it can be said that if the prior distribution has a relatively small variance, implying a high degree of belief about a random parameter, then the posterior mean will be close to the prior mean. Suppose, in Example 8.13, that the prior parameter values were $\alpha = 2$ and $\beta = 48$ instead of 1 and 24, respectively. Then the prior mean would be the same as before, or $2/(2 + 48) = 0.04$, but the prior variance would now be 0.0007529, which is smaller than the previous value of 0.0014769. As a result, the posterior mean is now $(2 + 2)/(25 + 2 + 48) = 0.0533$ and is closer to the prior mean than the previous estimate. On the other hand, if a prior distribution had a very large variance, it would be virtually flat and would imply that one's prior belief about the uncertainty of a random parameter is vague. In such a case, the sample evidence would have much more weight in the posterior distribution than the prior distribution, and the Bayes and ML estimates would be virtually the same.

The sample size n also has an effect on how close Bayes and ML estimates are to each other. In general, Bayes estimates and ML estimates will differ by an amount that is small when compared to $1/\sqrt{n}$. Thus for relatively large sample sizes, the two estimates will be close to each other.

8.5.2 Bayesian Interval Estimation

A Bayesian interval estimate for θ can also be determined by using the posterior density function of the random parameter Θ.

Definition 8.9 Let $f(\theta \mid \underline{x})$ be the posterior density function of Θ conditioned on the sample result $\underline{x} = \{x_1, x_2, \ldots, x_n\}$, and let the limits a and b be such that

$$P(a < \Theta < b \mid \underline{x}) = \int_a^b f(\theta \mid \underline{x})d\theta = \gamma, \qquad (8.59)$$

where a and b are some functions of the sample result $\underline{x}$. Then the interval (a,b) is a Bayesian interval such that the probability of θ being contained in (a,b) is γ.

Unlike the confidence intervals in Section 8.4, a Bayesian interval is indeed a probability interval. In other words we can say that with (8.59) the probability is γ that θ is contained in the interval (a,b), whereas with a confidence interval we can only say that in the long run $100\gamma\%$ of all such intervals will contain the true value of θ.

To illustrate a Bayesian probability interval, let $X_1, X_2, \ldots, X_n$ be a random sample from a normal distribution with unknown mean μ but a known variance σ^2. Assume the mean is a random parameter to which we are willing to assign a normal prior distribution with density function

$$f_M(\mu) = \frac{1}{\sigma_0\sqrt{2\pi}} \exp[-(\mu - \mu_0)^2/2\sigma_0^2] \qquad -\infty < \mu < \infty,$$

where μ_0 and σ_0^2 are the prior mean and variance, respectively. From previous discussion (see Example 8.7), the likelihood function given the realization μ is

$$L(x_1, x_2, \ldots, x_n \mid \mu) = (2\pi\sigma^2)^{-n/2}\exp[-\Sigma(x_i - \mu)^2/2\sigma^2].$$

Then it can be shown that the posterior density of the mean conditioned on $\underline{x}$ is also normal with mean

$$E(M \mid \underline{x}) = \frac{n\sigma_0^2\bar{x} + \mu_0\sigma^2}{n\sigma_0^2 + \sigma^2} \tag{8.60}$$

and variance

$$Var(M \mid \underline{x}) = \frac{\sigma^2\sigma_0^2}{n\sigma_0^2 + \sigma^2}. \tag{8.61}$$

Thus the Bayes estimate of μ for a squared error loss function is given by (8.60). As in Example 8.13, notice that a small prior variance σ_0^2 would yield a Bayes estimate for μ that is close to the prior mean μ_0. Moreover, for fixed μ_0 and σ_0^2, as n becomes large the Bayes estimate approaches the maximum likelihood estimate $\bar{x}$.

Example 8.14   Recall Example 8.9 in which we determined 90%, 95%, and 99% confidence intervals for the mean fill μ based on the weights of 16 randomly selected boxes of cereal, where the weights were assumed to be normally distributed with $\sigma = 5$ grams. Due to minor disturbances in the filling process, suppose the mean fill is also a normally distributed random variable with mean $\mu_0 = 500$ and standard deviation $\sigma_0 = 1$. Determine 0.9, 0.95, and 0.99 Bayesian probability intervals for μ.

From Example 8.9, $\bar{x} = 503.75$; then, using (8.60) and (8.61), the posterior mean and variance are computed to be

$$E(M \mid \underline{x}) = \frac{(16)(1)(503.75) + (500)(25)}{(16)(1) + 25} = 501.4634$$

and

$$Var(M \mid \underline{x}) = \frac{(25)(1)}{(16)(1) + 25} = 0.6098,$$

respectively. Since the posterior density of M is $N(501.4634, \sqrt{0.6098})$, and since for, say, $\gamma = 0.9$, $P(-1.645 < Z < 1.645) = 0.9$, where $Z \sim N(0, 1)$, it follows

TABLE 8.4   Bayesian probability intervals for Example 8.14

Probability	Lower limit	Upper limit
0.9	500.18	502.75
0.95	499.93	502.99
0.99	499.45	503.47

from (8.59) that a 0.9 probability interval for μ that is symmetric about the posterior mean is

$$E(M \mid \underline{x}) \pm 1.645 \sqrt{Var(M \mid \underline{x})}.$$

Thus the limits are $a = E(M \mid \underline{x}) - 1.645\sqrt{Var(M \mid \underline{x})}$ and $b = E(M \mid \underline{x}) + 1.645\sqrt{Var(M \mid \underline{x})}$. Substituting the values for $E(M \mid \underline{x})$ and $\sqrt{Var(M \mid \underline{x})}$, we obtain the 0.9 probability interval of (500.18, 502.75) for μ. In a similar manner, we can compute Bayesian intervals for $\gamma = 0.95$ and $\gamma = 0.99$. These are summarized in Table 8.4. Notice that the Bayesian probability intervals are uniformly narrower than the corresponding confidence intervals in Example 8.9.

8.6   Statistical Tolerance Limits

In Section 5.4 we briefly mentioned statistical tolerance limits and commented on their importance for assessing product variability. In this section we will develop statistical tolerance limits when sampling is from an unspecified probability distribution, or when sampling is from a normal distribution. The former limits are known as *distribution-free* tolerance limits because the underlying distribution is not specified.

8.6.1   Distribution-Free Tolerance Limits

Imagine a random phenomenon involving the manufacture of a product. Let X be the measurement variable of this phenomenon, and let $f(x; \theta)$ be the probability density function of X, where θ is some fixed parameter.

Definition 8.10   If D is the proportion of observations of the random variable X that fall between the limits L_1 and L_2, which are single-valued functions of the observations such that

$$D = \int_{L_1}^{L_2} f(x; \theta)dx = F_X(L_2; \theta) - F_X(L_1; \theta), \tag{8.62}$$

then L_1 and L_2 are called *statistical tolerance limits*.

Since L_1 and L_2 are single-valued functions of the observations, they are themselves random variables. In turn, the proportion D is a random variable, and the probability statement

$$P(D \geq d) = \gamma$$

is interpreted to mean that with probability γ the proportion of values of the distribution of X falling between L_1 and L_2 is no less than d.

Let $X_{(r)}$ and $X_{(n-r+1)}$ be the rth smallest and $(n - r + 1)$th largest values in a random sample of size n involving the measurement variable X. It has been shown that the proportion D of values of the distribution of X that fall between $L_1 = X_{(r)}$ and $L_2 = X_{(n-r+1)}$ is beta distributed with parameters $\alpha = n - 2r + 1$ and $\beta = 2r$, irrespective of the form of the probability density function of X, where L_1 and L_2 are of symmetric order. Thus

$$P(D \geqslant d) = 1 - F_B(d; n - 2r + 1, 2r) = \gamma. \tag{8.63}$$

Expression (8.63) is indeed powerful because it allows for the determination of statistical tolerance limits without requiring the specification of the distribution of the underlying random variable X. Such limits are known as distribution-free tolerance limits. Notice that the relation (8.63) involves the four quantities n, r, d, and γ. With the use of beta tables, knowledge of any three will produce the fourth.

The primary use of (8.63) is to determine the smallest sample size such that with probability γ at least a proportion d of the distribution of X will be included between the two extreme values of the sample, $X_{(1)}$ and $X_{(n)}$. That is, for $r = 1$, (8.63) reduces to

$$P(D \geqslant d) = 1 - F_B(d; n - 1, 2) = \gamma,$$

which further simplifies to

$$\gamma = 1 - [nd^{n-1} - (n - 1)d^n], \tag{8.64}$$

as a result of being able to express the beta distribution function as a summation if one of the shape parameters is a small integer (see [1]).

Figure 8.2 provides several useful proportions d as functions of the sample size n and the probability γ. For example, if a sample of size 25 is drawn at random from a distribution with unknown probability density function, the probability is 0.973 that at least 80 percent of the values of X will be included between the two extreme values of the sample.

Many times, one-sided tolerance limits are sought so that with probability γ at least a proportion d of the distribution of X will exceed a lower tolerance limit or be less than an upper tolerance limit. Again irrespective of the distribution of X, it can be shown that

$$P(D \geqslant d) = 1 - F_B(d; n - r + 1, r) = \gamma. \tag{8.65}$$

Notice that if $r = 1$, inference will be based on the smallest value in the sample, $X_{(1)}$; and if $r = n$, the inference will be based on the largest value, $X_{(n)}$. For $r = 1$, it can be shown that (8.65) reduces to

$$P(D \geqslant d) = 1 - d^n = \gamma.$$

Thus by solving for the sample size n, we obtain

$$n = \frac{\log(1 - \gamma)}{\log(d)}. \tag{8.66}$$

FIGURE 8.2 Proportions d as functions of sample size n and probability γ

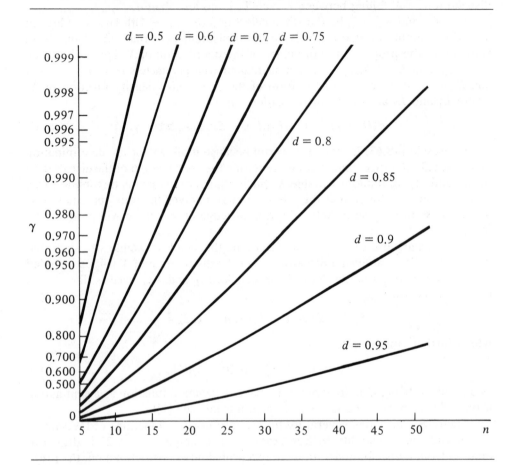

Expression (8.66) allows the determination of the required sample size for which, with probability γ, at least a proportion d of the values of X will exceed the smallest value in the sample.

8.6.2 Tolerance Limits When Sampling from a Normal Distribution

In some situations the underlying distribution can be adequately modeled by a normal distribution. In this section we examine statistical tolerance limits for these situations.

Recall that statistical tolerance limits place limits on actual measurements of the distribution, unlike confidence intervals, which determine intervals within which an unknown parameter is likely to be found. Thus if sampling is from $N(\mu; \sigma)$ such that both μ and σ are known, then for example, the limits $\mu \pm 1.645\sigma$, $\mu \pm 1.96\sigma$, and $\mu \pm 2.575\sigma$ will include 90%, 95%, and 99% of the distribution, respectively. Or for one-sided limits, 90% of the observations of the distribution will exceed the lower limit of $\mu - 1.28\sigma$, and 99% will be less than the upper limit of $\mu + 2.33\sigma$. The only problem, of course, is that we are not likely to know the mean μ and the variance σ^2.

Suppose we consider the estimators $\overline{X}$ and S^2. Since both of these are random variables and are subjected to sampling variability, it is not true to say, for example, that 90% of the distribution will be contained in the interval $\overline{X} \pm 1.645S$. Alternatively, consider the random interval $\overline{X} \pm kS$, where k is an appropriate constant pertinent to the joint distribution of $\overline{X}$ and S^2. Since $\overline{X} \pm kS$ are random limits, it is impossible to state with absolute certainty what percentage of the distribution will be contained within these limits. In other words, as with confidence intervals, we cannot find k such that the computed limits, which are based on some random sample, will always include a fixed percentage of the distribution. However, we can select k such that if we were to repeatedly draw samples of the same size from a normal distribution, a fixed proportion γ of these limits will contain at least $100d\%$ of the distribution values. That is, the random interval $\overline{X} \pm kS$ has probability γ of containing at least $100d\%$ of the sampled normal distribution. Based on a random sample of size n, two-sided $100\gamma\%$ tolerance limits for a $100d$ percentage of a normal distribution are $\overline{x} \pm ks$, where γ is the confidence coefficient and d is the distribution coverage. Table H of the Appendix contains k values for selected values of n, γ, and d.

Many times we are only interested in one-sided tolerance limits. For example, in the manufacture of pistons, if the diameter is below a certain tolerance, the piston must be scrapped. However, if the diameter of a piston exceeds an upper tolerance, it can be reworked to an acceptable level. As one would expect, the values k for one-sided tolerance limits are not the same as those found in Table H. These are found in Table I of the Appendix for frequently used values of n, γ, and d. Accordingly, we can determine a value k such that we are 100γ percent confident that at least a $100d$ percentage of the values of a normal distribution will exceed the lower tolerance limit $\overline{x} - ks$, or will be less than the upper tolerance limit $\overline{x} + ks$.

Example 8.15 In a highly competitive environment, the availability of a product upon demand is crucial to the success of a business. To determine an upper tolerance limit for actual monthly demand for a particular product, a retail establishment has collected what it believes is a random sample of monthly demands consisting of the following data: 129, 142, 145, 153, 136, 138, 163, 151, 146, 128, 133, 148, 144, 140, 143. If monthly demand for this product is well approximated by a normal distribution, determine an upper tolerance limit with $\gamma = 0.99$ and $d = 0.95$.

For $\gamma = 0.99$, $d = 0.95$, and $n = 15$, we determine from Table I of the Appendix that $k = 3.102$. Based on the data, the sample mean and standard deviation are computed to be $\overline{x} = 142.6$ and $s = 9.2798$, respectively. The upper tolerance limit is $142.6 + (3.102)(9.2798) = 171.39$. Thus we are 99% confident that 95% of all possible demands will be less than 171.39 units per month. In other words, if such a business establishment stocks approximately 172 units of the product per month, it will have a high assurance of meeting monthly demand for this product.

It should be emphasized once again that the statistical tolerance limits developed in this section are with respect to sampling from a normal distribution. If there is doubt about this assumption, one should use the distribution-free tolerance limits discussed in Section 8.6.1. It is reasonable to expect distribution-free tolerance limits to be more conservative than those based on the normal distribution since less information is available.

References

1. K. V. Bury, *Statistical models in applied science,* Wiley, New York, 1975.
2. R. V. Hogg and A. T. Craig, *Introduction to mathematical statistics,* 4th ed., MacMillan, New York, 1978.
3. A. M. Mood and F. A. Graybill, *Introduction to the theory of statistics,* 2nd ed., McGraw-Hill, New York, 1963.
4. C. R. Rao, *Advanced statistical methods in biometric research,* Wiley, New York, 1952.
5. S. S. Wilks, *Mathematical statistics,* Wiley, New York, 1962.
6. R. L. Winkler, *An introduction to Bayesian inference and decision,* Holt, Rinehart and Winston, New York, 1972.

Exercises

8.1. In a binomial experiment exactly x successes are observed in n independent trials. The following two statistics are proposed as estimators of the proportion parameter p: $T_1 = X/n$ and $T_2 = (X + 1)/(n + 2)$.

   a. Determine and compare the mean squared errors for T_1 and T_2.
   b. Graph the MSE of each statistic as a function of p for $n = 10$ and $n = 25$. Is one estimator uniformly better than the other?

8.2. Let X_1, X_2, X_3, and X_4 be a random sample of size 4 from a population whose distribution is exponential with unknown parameter θ. Which of the following statistics are unbiased estimators of θ?

$$T_1 = \frac{1}{6}(X_1 + X_2) + \frac{1}{3}(X_3 + X_4)$$

$$T_2 = (X_1 + 2X_2 + 3X_3 + 4X_4)/5$$

$$T_3 = (X_1 + X_2 + X_3 + X_4)/4$$

8.3. Show that the statistic T_1 in Exercise 8.1 is a consistent estimator of the binomial parameter p.

8.4. Use Tchebysheff's theorem to show that the statistic T_2 in Exercise 8.1 is a consistent estimator of the binomial parameter p.

8.5. Among the unbiased estimators of θ in Exercise 8.2, determine the one with the smallest variance. What are the relative efficiencies of the other unbiased estimators relative to the one with the smallest variance?

8.6. Let X_1, X_2, X_3, X_4, and X_5 be a random sample from a population whose distribution is normal with mean μ and variance σ^2. Consider the statistics $T_1 = (X_1 + X_2 + \cdots + X_5)/5$ and $T_2 = (X_1 + X_2 + 2X_3 + X_4 + X_5)/6$ as estimators of μ. Identify the statistic with the smaller variance.

8.7. Use the Cramér–Rao lower bound to determine the variance of the minimum variance unbiased estimator of θ when sampling from a population whose distribution is the exponential with density $f(x; \theta) = (1/\theta)\exp(-x/\theta)$, $x > 0$. Deduce that the efficient estimator of θ is the sample mean.

8.8. Let $X_1, X_2, \ldots, X_n$ be a random sample from a population whose distribution is gamma with known shape parameter. Show that the maximum likelihood estimator of the scale parameter is given by expression (8.8).

8.9. Let $X_1, X_2, \ldots, X_n$ be a random sample from a population whose distribution is the Poisson with parameter λ. Determine the maximum likelihood estimator of λ.

8.10. Let $X_1, X_2, \ldots, X_n$ be a random sample from a population whose distribution is the exponential with scale parameter θ. Determine the maximum likelihood estimator of θ and show that it is a sufficient statistic for θ.

8.11. Let $X_1, X_2, \ldots, X_n$ be a random sample from a population whose distribution is the Rayleigh with density $f(x; \sigma^2) = (x/\sigma^2)\exp(-x^2/2\sigma^2)$, $x > 0$. Determine the maximum likelihood estimator of σ^2. Is it a sufficient statistic for σ^2?

8.12. Equivalent to Definition 8.7, we define the rth sample moment about the sample mean to be

$$M_r = \frac{\sum_{i=1}^{n} (X_i - \overline{X})^r}{n},$$

where $X_1, X_2, \ldots, X_n$ is a random sample. Use sample moments about the sample mean to compute the sample shape factors for the data in Exercise 1.1. Can you infer anything about the nature of the underlying distribution based on the shape factors?

8.13. Repeat Exercise 8.12 using the data in Exercise 1.2.

8.14. Table 8.5 is a frequency distribution for automobile accidents compiled for a California driver record study.* Assuming the number of accidents is a negative binomial random variable, use the method of moments to estimate the negative binomial parameters k and p. Compare the observed frequencies with those determined by using the estimates of k and p.

8.15. The following is a random sample of observed lifetimes in hours of a certain electrical component: 142.84, 97.04, 32.46, 69.14, 85.67, 114.43, 41.76, 163.07, 108.22, 63.28. Assume the lifetime of such a component is a Weibull random variable with shape parameter $\alpha = 2$.

a. Determine a maximum likelihood estimate of the scale parameter θ.
b. Would the method of moments yield a different estimate of θ than the one determined in part a?
c. Use your answer in part a to estimate the reliability of such a component at $t = 150$ hours.

*Multivariate analysis of driver accident frequencies over a period of 14 years, California Department of Motor Vehicles, FHWA Project No. B0149, 1975.

TABLE 8.5

Number of accidents	Number of drivers
0	35,068
1	13,411
2	4,013
3	1,184
4	353
5	93
6	29
7	8
8	4
9 or more	2

8.16. Using the answer to part a in Exercise 8.15, determine the time at which the reliability of the component is 0.95.

8.17. The following are the ordered times to failure in hours of ten components that failed out of 40 subjected to a life test: 421, 436, 448, 474, 496, 499, 510, 525, 593, 675. Assume that time to failure is an exponentially distributed random variable.

 a. Determine a maximum likelihood estimate of the parameter θ.

 b. Use your answer in part a to estimate the reliability of such a component at $t = 4000$ hours.

8.18. A life test will be terminated when $m < n$ units fail. If time to failure is a Weibull random variable with known shape parameter, determine the maximum likelihood estimator of the scale parameter θ.

8.19. We wish to determine the likelihood of a successful business operation for specialty shops in large suburban shopping malls. In a large metropolitan area, a random sample of 30 such shops is selected from various malls with the characteristic of interest being the length of time the shops remain in operation. A meaningful data base would be established by observing when the first eight of these ceased to operate. The following are the ordered lengths of operation in months: 3.2, 3.9, 5.9, 6.5, 16.5, 20.3, 40.4, 50.9. Assume the length of time a shop of this kind remains in operation is a Weibull random variable with $\alpha = 0.8$.

 a. Use the result of Exercise 8.18 to determine the maximum likelihood estimate of θ.

 b. Based on your answer to part a, what is the probability that such a shop will be operating after two years from the time it opened? After ten years?

8.20. The throughput time of batch computer programs, defined as the time difference between the first card read and last line printed, is made up of three distinct components: input queue time, central processor time, and output queue time. The following are the throughput times in minutes of a random sample of 15 similar computer programs: 12.5, 5.2, 6.8, 3.6, 10.9, 12.8, 7.8, 8.6, 6.3, 6.9, 18.2, 15.4, 9.2, 10.3, 7.3. Assume the throughput time is adequately modeled by a gamma distribution with $\alpha = 3$.

 a. Determine the maximum likelihood estimate of the scale parameter θ.

 b. Would the method of moments yield a different estimate of θ than the one determined in part a?

c. Use your answer in part a to compute the probability of a throughput time exceeding 20 minutes.

8.21. A manufacturer of a synthetic fiber wishes to estimate the mean breaking strength of the fiber. An experiment is devised in which the breaking strengths in pounds are observed for 16 strands randomly selected from the process. The strengths are 20.8, 20.6, 21.0, 20.9, 19.9, 20.2, 19.8, 19.6, 20.9, 21.1, 20.4, 20.6, 19.7, 19.6, 20.3, and 20.7. Assuming the breaking strength of the fiber is adequately modeled by a normal distribution with a known standard deviation of 0.45 pounds, construct a 98% confidence interval estimate for the true average breaking strength of the fiber.

8.22. Referring to Exercise 8.21, which of the following statements are appropriate for the interpretation of the confidence interval?

a. The probability that the true average strength of the fiber is between the confidence limits is 0.98.
b. Approximately 98% of the confidence intervals computed as a result of repeated samples of size 16 from the process that produces the synthetic fiber would include the true average strength of the fiber.
c. The probability that the breaking strength of any such fiber is outside the confidence limits is 0.02.

8.23. Use the methods in Section 5.9 to generate 100 samples of size 16 each from a normal distribution with mean 100 and standard deviation 10. For each sample, construct a 95% confidence interval for μ. How many of the intervals include the known value of 100 for μ? See Exercise 8.36.

8.24. A doughnut shop is interested in estimating its daily average sales volume. Suppose the standard deviation is known to be $50.

a. If the sales volume is adequately approximated by a normal distribution, how large a sample is needed so that with probability 0.95 the sample mean will be within $20 of the true average sales volume?
b. Determine the needed sample size if the normal assumption cannot be made.

8.25. Referring to Exercise 8.24, generate 100 samples, each of the size determined in part a, from a normal distribution with mean and standard deviation 400 and 50, respectively. Compute the sample mean for each sample. How many of the sample means are within $20 of the known value of 400 for μ? Is your result in line with what is expected?

8.26. It is believed that the range of hourly wages paid to auto mechanics in a large city is $9. If we assume that hourly wages are approximately normally distributed, how large a sample is necessary so that with probability 0.99 the sample mean will be within one dollar of the true average hourly wages? Answer the same question without the use of the normal assumption.

8.27. The Chamber of Commerce in a large city is interested in estimating the average amount of money that people attending conventions spend for meals, lodging, and entertainment per day. Sixteen persons were randomly selected from various conventions taking place in this city and were asked to record their expenditures for a given day. The following information was obtained in dollars: 150, 175, 163, 148, 142, 189, 135, 174, 168, 152, 158, 184, 134, 146, 155, 163. If we assume the amount spent per day is a normally distributed random variable, determine 90%, 95%, and 98% confidence interval estimates for the true average amount.

8.28. Referring to Exercise 8.21, determine a 98% confidence interval estimate for the true average breaking strength without assuming knowledge of the population standard deviation. How does this interval compare with the one constructed in Exercise 8.21?

8.29. To check the sensitivity of the Student's t distribution to the assumption that sampling is from a normal distribution, generate 100 random samples of size ten each from an exponential distribution with $\theta = 20$. For each sample, construct a 95% confidence interval estimate for the mean. How many of the intervals contain the known mean value $\theta = 20$? Repeat the process, increasing the sample size to 30. Do you notice a difference? Comment on your results. See Exercise 8.37.

8.30. A random sample of hourly wages for nine auto mechanics yielded the following data (dollars): 10.5, 11, 9.5, 12, 10, 11.5, 13, 9, 8.5. Under the assumption that sampling is from a normal distribution, construct 90%, 95%, and 99% confidence interval estimates for the mean hourly wages of all auto mechanics and interpret your results.

8.31. Two state-supported universities have distinct methods of registering students at the beginning of each semester. The two universities wish to compare the average time it takes students to go through registration. The registration times of 100 randomly selected students were observed at each university. The sample means and sample standard deviations are as follows:

$$\bar{x}_1 = 50.2 \qquad \bar{x}_2 = 52.9$$

$$s_1 = 4.8 \qquad s_2 = 5.4$$

If we assume sampling is from independent normal populations with equal variances, determine 90%, 95%, and 99% confidence interval estimates for the difference of mean registration times at the universities. Based on this evidence, are you likely to conclude that a real difference in mean time exists?

8.32. A certain metal is currently manufactured by a standard process. A new process has been developed in which an alloy is added to the production of the metal. The manufacturers are interested in estimating the true difference between the mean breaking strengths of the metals produced by the two processes. Twelve specimens of the metal are randomly selected from each of the two production methods, and each specimen is subjected to stress until a crack is observed. The following are the breaking strengths of the specimens in kilograms per square centimeter:

Standard process	428	419	458	439	441	456	463	429	438	445	441	463
New process	462	448	435	465	429	472	453	459	427	468	452	447

If sampling is assumed to be from two independent normal distributions with equal variances, determine 90%, 95%, and 99% confidence interval estimates for $\mu_S - \mu_N$. Based on your results, are you likely to conclude that a real difference exists between μ_S and μ_N?

8.33. A cost-of-living survey was conducted for the two largest cities in a state by an appropriate agency to determine average grocery expenses for four-person families in the two cities. Twenty such families were randomly selected from each city, and their weekly grocery expenses were observed. The sample means and sample standard deviations are as follows:

$$\bar{x}_1 = 135 \qquad \bar{x}_2 = 122$$

$$s_1 = 15 \qquad s_2 = 10$$

If we assume sampling is from independent normal populations with equal variances, determine 95% and 99% confidence interval estimates for $\mu_1 - \mu_2$. Are you likely to conclude that a real difference exists between μ_1 and μ_2?

8.34. Some nominal random variation in the thickness of plastic sheets produced by a machine is expected. To determine whether the variation in the thickness is within acceptable limits, twelve plastic sheets were randomly selected from a day's production, and their thickness in millimeters was measured. The following are the recorded data: 12.6, 11.9, 12.3, 12.8, 11.8, 11.7, 12.4, 12.1, 12.3, 12.0, 12.5, 12.9. If we assume the thickness is a normally distributed random variable, determine 90%, 95%, and 99% confidence interval estimates for the unknown variance of the thickness. If a standard deviation in excess of 0.9 millimeters is not acceptable, is there reason for concern based on this evidence?

8.35. Using the data in Exercise 8.27, determine a 95% confidence interval estimate for the unknown variance and interpret your result.

8.36. Referring to Exercise 8.23, for each sample construct a 95% confidence interval for σ^2. How many of the intervals include the known value of 100 for σ^2? Is the result in line with what you expect?

8.37. To check the sensitivity of the chi-square distribution to the assumption that sampling is from a normal distribution, repeat Exercise 8.29, constructing for each sample a 95% confidence interval estimate for σ^2. Relative to the two sample sizes, how many of the intervals contain the known value of $\sigma^2 = 400$? Based on these results, compare the sensitivities of the Student's t distribution and the chi-square distribution to the assumption of normal sampling.

8.38. A state agency charged with the responsibility of monitoring water quality for commercial fishing is interested in comparing the variation of a certain toxic substance at two estuaries whose waters contain industrial waste from nearby plants. Eleven water samples selected at various locations in the first estuary are analyzed, and eight water samples are analyzed from the other estuary. The recorded measurements in ppm are shown in Table 8.6. If sampling is assumed to be from two independent

TABLE 8.6 Levels of a toxic substance (ppm)

Estuary 1	*Estuary 2*
10	11
10	8
12	9
13	7
9	10
8	8
12	8
12	10
10	
14	
8	

normal populations, determine a 95% confidence interval estimate for the ratio σ_1^2/σ_2^2 of the two unknown variances. Based on this result, are you likely to conclude the two variances are different? Why?

8.39. Refer to Exercise 8.32 to construct a 99% confidence interval estimate for the ratio σ_1^2/σ_2^2, where σ_1^2 is the variance of the standard process and σ_2^2 is the variance of the new process. Based on this result, is the assumption of equal variances a reasonable one?

8.40. The final poll in a recent senatorial election revealed that 1400 out of 2500 randomly selected individuals who are likely to vote on election day indicated a preference for candidate A over candidate B.

   a. Determine a lower one-sided 99% confidence interval for the true proportion of voters favoring candidate A. Based on this result, would you say that A is likely to win the election? Why?
   b. Suppose 225 persons were randomly sampled with the same sample proportion favoring candidate A as in part a. Are the results different this time?
   c. Are the assumptions for the approximate 99% confidence intervals reasonable in this case?

8.41. You receive a large lot of items from a manufacturer who claims that the production percent defective is 1%. Out of 200 items randomly selected and inspected, you find eight defectives. Determine approximate 90%, 95%, and 99% confidence intervals for the true proportion defective in this production process. Based on these results, what can you conclude about the manufacturer's claim?

8.42. A medical researcher wishes to estimate the proportion of middle-aged, heavy-smoking males who will develop lung cancer during the next five years. The researcher wants to select a number of these men who have been smoking at least two packs of cigarettes a day for no less than 20 years and observe them for the next five years to see how many develop lung cancer. How large a random sample of these men should the researcher select so that with an approximate probability of 0.95, the sample proportion will be within 0.02 units of the true proportion?

8.43. Auditing firms usually select a random sample of a bank's customers to confirm checking account balances as reported by the bank. If an auditing firm is interested in estimating the proportion of accounts for which there is a discrepancy between customer and bank, how many accounts should be selected so that with approximately 99% confidence the sample proportion will be within 0.05 units of the true proportion?

8.44. The weekly sales volume at a convenience store is adequately represented by a normal distribution with an unknown mean μ but a known standard deviation $\sigma = \$2{,}000$. Due to many minor influences, it is believed that the average weekly sales volume can also be considered a random variable. Suppose we are willing to assign a normal distribution to the weekly mean with $\mu_0 = \$20{,}000$ and $\sigma_0 = \$200$. A random sample of 16 weeks reveals a sample mean sales volume of $\$21{,}500$.

   a. For a squared error loss function, determine the Bayes estimate of μ.
   b. Determine a 95% Bayesian probability interval estimate for μ.
   c. Determine a 95% confidence interval for μ and compare it to your estimate in part b.
   d. Repeat parts a through c with $\sigma_0 = 100$, and comment on your result.
   e. Repeat parts a through c with $\sigma_0 = 800$, and comment on your result.
   f. Suppose $n = 64$; assuming that $\bar{x} = 21{,}500$, how would this affect your answers to parts a through c?

8.45. A real estate office has been able to determine that the daily number of incoming calls to the office is a Poisson random variable. Because of fluctuating real estate market conditions, the firm has also concluded that the Poisson parameter is a gamma distributed random variable with shape and scale parameters of 20 and 4, respectively. On a randomly selected day, 90 calls are received.

    a. For a squared error loss function, determine the Bayes estimate of the Poisson parameter.

    b. Determine a 99% Bayesian probability interval. (Hint: Use (5.51).)

8.46. A hotel builder is very much interested in the breaking strength of steel cables that will hold up a catwalk suspended above the hotel lobby. The contractor hires an independent testing organization and instructs them to determine a lower tolerance limit for the breaking strengths of the cables such that 99% of the strengths will exceed this limit with 0.95 probability. The testing organization selects at random 20 cable specimens and tests them for their breaking strengths. The test results in kilograms per square centimeter are 2130, 2158, 2192, 2110, 2145, 2208, 2201, 2195, 2125, 2148, 2166, 2172, 2192, 2138, 2210, 2215, 2108, 2105, 2120, and 2130. If we assume the breaking strength of such a cable is a normally distributed random variable, determine the desired tolerance limit.

8.47. The inside diameter of a bearing is a crucial measurement in the manufacture of these bearings. Based on a random sample of 25 bearings, the sample mean was 3 cm and the sample standard deviation was 0.005 cm. Determine two-sided tolerance limits such that with probability 0.99, 95% of the inside diameters of all bearings manufactured by this process will be inside the tolerance limits. Assume the inside diameter is a normally distributed random variable.

8.48. Suppose that in Exercise 8.47 we could not assume the normal distribution. If the largest and smallest diameters observed in the sample of 25 bearings were 3.013 and 2.984 respectively, and we are interested in an interval that covers 90%, 95%, or 99% of all inside diameters, what probability can be associated with the interval 2.984 to 3.013 for each proportion of coverage?

8.49. Suppose we could not assume the normal distribution in Exercise 8.46. For the same probability and sample size, what would be the proportion of breaking strengths that would exceed the smallest value of the twenty observations? How large a sample would be necessary in this case to have the same probability and proportion of coverage as in Exercise 8.46?

8.50. Suppose we are sampling from a population whose probability distribution is unknown. How large a sample is necessary so that with probability 0.99, at least 95% of the values of the random variable of interest will be included between the two extreme values in the sample?

8.51. Suppose we are sampling from a population whose probability distribution is unknown. How large a sample is necessary so that with probability 0.99, at least 97% of the values of the random variable will exceed the smallest value in the sample?

CHAPTER NINE

Testing Statistical Hypotheses

9.1 Introduction

In Chapter 8 we examined statistical inference with regard to point and interval estimation. In this chapter we take up the other primary area of statistical inference: testing a statistical hypothesis. As we will see, testing statistical hypotheses is strongly related to the concept of estimation.

A statistical hypothesis is a claim about some unknown feature of a population of interest. The essence of testing a statistical hypothesis is to decide whether the claim is supported by the experimental evidence obtained through a random sample. Usually, the claim involves either some unknown parameter or an unknown functional form of the underlying distribution from which we are sampling. The decision on whether the sample data statistically support the claim is based on probability. Simply put, the claim will be rejected if its chance of being correct is small in the face of the observed evidence.

To a large extent, our approach here will be more intuitive than theoretical because we feel that with this approach the reader stands to gain insight into the essence of statistical hypotheses. Initially, we will develop the foundation for testing statistical hypotheses. Then we will examine several areas of application with regard to means, variances, and proportions.

9.2 Basic Concepts for Testing Statistical Hypotheses

To illustrate the notion of statistical hypotheses, suppose, for example, that we are interested in the average time it takes units to be assembled in an assembly line operation. Under standard operating conditions, the target average time to assemble a unit is 10 minutes. The plant manager would like to allow the process to continue operating unless substantial evidence is found that the average time is not 10 minutes. The evidence will be in the form of a random sample of size n obtained from the underlying distribution for a unit's assembly time. How should one approach the problem of deciding whether to allow the process to continue operating?

The answer to such a question is the focal point of this chapter. Notice that here we are not interested, per se, in estimating the unknown mean time μ. Rather, we want to determine whether the value of μ is 10. In other words, even before the sample is selected, we have conjectured that we will be sampling from a distribution whose mean is 10. If the claim is statistically plausible based on the experimental evidence, then it will be assumed that the target average of 10 minutes is being realized, and the assembly process will be allowed to continue operating. On the other hand, if the claim is not statistically supported by the sample evidence, the plant manager may decide to stop the process and make appropriate adjustments.

Let us label the claim that $\mu = 10$ as the *null hypothesis* and write it as

$$H_0: \mu = 10.$$

Notice that with H_0 we have specified a single value for the parameter in question. In fact, if a statistical hypothesis assigns particular values to all unknown parameters and identifies the functional form of the underlying distribution, it is called a *simple hypothesis*. Otherwise it is known as a *composite hypothesis*. Thus $H_0: \mu = 10$ is a simple hypothesis only if the functional form of the underlying distribution and values for other unknown parameters (if any) have been specified. If the null hypothesis were stated as $H_0: \mu \le 10$ or $H_0: \mu \ge 10$, it would not be a simple hypothesis because it does not assign one specific value to μ.

A null hypothesis should be regarded as true unless sufficient evidence to the contrary is presented. In other words, we will reject the null hypothesis that the mean assembly time is 10 minutes only if the experimental evidence is strongly against it. A close parallel to this interpretation of the null hypothesis is found in our judicial process in which the accused is presumed not guilty until proven otherwise. That is, by defining the null hypothesis as "not guilty" we insist that it be rejected only if the prosecution provides sufficient evidence to the contrary.

Let us analyze the possible decisions one can make with regard to the null hypothesis $H_0: \mu = 10$. In doing this, we must take into account the consequences that may arise from the true state of nature: In reality μ may or may not be equal to 10. Simply put, there are two possible decisions about H_0 — *reject H_0* or *fail to reject H_0*.* However, each one of these decisions has the following two possible consequences with regard to the state of nature:

Reject H_0 $\begin{cases} \text{when in fact } H_0 \text{ is true,} \\ \text{when in fact } H_0 \text{ is false,} \end{cases}$ Fail to reject H_0 $\begin{cases} \text{when in fact } H_0 \text{ is true,} \\ \text{when in fact } H_0 \text{ is false.} \end{cases}$

If the decision is to reject H_0, then either we have rejected something that in reality is true (incorrect decision), or we have rejected something that in reality is false (correct decision). If we cannot reject H_0, either we cannot reject something that is true (correct decision), or we cannot reject something that in reality is false (incorrect decision). Therefore, whether the decision is to reject or to fail

*The reason why we have used the phrase "fail to reject H_0" rather than "accept H_0" will become apparent in due time.

to reject H_0, there is the possibility of making the wrong decision with regard to the true state of nature.

When a decision is made about a null hypothesis, two of the possible consequences relative to the true state of nature lead to inferential errors. The rejection of the hypothesis H_0 when in reality H_0 is true constitutes what is called *type I error*. Failure to reject H_0 when in reality H_0 is false constitutes *type II error*. The reader should note that type I error is possible only when the decision is to reject the null hypothesis, and type II error is possible only when the decision is not to reject H_0. In other words, if the null hypothesis is really true, only a type I error can be made, and if the null hypothesis is false, only a type II error is possible. One cannot commit both errors simultaneously. Obviously, one should be concerned with the possibility of committing either type of error. However, it is important to understand that a decision on a statistical hypothesis is an inferential process, which is always subject to error. The decision to reject H_0 does not necessarily mean that H_0 is false; but the sample evidence on which such a decision is based does provide some degree of confidence — parallel to that in interval estimation — with which one can proceed *as if H_0* were false.

It is imperative to have some quantity that measures the likelihood of committing either one of these errors. Such a measure is a probability.

Definition 9.1   The probability of rejecting H_0, given that H_0 is true, is defined to be the probability (or size) of type I error and is denoted by α, $0 \leq \alpha \leq 1$.

Definition 9.2   The probability of not rejecting H_0, given that H_0 is false, is defined to be the probability (or size) of type II error and is denoted by β, $0 \leq \beta \leq 1$.

Hence the probabilities of type I and type II errors are given by the statements

$$P(\text{reject } H_0 \mid H_0 \text{ is true}) = \alpha \qquad (9.1)$$

and

$$P(\text{cannot reject } H_0 \mid H_0 \text{ is false}) = \beta. \qquad (9.2)$$

Notice that both α and β are conditional probabilities. One cannot determine the probabilities of type I and type II errors in an absolute sense because the true state of nature is not known. Rather, we can compute the probability α of rejecting H_0 only if we assume H_0 is true, or the probability β of failing to reject H_0, if we assume H_0 is false.

When a claim is incorporated in the statement of the null hypothesis, we need to devise a rule that will tell us what decision to make about H_0 once the sample evidence becomes available. Such a rule is called a test of a statistical hypothesis.

Definition 9.3   A *test* of a statistical hypothesis concerning some unknown feature of a population of interest is any rule for deciding whether to reject the null hypothesis based on a random sample from the population.

The decision is based on some appropriate statistic called the *test statistic*. For certain values of the test statistic, the decision will be to reject the null hypothesis. These values constitute what is known as the *critical region* of the test. For illustration, recall the null hypothesis H_0: $\mu = 10$. For a given sample size n, suppose we decide to reject H_0 if we observe a value of the sample mean $\overline{X}$ that exceeds 12. Then $\overline{X}$ is the test statistic, the value $\overline{X} = 12$ is the *critical value,* and the set of values of $\overline{X}$ greater than 12 constitutes the critical region of the test.

To show the critical region graphically, assume that n is sufficiently large so that the sampling distribution of the test statistic $\overline{X}$, given that H_0 is true, is essentially a normal distribution. Figure 9.1 shows the critical region as the shaded area to the right of the critical value $\overline{X} = 12$. The area of the critical region is the same as the size of the type I error α. In other words, $P(\overline{X} > 12 | \mu = 10) = \alpha$. The interpretation of α is analogous to that in confidence intervals. That is, the probability α is only in reference to the region $\overline{X} > 12$ involving the random variable $\overline{X}$, given that $\mu = 10$. But the decision whether to reject H_0 will be based on a single sample of size n, from which the estimate $\overline{x}$ will be computed. Thus if $\overline{x} > 12$, it does not mean that the probability of H_0 being correct is α; rather, it implies a long-run relative frequency interpretation for α. In other words, if μ is really equal to 10, and if we were to repeatedly draw samples of size n from this population, we would expect $100\alpha\%$ of the time to find a value of the test statistic $\overline{X}$ to be greater than 12, and thus would reject the null hypothesis. Only in this sense are we willing to say that our confidence in rejecting H_0 when the estimate $\overline{x} > 12$ is the same as the complement of the type I error α, or $1 - \alpha$.

To construct a suitable decision rule for testing a statistical hypothesis, it is also necessary to state an *alternative hypothesis* that reflects the possible value or range of values of the parameter of interest if the null hypothesis is false. That is, the alternative hypothesis represents some form of negation of the null hypothesis. The alternative hypothesis is usually denoted by H_1 and may be simple or composite. Although no generalization is intended, often it is desired to state a null hypothesis that is more specific than the alternative. Thus the

FIGURE 9.1 The critical region as an area

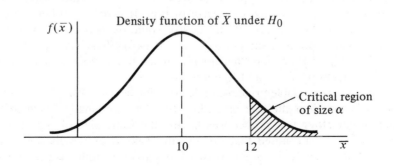

Density function of $\overline{X}$ under H_0

$f(\overline{x})$

Critical region of size α

10   12 $\overline{x}$

null is usually simple, while the alternative is usually a composite hypothesis. For example, suppose the plant manager suspects that the average assembly time is greater than 10 minutes. Then the appropriate null and alternative hypotheses would be

$$H_0: \mu = 10,$$

$$H_1: \mu > 10.$$

The rationale for this is that if the sample evidence does not support the rejection of the null hypothesis, then the plant manager may proceed as if H_0 is true. Otherwise, his or her suspicion would be substantiated, and some corrective action may be necessary.

According to Definition 9.3, the test procedure will be constructed such that the null hypothesis will or will not be rejected. In this sense, H_0 is referred to as the hypothesis to be tested. However, with the inclusion of the alternative hypothesis, it would be more descriptive to say that a statistical test of a hypothesis is to provide a decision between H_0 and H_1. In light of this, care must be exercised in stating the null and alternative hypotheses.

Let us return to the judicial process analogy to shed light on this matter. If the null hypothesis is "not guilty," then surely the alternative must be "guilty." The rejection of the null hypothesis would imply that the prosecution has been able to present sufficient evidence to warrant a guilty verdict. On the other hand, if the prosecution does not present sufficient evidence for conviction, the verdict will be not guilty. Such a decision does not necessarily imply that the accused is innocent; rather it emphasizes the lack of substantive evidence needed to convict the accused. Therefore, in some sense a guilty verdict (the rejection of H_0) is regarded as a stronger decision than a not guilty verdict (failure to reject H_0), which stems from the generally accepted judicial principle that it is worse to convict an innocent person than to let a guilty one go. If the verdict is guilty, we want to have a very high degree of assurance that an innocent person has not been convicted. In many situations, therefore, the type I error is thought to be more serious than the type II error.

In testing statistical hypotheses, the usual approach is to accept the premise that the type I error is a more serious error than type II and to formulate the null and alternative hypotheses accordingly. As a result, we often select in advance the maximum size of type I error we can tolerate and attempt to construct a test procedure that minimizes the size of type II error. In other words, it is not possible to fix both α and β and devise some decision rule for testing H_0 versus H_1, given a random sample of size n. It is for these reasons that we say "fail to reject H_0" rather than "accept H_0" when the sample evidence does not support the rejection of the null hypothesis.

A simple and reasonable principle in determining decision rules to test statistical hypotheses is to select the test procedure that has the smallest size of type II error among all other test procedures having the same size of type I error. In this context it must be noted that one cannot make α extremely small without increasing β as a result. In other words, for a given sample size n, the size of type II error will normally increase as the size of type I error decreases. In practice, what is usually done is to adjust the size of the type I error by changing the critical value of the test statistic and thus achieve a satisfactory balance between the two error sizes. When doing this, however, one must keep in mind the maximum size of type I error that can be tolerated in a particular situation. For illustration, recall once again the null hypothesis $H_0: \mu = 10$ against the alternative $H_1: \mu > 10$. Then β is the same as the probability of failing to reject H_0 when H_1 is true. As before, let $\overline{X}$ be the test statistic. Figure 9.2 shows how changing the critical value from 11 to 12 would decrease the size of type I error — shown under the left curve in both cases — but would increase the size of type II error — shown under the right curve.

The probability of type I error α is also known as the *level of statistical significance*. In this context the word "significance" implies only that the sample evidence is such that it warrants the rejection of H_0 at the given level for α. Consequently, the phrase, "The rejection of H_0 is *statistically discernible* at the given α level," is more appropriate. An example will illustrate the preceding concepts.

Example 9.1 Suppose we can tolerate a size of type I error up to 0.06 when testing the null hypothesis

$$H_0: \mu = 10$$

against the alternative

$$H_1: \mu > 10$$

for the assembly time problem. Assume the distribution of the time required to assemble a unit is normal with standard deviation $\sigma = 1.4$ minutes. Say we observe the assembly times of 25 randomly selected units and choose the sample

FIGURE 9.2 The effect on α and β of changing the critical value

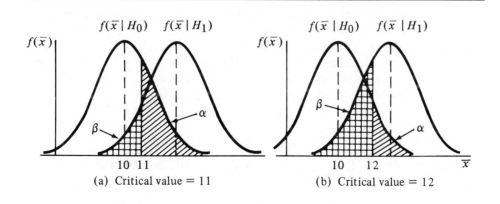

(a) Critical value = 11   (b) Critical value = 12

mean $\overline{X}$ as the test statistic. In particular, we want to compare the following three critical regions

$$\text{Test A:} \quad \text{Reject } H_0 \quad \text{if } \overline{X} > 10.65$$

$$\text{Test B:} \quad \text{Reject } H_0 \quad \text{if } \overline{X} > 10.45$$

$$\text{Test C:} \quad \text{Reject } H_0 \quad \text{if } \overline{X} > 10.25$$

to determine which one satisfies the size of type I error that can be tolerated and which has the smallest β among the three.

To determine the probability of type I error, we must assume that H_0 is true and compute

$$P(\overline{X} > c \mid \mu = 10) = \alpha,$$

where c is the critical value, or the boundary of the critical region. Since we assumed sampling from a normal distribution, under H_0, $\overline{X} \sim N(10, 1.4/\sqrt{25})$. It follows that for test A

$$\alpha = P(\overline{X} > 10.65 \mid \mu = 10)$$

$$= P[Z > (10.65 - 10)/0.28 \mid \mu = 10]$$

$$= P(Z > 2.32 \mid \mu = 10)$$

$$= 0.0102.$$

Similarly for test B,

$$\alpha = P(\overline{X} > 10.45 \mid \mu = 10) = P(Z > 1.61 \mid \mu = 10) = 0.0537,$$

and for test C

$$\alpha = P(\overline{X} > 10.25 \mid \mu = 10) = P(Z > 0.89 \mid \mu = 10) = 0.1867.$$

Notice the size of type I error for test C exceeds the imposed limit of 0.06, while those of tests A and B are less than this limit. Since test C does not meet the requirements, it will no longer be considered.

Since neither test A nor test B has violated the maximum size of type I error, let us determine which one has the smaller size of type II error. Recall that the occurrence of type II error implies that H_0 is false. Then for a given sample size and a maximum α value, the size of type II error will be strictly a function of the range of values of the unknown parameter as specified by the alternative hypothesis. In other words,

$$\beta(\mu) = P(\overline{X} \leqslant c \mid \mu > 10).$$

In particular, suppose μ is really equal to 10.4. Then for test A

$$\beta(10.4) = P(\overline{X} \leqslant 10.65 \mid \mu = 10.4) = P(Z \leqslant 0.89 \mid \mu = 10.4) = 0.8133,$$

while for test B

$$\beta(10.4) = P(\overline{X} \leqslant 10.45 \mid \mu = 10.4) = P(Z \leqslant 0.18 \mid \mu = 10.4) = 0.5714.$$

TABLE 9.1 Type II error probabilities for tests A and B

μ	10.2	10.4	10.6	10.8	11.0	11.2	11.4
Test A	0.9463	0.8133	0.5714	0.2946	0.1056	0.0250	0.0037
Test B	0.8133	0.5714	0.2946	0.1056	0.0250	0.0037	0.0003

Thus if $\mu = 10.4$, the probability of test A failing to reject the null hypothesis that $\mu = 10$ is 0.8133, and the corresponding probability for test B is 0.5714. For this particular value from the alternative hypothesis, test B is better than A.

To illustrate the range of β probabilities for these two tests, we continue this process of computing the size of type II error for other representative values. The pertinent information is given in Table 9.1. We will illustrate later that for a given alternative hypothesis and a fixed size of type I error, the size of type II error can be reduced by increasing the sample size.

Based on the information in Table 9.1, the following points can be made. As the size of type I error is decreased (test A), the size of type II error is increased. If the claim as stated by the null hypothesis is false but differs very slightly from the true value, the chance of not rejecting H_0 is high. However, if the null hypothesis is false by a large amount, the probability of failing to detect its incorrectness is small. Thus in comparing tests A and B, if a size of up to 0.06 can be tolerated for type I error, test B is better than test A because its β probabilities are uniformly smaller than those of test A.

9.3 Types of Critical Regions and the Power Function

We have suggested that it is desirable to state a simple null hypothesis. In fact, it is also desirable to state a simple alternative hypothesis because only then can we determine single values for the sizes of type I and type II errors. To illustrate, recall Example 9.1. Suppose we have also formulated a simple alternative hypothesis, say, H_1: $\mu = 10.8$. Then for tests A and B, the sizes of type I error would remain at 0.0102 and 0.0537, respectively. But now the probability of type II error for either test would be a single value rather than a range of values as in Example 9.1. It must be noted, however, that a simple alternative hypothesis would have limited real application. Accordingly, we will proceed under the assumption that the null hypothesis is simple and the alternative is composite.

In this context we want to investigate the types of critical regions that may arise. Consider the simple null hypothesis

$$H_0: \theta = \theta_0$$

about a parameter of interest θ when sampling from a distribution with probability density $f(x; \theta)$, where θ_0 is the claimed value of θ. If the alternative hypothesis is of the form

$$H_1: \theta > \theta_0$$

or

$$H_1: \theta < \theta_0,$$

H_1 is said to be a *one-sided alternative* hypothesis because the possible values of θ under H_1 lie to one side of the claimed value under H_0. The critical region is also called a one-sided rejection region because it is intuitively reasonable to reject H_0 for values of an appropriate test statistic that, if H_0 were true, are extreme in the direction as specified by the alternative hypothesis. It is worthwhile to note that one-sided alternative hypotheses should be formulated only if a value of the parameter from the other side is meaningless to the investigator. Otherwise, a *two-sided alternative* hypothesis should be stated. That is, if the alternative hypothesis does not provide direction with regard to the claimed value θ_0, then H_1 is said to be a two-sided alternative hypothesis of the form

$$H_1: \theta \neq \theta_0.$$

A two-sided alternative hypothesis implies the existence of a two-sided critical region* since H_1 includes values of θ that lie on both sides of the claimed value θ_0. In such a case one would be inclined to reject the null hypothesis for values of a test statistic that, if H_0 were true, are extreme in either direction.

Assuming a composite alternative hypothesis, we need to generalize the means by which the performance of a given test may be evaluated, especially in comparison with other competing tests. As illustrated in Example 9.1, the size of type II error varies for different values of θ from the alternative hypothesis when H_1 is composite. Thus the size of type II error is determined as a function of alternative values of θ under H_1. It should be noted that $\beta(\theta)$ is known as the *operating characteristic function,* and when $\beta(\theta)$ is plotted for various values of θ from H_1, an operating characteristic curve (OC) is obtained.

Since $\beta(\theta)$ is the probability that a value of a test statistic will not fall in the critical region when H_0 is false, then $1 - \beta(\theta)$ represents the probability that a value of a test statistic will be inside the critical region when H_0 is false. This probability is known as the *power function* of the test. In other words, the power and operating characteristic functions are complementary.

Definition 9.4 The function $P(\theta) = 1 - \beta(\theta)$ is called the power function and represents the probability of rejecting the null hypothesis when it is false; that is, when a value of the parameter from H_1 is true.**

In essence, the power of a test is the probability of detecting that H_0 is really false; thus the use of the word "power." For illustration, recall Example 9.1 and the contents of Table 9.1. The complements of the type II error probabilities in Table 9.1 are the powers of tests A and B for the indicated values of μ when testing H_0: $\mu = 10$ against H_1: $\mu > 10$. These are given in Table 9.2. It is apparent from the information in the table that test B is more powerful than test A. The power and characteristic functions of tests A and B may be plotted

---

*Usually a two-sided critical region is symmetric; the two parts of the region are selected such that they are equal in area.

**If H_0 is true, some authors also define the power to be the same as the size of type I error.

TABLE 9.2 Powers of tests A and B for Example 9.1

μ	10.2	10.4	10.6	10.8	11.0	11.2	11.4
Test A	0.0537	0.1867	0.4286	0.7054	0.8944	0.9750	0.9963
Test B	0.1867	0.4286	0.7054	0.8944	0.9750	0.9963	0.9997

against values of μ, giving power and operating characteristic curves, as illustrated in Figure 9.3.

Recall that for a fixed α and a given alternative hypothesis, the size of type II error can be reduced by increasing the sample size. It follows, therefore, that the power function will increase as the sample size is increased. For illustration, consider tests A and B of Example 9.1 for which the sample size is increased to, say, 50. Since we insist that the sizes of type I error remain the same for A and B, their critical values would shift downward because of the increase in the sample size. In particular, for test A

$$P(\overline{X} > c_A \,|\, \mu = 10) = 0.0102,$$

or

$$\frac{c_A - 10}{1.4/\sqrt{50}} = 2.32,$$

$$c_A = 10.46.$$

Similarly for test B

$$P(\overline{X} > c_B \,|\, \mu = 10) = 0.0537,$$

and $c_B = 10.32$. Table 9.3 contains information comparable to that in Tables 9.1 and 9.2 for $n = 50$.

FIGURE 9.3 Comparison of power and operating characteristic functions for A and B

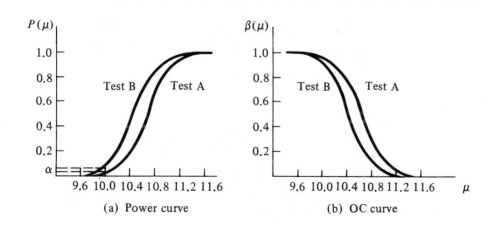

(a) Power curve   (b) OC curve

TABLE 9.3   Powers and β probabilities of tests A and B for $n = 50$

μ		10.2	10.4	10.6	10.8	11.0	11.2	11.4
Test A	$P(\mu)$	0.0951	0.3821	0.7611	0.9573	0.9968	0.9999	$\simeq 1$
	$\beta(\mu)$	0.9049	0.6179	0.2389	0.0427	0.0032	0.0001	$\simeq 0$
Test B	$P(\mu)$	0.2709	0.6554	0.9207	0.9922	0.9997	$\simeq 1$	$\simeq 1$
	$\beta(\mu)$	0.7291	0.3446	0.0793	0.0078	0.0003	$\simeq 0$	$\simeq 0$

We may also exhibit the power for different values of μ relative to the sampling distribution of the statistic $\overline{X}$. Consider for example test B, in which the critical value is $c_B = 10.32$ for $n = 50$. Figure 9.4 shows the distribution of $\overline{X}$ for various values of $\mu > 10$, where the shaded area is the power or the probability of rejecting H_0. Notice that as μ moves away from the claimed value under H_0, the power of the test increases.

FIGURE 9.4   Probabilities of rejection of H_0 for test B ($n = 50$)

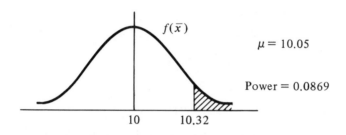

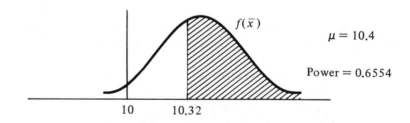

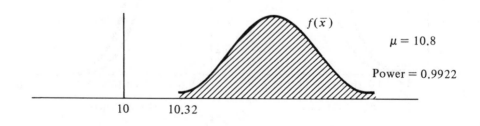

9.4 Best Tests

In the last section we determined that the evaluation of a test of a statistical hypothesis should be based on its power function. We now turn to the equally important problem of how to go about constructing a good test. In a theoretical sense, the method for constructing good tests is clearer when both null and alternative hypotheses are simple than when either one or both are composite. We now consider a theorem for constructing best tests in the simple H_0 versus simple H_1 case. It turns out that this theorem also has some application for the more practical cases.

Let $X_1, X_2, ..., X_n$ be a random sample of size n from a distribution with probability (density) function $f(x; \theta)$, and consider the hypothesis

$$H_0: \theta = \theta_0$$

against

$$H_1: \theta = \theta_1,$$

where θ_0 and θ_1 are specified. Say α is the maximum size of type I error that can be tolerated. Then a best test for H_0 versus H_1 is to select the test that has the smallest size of type II error — and thus the greatest power — among all tests having sizes of type I error that are no greater than α. The critical regions for such best tests can be determined by use of the following theorem, known as the Neyman–Pearson lemma:

Theorem 9.1 If there exists a critical region C of size α and a positive constant k such that

$$\frac{L_0(x_1, x_2, ..., x_n; \theta_0)}{L_1(x_1, x_2, ..., x_n; \theta_1)} \leq k \qquad \text{inside } C,$$

$$\frac{L_0(x_1, x_2, ..., x_n; \theta_0)}{L_1(x_1, x_2, ..., x_n; \theta_1)} \geq k \qquad \text{outside } C,$$

then C is the best critical region of size α for testing $H_0: \theta = \theta_0$ against $H_1: \theta = \theta_1$, where L_0 and L_1 are the likelihood functions relative to H_0 and H_1, respectively.

The proof of Theorem 9.1 is beyond the scope of this text. However, the usefulness of this theorem can be made clear with the following examples.

Example 9.2 Let $X_1, X_2, ..., X_n$ be a random sample of size n from a normal distribution with an unknown mean μ and a known variance σ^2. Determine the best critical region of size α for testing

$$H_0: \mu = \mu_0$$

against

$$H_1: \mu = \mu_1,$$

where $\mu_1 > \mu_0$.

Under H_0 the likelihood function is

$$L_0(x_1, x_2, ..., x_n; \mu_0) = (\sqrt{2\pi}\, \sigma)^{-n} \exp\left[-\sum_{i=1}^{n} (x_i - \mu_0)^2 \bigg/ 2\sigma^2\right],$$

and under H_1 it is

$$L_1(x_1, x_2, ..., x_n; \mu_1) = (\sqrt{2\pi}\, \sigma)^{-n} \exp\left[-\sum_{i=1}^{n} (x_i - \mu_1)^2 \bigg/ 2\sigma^2\right].$$

Then according to Theorem 9.1, the best critical region is one for which

$$\frac{\exp\left[-\sum(x_i - \mu_0)^2/2\sigma^2\right]}{\exp\left[-\sum(x_i - \mu_1)^2/2\sigma^2\right]} \leq k.$$

This inequality may be written as

$$\exp\left\{\frac{1}{2\sigma^2}\left[\sum(x_i - \mu_1)^2 - \sum(x_i - \mu_0)^2\right]\right\} \leq k, \tag{9.3}$$

which, after taking logarithms, reduces to

$$\sum(x_i - \mu_1)^2 - \sum(x_i - \mu_0)^2 \leq 2\sigma^2 \ln(k). \tag{9.4}$$

The left side of (9.4) simplifies as follows:

$$\sum(x_i - \mu_1)^2 - \sum(x_i - \mu_0)^2 = \sum x_i^2 - 2\mu_1\sum x_i + n\mu_1^2 - \sum x_i^2 + 2\mu_0\sum x_i - n\mu_0^2$$
$$= n(\mu_1^2 - \mu_0^2) - 2(\mu_1 - \mu_0)\sum x_i.$$

Substituting in (9.4) we have

$$n(\mu_1^2 - \mu_0^2) - 2(\mu_1 - \mu_0)\sum x_i \leq 2\sigma^2 \ln(k),$$

or

$$-2(\mu_1 - \mu_0)\sum x_i \leq 2\sigma^2 \ln(k) - n(\mu_1^2 - \mu_0^2).$$

Since $\mu_1 > \mu_0$, the quantity $-2(\mu_1 - \mu_0)$ is negative; thus

$$\sum x_i \geq \frac{n(\mu_1^2 - \mu_0^2) - 2\sigma^2 \ln(k)}{2(\mu_1 - \mu_0)},$$

or

$$\bar{x} \geq \frac{n(\mu_1^2 - \mu_0^2) - 2\sigma^2 \ln(k)}{2n(\mu_1 - \mu_0)}. \tag{9.5}$$

Expression (9.5) defines the *form* of the best critical region for testing $H_0: \mu = \mu_0$ versus $H_1: \mu = \mu_1$ where $\mu_1 > \mu_0$. Simply put, the best critical region is the right tail of the sampling distribution of $\bar{X}$ under the null hypothesis.

For a given α, the critical value, say, $\bar{x}_0$ can be found by properly choosing the positive constant k so that

$$P(\overline{X} \geq \bar{x}_0 \mid \mu = \mu_0) = \alpha.$$

In particular, suppose the size of type I error is chosen to be 0.05. Then the critical value $\bar{x}_0$ is such that

$$P(\overline{X} \geq \bar{x}_0 \mid \mu = \mu_0) = 0.05.$$

Since under H_0, $\overline{X}$ is normal with mean μ_0 and standard deviation $\sigma/\sqrt{n}$, then

$$P\left(Z \geq \frac{\bar{x}_0 - \mu_0}{\sigma/\sqrt{n}} \;\middle|\; \mu = \mu_0\right) = 0.05;$$

but

$$P(Z \geq 1.645 \mid \mu = \mu_0) = 0.05,$$

where $Z \sim N(0, 1)$. Accordingly, the critical value $\bar{x}_0$ is such that

$$\frac{\bar{x}_0 - \mu_0}{\sigma/\sqrt{n}} = 1.645,$$

or

$$\bar{x}_0 = \frac{1.645\sigma}{\sqrt{n}} + \mu_0.$$

Therefore, H_0: $\mu = \mu_0$ will be rejected in favor of H_1: $\mu = \mu_1 > \mu_0$ whenever a value of $\overline{X}$ is $\geq (1.645\sigma/\sqrt{n}) + \mu_0$.

It is important for the reader to note that the form of the best critical region as given by (9.5) for testing H_0: $\mu = \mu_0$ against H_1: $\mu = \mu_1$ is independent of the particular value μ_1 as long as $\mu_1 > \mu_0$. In other words, for all $\mu_1 > \mu_0$ the best critical region for testing H_0: $\mu = \mu_0$ is the right tail of the sampling distribution of $\overline{X}$. Thus, in reality, Expression (9.5) gives the form of the best critical region for testing the simple null H_0: $\mu = \mu_0$ against the composite alternative H_1: $\mu > \mu_0$. This best critical region is called a *uniformly most powerful region* (or test) for testing H_0: $\mu = \mu_0$ against H_1: $\mu > \mu_0$. We generalize the preceding remarks with the following definition of a best test.

Definition 9.5 A test of the hypothesis H_0: $\theta = \theta_0$ is said to be a uniformly most powerful test of size α if it is at least as powerful for every possible θ of the alternative hypothesis as any other test of size $\leq \alpha$. That is, the power function of such a test is at least as large as that of any other test of size $\leq \alpha$ for every θ of the alternative hypothesis.

Unfortunately, uniformly most powerful tests do not always exist. As illustrated in Example 9.2, the Neyman–Pearson lemma can be used to determine a uniformly most powerful test for a number of situations of practical interest in which the alternative hypothesis is composite but one-sided.

Example 9.3   Let $X_1, X_2, \ldots, X_n$ be a random sample of size n from a gamma distribution with unknown scale parameter θ and a known shape parameter a.* Determine the best critical region of size α for testing

$$H_0: \theta = \theta_0$$

against

$$H_1: \theta = \theta_1,$$

where $\theta_1 < \theta_0$.

We proceed in a manner similar to that of Example 9.2. Under H_0, the likelihood function is

$$L_0(x_1, x_2, \ldots, x_n; \theta_0) = [\Gamma(a)\theta_0^a]^{-n} \prod_{i=1}^{n} x_i^a \exp\left(-\sum_{i=1}^{n} x_i \Big/ \theta_0\right),$$

and for the alternative hypothesis it is

$$L_1(x_1, x_2, \ldots, x_n; \theta_1) = [\Gamma(a)\theta_1^a]^{-n} \prod_{i=1}^{n} x_i^a \exp\left(-\sum_{i=1}^{n} x_i \Big/ \theta_1\right).$$

Based on the Neyman–Pearson lemma, the best critical region is one for which

$$\frac{\theta_1^{na} \exp\left(-\sum x_i \Big/ \theta_0\right)}{\theta_0^{na} \exp\left(-\sum x_i \Big/ \theta_1\right)} \leq k.$$

That is,

$$\exp\left(-\frac{\sum x_i}{\theta_0} + \frac{\sum x_i}{\theta_1}\right) \leq (\theta_0/\theta_1)^{na} k$$

$$\exp\left[\left(\frac{1}{\theta_1} - \frac{1}{\theta_0}\right)\sum x_i\right] \leq (\theta_0/\theta_1)^{na} k$$

$$[(\theta_0 - \theta_1)/\theta_0\theta_1]\sum x_i \leq \ln[k(\theta_0/\theta_1)^{na}].$$

The quantity $\theta_0 - \theta_1$ is seen to be positive since by assumption $\theta_1 < \theta_0$; then

$$\sum x_i \leq \frac{\theta_0\theta_1 \ln[k(\theta_0/\theta_1)^{na}]}{\theta_0 - \theta_1}$$

or

$$\bar{x} \leq \frac{\theta_0\theta_1 \ln[k(\theta_0/\theta_1)^{na}]}{n(\theta_0 - \theta_1)}. \qquad (9.6)$$

---

*We have opted to denote the gamma shape parameter with a rather than α to prevent confusion with the size of type I error.

Accordingly, the best critical region for testing $H_0: \theta = \theta_0$ against $H_1: \theta = \theta_1$ where $\theta_1 < \theta_0$ is the left tail of the sampling distribution of $\overline{X}$. The critical value $\overline{x}_0$, which for a given size of type I error is such that

$$P(\overline{X} \le \overline{x}_0 \mid \theta = \theta_0) = \alpha,$$

may be found by appealing directly to the distribution of $\overline{X}$, which in this case is also gamma. We will need to use the incomplete gamma function to do this. Alternatively, if the sample size is sufficiently large, one could appeal to the Central Limit Theorem and use the normal approximation.

Of interest, once again, is the fact that the form of the best critical region as given by (9.6) does not depend on the particular value θ as long as $\theta_1 < \theta_0$. In reality, therefore, the critical region as indicated by (9.6) is a uniformly most powerful region for testing $H_0: \theta = \theta_0$ against $H_1: \theta < \theta_0$ when sampling from a gamma distribution with known shape parameter.

The reader is asked to verify that if in Example 9.2 the alternative hypothesis is of the form $H_1: \mu < \mu_0$, the best critical region for testing $H_0: \mu = \mu_0$ is the left tail of the sampling distribution of $\overline{X}$. It follows, therefore, that if in Example 9.3 the alternative hypothesis was $H_1: \theta > \theta_0$, the best critical region would be the right tail of the distribution of $\overline{X}$. However, if the alternative hypothesis in either of these examples were two-sided — that is, of the general form $H_0: \theta = \theta_0$ versus $H_1: \theta \ne \theta_0$ — no best critical region could be found because for all alternative values $\theta_1 < \theta_0$, the left tail of the sampling distribution of $\overline{X}$ would be best, while for all $\theta_1 > \theta_0$ the right tail would be best. Therefore, as a general rule, uniformly most powerful tests usually exist for one-sided alternative hypotheses, but they cannot be found for two-sided alternative hypotheses.

Now we illustrate the use of the Neyman–Pearson lemma to determine a best critical region when the underlying random variable is discrete.

Example 9.4 Let X_1, X_2, ..., X_n be a random sample of size n from a Poisson distribution with unknown parameter λ. Determine the best critical region of size α for testing

$$H_0: \lambda = \lambda_0$$

against

$$H_1: \lambda = \lambda_1,$$

where $\lambda_1 > \lambda_0$.

Proceeding in a manner similar to Examples 9.2 and 9.3, we have

$$L_0(x_1, x_2, ..., x_n; \lambda_0) = \frac{\exp(-n\lambda_0)\, \lambda_0^{\Sigma x_i}}{\prod x_i!}$$

and

$$L_1(x_1, x_2, ..., x_n; \lambda_1) = \frac{\exp(-n\lambda_1)\, \lambda_1^{\Sigma x_i}}{\prod x_i!}.$$

Thus the best critical region is one for which

$$\frac{\exp(-n\lambda_0)\,\lambda_0^{\Sigma x_i}}{\exp(-n\lambda_1)\,\lambda_1^{\Sigma x_i}} \leqslant k$$

or

$$\left(\frac{\lambda_0}{\lambda_1}\right)^{\Sigma x_i} \exp[n(\lambda_1 - \lambda_0)] \leqslant k.$$

After taking logarithms, we have

$$\ln(\lambda_0/\lambda_1)\sum x_i + n(\lambda_1 - \lambda_0) \leqslant \ln(k)$$

or

$$\ln(\lambda_0/\lambda_1)\sum x_i \leqslant \ln(k) - n(\lambda_1 - \lambda_0).$$

But if $\lambda_1 > \lambda_0$, then $0 < \lambda_0/\lambda_1 < 1$, and the natural logarithm of a number between zero and one is negative. As a result, the preceding inequality may be written as

$$\sum x_i \geqslant \frac{\ln(k) - n(\lambda_1 - \lambda_0)}{\ln(\lambda_0/\lambda_1)}. \tag{9.7}$$

Expression (9.7) defines the form of the best critical region for testing H_0: $\lambda = \lambda_0$ against H_1: $\lambda = \lambda_1 > \lambda_0$. In particular, since $Y = \Sigma X_i$ is also a Poisson random variable (see the Exercises in Chapter 7), the critical region of the form $y = \Sigma x_i \geqslant y_0$ is equivalent to inequality (9.7), where the critical value y_0 is chosen so that

$$P(Y \geqslant y_0) = \alpha.$$

Because Y is a discrete random variable, it is indeed difficult to determine the critical value y_0 such that $P(Y \geqslant y_0)$ is exactly equal to a previously selected size of type I error. There exists what is called a randomization procedure (see [2]), which can be implemented to overcome this difficulty. From a practical point of view, however, one simply chooses the critical region and, thus, the value y_0, whose area is close to the size of type I error that can be tolerated.

9.5   General Guidelines for Testing a Simple H_0 Against a Two-Sided or a One-Sided H_1

In the last section we developed a criterion with which best tests may be determined for testing statistical hypotheses. It was pointed out that uniformly most powerful tests do not exist for two-sided alternative hypotheses, although they usually do for one-sided alternatives. In this section we develop general test criteria for the following three cases involving simple null and composite alternative hypotheses.

Case 1	*Case 2*	*Case 3*
H_0: $\theta = \theta_0$	H_0: $\theta = \theta_0$	H_0: $\theta = \theta_0$
H_1: $\theta \neq \theta_0$	H_1: $\theta > \theta_0$	H_1: $\theta < \theta_0$

Since for Case 1 we cannot determine uniformly most powerful tests, we wish to compare the power functions of two competing tests for a specific example to typify the power function for this case.

Example 9.5   In a certain city assume that there are only two television stations, Channel 6 and Channel 10. It is widely believed that the audience share for the evening news is the same for both stations. A business firm is interested in testing the claim that the proportion of viewers for the evening news is 0.5 for either station. The firm does not have any prior information to suggest a one-sided alternative; thus it decides to test the null hypothesis

$$H_0: p = 0.5$$

against

$$H_1: p \neq 0.5.$$

The firm decides to poll 18 randomly selected residents and ask them on which channel they prefer to watch the evening news. The number X indicating Channel 6 will be recorded. The following two tests are proposed:

> Test A: Reject H_0 if $X \leq 4$ or $X \geq 14$.

> Test B: Reject H_0 if $X \leq 5$ or $X \geq 13$.

If the firm is willing to tolerate a maximum size of 0.1 for type I error, determine the better test to use in deciding between H_0 and H_1.

The test statistic X is a binomial random variable with $n = 18$ and, under the null hypothesis, $p = 0.5$. The critical regions for both tests are intuitively reasonable since one should reject the null hypothesis for values of X that are close to zero or close to 18. In other words, if p were really equal to 0.5, we would expect to observe a value of X around nine. The further away the observed value is from nine in either direction, the more we would be inclined to reject the null hypothesis. This stems from the fact that when testing statistical hypotheses, our thinking is based strictly on probability. For example, if p were equal to 0.5, the probability that X will assume a value between, say, 6 and 12 inclusive is

$$P(6 \leq X \leq 12) = 0.9038.$$

Therefore, it is unlikely that H_0 is correct when a small or a large value of X is realized. In fact, the probability of observing a large or a small value of X, given that H_0 is true, is precisely what we mean by the size of type I error.

For test A the probability of type I error is

$$\alpha_A = P(X \leq 4 \,|\, p = 0.5) + P(X \geq 14 \,|\, p = 0.5)$$

$$= 0.0154 + 0.0154$$

$$= 0.0308,$$

TABLE 9.4 Power functions of tests A and B

p	0.1	0.2	0.3	0.4	0.5	0.6	0.7	0.8	0.9
Test A $P(X \leq 4)$	0.9718	0.7164	0.3327	0.0942	0.0154	0.0013	$\simeq 0$	$\simeq 0$	$\simeq 0$
$P(X \geq 14)$	$\simeq 0$	$\simeq 0$	$\simeq 0$	0.0013	0.0154	0.0942	0.3327	0.7164	0.9718
Power	0.9718	0.7164	0.3327	0.0955	0.0308	0.0955	0.3327	0.7164	0.9718
Test B $P(X \leq 5)$	0.9936	0.8671	0.5344	0.2088	0.0481	0.0058	0.0003	$\simeq 0$	$\simeq 0$
$P(X \geq 13)$	$\simeq 0$	$\simeq 0$	0.0003	0.0058	0.0481	0.2088	0.5344	0.8671	0.9936
Power	0.9936	0.8671	0.5347	0.2146	0.0962	0.2146	0.5347	0.8671	0.9936

and for test B it is

$$\alpha_B = P(X \leq 5 \,|\, p = 0.5) + P(X \geq 13 \,|\, p = 0.5) = 0.0962.$$

It is worthwhile to note that the two-sided critical regions are symmetric for both tests. This is a theoretically best and a practically sound procedure for handling two-sided alternative hypotheses. Since both tests have α values that are less than the maximum size that can be tolerated, we will compare their power functions to decide which is the better test. The powers of tests A and B are given in Table 9.4 for representative values of p.

It is seen from the table that for every value of p, the power of test B is greater than that of test A. Accordingly, test B is uniformly more powerful than test A and is the better test to use for testing the indicated hypotheses. The power curves of tests A and B are given in Figure 9.5. Notice that in both instances the power curves increase in a symmetrical fashion as one moves away from the claimed value of p under H_0. This is a typical behavior of a power function for a two-sided alternative hypothesis as long as the corresponding two-sided critical region is symmetrical.

9.5.1 General Guidelines for Case 1

Consider testing the null hypothesis

$$H_0\!: \theta = \theta_0$$

against the alternative

$$H_1\!: \theta \neq \theta_0,$$

where θ_0 is the claimed value of some parameter θ under H_0. Given a random sample of size n from the underlying distribution, the general procedure for testing H_0 is to choose the best estimator of θ, say, T, and to reject H_0 when the estimate t, as determined from the sample, is "sufficiently" different from the claimed value θ_0. Such a procedure is based on the notion of a rare event that we have illustrated in earlier chapters. That is, if the estimate t is sufficiently different from the claimed value θ_0, either we have observed a rare event (and the null hypothesis is correct), or we have observed a value of the statistic that suggests a θ value different from the claimed θ_0. When the estimate t is sufficiently

FIGURE 9.5   Comparison of the power functions for tests A and B

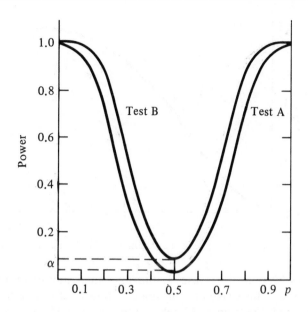

different from θ_0, we assume the latter possibility and let the size of type I error be the probability of the former. In particular, for a preselected size of type I error α, a two-sided critical region is determined at the tails of the sampling distribution of T such that the area on either side beyond the critical value is $\alpha/2$. Then H_0 is rejected in favor of H_1 when the estimate t falls inside the critical region. When the estimate t does not fall inside the critical region, the null hypothesis cannot be rejected. Thus any difference from θ_0 is regarded as being caused only by the sampling fluctuation of the estimator T.

    This approach is indeed similar to that for constructing a two-sided confidence interval for θ. For any claimed value θ_0 that lies within a $100(1 - \alpha)\%$ confidence interval for θ, H_0 will not be rejected. Given a $100(1 - \alpha)\%$ confidence interval for θ, only the claimed values under H_0 that lie outside such a confidence interval will cause rejection of the null hypothesis. In this context it is appropriate to regard a confidence interval as a more comprehensive statement of statistical inference for θ, since it includes all possible values θ_0 that would not lead to the rejection of the null hypothesis.

9.5.2   General Guidelines for Case 2

Consider the null hypothesis

$$H_0: \theta = \theta_0$$

versus the alternative

$$H_1: \theta > \theta_0.$$

FIGURE 9.6 Typical power curve for Case 2

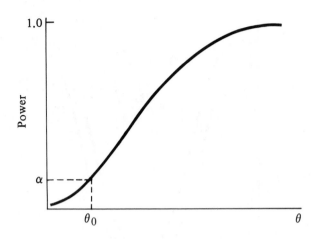

For this case as well as for Case 3, the one-sided nature of the alternative hypothesis suggests the existence of some a priori information that helps to define the one-sided direction of H_1 relative to the claimed value θ_0. The general procedure for testing H_0 is once again to select the best statistic T of θ and to reject H_0 when the estimate t is "sufficiently" greater than the claimed value θ_0. The word "sufficiently" implies that an allowance is made for the sampling fluctuation of the estimator T. However, if what is determined by way of a random sample is beyond this allowance, H_0 will be rejected. Thus for a size of type I error α, the critical region is located at the upper tail of the sampling distribution of T, and H_0 is rejected if the estimate t is no less than the critical value. The typical power curve for this case is illustrated in Figure 9.6.

9.5.3 General Guidelines for Case 3

For testing the hypothesis

$$H_0: \theta = \theta_0$$

against

$$H_1: \theta < \theta_0,$$

the general procedure is to reject H_0 whenever the estimate t is "sufficiently" less than the claimed value θ_0. The critical region of size α is located at the lower tail of the sampling distribution of T such that the area to the left of the critical value is the same as the size of type I error α. Any value t of the test statistic T that is in the critical region leads to the rejection of H_0. The typical power curve for this case is shown in Figure 9.7.

With regard to testing statistical hypotheses, the reader should take note of the following. Because we place greater emphasis on the size of type I error,

FIGURE 9.7 Typical power curve for Case 3

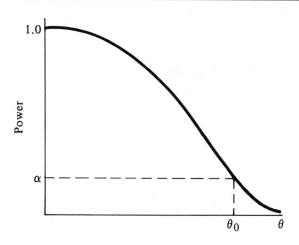

we usually set up the null hypothesis so as to reject it if the experimental evidence is supportive of that decision. In other words what we really like to conclude is that the alternative is correct. Thus when testing statistical hypotheses, we play the same role as the prosecutor, attempting to provide enough evidence for the rejection of the null hypothesis. It is the better practice to choose the size of type I error prior to the determination of the random sample. If it turns out that the null hypothesis cannot be rejected at the chosen α value, one should resist the temptation to simply increase the size of type I error post facto to reject the null hypothesis.

The preceding discussion constitutes what has been termed the classical method for testing statistical hypotheses. Some criticism has been directed toward this approach because the final decision of rejecting H_0 or not being able to reject it at the specified α value is too cut and dried and does not provide the actual strength that the decision is correct in terms of probability. What has been suggested is to compute the so-called p-value. The *p-value* is the probability, given H_0 is true, of the test statistic assuming a value as extreme or more so than the value computed based on the random sample. A relatively small p-value would suggest that if indeed H_0 is true, the observed value of the test statistic is rather unlikely. We would then opt to reject H_0 because that decision would have a higher probability of being correct.

We recommend the computation of the p-value coupled with the classical approach of selecting a size of type I error prior to the determination of the random sample. Then the decision to reject or not reject H_0 would be based on a critical region of size α, with the p-value providing the actual strength in terms of probability that the decision is correct. Accordingly, the following rule is suggested: If the p-value is less than or equal to α, H_0 is rejected; otherwise the null hypothesis cannot be rejected. The computation of the p-value will be illustrated in the examples of subsequent sections. It should be noted that many statistical computer packages, such as SAS, SPSS, BMD, and others, print out the *p*-value for nearly all situations involving the testing of statistical hypotheses.

9.6   Tests of Hypotheses Concerning Means When Sampling from Normal Distributions

In this section we shall discuss testing hypotheses on the mean of a normal distribution or on the means of two independent normal distributions. Both known and unknown variance scenarios will be examined. The reader is asked to consult Sections 8.4.1 through 8.4.3 for comparison to confidence intervals.

9.6.1   One-Sample Tests

Let $X_1, X_2, ..., X_n$ be a random sample from a normal distribution with unknown mean μ. Of interest is to test one of the following sets of hypotheses with regard to μ.

$$H_0: \mu = \mu_0 \qquad H_0: \mu = \mu_0 \qquad H_0: \mu = \mu_0$$
$$H_1: \mu \neq \mu_0 \qquad H_1: \mu > \mu_0 \qquad H_1: \mu < \mu_0$$

First assume that the population variance σ^2 is known. Then the test statistic is the sample mean $\overline{X}$, which under the null hypothesis is normally distributed with mean μ_0 and standard deviation $\sigma/\sqrt{n}$. For the two-sided hypothesis the critical region of size α is of the form

$$\text{Reject } H_0 \text{ if } \begin{cases} \overline{X} \geq \overline{x}_{1-\alpha/2} \\ \quad \text{or} \\ \overline{X} \leq \overline{x}_{\alpha/2}, \end{cases} \tag{9.8}$$

where $\overline{x}_{1-\alpha/2}$ and $\overline{x}_{\alpha/2}$ are the critical quantile values of $\overline{X}$ such that

$$P(\overline{X} \geq \overline{x}_{1-\alpha/2}) = \alpha/2 \quad \text{and} \quad P(\overline{X} \leq \overline{x}_{\alpha/2}) = \alpha/2.$$

Since under H_0, $\overline{X} \sim N(\mu_0, \sigma/\sqrt{n})$, then equivalently

$$P\left(Z \geq \frac{\overline{x}_{1-\alpha/2} - \mu_0}{\sigma/\sqrt{n}}\right) = \alpha/2 \quad \text{and} \quad P\left(Z \leq \frac{\overline{x}_{\alpha/2} - \mu_0}{\sigma/\sqrt{n}}\right) = \alpha/2$$

or

$$z_{1-\alpha/2} = \frac{\overline{x}_{1-\alpha/2} - \mu_0}{\sigma/\sqrt{n}} \quad \text{and} \quad z_{\alpha/2} = \frac{\overline{x}_{\alpha/2} - \mu_0}{\sigma/\sqrt{n}},$$

where $z_{1-\alpha/2}$ and $z_{\alpha/2}$ are the corresponding quantile values of Z. It follows, therefore, that H_0 is rejected when a value $\overline{x}$ of the sample mean $\overline{X}$ is such that

$$\overline{x} \geq \frac{\sigma\, z_{1-\alpha/2}}{\sqrt{n}} + \mu_0 \quad \text{or} \quad \overline{x} \leq \frac{\sigma\, z_{\alpha/2}}{\sqrt{n}} + \mu_0.$$

FIGURE 9.8 Critical regions for one-sided alternative hypotheses

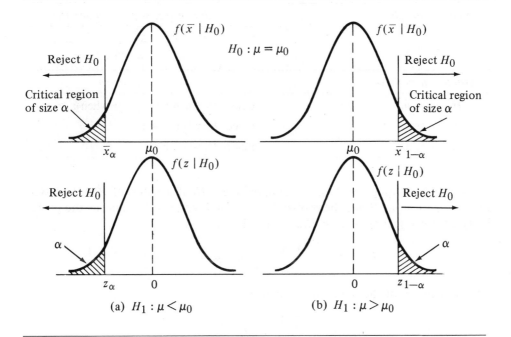

(a) $H_1 : \mu < \mu_0$ (b) $H_1 : \mu > \mu_0$

Equivalently, H_0 is rejected whenever

$$z \geq z_{1-\alpha/2} \quad \text{or} \quad z \leq z_{\alpha/2},$$

where $z = (\bar{x} - \mu_0)/(\sigma/\sqrt{n})$ is the value of the standard normal corresponding to the value $\bar{x}$ of $\overline{X}$.

For the one-sided alternative hypothesis $H_1: \mu > \mu_0$, the critical region of size α is the right tail of the sampling distribution of $\overline{X}$; it is of the form

$$\text{Reject } H_0 \quad \text{if } \overline{X} \geq \bar{x}_{1-\alpha}, \tag{9.9}$$

where $\bar{x}_{1-\alpha}$ is the quantile value of $\overline{X}$ such that $P(\overline{X} \geq \bar{x}_{1-\alpha}) = \alpha$. Similarly, for the alternative hypothesis $H_1: \mu < \mu_0$, the critical region is of the form

$$\text{Reject } H_0 \quad \text{if } \overline{X} \leq \bar{x}_{\alpha}, \tag{9.10}$$

where the value $\bar{x}_{\alpha}$ is such that $P(\overline{X} \leq \bar{x}_{\alpha}) = \alpha$.

The critical regions for the one-sided hypotheses are illustrated in Figure 9.8 in terms of the statistic $\overline{X}$ and its transformation to the standard normal random variable Z. A summary of the rejection criteria for testing hypotheses on the mean of a normal distribution with known variance is given in Table 9.5.

Before working an example, let us develop a general expression for the determination of type II error for one of these cases. Consider the null hypothesis $H_0: \mu = \mu_0$ against the alternative $H_1: \mu > \mu_0$. Suppose that in reality $\mu =$

TABLE 9.5 Rejection criteria for testing hypotheses on the mean of a normal distribution with known variance

Null hypothesis	Value of test statistic under H_0
$H_0: \mu = \mu_0$	$z = \dfrac{\bar{x} - \mu_0}{\sigma/\sqrt{n}}$

Alternative hypothesis	Rejection criteria
$H_1: \mu \neq \mu_0$	Reject H_0 when $z \leq z_{\alpha/2}$ or when $z \geq z_{1-\alpha/2}$
$H_1: \mu > \mu_0$	Reject H_0 when $z \geq z_{1-\alpha}$
$H_1: \mu < \mu_0$	Reject H_0 when $z \leq z_\alpha$

$\mu_1 > \mu_0$. According to (9.9), we cannot reject H_0 if a value of $\bar{X}$ is less than $(\sigma z_{1-\alpha}/\sqrt{n}) + \mu_0$. Since the probability of type II error is the same as the probability of not rejecting a false H_0, we need to determine

$$\beta = P\left(\bar{X} < \frac{\sigma z_{1-\alpha}}{\sqrt{n}} + \mu_0 \,\middle|\, \mu = \mu_1 > \mu_0\right),$$

which in terms of the standard normal is

$$\beta = P\left[Z < \frac{\dfrac{\sigma z_{1-\alpha}}{\sqrt{n}} + \mu_0 - \mu_1}{\sigma/\sqrt{n}} \,\middle|\, \mu = \mu_1\right]. \tag{9.11}$$

By substituting any value μ_1 from the alternative hypothesis in (9.11), we can compute the corresponding probability of type II error and, thus, the power. Notice that β — and thus power — depends on the sample size n, the size of type I error α, the difference $(\mu_0 - \mu_1)$ between the claimed value μ_0 under H_0 and the true value μ_1 under H_1, and the population standard deviation σ. For fixed α, $(\mu_0 - \mu_1)$, and σ, the size of type II error decreases as n increases. For fixed n, $(\mu_0 - \mu_1)$, and σ, β increases as α decreases. And for fixed n, α, and σ, β decreases as the difference $(\mu_0 - \mu_1)$ increases.

Expressions similar to (9.11) can be developed for the other cases. The general behavior of the size of type II error as a function of n, α, $(\mu_0 - \mu_1)$, and σ is the same as before.

Example 9.6 The following data represent the assembly times of 20 randomly selected units: 9.8, 10.4, 10.6, 9.6, 9.7, 9.9, 10.9, 11.1, 9.6, 10.2, 10.3, 9.6, 9.9, 11.2, 10.6, 9.8, 10.5, 10.1, 10.5, 9.7. Assume that a unit's assembly time is a normal random variable with mean μ and standard deviation $\sigma = 0.6$ minutes. Based on this sample, is there reason to believe at the 0.05 level that the average assembly time exceeds 10 minutes?

Consider the null hypothesis

$$H_0: \mu = 10$$

against the alternative

$$H_1: \mu > 10.$$

If H_0 can be rejected with $\alpha = 0.05$, there would be reason to believe that the average assembly time is greater than 10 minutes. Since $P(Z \geqslant 1.645) = 0.05$, the critical value in terms of the standard normal is $z_{0.95} = 1.645$. From the sample data we compute $\bar{x}$ to be 10.2 minutes. Then

$$z = \frac{\bar{x} - \mu_0}{\sigma/\sqrt{n}} = \frac{10.2 - 10}{0.6/\sqrt{20}} = 1.4907.$$

Since $z = 1.4907 < z_{0.95} = 1.645$, the null hypothesis cannot be rejected. The p-value in this case is the probability that a standard normal random variable is greater than or equal to the value of 1.4907, given H_0 is true. From Table D of the Appendix it is seen that

$$P(Z \geqslant 1.4907 \mid \mu = 10) = 0.0681.$$

Since $p = 0.0681 > \alpha = 0.05$, we conclude that based on this sample there is insufficient evidence to reject the hypothesis that the mean assembly time is 10 minutes.

In the context of this example, suppose we ask the following question. If the true mean assembly time is 10.3 minutes, what is the probability of rejecting the null hypothesis? Here we wish to determine the power of the test for detecting the incorrectness of H_0 when the true mean is 10.3 minutes. Let us first determine the size of type II error. Using (9.11) we have

$$\beta = P\left(Z < \frac{\dfrac{(0.6)(1.645)}{\sqrt{20}} + 10 - 10.3}{0.6/\sqrt{20}} \;\middle|\; \mu = 10.3 \right)$$

$$= P(Z < -0.59 \mid \mu = 10.3)$$

$$= 0.2776.$$

Thus the probability of failing to reject H_0 when the mean is 10.3 minutes is 0.2776. Therefore, power $= 1 - \beta = 0.7224$. Following this procedure, we determine β and power probabilities for other values of μ under the alternative hypothesis, as summarized in Table 9.6. Notice that as the difference between the claimed value of the mean under H_0 and the true value under H_1 increases, the power of the test increases.

Now let us assume the same situation as before with the exception that the population variance σ^2 is unknown. Based on Section 8.4.2, the best test statistic

TABLE 9.6 Type II error and power probabilities for Example 9.6

μ	*10.01*	*10.1*	*10.2*	*10.3*	*10.4*	*10.5*	*10.6*	*10.7*
β	0.9418	0.8159	0.5596	0.2776	0.0901	0.0188	0.0024	0.0002
Power	0.0582	0.1841	0.4404	0.7224	0.9099	0.9812	0.9976	0.9998

TABLE 9.7   Rejection criteria for testing hypotheses on the mean of a normal distribution with unknown variance

Null hypothesis	Value of test statistic under H_0
H_0: $\mu = \mu_0$	$t = \dfrac{\bar{x} - \mu_0}{s/\sqrt{n}}$

Alternative hypothesis	Rejection criteria
H_1: $\mu \neq \mu_0$	Reject H_0 when $t \leq t_{\alpha/2, n-1}$ or when $t \geq t_{1-\alpha/2, n-1}$
H_1: $\mu > \mu_0$	Reject H_0 when $t \geq t_{1-\alpha, n-1}$
H_1: $\mu < \mu_0$	Reject H_0 when $t \leq t_{\alpha, n-1}$

to use in this case has the Student's t distribution. That is, under the null hypothesis H_0: $\mu = \mu_0$ the statistic

$$T = \frac{\bar{X} - \mu_0}{S/\sqrt{n}}$$

has a Student's t distribution with $n - 1$ degrees of freedom. The reader should have little difficulty in recognizing that by using the Student's t distribution, the critical regions for this case would parallel those of the previous case with regard to the two-sided or one-sided alternative hypotheses. A summary is provided in Table 9.7.

Example 9.7   Using the data from Example 8.9, show that for any claimed value μ_0 for μ that is inside, say, a 95% confidence interval, a test of the hypothesis

$$H_0: \mu = \mu_0$$

against the alternative

$$H_1: \mu \neq \mu_0$$

would not lead to the rejection of H_0 for $\alpha = 0.05$.

Recall from Section 8.4.2 that a 95% confidence interval for μ was determined to be 500.45–507.05. We need to show that the limits 500.45 and 507.05 coincide with the boundaries of the claimed values μ_0 under H_0 that would lead to the rejection of the null hypothesis. Since $\bar{x} = 503.75$ and $s = 6.2$, for the limit 500.45 we have

$$t = \frac{503.75 - 500.45}{6.2/\sqrt{16}} = 2.131,$$

and for the limit 507.05 we have

$$t = \frac{503.75 - 507.05}{6.2/\sqrt{16}} = -2.131.$$

But ± 2.131 are the boundaries of the two-sided critical region of size $\alpha = 0.05$ and 15 degrees of freedom. In other words, if $\mu_0 \leq 500.45$, then $t \geq 2.131$, and if $\mu_0 \geq 507.05$, $t \leq -2.131$. Thus any claimed value μ_0 interior to 500.45 and 507.05 would not lead to the rejection of H_0 with $\alpha = 0.05$.

To illustrate the computation of a p-value in the context of this example, consider the null hypothesis

$$H_0: \mu = 508$$

against the alternative

$$H_1: \mu \neq 508.$$

Since the claimed value of 508 is outside the 95% confidence interval, H_0 will be rejected at the $\alpha = 0.05$ level. To determine the p-value we compute the value of the test statistic, which is

$$t = \frac{503.75 - 508}{6.2/\sqrt{16}} = -2.742.$$

Since the alternative hypothesis is two-sided, the p-value is given by

$$P(|T| \geq 2.742) = P(T \leq -2.742) + P(T \geq 2.742),$$

where T is a Student's t random variable with 15 degrees of freedom. From Table F of the Appendix we see that it is necessary to interpolate between the quantile values $t_{0.99, \, 15} = 2.602$ and $t_{0.995, \, 15} = 2.947$. Then $t_{0.992, \, 15} = 2.742$, and the p-value is approximately 0.016. Therefore, if the null hypothesis is true, there is less than 2 percent chance of observing a value of a Student's t distribution with 15 degrees of freedom whose magnitude is as large or larger than the observed value of 2.742.

The determination of power and type II error probabilities for the T statistic is somewhat more difficult than it was in the previous case involving the normal distribution. The difficulty arises because the distribution of the test statistic if H_0 is false is not exactly the same as the Student's t distribution. In fact, under the alternative hypothesis the statistic has the so-called *noncentral t distribution*, which differs from the ordinary Student's t because an additional parameter is introduced. The parameter, denoted by δ, is defined by

$$\delta = \frac{\mu - \mu_0}{\sigma}$$

and expresses the difference between the true value μ under H_1 and the claimed value μ_0 under H_0 in terms of σ. As a result, the power function of the statistic T is a function of both the degrees of freedom ν and δ. OC curves as functions of δ and the sample size n exist for both one-sided and two-sided alternative hypotheses (see [1]). These reveal the same behavior for the size of type II error with regard to n, α, and the difference between the values under H_1 and H_0 as in the previous case. It should be noted that for relatively large sample sizes, say greater than 30, the computation of power for the T statistic can be adequately handled using the normal approximation.

9.6.2 Two-Sample Tests

Let $X_1, X_2, \ldots, X_{n_x}$ and $Y_1, Y_2, \ldots, Y_{n_y}$ be two random samples from independent normal distributions with means μ_X and μ_Y and variances σ_X^2 and σ_Y^2, respectively. Suppose we wish to test the null hypothesis

$$H_0: \mu_X - \mu_Y = \delta_0$$

against one of the following alternatives:

$$H_1: \mu_X - \mu_Y \neq \delta_0 \qquad H_1: \mu_X - \mu_Y > \delta_0 \qquad H_1: \mu_X - \mu_Y < \delta_0,$$

where δ_0 is some positive quantity or zero representing the claimed difference between the two unknown means. Assume the population variances are known. From the discussions in Sections 7.7, 8.4.3, and the preceding material of this chapter, it is reasonable to conclude that the appropriate test statistic is the sample mean difference $\overline{X} - \overline{Y}$. In particular, the null hypothesis will be rejected if a value of $\overline{X} - \overline{Y}$ based on a random sample is sufficiently different, greater than, or less than δ_0, depending on the alternative hypothesis in question. A transformation to the standard normal distribution gives rise to an equivalent form of the test statistic given by (8.41). A summary of the pertinent information is given in Table 9.8.

Example 9.8   Suppose that random samples of equal size n from two independent normal distributions with known variances σ_X^2 and σ_Y^2 are to be used to test the null hypothesis

$$H_0: \mu_X - \mu_Y = \delta_0$$

against the alternative

$$H_1: \mu_X - \mu_Y = \delta_1 > \delta_0.$$

If the particular sizes of type I and type II errors are specified to be α and β, respectively, determine an expression for n.

TABLE 9.8 Rejection criteria for testing hypotheses on the means of two independent normal distributions with known variances

Null hypothesis	Value of test statistic under H_0
$H_0: \mu_X - \mu_Y = \delta_0$	$z = \dfrac{\bar{x} - \bar{y} - \delta_0}{\sqrt{\dfrac{\sigma_X^2}{n_X} + \dfrac{\sigma_Y^2}{n_Y}}}$

Alternative hypothesis	Rejection criteria
$H_1: \mu_X - \mu_Y \neq \delta_0$	Reject H_0 when $z \leq z_{\alpha/2}$ or when $z \geq z_{1-\alpha/2}$
$H_1: \mu_X - \mu_Y > \delta_0$	Reject H_0 when $z \geq z_{1-\alpha}$
$H_1: \mu_X - \mu_Y < \delta_0$	Reject H_0 when $z \leq z_\alpha$

We are given that if H_0 is really true, the probability of rejecting it is α; and if H_0 is really false ($\mu_X - \mu_Y = \delta_1 > \delta_0$), the probability of not rejecting H_0 is β. With regard to the sampling distribution of $\overline{X} - \overline{Y}$, let c_0 be the critical value. Then H_0 is rejected when $\bar{x} - \bar{y} \geq c_0$ such that

$$P(\overline{X} - \overline{Y} \geq c_0 \mid \mu_X - \mu_Y = \delta_0) = \alpha.$$

In terms of the standard normal variable, this is equivalent to

$$P\left(Z \geq \frac{c_0 - \delta_0}{\sqrt{\dfrac{\sigma_X^2 + \sigma_Y^2}{n}}} \,\middle|\, \mu_X - \mu_Y = \delta_0 \right) = \alpha.$$

Since we can determine the quantile value $z_{1-\alpha}$ of the standard normal such that

$$P(Z \geq z_{1-\alpha}) = \alpha,$$

we have

$$\frac{c_0 - \delta_0}{\sqrt{\dfrac{\sigma_X^2 + \sigma_Y^2}{n}}} = z_{1-\alpha}. \qquad (9.12)$$

If $\mu_X - \mu_Y = \delta_1 > \delta_0$, then the probability of not rejecting H_0 is β. Hence

$$P(\overline{X} - \overline{Y} < c_0 \mid \mu_X - \mu_Y = \delta_1) = \beta,$$

which in terms of the standard normal variable is

$$P\left(Z < \frac{c_0 - \delta_1}{\sqrt{\dfrac{\sigma_X^2 + \sigma_Y^2}{n}}} \,\middle|\, \delta_1 \right) = \beta.$$

But the quantile value z_β must be the point of the standard normal such that

$$P(Z < z_\beta) = \beta.$$

Then it follows that

$$\frac{c_0 - \delta_1}{\sqrt{\dfrac{\sigma_X^2 + \sigma_Y^2}{n}}} = z_\beta. \qquad (9.13)$$

It should be noted that since β is likely to be less than 0.5, the quantile value z_β is negative.

Notice that equations (9.12) and (9.13) contain two unknowns: c_0 and n. To solve for n, let us first solve both of these equations for c_0.

$$c_0 = z_{1-\alpha}\sqrt{\frac{\sigma_X^2 + \sigma_Y^2}{n}} + \delta_0,$$

and

$$c_0 = z_\beta \sqrt{\frac{\sigma_X^2 + \sigma_Y^2}{n}} + \delta_1.$$

Equating the terms on the right side, we have

$$z_{1-\alpha} \sqrt{\frac{\sigma_X^2 + \sigma_Y^2}{n}} + \delta_0 = z_\beta \sqrt{\frac{\sigma_X^2 + \sigma_Y^2}{n}} + \delta_1,$$

or

$$\sqrt{\frac{\sigma_X^2 + \sigma_Y^2}{n}} (z_{1-\alpha} - z_\beta) = \delta_1 - \delta_0.$$

Since for the standard normal $-z_\beta = z_{1-\beta}$,

$$\sqrt{\frac{\sigma_X^2 + \sigma_Y^2}{n}} (z_{1-\alpha} + z_{1-\beta}) = \delta_1 - \delta_0,$$

which, after solving for n, reduces to

$$n = \frac{(\sigma_X^2 + \sigma_Y^2)(z_{1-\alpha} + z_{1-\beta})^2}{(\delta_1 - \delta_0)^2}. \tag{9.14}$$

Expression (9.14) determines the size of each of two random samples from two independent normal distributions to assure probabilities α and β for type I and type II errors, respectively, when testing

$$H_0: \mu_X - \mu_Y = \delta_0$$

against

$$H_1: \mu_X - \mu_Y = \delta_1 > \delta_0.$$

For a specific example, let $\sigma_X^2 = 25$, $\sigma_Y^2 = 20$, $\delta_0 = 5$, $\delta_1 = 8$, $\alpha = 0.05$, and $\beta = 0.10$. Then $z_{0.95} = 1.645$, $z_{0.90} = 1.28$, and

$$n = \frac{(25 + 20)(1.645 + 1.28)^2}{(8 - 5)^2} = 43.$$

The reader is asked to determine an equivalent expression for the left-sided alternative hypothesis. For a two-sided alternative hypothesis an approximation to the size n is possible by using Expression (9.14) and replacing α with $\alpha/2$. Although this approach is not exact, it is sufficient for most practical situations.

Let us examine the case with unknown variance. If the variances σ_X^2 and σ_Y^2 are unknown but can be assumed to be equal, then for the null hypothesis

$$H_0: \mu_X - \mu_Y = \delta_0$$

the test statistic is

$$T = \frac{\overline{X} - \overline{Y} - \delta_0}{S_p \sqrt{\dfrac{1}{n_X} + \dfrac{1}{n_Y}}}, \tag{9.15}$$

TABLE 9.9 Rejection criteria for testing hypotheses on the means of two independent normal distributions with unknown but equal variances

Null hypothesis	Value of test statistic under H_0
$H_0: \mu_X - \mu_Y = \delta_0$	$t = \dfrac{\bar{x} - \bar{y} - \delta_0}{s_p \sqrt{\dfrac{1}{n_X} + \dfrac{1}{n_Y}}}$

Alternative hypothesis	Rejection criteria
$H_1: \mu_X - \mu_Y \neq \delta_0$	Reject H_0 when $t \leq t_{\alpha/2, m}$ or when $t \geq t_{1-\alpha/2, m}$, where $m = n_X + n_Y - 2$
$H_1: \mu_X - \mu_Y > \delta_0$	Reject H_0 when $t \geq t_{1-\alpha, m}$
$H_1: \mu_X - \mu_Y < \delta_0$	Reject H_0 when $t \leq t_{\alpha, m}$

which has a Student's t distribution with $n_X + n_Y - 2$ degrees of freedom. The pooled estimator S_p^2 of the common variance σ^2 is as given by expression (7.28). The critical regions of size α for the two-sided and one-sided alternative hypotheses should be apparent from previous discussion. They are summarized in Table 9.9.

Example 9.9 Recently there has been increased interest in assessing the effect of offensive noise on one's ability to perform a given task. A researcher has devised an experiment in which a number of subjects will be asked to perform a task in a controlled environment under two levels of background noise. The researcher selects 32 persons who are equally capable of performing the task in about the same time. Of these, 16 are selected at random and are asked to perform the given task under a modest level of background noise. The remaining 16 will perform the same task under Level 2, a more severe level of offensive noise than Level 1. The following sample data represent the observed times (in minutes) required to complete the task by the 16 persons for each level.

Level 1	14	12	15	15	11	16	17	12	14	13	18	13	18	15	16	11
Level 2	20	22	18	18	19	15	18	15	22	18	19	15	21	22	18	16

Assuming that these data constitute random samples from two independent normal distributions with unknown but equal variances, is there reason to believe that the average time for Level 2 exceeds that for Level 1 by more than two minutes with $\alpha = 0.01$?

Let μ_1 and μ_2 be the unknown means for Levels 1 and 2, respectively. The claimed value for the difference between μ_2 and μ_1 is $\delta_0 = 2$. In other words, we claim that μ_2 is greater than μ_1 by two minutes; but we really would like to show that μ_2 is greater than μ_1 by more than two minutes. Accordingly, consider the null hypothesis

$$H_0: \mu_2 - \mu_1 = 2$$

against the alternative

$$H_1: \mu_2 - \mu_1 > 2.$$

Since $\alpha = 0.01$ and $n_1 = n_2 = 16$, the critical value is $t_{0.99,\,30} = 2.457$. From the data we determine that $\bar{x}_1 = 14.375$, $\bar{x}_2 = 18.5$, $s_1 = 2.2767$, and $s_2 = 2.4495$; thus the pooled estimate of the common variance is

$$s_p^2 = \frac{(15)(2.2767)^2 + 15(2.4495)^2}{16 + 16 - 2} = 5.5917,$$

or

$$s_p = 2.3647.$$

Then the value of the test statistic is

$$t = \frac{(18.5 - 14.375) - 2}{2.3647 \sqrt{\dfrac{1}{16} + \dfrac{1}{16}}} = 2.5417.$$

Since the realized value of 2.5417 is inside the critical region of size 0.01, the null hypothesis is rejected. Under H_0, the p-value is the probability that $T \geq 2.5417$, where $T \sim$ Student's t with 30 degrees of freedom. Using Table F in the Appendix and after interpolation, we determine that

$$P(T \geq 2.5417) = 0.0085.$$

Therefore, based on this experiment, we conclude that the difference between the means of Level 2 and Level 1 exceeding two minutes is statistically discernible with a p-value of 0.0085.

9.6.3 Reflection on Assumptions and Sensitivity

Before proceeding to the next section, it would be beneficial to pause a moment and reflect on the assumptions that have been made about testing statistical hypotheses on means. As we have emphasized before, statistical inferential procedures provide a sound and objective way of making inferences about population characteristics based on random samples. This process usually succeeds only when the assumptions that were made for the development of the appropriate sampling distributions are reasonably adhered to. The casual and haphazard approach to the application of statistical methods, without an understanding of the assumptions and possible consequences if they are not met, often leads to misinterpretation and wrong conclusions.

As we have seen, the Student's t distribution plays an important role for inferences on means, especially with regard to samples of modest size. But the t distribution is based on the assumption that sampling is from a normal distribution. If sampling is not from a normal distribution, the use of the Student's t distribution is actually incorrect because, for example, critical regions of size α are likely to be larger than the value we specify for α. Fortunately, however, the t distribution is largely *robust,* or insensitive to the assumption of normality, especially when the sample size is, say, 15 or more.

When the Student's t distribution is used to compare two means, the violation of the equal variance assumption is much more severe than the violation of the normality assumption. For an intuitive reason of the apparent effect, suppose in reality we are sampling from two normal distributions, one with mean $\mu = 100$ and standard deviation $\sigma = 20$, the other with $\mu = 120$ and $\sigma = 30$. The four-sigma range of the first is seen to be 60 to 140, while that of the second is 60 to 180. In essence, therefore, a value of less than 140 can just as easily be observed from either one of the two populations. Such values would not imply, however, that a difference between the two means exists. Only observations of the second sample in excess of 140 would begin to suggest an apparent mean difference, but their number is likely to be too small to make the difference in means discernible. Thus, based on the T statistic, the wrong conclusion of no difference between means is likely to occur with unacceptable frequency because of the imbalance in the inherent variation of the two distributions.

To quantify the effect of unequal variances, we simulated 1000 random samples of size 20 each from two independent normal distributions using the IMSL package. For the first distribution we set the mean and the standard deviation at 100 and 20, respectively. For the second, the values of 110, 120, and 130 were used for the mean, and the values of 25, 30, and 40 were used for the standard deviation. Accordingly, twelve cases were simulated in which for each generated pair of random samples we tested the hypothesis

$$H_0: \mu_1 - \mu_2 = 0$$

against the alternative

$$H_1: \mu_1 - \mu_2 < 0$$

using the Student's T statistic as given by (9.15). For each case we determined the number of times out of the 1000 trials the false null hypothesis could not be rejected with $\alpha = 0.05$. Thus we are able to compare the size of type II error for each case against the corresponding value, which can be obtained from OC curves in [1], when both standard deviations are equal to 20. The type II error probabilities are given in Table 9.10. When compared to the β values for equal variances, there is an appreciable increase in the size of type II error as the difference between the variances becomes more pronounced. Therefore, the effect of the violation of the equal variance assumption when comparing means can be substantial.

Now let us see the effect on the size of type I error if the assumption of equal variances is violated. That is, assuming H_0 is true, what effect would

TABLE 9.10 Simulated β probabilities for the effect of unequal variances when comparing two means ($\mu_1 = 100$, $\sigma_1 = 20$)

	$\sigma_2 = 20$	$\sigma_2 = 25$	$\sigma_2 = 30$	$\sigma_2 = 40$
$\mu_2 = 110$	0.550	0.626	0.687	0.758
$\mu_2 = 120$	0.065	0.139	0.209	0.389
$\mu_2 = 130$	0.002	0.008	0.021	0.093

TABLE 9.11 α probabilities for the effect of unequal variances when comparing two means

		σ_1^2/σ_2^2				
		1/5	1/2	1	2	5
	1	0.050	0.050	0.050	0.050	0.050
n_1/n_2	2	0.120	0.080	0.050	0.029	0.014
	5	0.220	0.120	0.050	0.014	0.002

unequal variances have on α? Scheffé [4] has determined that if the sample sizes n_1 and n_2 are large but equal, the T statistic is remarkably robust to the assumption of equal variances when comparing two means. Table 9.11 (see [4] for details) contains the actual size of type I error based on a 95% confidence interval for $\mu_1 - \mu_2$ as a function of the ratio of the two sample sizes and the ratio of the two variances. Notice that the size of type I error does not change in the first row from its prescribed value of 0.05, even though the variance ratio does change.

Throughout the discussion of statistical inference, we have assumed that a sample is drawn at random, and that the observations are therefore independently distributed. If these assumptions are not met, any statistical inference is likely to be in serious error regardless of the sample size. Yet the assumption of a random sample is the one that is likely to be violated most often.

Closely related to the concept of randomness is the selection of the sample when the means of two levels — or more, as we will examine later — are to be compared. To illustrate, recall Example 9.9. Since 16 persons were randomly selected to perform the given task under Level 1, it follows that the remaining 16 who performed the task under Level 2 were also randomly selected. This procedure assures an impartial assignment of which of the 32 persons will be subjected to which noise level. In statistical inference the process of impartial selection is called *randomization*. The principle of randomization protects against the introduction of systematic bias in the assignment of persons or things to different levels, thereby strengthening the credibility of the impending comparison.

We have already seen how inherent differences in variability can cloud the comparison between two means. Many times in the process of observing sample data, uncontrolled external factors can cause differences in variability. However, by adhering to the principle of randomization, such external factors are likely to have a balanced effect on the measurements under the two levels of interest. In the noise problem, for example, such factors as a subject's mood at the time the task is performed cannot be controlled. The principle of randomization tends to neutralize such effects.

9.6.4 Test on Means When the Observations Are Paired

Recall from the last section that when the means of two levels are to be compared, it is desirable to have the persons or things that will produce the measurements within each level as nearly homogeneous as possible. If there is an effect due to external factors, it can be neutralized by applying the principle of randomization.

It is also possible to neutralize undesirable variation by actually controlling the extraneous factors. This is accomplished by taking observations in pairs, where the conditions of external factors are assumed to be the same within each pair but may vary from pair to pair. Usually there is a natural relationship between the observations in a pair. That is, for each pair a single person or thing is selected at random and subjected to both levels of interest. Even though we still want to determine if there is a difference between the means, we can no longer regard the pairs as forming two independent samples.

For illustration, let us examine the following problem. A medical researcher is interested in determining whether an experimental drug has the undesirable side effect of raising systolic blood pressure. To conduct a broad-based study, she selects at random n persons of varying age and health conditions. In a controlled laboratory environment she records the blood pressure of the n subjects, administers the drug to them for a suitable length of time, then records the blood pressure again.

Let (X_1, Y_1), (X_2, Y_2), ..., (X_n, Y_n) be the n pairs, where (X_i, Y_i) denotes the systolic blood pressure of the ith subject before and after the drug. Notice here that the external factors deal with the condition of an individual relative to age, health, and other peculiarities that may have a unique effect on the blood pressure. Since each subject forms a pair, the effect of external factors on blood pressure is between pairs, and any substantive difference in blood pressure within each pair can reasonably be attributed to the effect of the drug. Thus by taking the difference between the two observations in each pair, we are able to remove (block out) the variability in blood pressure due to external factors. This makes possible a valid comparison of the blood pressure before and after the drug is administered. Of interest, therefore, is the column of differences created by subtracting one observation of each pair from the other, as in Table 9.12.

It is assumed that the differences $D_1, D_2, ..., D_n$ constitute independent normally distributed random variables such that $E(D_i) = \mu_D$ and $Var(D_i) = \sigma_D^2$ for all $i = 1, 2, ..., n$. This is possible if we assume independence between the pairs (but not necessarily within) so that $E(X_i) = \mu_i$ and $E(Y_i) = \mu_i + \mu_D$ for $i = 1, 2, ..., n$. Thus for the ith pair the expected values differ by a constant, which is the expected value of D_i for $i = 1, 2, ..., n$. Moreover, $Var(X_i) = \sigma_X^2$ and $Var(Y_i) = \sigma_Y^2$ are unknown and not necessarily equal, but are assumed to be constant for all $i = 1, 2, ..., n$.

TABLE 9.12 Differences between observations in an experiment

Pair number (person)	*Level 1 (BP before)*	*Level 2 (BP after)*	*Difference $Y - X$**
1	X_1	Y_1	$D_1 = Y_1 - X_1$
2	X_2	Y_2	$D_2 = Y_2 - X_2$
.	.	.	.
.	.	.	.
.	.	.	.
n	X_n	Y_n	$D_n = Y_n - X_n$

*One can just as easily take the difference $X - Y$.

In the context of the blood pressure problem, what we are saying here is the following. The constant μ_D is the mean difference in blood pressure due to the drug. Even though the blood pressure averages will vary from person to person because of differences in health conditions, we believe that μ_D is likely to be the same from person to person. Notice that if μ_D is zero, it would suggest that the drug has no effect on the blood pressure. On the other hand, if μ_D is greater than zero, it would indicate an increase in the blood pressure average due to the drug. The variance σ_D^2 of the differences in blood pressure is unknown and depends on the variances before and after the drug is administered. Although the variances σ_X^2 and σ_Y^2 may be different, they are assumed to be constant from person to person.

The preceding discussion demonstrates that statistical inferences on the means of two levels when the observations are paired can be made by treating the column of differences as a single random sample and applying the methods of Section 9.6.1. Under the null hypothesis

$$H_0: \mu_D = \delta_0,$$

the statistic

$$T = \frac{\overline{D} - \delta_0}{S_D/\sqrt{n}} \tag{9.16}$$

has a Student's t distribution with $n - 1$ degree of freedom, where

$$\overline{D} = \sum_{i=1}^{n} D_i/n$$

and

$$S_D^2 = \sum_{i=1}^{n} (D_i - \overline{D})^2/(n - 1).$$

The critical regions of size α for the two-sided and one-sided alternative hypotheses are summarized in Table 9.13.

TABLE 9.13 Rejection criteria for testing hypotheses on means when the observations are paired

Null hypothesis	Value of test statistic under H_0
$H_0: \mu_D = \delta_0$	$t = \dfrac{\overline{d} - \delta_0}{s_d/\sqrt{n}}$

Alternative hypothesis	Rejection criteria
$H_1: \mu_D \neq \delta_0$	Reject H_0 when $t \leq t_{\alpha/2,\, n-1}$ or when $t \geq t_{1-\alpha/2,\, n-1}$
$H_1: \mu_D > \delta_0$	Reject H_0 when $t \geq t_{1-\alpha,\, n-1}$
$H_1: \mu_D < \delta_0$	Reject H_0 when $t \leq t_{\alpha,\, n-1}$

TABLE 9.14 Sample data for Example 9.10

Subject	BP before	BP after	Difference (after − before)
1	128	134	6
2	176	174	−2
3	110	118	8
4	149	152	3
5	183	187	4
6	136	136	0
7	118	125	7
8	158	168	10
9	150	152	2
10	130	128	−2
11	126	130	4
12	162	167	5

Example 9.10 In the blood pressure problem above, let $\alpha = 0.01$ and test the null hypothesis

$$H_0: \mu_D = 0$$

against the alternative

$$H_1: \mu_D > 0,$$

based on the sample data in Table 9.14.

From the column of differences we find that $\bar{d} = 3.75$ and $s_D = 3.7929$. Thus the value of the test statistic is

$$t = \frac{3.75 - 0}{3.7929/\sqrt{12}} = 3.425.$$

Since the critical value is $t_{0.99,\,11} = 2.718$, the null hypothesis of no drug effect is rejected. Therefore, based on the results of this study, an increase in the average blood pressure is statistically discernible with a p-value of 0.0036.

It is worthwhile to note that in the preceding example there is no opportunity to apply the principle of randomization to remove possible systematic bias. This is typical of before–after situations in which the observations are paired to remove external effects. It is possible, however, that another external factor may intervene between measurements and cause substantive differences in the observations of some pairs; this influence will be wrongly credited to the effect being tested. In the blood pressure problem, for example, some of the subjects may undergo changes in health that are independent of the drug being administered to them, and the changes may cause an increase (or decrease) in blood pressure. The following example illustrates a more ideal experiment for comparing two means by pairing observations.

Example 9.11 Research goes on to develop superior varieties of corn that will yield larger quantities per unit of land. A researcher has developed a new hybrid

TABLE 9.15 Sample data for Example 9.11

Type	L_1	L_2	L_3	L_4	L_5	L_6	L_7	L_8	L_9	L_{10}
Variety X (standard)	23	35	29	42	33	19	37	24	35	26
Variety Y (new)	26	39	35	40	38	24	36	27	41	27

variety of corn that he feels is superior to the best variety currently available. He believes this new variety of corn will outproduce the standard one in most geographical locations. To verify this he devises the following experiment. He selects ten equal-sized plots from distinct geographical locations. Each plot is divided into two equal sections so that both varieties can be planted at each location. To remove possible systematic bias, he applies the principle of randomization in all plots to decide which section is planted with which variety. He accomplishes this by tossing a coin to decide the variety. He controls as many factors, such as planting time, type of fertilizer, and application interval, as possible. At harvest time he records the yield in bushels per unit of area. Suppose the data in Table 9.15 are obtained. Based on this data, determine a 95% confidence interval on the mean difference in yield between varieties X and Y.

Before proceeding with the analysis, we should recognize that the external factor being blocked out as a result of the pairing is the geographic location. In this type of situation there is little doubt that soil conditions and other effects are unlikely to be the same at different locations. Thus the opportunity exists for a substantial location effect on yield. Also notice that the opportunity is presented to randomize the assignment of varieties to plots to remove any systematic bias.

To determine the desired confidence interval, the differences in yield between X and Y at the ten locations are $-3, -4, -6, 2, -5, -5, 1, -3, -6$, and -1. Based on these, we compute $\overline{d} = -3$ and $s_D = 2.8284$. Assuming that these differences are values of independent normally distributed random variables, a 95% confidence interval on μ_D is

$$\overline{d} \pm t_{0.975,\, 9} \frac{s_D}{\sqrt{10}},$$

or

$$-3 \pm (2.262)(2.8284/\sqrt{10}),$$

which reduces to the interval $(-5.0232, -0.9768)$. Since the value zero is not included in this interval, the corresponding null hypothesis that the difference is zero will be rejected at the $\alpha = 0.05$ level.

It is appropriate to place the problem of comparing the means of two levels in a better perspective to justify the planning of an experiment based on independent samples or based on paired samples. Let X and Y represent the two levels of interest, assuming equal sample size n for the two independent samples and n

pairs of observations. Since in either case what is desired is an inference on the difference between the means, the statistic for both cases is $\overline{X} - \overline{Y}$. Thus under the assumption of normal sampling a $100(1 - \alpha)\%$ confidence interval for the mean difference in either case is of the general form

$$(\overline{X} - \overline{Y}) \pm t_{1-\alpha/2,\, m}\, s.d.(\overline{X} - \overline{Y}), \tag{9.17}$$

where m is the degrees of freedom. In expression (9.17), two terms differ between the two cases. One is the quantile value $t_{1-\alpha/2,m}$; the other is the standard deviation of the statistic $\overline{X} - \overline{Y}$. When the observations are paired, the quantile value is a function of $m = n - 1$ degrees of freedom, while that for independent samples is based on $m = 2(n - 1)$ degrees of freedom. For a given α, the quantile value will increase as the degrees of freedom decrease. Then, everything else being equal, a confidence interval for paired samples is wider because of the loss of degrees of freedom.

In light of the preceding information, the standard deviation of $\overline{X} - \overline{Y}$ becomes a trade-off to keep in mind when choosing between independent and paired samples. If a potentially influential extraneous factor is allowed to vary when taking independent samples, the likely consequence is a substantial variability among the measurements, thereby producing a large $s.d.(\overline{X} - \overline{Y})$. By pairing the observations, we can neutralize the influence of the extraneous factor and keep its effect the same within each pair. Then the observations within each pair are likely to be correlated. That is, for a given pair, a large value of X is likely to result in a large value of Y or vice versa, resulting in a positive covariance between X and Y. It follows then that since $Var(X - Y) = Var(X) + Var(Y) - 2Cov(X, Y)$, the variance of $X - Y$ (as well as that of $\overline{X} - \overline{Y}$) will be smaller for paired samples than for independent samples. Therefore, in a well-planned experiment for paired observations, the reduction in the standard deviation of $\overline{X} - \overline{Y}$ will usually more than offset the increase in the critical value due to the loss of degrees of freedom.

For illustration, in Example 9.11 we computed the estimate $s_D = 2.8284$. If the data are considered as independent samples from two normal distributions with equal variances, an estimate of the common variance is

$$s_p^2 = \frac{9(52.6778) + 9(43.1222)}{18} = 47.9,$$

or $s_p = 6.921$. The value $s_p = 6.921$ is more than double the comparable value $s_D = 2.8284$. Constructing a 95% confidence interval for independent samples, we obtain

$$-3 \pm (2.101)(6.921)\sqrt{\frac{1}{10} + \frac{1}{10}},$$

or

$$(-9.5029, 3.5029).$$

It is obvious that a null hypothesis of no difference in means could not be rejected if the data were considered as independent samples.

9.7 Tests of Hypotheses Concerning Variances When Sampling from Normal Distributions

As we have argued before, an inference on a variance is of equal importance to an inference on a mean. In industrial environments, for example, product variability may be a more important quantity than a product average. For this reason as well as the need to check assumptions of equal variances, we will present criteria to test hypotheses on variances based on a single random sample or based on two independent samples from normal distributions. As expected, the criteria for testing hypotheses on variances are based on the corresponding methods for constructing confidence intervals, as discussed in Sections 8.4.4 and 8.4.5. It is imperative to emphasize again that these procedures are especially sensitive to the assumption of normality.

9.7.1 One-Sample Tests

Let $X_1, X_2, \ldots, X_n$ be a random sample from a normal distribution with unknown mean μ and unknown variance σ^2. Consider testing the null hypothesis

$$H_0: \sigma^2 = \sigma_0^2$$

against one of the following alternatives:

$$H_1: \sigma^2 \neq \sigma_0^2, \qquad H_1: \sigma^2 > \sigma_0^2, \qquad H_1: \sigma^2 < \sigma_0^2,$$

where σ_0^2 is the claimed value for σ^2. The statistic of interest is the sample variance S^2. The null hypothesis will be rejected if the realization of S^2 computed from the sample is sufficiently different, greater than, or less than σ_0^2, depending on the alternative hypothesis. But under H_0, the quantity $(n-1)s^2/\sigma_0^2$ is a value of chi-square random variable with $n-1$ degrees of freedom. Then, for example, if the alternative hypothesis is $H_1: \sigma^2 > \sigma_0^2$, we will reject H_0 whenever the value $(n-1)s^2/\sigma_0^2$ is inside the critical region of size α on the right side of the chi-square distribution with $n-1$ degrees of freedom. A summary of the relevant information is provided in Table 9.16.

As we have noted before, the violation of the assumption that sampling is from a normal distribution has a substantial effect when using the chi-square

TABLE 9.16 Rejection criteria for testing hypotheses on the variance of a normal distribution with unknown mean

Null hypothesis	*Value of test statistic under H_0*
$H_0: \sigma^2 = \sigma_0^2$	$\chi^2 = \dfrac{(n-1)s^2}{\sigma_0^2}$

Alternative hypothesis	*Rejection criteria*
$H_1: \sigma^2 \neq \sigma_0^2$	Reject H_0 when $\chi^2 \geq \chi^2_{1-\alpha/2,\, n-1}$, or when $\chi^2 \leq \chi^2_{\alpha/2,\, n-1}$
$H_1: \sigma^2 > \sigma_0^2$	Reject H_0 when $\chi^2 \geq \chi^2_{1-\alpha,\, n-1}$
$H_1: \sigma^2 < \sigma_0^2$	Reject H_0 when $\chi^2 \leq \chi^2_{\alpha,\, n-1}$

TABLE 9.17 Rejections of the null hypothesis out of 1000 samples from each of three distributions of equal variance

Type of distribution and parameter values		
Uniform $(0, \sqrt{1200})$	*Gamma* *Shape* = 2; *scale* = $\sqrt{50}$	*Exponential* *Mean* = 10
8	107	156

statistic for inferences on variances. To illustrate this effect, we simulated an experiment similar to that described in Section 8.4.3. For the modest sample size of $n = 30$ we generated 1000 random samples from each of a uniform, an exponential, and a gamma distribution. The parameter values for each distribution were selected to yield a variance of 100 in each case. For each random sample we tested the null hypothesis

$$H_0: \sigma^2 = 100$$

against the alternative

$$H_1: \sigma^2 > 100,$$

using the chi-square statistic with $\alpha = 0.05$. For each imposed distribution we counted the number of times the null hypothesis was rejected. The results are listed in Table 9.17.

Since $\alpha = 0.05$ represents the probability of rejecting a true hypothesis — which is the case here — we expect 50 out of 1000 random samples to yield this decision under normal sampling. Based on the results, however, there is enough discrepancy to believe that the chi-square statistic is sensitive to departures from normal sampling. It is worthwhile to note that the results of the simulation study are somewhat predictable, especially if we compare the shape factors of the selected distributions with those of the normal distribution. The uniform distribution is symmetric, like the normal, but it is defined in the finite interval $(0, \sqrt{1200})$. Consequently, the likelihood is diminished that some random samples would contain extreme values that would inflate the sample variance. Thus the number of rejections is less than what is expected. The exponential distribution is the most skewed of the three selected distributions and has the largest relative kurtosis. Hence it is not surprising that the number of rejections is quite a bit larger than that for the normal distribution. The gamma distribution, with shape and scale parameters of 2 and $\sqrt{50}$, respectively, falls somewhere in between since its coefficient of skewness is $\sqrt{2}$ and its relative kurtosis is 6.

9.7.2 Two-Sample Tests

Let $X_1, X_2, ..., X_{n_X}$ and $Y_1, Y_2, ..., Y_{n_Y}$ be two random samples from independent normal distributions with unknown means μ_X and μ_Y and unknown variances σ_X^2 and σ_Y^2. Consider testing the null hypothesis

$$H_0: \sigma_X^2 = \sigma_Y^2$$

against one of the following alternatives:

$$H_1: \sigma_X^2 \neq \sigma_Y^2, \qquad H_1: \sigma_X^2 > \sigma_Y^2, \qquad H_1: \sigma_X^2 < \sigma_Y^2.$$

The statistics of interest are the sample variances S_X^2 and S_Y^2. With regard to the two-sided alternative hypothesis, for example, we would be inclined to reject the null hypothesis whenever the estimate s_X^2 is sufficiently different from the estimate s_Y^2. Recall from Section 7.8 that by virtue of independence, the quantities $(n_X - 1)S_X^2/\sigma_X^2$ and $(n_Y - 1)S_Y^2/\sigma_Y^2$ are two independent chi-square random variables with $n_X - 1$ and $n_Y - 1$ degrees of freedom, respectively. Then it follows that the statistic

$$F = \frac{S_X^2/\sigma_X^2}{S_Y^2/\sigma_Y^2}$$

has an F distribution with $n_X - 1$ and $n_Y - 1$ degrees of freedom. But under the null hypothesis, $\sigma_X^2 = \sigma_Y^2$; thus, the test statistic reduces to

$$F = S_X^2/S_Y^2.$$

For a two-sided alternative hypothesis and a size α for type I error, the null hypothesis will be rejected when $f = s_X^2/s_Y^2 \geq f_{1-\alpha/2,\, n_X-1,\, n_Y-1}$, or when $f \leq 1/f_{1-\alpha/2,\, n_Y-1,\, n_X-1}$. A complete summary of rejection criteria is provided in Table 9.18.

   To illustrate, recall that in Example 9.9 we assumed equal variances in comparing the means for two levels of noise. To check the validity of this assumption at the $\alpha = 0.1$ level, suppose we test the hypothesis

$$H_0: \sigma_1^2 = \sigma_2^2$$

against the alternative

$$H_1: \sigma_1^2 \neq \sigma_2^2.$$

   The right-side and left-side critical values are seen to be $f_{0.95,\, 15,\, 15} = 2.40$ and $1/f_{0.95,\, 15,\, 15} = 1/2.40 = 0.42$, respectively. Based on the sample data, we compute $s_1^2 = 5.1833$ and $s_2^2 = 6.0$. Thus the value of the test statistic is

$$f = 5.1833/6 = 0.8639.$$

TABLE 9.18 Rejection criteria for testing hypotheses on the variances of two independent normal distributions

Null hypothesis	Value of test statistic under H_0
$H_0: \sigma_X^2 = \sigma_Y^2$	$f = s_X^2/s_Y^2$

Alternative hypothesis	Rejection criteria
$H_1: \sigma_X^2 \neq \sigma_Y^2$	Reject H_0 when $f \geq f_{1-\alpha/2,\, n_X-1,\, n_Y-1}$, or when $f \leq 1/f_{1-\alpha/2,\, n_Y-1,\, n_X-1}$
$H_1: \sigma_X^2 > \sigma_Y^2$	Reject H_0 when $f \geq f_{1-\alpha,\, n_X-1,\, n_Y-1}$
$H_1: \sigma_X^2 < \sigma_Y^2$	Reject H_0 when $f \leq 1/f_{1-\alpha,\, n_Y-1,\, n_X-1}$

Since $f = 0.8639$ is neither greater than or equal to 2.4 nor less than or equal to 0.42, the null hypothesis cannot be rejected. Accordingly, the sample results do not provide a reason to suspect that the equal variance assumption is being violated.

9.8 Inferences on the Proportions of Two Independent Binomial Distributions

In Section 8.4.6 we developed criteria for the construction of confidence intervals of the proportion parameter p when sampling from a binomial distribution. Many times we are interested in comparing the proportion of one distinct group with that of another, relative to some common characteristic. For example, we might be interested in comparing the proportion of defective units of a given product produced by two competing manufacturers. Or there might be an interest in comparing the proportions of high school students in two geographical locations who had SAT scores above a certain level. Thus we need to extend the ideas presented in Section 8.4.6 to compare the proportion parameters when sampling from two independent binomial distributions.

To illustrate, a recent study compared the proportions of left-handers and right-handers who smoke. Let the general population be divided into two groups, consisting of left-handers and right-handers, and let each group be further subdivided into smokers and nonsmokers. Let p_1 be the proportion of left-handers who smoke and p_2 be the proportion of right-handers who smoke. Of interest is a comparison between p_1 and p_2.

Assume the left-handers and right-handers constitute two independent binomial distributions such that the proportions of smokers in the two groups are p_1 and p_2, respectively. Based on random samples of sizes n_1 and n_2, let X and Y be the observed numbers of left-handers and right-handers who smoke, respectively. The sample proportions

$$\hat{P}_1 = X/n_1,$$

$$\hat{P}_2 = Y/n_2$$

are the maximum likelihood estimators of p_1 and p_2, respectively. Since by assumption X and Y are binomial random variables, the variances of the estimators are given by

$$Var(\hat{P}_1) = Var(X/n_1) = p_1(1 - p_1)/n_1,$$

$$Var(\hat{P}_2) = Var(Y/n_2) = p_2(1 - p_2)/n_2.$$

Suppose we wish to construct a large sample confidence interval for the difference between p_1 and p_2. The statistic of interest is the difference between the two sample proportions. Since

$$E(\hat{P}_1) = p_1, \qquad E(\hat{P}_2) = p_2,$$

then based on Theorem 6.1 and its corollary, as given by expression (7.2),

$$E(\hat{P}_1 - \hat{P}_2) = p_1 - p_2, \tag{9.18}$$

and

$$Var(\hat{P}_1 - \hat{P}_2) = Var(\hat{P}_1) + Var(\hat{P}_2)$$

$$= \frac{p_1(1 - p_1)}{n_1} + \frac{p_2(1 - p_2)}{n_2}. \tag{9.19}$$

Based on earlier discussion (see Chapter 5), it can be shown that for large n_1 and n_2 the distribution of the statistic $\hat{P}_1 - \hat{P}_2$ is approximately normal with mean and variance given by (9.18) and (9.19), respectively. In other words, the distribution of

$$Z = \frac{(\hat{P}_1 - \hat{P}_2) - (p_1 - p_2)}{\sqrt{\dfrac{\hat{P}_1(1 - \hat{P}_1)}{n_1} + \dfrac{\hat{P}_2(1 - \hat{P}_2)}{n_2}}} \tag{9.20}$$

is approximately $N(0, 1)$ for large n_1 and n_2. Notice that the denominator in expression (9.20) provides for an estimate of the standard deviation of the statistic $\hat{P}_1 - \hat{P}_2$, since the sample proportions have replaced p_1 and p_2. It follows, therefore, that for large n_1 and n_2 the probability of the random interval

$$[(\hat{P}_1 - \hat{P}_2) - z_{1-\alpha/2} \, s.d.(\hat{P}_1 - \hat{P}_2), \qquad (\hat{P}_1 - \hat{P}_2) + z_{1-\alpha/2} \, s.d.(\hat{P}_1 - \hat{P}_2)]$$

is approximately $1 - \alpha$, and an approximate $100(1 - \alpha)\%$ confidence interval for $p_1 - p_2$ is

$$(\hat{p}_1 - \hat{p}_2) \pm z_{1-\alpha/2} \sqrt{\frac{\hat{p}_1(1 - \hat{p}_1)}{n_1} + \frac{\hat{p}_2(1 - \hat{p}_2)}{n_2}}, \tag{9.21}$$

where $\hat{p}_1 = x/n_1$ and $\hat{p}_2 = y/n_2$ are the respective maximum likelihood estimates of p_1 and p_2.

Example 9.12   In a study of the smoking habits of left-handers and right-handers, a random sample of 400 left-handers revealed 190 smokers, and a random sample of 800 right-handers produced 300 smokers. Based on this evidence, construct a 98% confidence interval for the true difference between the proportions p_1 and p_2.

The estimates of the proportions are

$$\hat{p}_1 = 190/400 = 0.475, \qquad \hat{p}_2 = 300/800 = 0.375.$$

Since the sample sizes are large, the normal approximation will be adequate. For a 98% confidence interval $z_{0.99} = 2.33$, and the confidence interval is

$$(0.475 - 0.375) \pm 2.33 \sqrt{\frac{(0.475)(1 - 0.475)}{400} + \frac{(0.375)(1 - 0.375)}{800}},$$

which reduces to the interval $(0.0295, 0.1705)$. Since this confidence interval does not include the origin and, in fact, lies to the right of it, we can conclude with 98% confidence that the percentage of left-handers who smoke exceeds that of right-handers.

Suppose we are interested in testing the null hypothesis

$$H_0: p_1 - p_2 = 0$$

against one of the following alternatives:

$$H_1: p_1 - p_2 \neq 0, \qquad H_1: p_1 - p_2 > 0, \qquad H_1: p_1 - p_2 < 0.$$

Given random samples of sizes n_1 and n_2, consider the statistic $\hat{P}_1 - \hat{P}_2$. Our intuition suggests that we should reject the null hypothesis whenever a value of this statistic is sufficiently different, greater than, or less than zero, depending on the alternative hypothesis. Equivalently, we may base the decision on a test statistic similar to that given by (9.20), which is approximately $N(0, 1)$ for large n_1 and n_2.

Since under H_0 the two proportions are assumed equal, let $p = p_1 = p_2$ be the common proportion. Then if the null hypothesis is true, the statistic $\hat{P}_1 - \hat{P}_2$ is approximately normally distributed with mean

$$E(\hat{P}_1 - \hat{P}_2) = 0$$

and standard deviation

$$s.d.(\hat{P}_1 - \hat{P}_2) = \sqrt{\frac{p(1 - p)}{n_1} + \frac{p(1 - p)}{n_2}}$$

$$= \left(\sqrt{p(1 - p)}\right)\left(\sqrt{\frac{1}{n_1} + \frac{1}{n_2}}\right).$$

Since p is unknown, we pool the information from the two samples to determine the pooled estimator

$$\hat{P} = \frac{X + Y}{n_1 + n_2},$$

where X and Y are the observed random variables possessing the characteristic of interest. Then an estimate of the standard deviation of $\hat{P}_1 - \hat{P}_2$ is

$$s.d. (\hat{P}_1 - \hat{P}_2) = \left(\sqrt{\hat{p}(1 - \hat{p})}\right)\left(\sqrt{\frac{1}{n_1} + \frac{1}{n_2}}\right),$$

where $\hat{p} = (x + y)/(n_1 + n_2)$ is the pooled estimate of p. Under H_0 the statistic

$$Z = \frac{\hat{P}_1 - \hat{P}_2}{\left(\sqrt{\hat{P}(1 - \hat{P})}\right)\left(\sqrt{\frac{1}{n_1} + \frac{1}{n_2}}\right)} \tag{9.22}$$

is approximately $N(0, 1)$ for large n_1 and n_2. Depending on the alternative hypothesis, the reader should have no difficulty deciding when to reject H_0 based on (9.22) and a given size of type I error.

References

1. A. H. Bowker and G. J. Lieberman, *Engineering statistics,* Prentice-Hall, Englewood Cliffs, N.J., 1959.
2. P. G. Hoel, *Introduction to mathematical statistics,* 4th ed., Wiley, New York, 1971.
3. B. W. Lindgren, *Statistical theory,* 3rd ed., Macmillan, New York, 1976.
4. H. Scheffé, *The analysis of variance,* Wiley, New York, 1959.

Exercises

9.1. Suppose you wish to test the hypothesis

$$H_0: \theta = 5$$

against the alternative

$$H_1: \theta = 8$$

by means of a single observed value of a random variable with probability density function $f(x; \theta) = (1/\theta)\exp(-x/\theta)$, $x > 0$. If the maximum size of type I error that can be tolerated is 0.15, which of the following tests is best for choosing between the two hypotheses?

a. Reject H_0 if $X \geq 9$
b. Reject H_0 if $X \geq 10$
c. Reject H_0 if $X \geq 11$

9.2. Suppose you observe a single value of a random variable whose density is $f(x; \theta) = 1/\theta$, $0 < x < \theta$, and you wish to test the hypothesis

$$H_0: \theta = 20$$

against the alternative

$$H_1: \theta = 15.$$

Which of the two tests — (a) reject H_0 if $X \leq 8$, or (b) reject H_0 if $X > 8$ — is better for deciding between the two hypotheses?

9.3. The proportion defective of a production process is known to be 0.05. The process is checked periodically by taking random samples of size 20 and inspecting the units. If two or more units in the sample of 20 are found defective, the process is stopped and is considered to be "out of control."

a. State the appropriate null and alternative hypotheses.
b. Determine the probability of type I error.
c. Determine and graph the power function for the following alternative proportion defective values: 0.06, 0.08, 0.1, 0.15, 0.2, and 0.25.
d. Compare your answers to part b and part c to the case where the process is judged out of control when three or more units are found defective.

9.4. The average amount being poured in a container by a filling process is supposed to be 20 ounces. Periodically, 25 containers are randomly chosen and their contents weighed. The process is judged to be out of control when the sample mean $\overline{X}$ is either less than or equal to 19.8 or greater than or equal to 20.2 ounces. The amount being poured in each container is assumed to be adequately approximated by a normal distribution with standard deviation 0.5 ounces.

    a. State the appropriate null and alternative hypotheses.

    b. Determine the probability of type I error.

    c. Determine and graph the power function for the following values of the mean fill: 19.5, 19.6, 19.7, 19.8, 19.9, 20.0, 20.1, 20.2, 20.3, 20.4, and 20.5.

    d. As an alternative test, consider rejecting H_0 when $\overline{X} \leqslant 19.75$ or when $\overline{X} \geqslant 20.25$. If the maximum size of type I error is 0.05, which of these two tests is better?

9.5. Referring to Exercise 9.4, suppose the sample size is increased to 36 containers. Given the same sizes of type I error for the proposed tests, determine the new critical values and compare the power functions of the two tests.

9.6. The following are the observed system times (queue wait time plus service time) of ten randomly selected customers in a service-providing facility: 8.7, 2.4, 18.2, 10.5, 9.7, 4.8, 11.2, 29.3, 10.8, 15.6. Assume the system time is a gamma distributed random variable with unknown scale parameter θ and a shape parameter equal to 2. (Hint: See expression (5.51) and Theorem 7.1.)

    a. Test the null hypothesis

$$H_0: \theta = 5$$

    against the alternative

$$H_1: \theta > 5,$$

    with a maximum size of type I error of 0.05.

    b. If θ were really equal to 7, what would be the probability of type II error?

9.7. Let $X_1, X_2, \ldots, X_n$ be a random sample of size n from a normal distribution with an unknown mean μ and a known variance σ^2. Determine the best critical region of size α for testing

$$H_0: \mu = \mu_0$$

against

$$H_1: \mu = \mu_1,$$

where $\mu_1 < \mu_0$.

9.8. Let $X_1, X_2, \ldots, X_n$ be a random sample of size n from a Poisson distribution with unknown parameter λ. Determine the best critical region of size α for testing

$$H_0: \lambda = \lambda_0$$

against

$$H_1: \lambda = \lambda_1,$$

where $\lambda_1 < \lambda_0$.

9.9. The number of accidents at a busy intersection is adequately modeled by a Poisson distribution with a mean of 2.5 accidents per week. The traffic engineer has decided to reduce the speed limit of the two intersecting highways. The decision about whether the reduction in the speed limit has decreased the average number of accidents per week will be based on the total number of accidents observed during a four-week period following the reduction in the speed limit.

    a. State the appropriate null and alternative hypotheses.

    b. For a maximum size of type I error of 0.1, determine the critical value of the test statistic for the rejection of the null hypothesis. (Hint: See Example 9.4 and Exercise 7.6.)

c. If the average number of accidents has been decreased to 2, determine the probability of type II error.

9.10. Let $X_1, X_2, \ldots, X_n$ be a random sample of size n from an exponential distribution with unknown scale parameter θ. Determine the best critical region of size α for testing

$$H_0: \theta = \theta_0$$

against

$$H_1: \theta = \theta_1,$$

where $\theta_1 > \theta_0$.

9.11. Four units of a video game are randomly selected and tested until a breakdown occurs. The observed times until the occurrence of a breakdown are 148.2, 120.6, 165.5, and 145.7 hours. Assuming the time until a breakdown is an exponential random variable, use Example 7.4 to test the null hypothesis that the mean time to breakdown is 140 hours against the alternative that it exceeds 140 hours with probability of type I error of 0.1. (Hint: Use an iterative technique in conjunction with expression (5.56).)

9.12. A contractor has ordered a large number of steel beams whose average length should be 5 meters. The length of a beam is known to be normally distributed with a standard deviation of 0.02 meters. Upon receiving the shipment the contractor selects 16 beams at random and measures their lengths. The decision will be to return the shipment to the producer if the sample mean is smaller than expected.

   a. If the probability of rejecting a good shipment is 0.04, for what value of the sample mean should the shipment be returned?
   b. If the true mean length is 4.98 meters, what is the power of the test in part a?

9.13. In Exercise 9.12, what is the required sample size such that the probability of detecting a decrease of 0.015 meters in mean length is 0.99?

9.14. An owner of a subcompact car suspects that the average gasoline mileage is less than the EPA rating of 30 miles per gallon. The owner observes the mileage per gallon for nine tanks of gasoline as follows: 28.3, 31.2, 29.4, 27.2, 30.8, 28.7, 29.2, 26.5, 28.1. Upon further investigation the owner concludes the mileage per gallon is a normally distributed random variable with a known standard deviation of 1.4 mpg. Based on this information, can the owner's suspicion be supported with $\alpha = 0.01$? What is the p-value in this case?

9.15. In Exercise 9.14, for how many tanks should the gasoline mileage be observed so that if the average mpg is as low as 28 it will be detected with probability 0.9?

9.16. In a certain county in Iowa, the average corn yield has been 100 bushels per acre. For a given year in which the weather was particularly good, twelve randomly selected large plots in the county yielded an average of 106 bushels per acre for the same variety of corn. If the yield per acre is adequately modeled by a normal distribution with standard deviation of 8 bushels per acre, is there reason to believe that this year's yield has been better than normal? Use $\alpha = 0.01$. What is the p-value in this case?

9.17. For Exercise 9.16, determine the corresponding lower 99% confidence interval estimate for the true average yield per acre, and deduce the range of possible values for μ under the null hypothesis for which H_0 could not be rejected at the same value of α.

9.18. In an assembly plant a specific operation is designed to take an average of 5 minutes. The plant manager suspects that for a particular operator the average time is different. The manager samples eleven operation times for this worker with the following results (in minutes): 4.8, 5.6, 5.3, 5.2, 4.9, 4.7, 5.7, 4.9, 5.7, 4.9, 4.6. Assume the operation time is adequately modeled by a normal distribution.

   a. Can the manager's suspicion be supported with $\alpha = 0.02$? What is the p-value?
   b. Determine the corresponding 98% confidence interval estimate for the true average time, and deduce the range of possible values of μ under H_0 for which the null hypothesis could not be rejected.

9.19. At times, mildly radioactive industrial byproducts find their way into our fresh water supply. For reasons such as this, state health agencies periodically monitor fresh water sources by taking and analyzing water samples. It has been mandated that the average amount of radiation in drinking water must not exceed 4 picocuries per liter of water. A random sample of 16 water specimens from the water supply of a densely populated area yielded a sample mean and sample standard deviation of 4.2 and 1.2 picocuries per liter, respectively. Assume the amount of radiation per liter of water from this supply is adequately approximated by a normal distribution.

   a. Should one use a particularly small value for the probability of Type I error here? Why?
   b. Select an alpha value and test the appropriate hypothesis. What is the p-value?
   c. Should you be concerned about the assumption of normality? Comment.

9.20. In Exercise 9.14, suppose the standard deviation of the gasoline mileage is not known. Test the same hypothesis as in Exercise 9.14 and compare your results.

9.21. In Exercise 9.11, suppose you assumed the time to breakdown is normally distributed. Test the same hypothesis as in Exercise 9.11 and compare your results.

9.22. Consider testing $H_0: p = p_0$ against $H_1: p = p_1$ for the binomial parameter p, where $p_1 > p_0$. Use the Neyman–Pearson lemma to show the best critical region of size α is based on the observed number of "successes" out of n independent trials.

9.23. A manufacturer of washing machines claims that only five percent of all units sold will experience some malfunction during the first year of normal operation. A consumer organization has asked 20 randomly selected equal-sized families who have bought these washers to report any malfunctions during the first year. By the end of the year three families have reported malfunctions.

   a. If the consumer organization believes the proportion of washers that will experience a malfunction is higher than the claimed value, use Exercise 9.22 to determine whether $H_0: p = 0.05$ can be rejected with a maximum size of type I error of 0.1.
   b. Use an approximate method based on the material of Section 8.4.6 to test the null hypothesis and compare the probabilities of the test statistics, assuming values as extreme or more so than those determined, given that H_0 is true.

9.24. Suppose that in a random sample of 20 babies conceived by an in vitro fertilization process, 15 are girls.

   a. Use Exercise 9.22 to determine how likely is the result of 15 or more girls if the true proportion of females is 0.5.
   b. Compare the probability in part a with that obtained by using the normal approximation.

9.25. A health organization is interested in updating its information about the proportion of males who smoke. Based on previous studies, the proportion is believed to be 40%. The organization commissions a poll in which 1200 randomly selected males of all ages are queried about their smoking habits. Of the 1200, 420 are smokers. Use an approximate method to determine whether this evidence supports the notion that the proportion of male smokers is different from 40% for $\alpha = 0.01$.

9.26. The campaign manager for Candidate A is thinking about a media blitz in the last weeks prior to the election. He feels his candidate has been even with her opponent, Candidate B, but may have slipped somewhat recently. The manager commissions a poll of 1500 potential voters. If out of the 1500 polled 720 indicate a preference for A, is there reason to believe that Candidate A now trails Candidate B? Use $\alpha = 0.05$.

9.27. A manufacturer wishes to compare the average strength of his yarn with that of his major competitor. The strengths of 100 yarn specimens for each make are observed under controlled conditions. The sample means and sample standard deviations are as follows:

$$\bar{x}_1 = 110.8 \qquad \bar{x}_2 = 108.2$$
$$s_1 = 10.2 \qquad s_2 = 12.4.$$

If we assume sampling is from two independent normal populations, is there reason to believe that a difference exists between the average strengths of the two yarns? Use $\alpha = 0.02$. What is the p-value? (Hint: The statistic given by (8.41) in which the estimates s_1^2 and s_2^2 replace the corresponding population variances is approximately $N(0, 1)$ for large n_1 and n_2).

9.28. In Exercise 9.27, determine the operating characteristic and power curves.

9.29. Determine an equivalent expression to (9.14) for testing $H_0: \mu_X - \mu_Y = \delta_0$ against $H_1: \mu_X - \mu_Y = \delta_1 < \delta_0$.

9.30. It is believed that the average verbal SAT score for college-bound females exceeds that of males by more than 10 points. Random samples from both sexes produced the following results:

	Female		*Male*
	$n_1 = 125$		$n_2 = 100$
	$\bar{x}_1 = 480$		$\bar{x}_2 = 460$
	$s_1 = 60$		$s_2 = 52$

a. If sampling is from two independent normal populations, is the belief supported at the $\alpha = 0.05$ level? What is the p-value?

b. Suppose the true difference is 15 points. What is the power of the preceding test?

9.31. Use the data in Exercise 8.32 to determine whether statistically discernible differences exist between the mean breaking strengths of metals produced by the two processes with $\alpha = 0.05$. What is the p-value?

9.32. In the late 1970s it was discovered that the carcinogen nitrosodimethylamine (NDMA) was formed during the drying of green malt, which is used in brewing beer. Beginning in 1980 a new malt drying process was developed that minimized the formation of NDMA. Random samples of a domestic beer that was brewed using both drying processes were taken and the levels of NDMA in parts per billion were measured. The results are as follows:

Old Process	6	4	5	5	6	5	5	6	4	6	7	4
New Process	2	1	2	2	1	0	3	2	1	0	1	3

If sampling is assumed to be from two independent normal distributions with equal variances, is there reason to believe at the $\alpha = 0.05$ level that the average amount of NDMA has been decreased by more than 2 parts per billion through the new process?

9.33. Two machine operators are expected to produce on the average the same number of finished units over time. The following are the observed number of finished units per day for the two workers over a week's time.

Operator 1	Operator 2
12	14
11	18
18	18
16	17
13	16

If we assume the numbers of units produced daily by these workers are independent normally distributed random variables with equal variances, can we discern a difference in the means at the $\alpha = 0.1$ level?

9.34. In Exercise 9.33, since the data are daily observations over a week's time, should you consider an alternative approach to this problem? Discuss the merits of such an approach and show that a different result is obtained from that of Exercise 9.33. Why were you able to obtain a different result?

9.35. A medical researcher is interested in comparing the effectiveness of two popular diet plans, A and B. In particular, the investigator wants to determine whether one plan is more effective for reducing the weight of obese persons in a specified length of time. Discuss fully how the medical researcher should go about carrying out this experiment. Be sure to indicate necessary assumptions.

9.36. An educator has developed a new aptitude test that is much shorter than the one currently in use. The educator would like to compare the two tests. Discuss the approach the educator should use in making the comparison possible.

9.37. A manufacturer wishes to compare the current assembly process for one of his products with a proposed method that supposedly reduces the average assembly time. Eight workers are randomly selected from the assembly plant and are asked to assemble units of this product. The following are the observed times in minutes.

Worker	Current process	Proposed process
1	38	30
2	32	32
3	41	34
4	35	37
5	42	35
6	32	26
7	45	38
8	37	32

a. At the $\alpha = 0.05$ level, is there reason to believe the average assembly time for the current method exceeds that of the proposed method by more than 2 minutes?

b. What assumptions are necessary for testing the hypothesis in part a, and what is the *p*-value?

c. Determine a 95% confidence interval for the difference in mean assembly times.

9.38. A study was conducted to determine the extent that alcohol blunts a person's thinking ability for performing a given task. Ten persons of varying characteristics were selected at random and asked to participate in the experiment. After suitable briefing, each person performed the task with no alcohol in his or her system. Then the task was performed again after each person had consumed enough alcohol to raise alcohol content in his or her system to 0.1%.

a. Discuss the important aspects of control that the experimenter must consider in conducting such an experiment.

b. Suppose the "before" and "after" times (in minutes) of the ten participants are as follows:

Participant	Before	After
1	28	39
2	22	45
3	55	67
4	45	61
5	32	46
6	35	58
7	40	51
8	25	34
9	37	48
10	20	30

Can one conclude at the $\alpha = 0.05$ level that the average "before" time is less than the average "after" time by more than 10 minutes?

9.39. In Exercise 9.19, is there reason to believe the variance of the amount of radiation in the water supply exceeds 1.25 squared picocuries? Use $\alpha = 0.05$.

9.40. Develop general expressions for computing the probability of type II error when testing the hypothesis $H_0: \sigma^2 = \sigma_0^2$ against either $H_1: \sigma^2 > \sigma_0^2$ or $H_1: \sigma^2 < \sigma_0^2$.

9.41. Use the results of Exercise 9.40 to determine the power for the test of the hypothesis in Exercise 9.39 if $\sigma^2 = 1.4$.

9.42. A plant manager suspects the number of pieces produced by a particular worker per day fluctuates beyond normal expectation. The manager decides to observe the number of pieces produced by this worker for ten randomly selected days. The results are 15, 12, 8, 13, 12, 15, 16, 9, 8, and 14. If the standard deviation for all such workers in the plant is known to be 2 units and if the number of units produced per day is adequately modeled by a normal distribution, is the manager's suspicion supported at the $\alpha = 0.05$ level? What is the *p*-value?

9.43. In a filling process the tolerance for the weight of the containers is 8 grams. To meet this tolerance the standard deviation in the weight should be 2 grams. The weights of 25 randomly selected containers yielded a standard deviation of 2.8 grams.

a. If the weights are normally distributed, determine whether the variance of the weights is different from the needed value. Use $\alpha = 0.02$.

b. For what values of the sample variance could one not reject the null hypothesis in part a? Are these values equidistant from the needed value of the variance? Should they be? Comment.

9.44. Consider the data in Exercise 9.32. At the $\alpha = 0.05$ level, is there reason to believe the variances are not equal?

9.45. An investor wishes to compare the risks associated with two different stocks, A and B. The risk of a given stock is measured by the variation in daily price changes. The investor believes the risk associated with Stock B is greater than that of Stock A. Random samples of 21 daily price changes for Stock A and 16 daily price changes for Stock B are obtained. The following results are determined.

Stock A	Stock B
$\bar{x}_A = 0.3$	$\bar{x}_B = 0.4$
$s_A = 0.25$	$s_B = 0.45$

a. If sampling is assumed to be from two independent normal populations, can the investor's belief be substantiated at the $\alpha = 0.05$ level?
b. If the sample variance for A is as given, what is the maximum value for the sample variance of B based on $n = 16$ that would not lead to the rejection of the null hypothesis in part a?

9.46. For Exercise 9.33, can you support the contention that the variation in the daily number of finished units for Operator 2 is less than that for Operator 1 at the $\alpha = 0.05$ level?

9.47. In a recent study spanning 25 years, the possible protection against the development of lung cancer from eating a form of vitamin A, called carotene, was investigated. It was found that of 488 men who had the lowest carotene intake during this time, 14 developed lung cancer, but in a group of the same size who consumed the most carotene, only two developed cancer. Under suitable assumptions, can we conclude that regular intake of carotene reduces the risk of developing lung cancer in men? Use $\alpha = 0.01$. What is the p-value? From a statistical point of view, what advice would you offer to a medical researcher who is interested in a project such as this?

9.48. For Exercise 9.47, determine an approximately 99% confidence interval estimate for the true difference in the two proportions.

9.49. An economist for a state agency wants to determine whether the current unemployment rates at the two largest urban areas in the state are different. Based on random samples of 500 persons from each of the two areas, the economist finds 35 persons unemployed in one area and 25 persons unemployed in the other area. Under suitable assumptions, is there reason to believe at the $\alpha = 0.05$ level that the unemployment rates of the two areas are different? What is the p-value?

9.50. A user of large quantities of electrical components purchases the components primarily from two suppliers, A and B. Because of a better pricing structure, the user would really like to do business solely with B if the proportions of defective units for A and B are the same. From two large lots, the user randomly selects 125 units from A and 100 units from B, inspects the selected units, and finds 7 and 7 defective units, respectively. Under suitable assumptions and based on this information, is there reason not to buy the components solely from B? Use $\alpha = 0.02$.

CHAPTER TEN

Goodness of Fit Tests and Analysis of Contingency Tables

10.1 Introduction

Recall that a statistical hypothesis is a claim about some unknown feature of a population of interest. In Chapter 9 the unknown feature was exclusively a value of some parameter θ. In this chapter we will examine the testing of statistical hypotheses in which the unknown feature is some property of the functional form of the distribution being sampled. In addition, we will discuss tests of independence between two random variables in which sample evidence is obtained by classifying each random variable into a number of categories.

Traditionally, this type of test is known as *goodness of fit* because it compares the results of a random sample with the results one expects to observe if the null hypothesis is correct. The comparison is made by classifying the observed data into a number of distinct categories and then comparing the observed and expected frequencies for each category. For a specified size of type I error, the null hypothesis is rejected if there is sufficient disparity between the observed and expected frequencies.

It is worthwhile to note that for situations of this type the alternative hypothesis is composite, and often it is not even explicitly identified. As a result, the power function is very difficult to obtain analytically. Consequently, goodness of fit tests should not be used by themselves to accept the claim of the null hypothesis. The decision remains not to reject H_0 (rather than accept it) if the disparity between the observed and the expected frequencies is relatively small.

10.2 The Chi-Square Goodness of Fit Test

A goodness of fit test is used to decide whether a given set of data conforms to a specified probability distribution. Let a random sample of size n from the

336

distribution of a random variable X be divided into k mutually exclusive and exhaustive classes, and let N_i, $i = 1, 2, \ldots, k$, be the number of observations in the ith class. Consider testing the null hypothesis

$$H_0: F(x) = F_0(x), \tag{10.1}$$

where the claimed probability model $F_0(x)$ is completely specified with regard to all parameters. Thus the null hypothesis is simple. Since $F_0(x)$ is specified, we can determine the probability p_i of obtaining an observation in the ith class under H_0, where by necessity $\Sigma_{i=1}^{k} p_i = 1$.

Let n_i be the realization of N_i for $i = 1, 2, \ldots, k$ so that $\Sigma_{i=1}^{k} n_i = n$. The probability of exactly n_i observations in the ith class is $p_i^{n_i}$ for $i = 1, 2, \ldots, k$. Since there are k mutually exclusive categories with probabilities $p_1, p_2, \ldots, p_k$, then under the null hypothesis the probability of the grouped sample is the same as the probability function of a multinomial distribution as given by (6.3).

To deduce an appropriate test statistic for H_0, consider the case for $k = 2$. This is the binomial distribution with probability function given by (4.1) in which $x = n_1$, $p = p_1$, $n - x = n_2$, and $1 - p = p_2$. Consider the standardized random variable

$$Y = \frac{N_1 - np_1}{\sqrt{np_1(1 - p_1)}}.$$

Recall from Chapter 5 that for sufficiently large n, the distribution of Y is approximately the standard normal. Moreover, we know from Example 5.14 that the square of a standard normal random variable is chi-square distributed with one degree of freedom. Then the statistic

$$\frac{(N_1 - np_1)^2}{np_1(1 - p_1)} = \frac{(N_1 - np_1)^2}{np_1} + \frac{(N_1 - np_1)^2}{np_2}$$

$$= \frac{(N_1 - np_1)^2}{np_1} + \frac{[n - N_2 - n(1 - p_2)]^2}{np_2}$$

$$= \frac{(N_1 - np_1)^2}{np_1} + \frac{(N_2 - np_2)^2}{np_2}$$

$$= \sum_{i=1}^{2} \frac{(N_i - np_i)^2}{np_i}$$

is approximately chi-square distributed with one degree of freedom as n becomes sufficiently large.

Following this type of reasoning, it can be shown that for $k \geqslant 2$ distinct categories the statistic

$$\sum_{i=1}^{k} \frac{(N_i - np_i)^2}{np_i} \tag{10.2}$$

is approximately chi-square distributed with $k - 1$ degrees of freedom for sufficiently large n. Notice that N_i is the observed frequency of the ith class, and np_i is the corresponding expected frequency under the null hypothesis. Accordingly, the statistic is the ratio of the squared difference between corresponding observed and expected frequencies to the expected frequency summed over all k classes. The statistic given by (10.2) is known as Pearson's *chi-square goodness of fit test*. If there is perfect agreement between the observed and expected frequencies, the statistic has the value zero; if there is much disparity, the statistic will assume a large value. It follows, therefore, that for a given size of type I error, the critical region is the upper tail of a chi-square distribution with $k - 1$ degrees of freedom.

Example 10.1   A manager of a large industrial plant wants to determine whether the number of employee visits to the plant dispensary is evenly distributed for the five working days of the week. Based on a random sample of four full weeks, the following number of visits were observed:

Monday	Tuesday	Wednesday	Thursday	Friday
49	35	32	39	45

With $\alpha = 0.05$, is there reason to believe that the number of employee visits to the dispensary is not evenly distributed among the working days of the week?

An even distribution would imply that the proportions for each day of the working week are all the same. Therefore we will test the null hypothesis

$$H_0: p_i = 0.2, \quad i = 1, 2, ..., 5.$$

Since the sample size is $n = 200$, the expected frequency for each day is $np_i = 40$. Then the computed value of the test statistic is

$$\chi^2 = \frac{(49 - 40)^2}{40} + \frac{(35 - 40)^2}{40} + \frac{(32 - 40)^2}{40} + \frac{(39 - 40)^2}{40} + \frac{(45 - 40)^2}{40} = 4.9.$$

For $k = 5$ classes, the critical value is seen to be $\chi^2_{0.95, 4} = 9.49$. Since $\chi^2 = 4.9 < \chi^2_{0.95, 4} = 9.49$, the null hypothesis cannot be rejected. Based on this evidence there is no reason to believe that the number of employee visits is not evenly distributed among the five working days.

An advantage of the chi-square goodness of fit test is that for large n, the limiting chi-square distribution of the statistic is independent of the form of the claimed distribution $F_0(x)$ under H_0. As a result, the chi-square goodness of fit test is also used in situations in which $F_0(x)$ is continuous. It must be emphasized, however, that the nature of the chi-square goodness of fit test remains discrete in the sense that it compares the observed and expected frequencies for a finite number of categories. Accordingly, if $F_0(x)$ is continuous, the test does not compare the smoothed observed frequency with the claimed probability density function as implied by the null hypothesis. Rather, the comparison is made by approximating the continuous distribution under H_0 with a finite number of class intervals. Even with this limitation, the chi-square goodness of fit test is a reasonably adequate procedure for testing assumptions of, say, normality as long as the sample size is moderately large. On the question of how large the sample size should be, it has been found that n should be about five times the number of classes. A more conservative rule of thumb is to select a sample so that each expected frequency is no less than five. This can also be accomplished by combining neighboring classes, but for each pair of classes that is combined, the number of degrees of freedom is reduced by one.

Unless one can specify an alternative hypothesis consisting of a particular alternative model $F_1(x)$, the power of the chi-square goodness of fit test is indeed difficult to determine analytically. However, it can be shown that the power tends to 1 as n tends to ∞. This result implies that for extremely large sample sizes, it is almost certain to reject the null hypothesis because one would not be able to specify H_0 close enough to the true distribution. Thus the application of the chi-square goodness of fit test is questionable when extremely large sample sizes are involved.

Example 10.2   The grouped data of SAT math scores for 1979–80 college-bound male high school seniors are given in Table 5.2. Recall that in Example 5.5 we compared the observed frequencies with the expected frequencies, where the latter were determined based on a normal distribution with mean 491 and standard deviation 120. Based on the chi-square goodness of fit test, is there reason to believe that the SAT math scores are not normally distributed with mean 491 and standard deviation 120 at the $\alpha = 0.01$ level?

Consider testing the null hypothesis

$$H_0: F(x) = F_0(x),$$

where $F_0(x)$ is the normal probability model with mean 491 and standard deviation 120. Under the null hypothesis the expected frequencies for the 12 classes are as given in the last column of Table 5.2. These were determined by first converting the interval of each class to the corresponding standard normal interval, using $\mu = 491$ and $\sigma = 120$. Then the probability of the interval was determined under H_0. Finally, for each class the probability was multiplied by the sample size $n = 478{,}193$ to yield the expected frequency. Notice that the probabilities in the next to the last column of Table 5.2 do not add to one. But under the null hypothesis the classes must be exhaustive so that $\Sigma_{i=1}^{k} p_i = 1$. This can be accomplished by adjusting the first and last class such that the first class has no lower limit and the last class has no upper limit. Since under H_0, $X \sim N(491, 120)$,

$$P(X \leq 250) = P(Z \leq -2.01) = 0.0222,$$

and the revised expected frequency for the first class is $(478{,}193)(0.0222) = 10{,}615.88$. Similarly for the last class,

$$P(X \geq 750) = P(Z \geq 2.16) = 0.0154,$$

which results in an expected frequency of 7364.17.

Based on the twelve classes, the computed value of the chi-square statistic is

$$\chi^2 = \frac{(3{,}423 - 10{,}615.88)^2}{10{,}615.88} + \frac{(18{,}434 - 16{,}115.10)^2}{16{,}115.10} + \cdots + \frac{(6{,}414 - 7{,}364.17)^2}{7{,}364.17}$$

$$= 13{,}067.02,$$

which is clearly beyond the critical value $\chi^2_{0.99,\ 11} = 24.75$. Accordingly, the null hypothesis that the SAT math scores for high school male seniors are normally distributed with mean 491 and standard deviation 120 is rejected. This example illustrates the comment made previously that for very large sample sizes, the simple null hypothesis is almost certain to be rejected.

Recall that the null hypothesis given by (10.1) is simple since the claimed probability model $F_0(x)$ is completely specified with regard to all its parameters. However, for many applications involving goodness of fit, we can only specify the form of $F_0(x)$. For example, we may want to test the null hypothesis that a set of observations of a measurement of interest X conforms to a normal distribution, but we cannot specify the value of the mean or the variance. As a result, the null hypothesis

$$H_0: F(x) = F_0(x)$$

is composite. Consequently, the expected frequencies np_i for the $i = 1, 2, \ldots,$ k classes cannot be determined, since they are functions of the unknown parameters of $F_0(x)$.

Suppose T is a statistic for an unknown parameter θ of $F_0(x)$. In the context of goodness of fit, both the observable frequencies N_i and the expected frequencies $np_i(T)$ are random variables, where $p_i(T)$ indicates that the probabilities under the null hypothesis are functions of the statistic T of θ. It can be shown that if for every unknown parameter θ the statistic T is the maximum likelihood estimator of θ, and if the expected frequencies are determined as functions of maximum likelihood estimators, then

$$\sum_{i=1}^{k} \frac{[N_i - np_i(T)]^2}{np_i(T)} \tag{10.3}$$

is approximately chi-square distributed with $k - 1 - r$ degrees of freedom for sufficiently large n, where r is the number of parameters being estimated.

As in the previous case of a simple H_0, the critical region is the upper tail of the chi-square distribution. But the number of degrees of freedom now is reduced by the number of parameters being estimated. Consequently, there is a leftward shift in the critical value for the same size of type I error, and the null hypothesis can be rejected for a smaller observed value of (10.3) than in the previous case. This is logical since the fit should be better because the unknown parameters are estimated based on the sample observations.

The important features for application of the chi-square goodness of fit test for the composite case are the same as those previously outlined for the simple null hypothesis. A relatively minor problem arises in whether the unknown parameters should be estimated based on the grouped data or the ungrouped data. Theoretically, neither approach may be correct because the maximum likelihood estimates should be determined by maximizing the likelihood function based on the multinomial distribution. But it may be difficult to obtain the estimates by this method. Fortunately, it turns out that for many cases the error is not serious. Thus, one can safely use the maximum likelihood estimates determined from either the grouped or ungrouped data.

Example 10.3 Recall Example 4.5 in which we compared the observed number of touchdowns scored by each team per game in the NFL with the expected number, if the number of touchdowns is Poisson distributed. Based on the information contained in Table 4.3, is there reason to believe at the 0.05 level that the number of touchdowns is not a Poisson random variable?

Since the value of the Poisson parameter λ is not specified, the maximum likelihood estimate of λ is determined to be $\hat{\lambda} = 2.435$ based on the information in Table 4.3. The probability of exactly zero touchdowns under the null hypothesis of a Poisson distribution is

$$p(0) = (2.435)^0 \exp(-2.435)/0! = 0.0876.$$

For $n = 448$ the expected number of zero touchdowns is $(448)(0.0876) = 39.24$. Following this procedure, we can determine the other expected frequencies. The computation of the chi-square statistic is outlined in Table 10.1.

For $k = 8$ categories and one parameter estimated, the degrees of freedom will be 6. For $\alpha = 0.05$ the critical value is $\chi^2_{0.95,6} = 12.60$. Since $\chi^2 = 6.477 < \chi^2_{0.95, 6} = 12.60$, the null hypothesis that the distribution of the number of touchdowns scored by each team per NFL game is Poisson cannot be rejected.

TABLE 10.1 Computation of the chi-square statistic for Example 10.3

Number of touchdowns	Observed frequency	Expected frequency	$\dfrac{[n_i - np_i(\hat{\lambda})]^2}{np_i(\hat{\lambda})}$
0	35	39.24	0.458
1	99	95.56	0.124
2	104	116.34	1.309
3	110	94.44	2.564
4	62	57.48	0.355
5	25	28.00	0.321
6	10	11.38	0.167
7	3	5.56	1.179
Totals	448	448	6.477

10.3   The Kolmogorov–Smirnov Statistic

Recall that to apply the chi-square goodness of fit test when the claimed model under H_0 is continuous, it is necessary to approximate $F_0(x)$ by grouping the observed data into a finite number of class intervals. The requirement to group the data implies that the sample size has to be moderately large. Thus the chi-square goodness of fit test may be limited when $F_0(x)$ is continuous and a random sample of only a small size is available. A more appropriate goodness of fit test than the chi-square when $F_0(x)$ is continuous is the Kolmogorov–Smirnov statistic. The Kolmogorov–Smirnov test does not require groupings, and it is applicable for small sample sizes. It is based on a comparison between the observed cumulative distribution function of the ordered sample and the claimed distribution under the null hypothesis. If such a comparison reveals a sufficient difference between the sample and assumed distribution functions, then the null hypothesis that the distribution is $F_0(x)$ is rejected.

Consider the null hypothesis as given by (10.1), where $F_0(x)$ is completely specified. Let $X_{(1)}$, $X_{(2)}$, ..., $X_{(n)}$ denote the ordered observations of a random sample of size n and define the sample cumulative distribution function as

$$S_n(x) = \begin{cases} 0 & x < x_{(1)}, \\ k/n & x_{(k)} \leqslant x < x_{(k+1)}, \\ 1 & x \geqslant x_n. \end{cases} \qquad (10.4)$$

In other words, for any ordered value x of the random sample, $S_n(x)$ is the proportion of the number of sample values less than or equal to x. Since $F_0(x)$ is completely specified, it is possible to evaluate $F_0(x)$ for some desired x and compare it to the corresponding $S_n(x)$. If the null hypothesis is true, then it is logical to expect such differences to be relatively small. The Kolmogorov–Smirnov statistic is now defined to be

$$D_n = \max_x |S_n(x) - F_0(x)|. \qquad (10.5)$$

The statistic D_n has a distribution that is independent of the claimed model under the null hypothesis. For this reason D_n is said to be a *distribution-free* statistic. As a result, the distribution function of D_n can be evaluated as a function of the sample size alone and then used for any $F_0(x)$. In Table J of the Appendix upper quantile values of the distribution of D_n are given for various sample sizes. The reader should note that the asymptotic values of D_n found at the bottom of the table provide adequate approximation for n greater than 50.

For a size α of type I error, the critical region is of the form

$$P\left(D_n > \frac{c}{\sqrt{n}}\right) = \alpha.$$

Accordingly, H_0 is rejected if for some x the observed value of D_n is inside the critical region of size α.

As we have noted earlier, the Kolmogorov–Smirnov statistic is generally superior to the chi-square goodness of fit test when the data involve a continuous random variable because no grouping is required. In addition, the Kolmogorov–Smirnov test has the attractive property of being applicable to small sample sizes. On the other hand, the statistic is somewhat limited because the claimed model under H_0 must be completely specified. Further, the Kolmogorov–Smirnov statistic should not be applied to cases in which the observations are not inherently quantitative because ambiguities could arise about the ordering of the observations.

Example 10.4 The following are the ordered values of a random sample of SAT scores from the entering freshman class at a large public university: 852, 875, 910, 933, 957, 963, 981, 998, 1007, 1010, 1015, 1018, 1023, 1035, 1048, 1063. In past years the SAT scores at this institution were adequately represented by a normal distribution with mean 985 and standard deviation 50. Based on this sample, is there reason to believe that a change in the distribution of the SAT scores has occurred at this university? Use $\alpha = 0.05$.

Let X be a random variable representing SAT scores at this university. Consider testing the null hypothesis

$$H_0: F(x) = F_0(x),$$

where $F_0(x)$ is the normal distribution function with mean 985 and standard deviation 50. Since X is a continuous random variable and the sample size on X is small, the Kolmogorov–Smirnov statistic will be used to test H_0. The sample distribution function is obtained by using (10.4) for the ordered values. This involves nothing more than adding the increment $1/16 = 0.0625$ to the previous value of the sample distribution. The corresponding values of the claimed normal model are obtained by first standardizing to $N(0, 1)$ and then using Table D of the Appendix. The relevant information is contained in Table 10.2.

TABLE 10.2 Computation of the Kolmogorov–Smirnov statistic for Example 10.4

Ordered values	$S_n(x)$	$F_0(x)$	$|S_n(x) - F_0(x)|$
852	0.0625	0.0039	0.0586
875	0.1250	0.0139	0.1111
910	0.1875	0.0668	0.1207
933	0.2500	0.1492	0.1008
957	0.3125	0.2877	0.0248
963	0.3750	0.3300	0.0450
981	0.4375	0.4681	0.0306
998	0.5000	0.6026	0.1026
1007	0.5625	0.6700	0.1075
1010	0.6250	0.6915	0.0665
1015	0.6875	0.7257	0.0382
1018	0.7500	0.7454	0.0046
1023	0.8125	0.7764	0.0361
1035	0.8750	0.8413	0.0337
1048	0.9375	0.8962	0.0413
1063	1.0000	0.9406	0.0594

The maximum deviation is seen to be 0.1207. From Table J of the Appendix the critical value of D_{16} for $\alpha = 0.05$ is 0.328. Since $0.1207 < 0.328$, the null hypothesis cannot be rejected. Accordingly, we cannot detect a change in the distribution of the current SAT scores from the established $N(985, 50)$.

10.4   The Chi-Square Test for the Analysis of Two-Way Contingency Tables

Many times the need arises to determine whether there is a relationship between two distinct traits on which a population of objects has been classified, and where each trait is subdivided into a number of categories. For example, is there a relationship between cigarette smoking and the propensity to develop lung cancer; or, is there a relationship between political affiliation and how one feels about the proposal to increase the defense budget. In both instances the population has been classified into two traits, each of which is assumed to have at least two mutually exclusive and exhaustive categories. In the first example the two traits are whether one smokes and whether one develops lung cancer. The categories for the two traits might be heavy smoker, moderate smoker, and nonsmoker for the first, and whether one does or does not develop lung cancer for the second.

When a random sample is obtained from a population that has been classified in this manner, the result is what is called a *two-way contingency table*. Such a table is made up of the observed frequencies relative to the two traits and their categories. Although we will analyze a two-way contingency table, it is possible to analyze contingency tables involving more than two traits.

The analysis of a two-way contingency table assumes that the two traits are independent. That is, under the null hypothesis of independence we want to determine whether there is a sufficient disparity between the observed frequencies and the corresponding expected frequencies so as to reject the null hypothesis. The chi-square test, discussed in Section 10.2, provides the appropriate means to analyze a contingency table.

Let n be a random sample from a population that has been classified according to traits A and B, each of which contains r and c number of categories, respectively. Further, let N_{ij} be the number of observations in the (i, j) category of traits A and B, respectively, for $i = 1, 2, ..., r$ and $j = 1, 2, ..., c$. Then a contingency table is an $r \times c$ array, as given by Table 10.3, where the entries in the table represent the realizations of the random variables N_{ij}.

Notice that the ith row total is the observed frequency of the ith category of trait A summed over all categories of trait B. Similarly, the jth column total is the observed frequency of the jth category of B summed over all categories of A. Let

$$n_{i\cdot} = \sum_{j=1}^{c} n_{ij} \qquad i = 1, 2, ..., r,$$

$$n_{\cdot j} = \sum_{i=1}^{r} n_{ij} \qquad j = 1, 2, ..., c,$$

TABLE 10.3 A two-way contingency table

		Trait B				
	Categories	1	2	$\cdots$	c	*Totals*
Trait A	1	n_{11}	n_{12}	$\cdots$	n_{1c}	$n_{1\cdot}$
	2	n_{21}	n_{22}	$\cdots$	n_{2c}	$n_{2\cdot}$
	.	.	.	$\cdots$	.	.
	.	.	.	$\cdots$	.	.
	.	.	.	$\cdots$	.	.
	r	n_{r1}	n_{r2}		n_{rc}	$n_{r\cdot}$
	Totals	$n_{\cdot1}$	$n_{\cdot2}$	$\cdots$	$n_{\cdot c}$	n

denote the row and column sums, respectively, where the "dot" notation indicates the subscript over which summation has taken place.

Let p_{ij} be the probability that an object selected at random from the population of interest will fall in the (i, j) category of the contingency table. Let $p_{i\cdot}$ be the (marginal) probability that an object will be in category i of trait A, and let $p_{\cdot j}$ be the (marginal) probability that an object will be in category j of trait B. If the two traits are independent, the joint probability must be the product of the corresponding marginal probabilities. Thus the null hypothesis of independence may be stated as follows:

$$H_0: p_{ij} = p_{i\cdot}p_{\cdot j} \qquad i = 1, 2, \ldots, r; \ j = 1, 2, \ldots, c. \qquad (10.6)$$

If the marginal probabilities $p_{i\cdot}$ and $p_{\cdot j}$ can be specified, then under the null hypothesis the statistic

$$\sum_{i=1}^{r} \sum_{j=1}^{c} \frac{(N_{ij} - np_{i\cdot}p_{\cdot j})^2}{np_{i\cdot}p_{\cdot j}} \qquad (10.7)$$

is approximately chi-square distributed with $rc - 1$ degrees of freedom for large n. The majority of times, however, the marginal probabilities are not likely to be known and, thus, must be estimated based on the sample. Fortunately, the chi-square goodness of fit test remains the appropriate statistic to use to test (10.6) as long as maximum likelihood estimates of the marginal probabilities are used, and one degree of freedom is subtracted from the total for each parameter being estimated. Since $\Sigma_{i=1}^{r} p_{i\cdot} = 1$ and $\Sigma_{j=1}^{c} p_{\cdot j} = 1$, there are $r - 1$ row parameters and $c - 1$ column parameters to be estimated. Thus the degrees of freedom will be $rc - 1 - (r - 1) - (c - 1) = rc - r - c + 1 = (r - 1)(c - 1)$.

It can be shown that the maximum likelihood estimates of $p_{i\cdot}$ and $p_{\cdot j}$ are given by

$$\hat{p}_{i\cdot} = n_{i\cdot}/n, \qquad (10.8)$$

and

$$\hat{p}_{\cdot j} = n_{\cdot j}/n, \qquad (10.9)$$

respectively. Substituting (10.8) and (10.9) in (10.7), we obtain the statistic

$$\sum_{i=1}^{r} \sum_{j=1}^{c} \frac{\left(N_{ij} - \frac{n_i.n_{.j}}{n}\right)^2}{\frac{n_i.n_{.j}}{n}}, \qquad (10.10)$$

which for large n is approximately a chi-square random variable with $(r - 1) \times (c - 1)$ degrees of freedom.

Example 10.5   A corporation is evaluating a proposed merger. The board of directors wishes to sample the opinion of the shareholders to determine whether opinion concerning the proposed merger is independent of the number of shares held. A random sample of 250 shareholders reveals the information in Table 10.4. Based on this information, is there reason to doubt that opinion on the proposed merger is independent of the number of shares held? Use $\alpha = 0.10$.

Let the null hypothesis be stated as follows:

$$H_0: p_{ij} = p_i.p_{.j}, \qquad i = 1, 2, 3; \quad j = 1, 2, 3.$$

Here p_{ij} is the probability that a shareholder selected at random will fall in the (i, j) category; $p_i.$ is the marginal probability that the number of shares held by a randomly selected shareholder is in category i; and $p_{.j}$ is the marginal probability that a randomly selected shareholder will have opinion j. By (10.10) the expected frequency of the (i, j) cell is the product of the ith row total and the jth column total divided by the sample size $n = 250$. For example, the expected number of shareholders who favor the proposal and own more than 1000 shares is (95)(100)/250 = 38. By continuing this process we are able to determine the expected frequencies for each combination. In each cell of Table 10.5, the first line represents the observed frequency, the second line the expected frequency, and the third line the contribution of that cell to the value of the statistic, as given by (10.10).
  Thus the value of the statistic is

$$\chi^2 = \frac{(38 - 30.4)^2}{30.4} + \frac{(29 - 39.52)^2}{39.52} + \cdots + \frac{(4 - 7.6)^2}{7.6} = 10.80.$$

Since $r = c = 3$, the degrees of freedom is 4. For $\alpha = 0.1$, the critical value is $\chi^2_{0.9, 4} = 7.78$. Then the observed value of the test statistic is inside the critical

TABLE 10.4 Sample data for Example 10.5

		Opinion		
Shares held	*Favor*	*Oppose*	*Undecided*	*Totals*
Under 200	38	29	9	76
200–1000	30	42	7	79
Over 1000	32	59	4	95
Totals	100	130	20	250

TABLE 10.5 Expected and observed frequencies for Example 10.5

Shares held	Favor	Oppose	Undecided	Totals
Under 200	38 30.40 1.90	29 39.52 2.80	9 6.08 1.40	76 76 6.10
200–1000	30 31.60 0.08	42 41.08 0.02	7 6.32 0.07	79 79 0.17
Over 1000	32 38 0.95	59 49.40 1.87	4 7.60 1.71	95 95 4.53
Totals	100 100 2.93	130 130 4.69	20 20 3.18	250 250 10.80

region, and the null hypothesis of independence is rejected. Accordingly, there is reason to believe that opinion concerning the proposed merger and the number of shares held are not independent.

References

1. P. G. Hoel, *Introduction to mathematical statistics,* 4th ed., Wiley, New York, 1971.
2. B. W. Lindgren, *Statistical theory*, 3rd ed., Macmillan, New York, 1976.

Exercises

10.1. Based on the records of a boutique, 50 percent of the dresses bought by the shop for a season will be sold at the full retail price, 25 percent will be sold at 20 percent off the retail price, 15 percent will be sold after a 40% price reduction, and the remaining dresses will be sold with a 60% reduction. For the current season, 300 dresses were bought and sold as follows:

Full price	20% off	40% off	60% off
140	90	30	40.

Is there reason to believe the breakdown for this season was different from past seasons? Use $\alpha = 0.05$. What is the p-value?

10.2. In a large hospital the observed number of births for each month of a given year is as follows:

Jan	Feb	March	April	May	June	July	Aug	Sept	Oct	Nov	Dec
95	105	95	105	90	95	105	110	105	100	95	100

If $\alpha = 0.01$, is there any reason to believe the number of births is not uniformly distributed over the months of the year? What is the p-value?

10.3. In Exercise 10.2, suppose the observed number of births for each month over a ten-year period is simply ten times the observed numbers given in Exercise 10.2 for one year.

    a. Will this change the conclusion of Exercise 10.2?

    b. What can one conclude about the use of the chi-square goodness of fit test for large n?

10.4. A manufacturer claims that a process produces only 5% defective units. A large buyer randomly selects 100 such units and finds ten to be defective.

    a. Using the chi-square goodness of fit test, determine whether there is reason to doubt the claim. Use $\alpha = 0.05$.

    b. Compare your answer in part a to an answer using the approximate method discussed in Chapter 9 to test the null hypothesis that the true proportion defective is 0.05.

    c. Is there any relationship between the values of the test statistics obtained in part a and part b? Are there conditions for this relationship?

10.5. A traffic safety organization wanted to determine whether the number of fatal automobile accidents is evenly distributed over the color of the automobile involved in the accident. The organization obtained a random sample of 600 automobile accidents in which at least one fatality occurred in each accident and noted the color of the automobile. The following breakdown was determined:

Red	Brown	Yellow	White	Gray	Blue
75	125	70	80	135	115

Is there reason to believe the color proportions are not the same? Use $\alpha = 0.01$.

10.6. In a medical study spanning 30 years and conducted to determine, among other things, whether smoking habits may influence the development of heart disease, 160 men developed heart disease during the 30-year period. These men were classified as heavy smokers (more than two packs of cigarettes per day), moderate smokers (one to two packs), light smokers (less than one pack), or nonsmokers. The number of men in each category who developed heart disease was observed to be as follows:

Heavy smoker	Moderate smoker	Light smoker	Nonsmoker
58	54	36	12

    a. If we assume at the beginning of the study there was an equal number of men in each of the four categories, is there reason to believe at the $\alpha = 0.01$ level that the proportions for these categories are not the same?

    b. How would you caution the medical investigator in using the chi-square goodness of fit test in this situation?

10.7. In a production process a random sample of 100 units is taken from each day's production and inspected for defective units. For a given week the following number of defective units are observed for the five operating days:

Monday	Tuesday	Wednesday	Thursday	Friday
12	7	6	5	10

If the overall percent defective is 8%, can we conclude at the $\alpha = 0.05$ level that there is a discernible difference in the daily percent defective?

10.8. Refer to the data in Exercise 1.1. Using the chi-square goodness of fit test, can we conclude the time lengths are not exponentially distributed with $\theta = 3.2$ minutes? Use $\alpha = 0.01$.

10.9. Consider the data in Exercise 1.7.

a. For $\alpha = 0.05$, use the chi-square goodness of fit method to test the null hypothesis that the distribution of the number of touchdowns scored per team per NFL game is Poisson with parameter $\lambda = 2.7$.

b. Suppose you estimate the value of λ from the data. How would this change affect your answer in part a?

10.10. Use the Kolmogorov–Smirnov statistic on the data of Exercise 1.1 and compare your result with that obtained in Exercise 10.8.

10.11. Use the Kolmogorov–Smirnov statistic to test the null hypothesis that the data in Exercise 1.2 are normally distributed with mean 50 and standard deviation 10. Use $\alpha = 0.05$.

10.12. As we have noted, a limitation of the Kolmogorov–Smirnov statistic is that the claimed model under H_0 must be completely specified. Although no analytical treatment is available when some of the parameters are not specified, Lilliefors* has obtained rejection limits through a simulation study for the specific problem of testing for normality. If the sample mean and sample standard deviation are used as parameters of the normal distribution under the null hypothesis, the statistic D_n has a distribution whose quantiles have been obtained by Lilliefors. Specifically, for $\alpha = 0.05$ the 95th percentile values of the distribution of this statistic under H_0 are as follows:

n	10	12	14	15	16	18	20	25	>25
95th percentile	0.258	0.242	0.227	0.220	0.213	0.200	0.190	0.173	$0.886/\sqrt{n}$

Use the Lilliefors modification to the Kolmogorov–Smirnov statistic to test for normality of the data in Exercise 1.2 and compare your result with that in Exercise 10.11.

10.13. Use the chi-square goodness of fit procedure to test the null hypothesis that the data of Exercise 1.2 are normally distributed at the $\alpha = 0.01$ level.

10.14. A random sample of 25 married males were asked their age when first married, and the following data were obtained: 24, 19, 20, 22, 50, 23, 23, 21, 25, 27, 45, 27, 26, 26, 35, 29, 28, 30, 31, 32, 31, 33, 34, 38, 41. Use the Kolmogorov–Smirnov statistic to test the null hypothesis that the distribution of the male's age when first married is gamma with $\theta = 2$ and $\alpha = 16$. Use $\alpha = 0.05$. (Hint: To compute the gamma probabilities, seek a tabulation of the incomplete gamma function given by (5.55).)

10.15. In Example 4.10, use the chi-square goodness of fit test to show that the null hypothesis of a negative binomial distribution for the number of touchdowns cannot be rejected with $\alpha = 0.05$.

10.16. Use the chi-square goodness of fit test to determine whether the null hypothesis that the accident data in Exercise 8.14 follow a negative binomial distribution can be rejected at the $\alpha = 0.05$ level.

---

*On the Kolmogorov–Smirnov test for normality with mean and variance unknown, J. Amer. Statistical Assoc. **64** (1967), 399–402. 1967.

10.17. The row and column totals of a two-way contingency table are as follows:

				10
				12
				15
8	14	10	5	37

Under the null hypothesis of independence, determine the table of expected frequencies.

10.18. A production process uses five machines in its three-shift operation. A random sample of 164 breakdowns was classified according to machine and the shift in which the breakdown occurred, as given in Table 10.6. Based on this information, is there reason to doubt the independence of shift and machine breakdown? Use $\alpha = 0.01$.

TABLE 10.6 Breakdowns by machine and shift

	Machine				
Shift	*A*	*B*	*C*	*D*	*E*
1	10	12	8	14	8
2	15	8	13	8	11
3	12	9	14	12	10

10.19. A random survey of voting citizens was conducted to determine if there is a relation between party affiliation and opinion on handgun control. The information in Table 10.7 was obtained. For $\alpha = 0.01$, is there reason to believe there is a dependency between opinion and party affiliation?

TABLE 10.7 Party affiliation and opinions on gun control

	Favor	*Oppose*	*Undecided*
Democrats	110	64	26
Republicans	90	116	14
Independents	55	35	10

10.20. In a random sample of recent college graduates, two traits were recorded — grade point average and SAT score. The information was classified as in Table 10.8.

TABLE 10.8 Grade point averages and SAT scores

	SAT score		
GPA	*900–1100*	*1100–1300*	*1300–1500*
>3.5	50	65	38
3.0–3.5	78	72	42
2.5–3.0	97	80	25
2.0–2.5	105	25	18

a. Is a dependence between SAT score and grade point average statistically discernible at the $\alpha = 0.01$ level?

b. Do you have reservations about this classification? Can you think of other traits that should have been considered?

10.21. In a recent study involving a random sample of 300 automobile accidents, the information was classified by the size of the automobile and whether a fatality had occurred.

	Small	Medium	Large
At least one fatality	42	35	20
No fatality	78	65	60

Given the data, is the frequency of fatal accidents dependent on the size of the automobile? Use $\alpha = 0.05$.

10.22. A consumer preference survey was conducted to determine whether consumer sentiment for three competing brands — A, B, and C — depended on the consumer's geographic region. The following information was obtained based on a random sample of consumers from three distinct regions.

	Region 1	Region 2	Region 3
Brand A	40	52	25
Brand B	52	70	35
Brand C	68	78	60

Based on this information, is brand preference dependent on the geographic region at the $\alpha = 0.05$ level?

CHAPTER ELEVEN

Methods for Quality Control and Acceptance Sampling

11.1 Introduction

In recent years awareness about the quality of a manufactured product has increased for both producers and consumers. A manufacturer who wishes to maintain a certain quality in the finished product must institute a procedure to detect serious deviations from the prescribed quality. To this end periodic sampling and statistical control charts have proven to be effective means of controlling the quality of manufactured products.

On the other hand, a consumer wants to make sure that the product purchased meets certain standards of quality. This is especially true if the consumer, as a matter of practice, purchases large lots of the product. In such cases what is necessary is to institute a procedure to inspect a relatively small sample of the product to decide whether the lot meets the prescribed standards of quality. Such a procedure involves the notion of acceptance sampling.

In this chapter we will discuss the basic principles and methods of statistical control charts and acceptance sampling procedures. The reader should view the material of this chapter as only an introduction to statistical quality control and acceptance sampling procedures, but the material should prove useful as background to further reading. References [2] and [3] are suggested for this purpose.

11.2 Statistical Control Charts

A statistical control chart is an inferential procedure based on repetitive sampling to study an ongoing process. According to its originator, W. A. Shewhart, a control chart is used to define a standard of quality for a manufacturing process and to determine whether that standard of quality is being maintained by the process.

In the development of control charts, the key factor is the variability in quality of the finished product. For any process a certain amount of variability in quality is inherent no matter how much attention has been directed toward its control. This type of variability is a function of random forces that are likely to be beyond control. Such random variation is usually acceptable and does not compromise the prescribed standard of quality. Variability can also be due to nonrandom or assignable causes. These could take the form of serious machine malfunctions, worker indifference, variability in quality of raw materials, and so on. Thus a statistical control chart is the inferential procedure with which to decide whether an observed deviation from the prescribed norm is due to chance alone or is due to some assignable cause. If the decision is for chance variation, then the process of interest is said to be in control. Otherwise, it will be judged to be out of control, in which case it usually is stopped and an effort is made to locate the cause of the problem.

Since the inference is based on probability, it is possible for a process to be declared out of control when, in fact, it is in control or to be declared in control when, in fact, it is out of control. The consequences of these errors can be severe. For example, if a process is declared out of control when in reality it is in control, we will be looking for an assignable cause that is nonexistent. On the other hand, if a process which in reality is out of control is allowed to continue, the prescribed standard of quality will not be achieved. It should be noted that these errors are facsimiles of the type I and type II errors discussed in Chapter 9.

Typically, the determination of a control chart depends on the periodic drawing of random samples of size n from the process, each time determining a value for some statistic of interest such as a sample mean or variance. Then the control chart is a graph in which the observed value of the statistic is plotted against the sample number or against the time period at which the sample was taken. The chart contains upper and lower control limits, which are the decision criteria for the process. That is, as long as values of the statistic are within the control limits, the process will be judged to be in control. If a value of the statistic falls outside the control limits, the process will be judged to be out of control. There is also a center line, which defines the prescribed norm for the process.

A user decides on what the control limits should be, how often to sample, what size sample to take, and what action should be taken once a process is judged out of control. However, some guidelines are available to the user. Shewhart argued that a proper balance between cost of sampling and accuracy of estimate can be achieved if a sample of four or five observations is taken each time. Also, "three-sigma" control limits have proven to be satisfactory and are the ones used in the United States as well as many other countries.

We now turn to control charts for the mean and the standard deviation. The former is known as an $\overline{X}$ chart, and the latter is called an S chart. It should be noted that traditionally the range R has been used to determine charts for the variability of the process because of its ease of computation. But the S chart is better and should not pose a computational problem with the computer packages readily available today. In the determination of $\overline{X}$ and S charts, we will assume sampling is from a normal distribution. In one case we will assume the mean or the variance is known, and in the other, we will assume both mean and variance are unknown.

11.2.1 $\overline{X}$ Charts — Population Mean Known

A control chart can be constructed based on the sample mean when the measurement of interest is normally distributed with known mean μ and known standard deviation σ. Knowledge of μ and σ may be due to the particular nature of the process of interest, which may provide sufficient information about the mean and the standard deviation. For this case, an $\overline{X}$ chart provides the inferential procedure by which we can decide whether the mean of the process is what we say it is.

Let X_1, X_2, ..., X_n be a random sample of size n from the process. Since by assumption $X_i \sim N(\mu, \sigma)$, the sample mean $\overline{X} \sim N(\mu, \sigma/\sqrt{n})$, and the probability that $|\overline{X} - \mu|$ is less than $3\sigma/\sqrt{n}$ is

$$P(|\overline{X} - \mu| < 3\sigma/\sqrt{n}) = 0.9974.$$

Thus the three-sigma control limits are $\mu \pm 3\sigma/\sqrt{n}$. That is, when a sample of size n is taken, a value of the sample mean is computed and plotted. If it falls inside the control limits $\mu \pm 3\sigma/\sqrt{n}$, the process is assumed to be in control; otherwise, it is out of control. In essence, therefore, each time a sample is taken, we are testing the null hypothesis that the process mean equals μ against the alternative that there has been a shift in the process mean. Rejection of the null hypothesis implies that the process is out of control.

Example 11.1   In a filling process, the machine is set to pour an average of 500 grams into each container with a standard deviation of 2 grams. Each operating day 10 samples of 5 containers each are taken, and the weight of each container is measured. The average weights for the 10 samples of a given week are as follows:

Sample No.	1	2	3	4	5
Sample Mean	498.37	499.49	501.25	498.63	502.97

Sample No.	6	7	8	9	10
Sample Mean	500.56	499.23	498.76	501.05	500.27

For 3σ control limits, was the process in control during this week? With these limits, what is the probability of not being able to detect a shift in the mean from 500 grams to 503 grams?

Since $n = 5$, $\mu = 500$, and $\sigma = 2$, the 3σ control limits are $500 \pm 3(2/\sqrt{5}) = 500 \pm 2.6833$ or $(497.3167, 502.6833)$. The control chart for the sample means is given in Figure 11.1. Notice that the fifth sample mean is outside

FIGURE 11.1 $\overline{X}$ chart for the data in Example 11.1

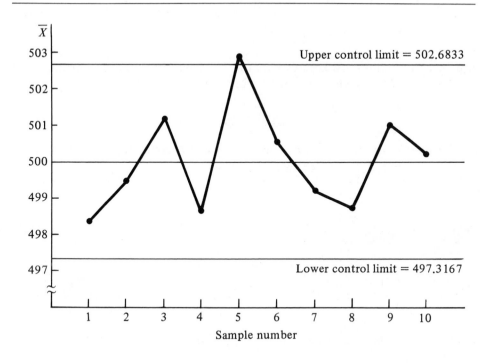

the upper control limit; thus, during this time the process is judged to be out of control relative to the average of the process. The probability of observing a value of $\overline{X}$ outside the control limits if the process is actually in control is

$$P(|\overline{X} - 500| > 2.6833) = 0.0026.$$

The probability of not being able to detect a shift in the mean from 500 to 503 grams is

$$P(497.3167 < \overline{X} < 502.6833 \mid \mu = 503) = P\left(\frac{497.3167 - 503}{2/\sqrt{5}} < Z < \frac{502.6833 - 503}{2/\sqrt{5}}\right)$$

$$= P(-6.35 < Z < -0.35)$$

$$= 0.3632.$$

11.2.2 S Charts — Population Standard Deviation Known

Many times the variability of a process is at least as important as the mean of the process. For example, in the manufacture of precision instruments, keeping the variation in the measurement of interest to an acceptable level is likely to be as important as the average.

We will consider control charts for process variability using the sample standard deviation

$$S = \left[\sum (X_i - \bar{X})^2 / (n - 1) \right]^{1/2}.$$

The 3σ control limits are $E(S) \pm 3 \; s.d.(S)$. To determine $E(S)$ and $Var(S)$, recall from Section 7.5 that the random variable

$$Y = \frac{(n - 1)S^2}{\sigma^2}$$

is chi-square distributed with $n - 1$ degrees of freedom, where the probability density function of Y is given by (7.16). Since

$$S^2 = \frac{\sigma^2 Y}{n - 1},$$

then

$$S = \frac{\sigma Y^{1/2}}{(n - 1)^{1/2}},$$

and

$$E(S) = \frac{\sigma}{(n - 1)^{1/2}} E(Y^{1/2}).$$

But

$$E(Y^{1/2}) = c \int_0^\infty y^{1/2} \, y^{(n-3)/2} \exp(-y/2) dy, \tag{11.1}$$

where

$$c = \frac{1}{\Gamma[(n - 1)/2] \, 2^{(n-1)/2}}.$$

In (11.1) let $u = y/2$; then $dy = 2du$ and

$$E(Y^{1/2}) = 2^{n/2} c \int_0^\infty u^{(n-2)/2} \exp(-u) du = 2^{n/2} c \Gamma(n/2).$$

Then

$$E(S) = \frac{\sigma}{(n - 1)^{1/2}} \, 2^{n/2} \, c\Gamma(n/2)$$

$$= \sigma \frac{2^{1/2} \Gamma(n/2)}{(n - 1)^{1/2} \Gamma[(n - 1)/2]}. \tag{11.2}$$

It is preferable to use quality control notation and write

$$E(S) = c_4 \sigma,$$

where

$$c_4 = \frac{2^{1/2} \Gamma(n/2)}{(n - 1)^{1/2} \Gamma[(n - 1)/2]}. \tag{11.3}$$

TABLE 11.1 Values of c_4 and c_5 for typical sample sizes n

n	4	5	6	7	8	9	10
c_4	0.9213	0.9400	0.9515	0.9594	0.9650	0.9693	0.9727
c_5	0.3889	0.3412	0.3076	0.2820	0.2622	0.2459	0.2321

For the variance of S, by definition

$$Var(S) = E(S^2) - E^2(S).$$

But we showed in Section 7.5 that $E(S^2) = \sigma^2$, so

$$Var(S) = \sigma^2 - c_4^2\sigma^2 = \sigma^2(1 - c_4^2),$$

or in the preferred notation,

$$Var(S) = c_5^2\sigma^2.$$

Therefore, $s.d.(S) = c_5\sigma$, and the 3σ control limits are

$$c_4\sigma \pm 3c_5\sigma, \tag{11.4}$$

where c_4 is as given by (11.3) and $c_5 = (1 - c_4^2)^{1/2}$. Notice that since σ is assumed to be known, the control limits are functions only of the size of each sample. In Table 11.1, the values of c_4 and c_5 are determined for typical sample sizes n.

For illustration, if $\sigma = 2$, the 3σ control limits for the sample standard deviation based on $n = 5$ are $(0.94)(2) \pm (3)(0.3412)(2)$ or $(0, 3.9272)$. In the S chart for this example the lower control limit is zero, the center line is 1.88, and the upper control limit is 3.9272. For $n = 5$ and $\sigma = 2$, the process variability is considered to be in control so long as a value of the sample standard deviation is inside these control limits.

11.2.3 $\overline{X}$ and S Charts — Population Mean and Variance Unknown

We now consider control charts for cases in which the population distribution is still normal but the mean and variance are unknown. For this situation, the control limits must be based on estimates for μ and σ.

Since the process average is unknown, the center line of the control chart is also unknown. If the center line is an estimate based on a large number of samples, the control limits thus obtained should be viewed only as *trial limits* because they may need to be modified before they can be used to gauge, say, product quality for future production operations. That is, the trial control limits are appropriate for determining whether the past operations of a production process were in control. To extend them to future production, the usual procedure is to eliminate all points falling outside the trial control limits and recompute new trial limits based on the remaining sample information. This process is continued until all points fall within the control limits for both $\overline{X}$ and S charts. The rationale for such a procedure is that control limits for future production should be functions of observations obtained while the production process is in control.

According to Shewhart, trial control limits should be based on at least 20 samples, each sample consisting of about four or five observations. Shewhart called such samples *rational subgroups*. They should be selected in a way that makes each subgroup practically homogeneous and that provides the maximum opportunity for variation from one subgroup to another. In a production process this implies that the observations in one subgroup should be taken in one time frame, and observations of another subgroup should be taken in a different time frame. The relatively small subgroup size of about four or five has been used not only for the need to balance cost of sampling and accuracy of estimate but also to give minimum opportunity for variation within a subgroup.

Let m be the number of samples and assume that $n_i = n$ for all $i = 1, 2, \ldots, m$. Further, let $\overline{X}_i$ be the sample mean and S_i the sample standard deviation of the ith sample. For all m samples, define the statistics

$$\overline{\overline{X}} = \frac{1}{m} \sum_{i=1}^{m} \overline{X}_i \tag{11.5}$$

and

$$\overline{S} = \frac{1}{m} \sum_{i=1}^{m} S_i. \tag{11.6}$$

It is apparent that $E(\overline{\overline{X}}) = \mu$; thus the average over all m samples is an unbiased estimator of μ. Similarly,

$$E(\overline{S}) = \frac{1}{m} \sum E(S_i) = \frac{1}{m} (m c_4 \sigma) = c_4 \sigma,$$

which suggests that an estimator for σ is $\overline{S}/c_4$. The 3σ trial limits for the sample mean when both μ and σ are unknown are

$$\overline{\overline{X}} \pm 3 \frac{\overline{S}}{c_4 \sqrt{n}}, \tag{11.7}$$

and those for the sample standard deviation are

$$\overline{S} \pm 3 \frac{c_5 \overline{S}}{c_4}, \tag{11.8}$$

where c_4 and c_5 are as previously defined.

Example 11.2   The data in Table 11.2 are 20 samples, each with five observations taken at two-hour intervals, of the tensile strength of a yarn in pounds. For each sample the mean and standard deviation are as indicated. Construct $\overline{X}$ and S control charts based on these data.

Averaging the $m = 20$ sample means we obtain $\overline{\overline{x}} = 47.12$, and averaging the sample standard deviations we have $\overline{s} = 2.326$. For $n = 5$, $c_4 = 0.94$ and

TABLE 11.2 Sample data on tensile strength of a yarn in pounds

Sample number		Sample values				$\overline{X}$	S
1	44	46	48	52	49	47.8	3.03
2	44	47	49	46	44	46.0	2.12
3	47	49	47	43	44	46.0	2.45
4	45	47	51	46	48	47.4	2.30
5	44	41	50	46	50	46.2	3.90
6	49	46	45	46	49	47.0	1.87
7	47	48	50	46	47	47.6	1.52
8	49	46	51	48	46	48.0	2.12
9	47	42	48	44	46	45.4	2.41
10	46	48	45	51	50	48.0	2.55
11	45	47	51	48	46	47.4	2.30
12	52	51	48	48	45	48.8	2.77
13	45	45	47	49	44	46.0	2.00
14	46	47	43	48	45	45.8	1.92
15	48	49	52	46	51	49.2	2.39
16	44	46	45	47	52	46.8	3.11
17	48	50	47	46	49	48.0	1.58
18	48	52	51	47	46	48.8	2.59
19	47	51	50	46	49	48.6	2.07
20	44	43	42	43	46	43.6	1.52

$c_5 = 0.3412$. Then by (11.7) and (11.8), the 3σ trial control limits for the sample means are

$$47.12 \pm \frac{(3)(2.326)}{(0.94)\sqrt{5}} = (43.80, 50.44),$$

and the limits for the sample standard deviations are

$$2.326 \pm \frac{(3)(0.3412)(2.326)}{0.94} = (0, 4.8589).$$

The control charts are given in Figure 11.2. Notice that the process variability appears to be in control, but the sample mean for the 20th sample is outside the trial limits. Since the mean of the 20th sample is outside the trial limits, new limits are determined after deleting this sample. We obtain the limits

$$47.31 \pm \frac{(3)(2.368)}{(0.94)\sqrt{5}} = (43.93, 50.69)$$

for $\overline{X}$ and the limits

$$2.368 \pm \frac{(3)(0.3412)(2.368)}{0.94} = (0, 4.9466)$$

for S. Now all points fall within the new trial limits for both the $\overline{X}$ and the S charts.

FIGURE 11.2 $\overline{X}$ and S charts for the data in Example 11.2

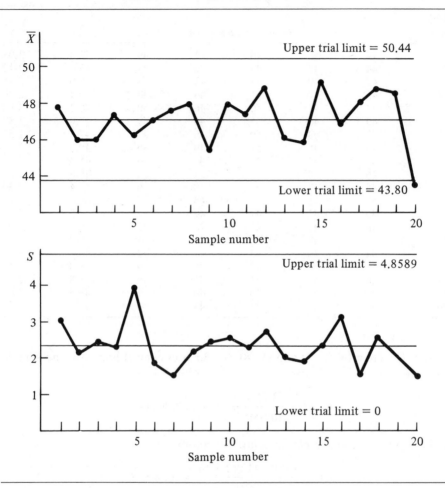

The construction of $\overline{X}$ and S charts is based on the normal distribution. The $\overline{X}$ chart is relatively insensitive to the assumption of normality because of the central limit theorem. However, the S chart is much more sensitive to the assumption of normality.

The existence of the p chart is worth a mention. The p chart can be constructed when sampling is assumed to be from a binomial distribution with proportion parameter p. Control limits are determined for the sample proportions of units falling into one of the two possible categories. What is usually of interest in this situation is to monitor the proportion of defective units produced by a manufacturing process.

To construct control limits for the sample proportions, assume p is unknown. Let m be the number of samples available, and let X_i be the number of defective units in the ith sample of size n. Then X_i/n is an estimator of p based on the *i*th sample, and $\overline{P} = (1/mn) \sum_{i=1}^{m} X_i$ is an estimator of p based on all m samples. Accordingly, 3σ trial limits for the sample proportions X_i/n are

$$\overline{P} \pm 3\sqrt{\frac{\overline{P}(1 - \overline{P})}{n}}. \tag{11.9}$$

11.3 Acceptance Sampling Procedures

A consumer may choose one of the following three ways to verify the quality of the items in a shipment that he or she has just received: Inspect every item in the lot, inspect items in a random sample from the lot, or accept the lot as is with no inspection. The first option is often prohibitively expensive, and the last option is not likely to be accepted by a consumer who is serious about the quality of purchased items. Therefore, the option that achieves a proper balance between the cost of inspection and the cost of accepting and thus using defective items is to inspect items in a random sample from the purchased lot. Based on the inspection process, the usual decision is either to accept the lot, to reject the lot, or to take another random sample. If acceptance or rejection is based on measured values of the items in the sample with regard to some continuous physical measurement, then inspection is said to be *by variables*. If the inspected items in the random sample are classified as either defective or nondefective and the lot is accepted or rejected based on the number of defectives in the sample, then inspection is said to be *by attributes*.

We consider now the fundamentals for developing single sampling plans based on attributes to decide whether to accept or reject a submitted lot. Later we will briefly examine acceptance sampling by variables. Let N be the lot size. Then a basic acceptance sampling plan calls for the random selection of n items from the lot of size N, and as long as the number of defective items in the sample is less than or equal to a predetermined acceptance number c, the lot is accepted. Otherwise the lot is rejected. For example, a sampling plan might be defined as $N = 10,000$, $n = 100$, and $c = 1$. This means that 100 items will be randomly selected from the 10,000, and if either zero or one defective is found in the sample, the lot of $N = 10,000$ items is accepted. If more than one defective is found, the entire lot is rejected. A consumer may choose to return a rejected lot to its manufacturer or to subject the lot to a 100 percent inspection. The former constitutes what is known as a *nonrectifying inspection* procedure, and the latter is a *rectifying inspection* process.

Assume the information available to the consumer about the quality of the items in the lot is the average proportion defective of the manufacturing process that produced the items. One very important criterion in a sampling plan is the probability of lot acceptance $P(A)$, given a proportion defective p. Under suitable assumptions and for some p and c, the probability that the lot will be accepted based on a random sample of size n is the binomial cumulative probability

$$P(A) \equiv P(X \leqslant c) = \sum_{x=0}^{c} \binom{n}{x} p^x (1 - p)^{n-x}, \tag{11.10}$$

TABLE 11.3 Probabilities of acceptance for the sampling plan $n = 100$, $c = 2$

p	0.01	0.02	0.03	0.04	0.05	0.06	0.07	0.08	0.09
$P(A)$	0.9197	0.6767	0.4232	0.2381	0.1247	0.0620	0.0296	0.0138	0.0062

where the random variable X represents the number of defective items found in the sample. If np is of moderate size, the binomial probability given by (11.10) can be adequately approximated by the Poisson cumulative probability

$$P(A) = \sum_{x=0}^{c} \frac{\lambda^x}{x!} \exp(-\lambda), \tag{11.11}$$

where $\lambda = np$.

A plot of the probability of acceptance against p is the operating characteristic (OC) curve. To illustrate, let us analyze the sampling plan $n = 100$ and $c = 2$. Using the Poisson approximation (11.11), we determine the probability of acceptance for values of p ranging from 0.01 to 0.09. The probabilities of acceptance are given in Table 11.3 and are plotted against p in Figure 11.3.

The nature of an OC curve is affected by the sample size n and the acceptance number c. For illustration, let us consider the sampling plans $n = 50$, $c = 1$; $n = 100$, $c = 2$; and $n = 200$, $c = 4$. The OC curves for these plans are given in Figure 11.4. Notice that although the ratio of c to n is constant, the OC curves are somewhat different. In fact, the curves are most sensitive to the sample size. As n increases, the slope of the OC curve becomes steeper. Thus for larger sample sizes, the probability of acceptance decreases rapidly as p increases. If n is fixed, increasing the acceptance number c tends to slide the OC curve to the right. This implies the expected result that for a given p, the probability of acceptance is higher as c increases. Consequently, one would think that the closer c is to zero, the better is the sampling plan. But as Figure 11.4 indicates, plans with larger c values are better as long as the sample size is also appreciably larger.

The development of good sampling plans involves both the producer and the consumer of the lot. Typically, the producer is the seller and the consumer is the buyer. A producer would certainly like to have the consumer reject a very small percentage of the submitted lots that are actually good, and the consumer would like to accept a very small percentage of the lots that are bad. Thus both experience a certain risk. Suppose they both agree that a lot is acceptable if the proportion defective $p \leq p_1$, and a lot is unacceptable if $p \geq p_2$. The following definitions of the risks involved are now given.

Definition 11.1 The producer's risk α is the probability that the consumer will reject a lot whose proportion defective is no more than p_1.

Definition 11.2 The consumer's risk β is the probability of accepting a lot whose proportion defective is greater than or equal to p_2.

FIGURE 11.3 Operating characteristic curve for the sampling plan $n = 100$, $c = 2$

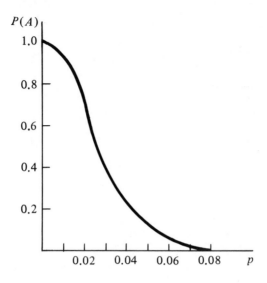

FIGURE 11.4 Operating characteristic curves for three sampling plans

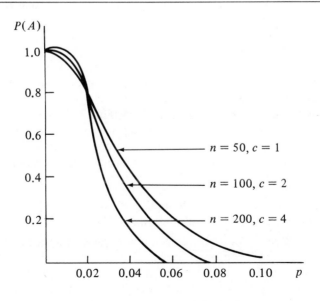

FIGURE 11.5 OC curve for specified producer and consumer risk points

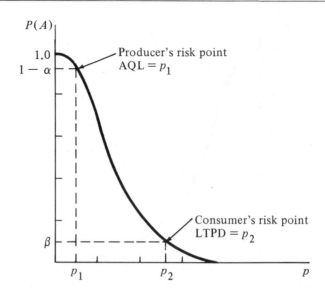

Based on these definitions, the producer's risk is the probability of type I error since it represents the probability of rejecting an acceptable lot. Similarly, the consumer's risk is the probability of type II error since it is the probability of failing to reject an unacceptable lot. In other words, the preceding situation is analogous to testing the null hypothesis H_0: $p = p_1$ against the alternative H_1: $p = p_2$.

The producer and consumer risks can be represented by two points on an operating characteristic curve, as depicted in Figure 11.5. In this context p_1 is called the *acceptable quality level* (AQL), and p_2 is known as the *lot tolerance proportion defective* (LTPD). The usual practice has been to set the probability of acceptance $P(A) = 1 - \alpha$ at the AQL near the 0.95 point on the OC curve, and the probability of acceptance $P(A) = \beta$ at the LTPD near the 0.10 point on the curve. Then 95 percent of the lots coming from a process whose proportion defective is at the AQL or better will be accepted, while only 10 percent will be accepted if they come from a process with a proportion defective at the LTPD or worse.

11.3.1 The Development of Single Sampling Plans for Stipulated Producer and Consumer Risks

We now examine a procedure for determining single sampling plans for specified values of producer and consumer risks. The essence of the procedure is to determine the sample size n and the acceptance number c, given the probabilities of acceptance at the AQL and at the LTPD. For example, suppose we desire a single sampling plan for which the operating characteristic curve passes through a producer's risk $\alpha = 0.05$ at an AQL of 0.01 and passes through a consumer's risk $\beta = 0.1$ at an LTPD of 0.05. Thus, the probabilities of acceptance at AQL = 0.01 and LTPD = 0.05 are 0.95 and 0.1, respectively.

Assume the conditions are such that the Poisson distribution will provide an adequate approximation. Let X be the random variable representing the number of defective items in a sample of size n. Then for the producer's risk, we desire to determine n and c such that

$$P(A) \equiv P(X \leq c) = \sum_{x=0}^{c} \frac{\lambda^x \exp(-\lambda)}{x!} = 1 - \alpha, \qquad (11.12)$$

where $\lambda = np_1$. Similarly, for the consumer's risk, we want to determine n and c such that

$$P(A) \equiv P(X \leq c) = \sum_{x=0}^{c} \frac{\lambda^x \exp(-\lambda)}{x!} = \beta, \qquad (11.13)$$

where now $\lambda = np_2$. Since α, β, p_1, and p_2 are given, the procedure reduces to the simultaneous solution of (11.12) and (11.13) for n and c. No direct method is available to solve these two equations. In other words, it is virtually impossible to determine a sampling plan whose OC curve passes exactly through the two points $(p_1, 1 - \alpha)$ and (p_2, β) because both n and c must be integers. What is usually done is to determine four plans, two of which will have the given value of α but a slightly different value for β, while the other two will have the given β but slightly different α.

Given $\alpha = 0.05$, $\beta = 0.1$, $p_1 = 0.01$, and $p_2 = 0.05$, the procedure is as follows: Let $\lambda_1 = np_1$ and $\lambda_2 = np_2$ and form the ratio of λ_2 to λ_1. For the example this is seen to be 5. Ideally, what we are looking for is to determine c when λ_2/λ_1 is exactly 5. Since this value of the ratio is not likely to be achieved precisely, what we would like to determine are two values of c that bracket the ratio of 5. This can be accomplished by starting with $c = 0$ and by interpolation, finding values for λ_1 such that $P(A) = 1 - \alpha$, and for λ_2 such that $P(A) = \beta$, using the cumulative Poisson distribution (Table B of the Appendix). Then, by incrementing c, the process is continued until two values of c are found that bracket the desired ratio. The corresponding sample sizes are determined by first holding the probability of acceptance at the producer's risk as given, then holding the probability of acceptance at the consumer's risk as given. Such a procedure will give four distinct sampling plans.

Given that $P(A) = 0.95$ and $c = 0$, we determine that $\lambda_1 = 0.05$. Similarly for $P(A) = 0.1$ and $c = 0$, λ_2 is found to be 2.30, and the ratio $\lambda_2/\lambda_1 = 46$. Now for $P(A) = 0.95$ and $c = 1$, $\lambda_1 = 0.36$, and for $P(A) = 0.10$, $\lambda_2 = 3.9$. Thus $\lambda_2/\lambda_1 = 10.83$. The process is continued, with the results listed in Table 11.4. The two values of c that bracket the ideal ratio of 5 are 2 and 3.

To determine n, suppose we hold the producer's risk at $\alpha = 0.05$. Then for $c = 2$, $np_1 = 0.82$; but $p_1 = 0.01$ and $n = 82$. For the plan $n = 82$ and $c = 2$, the probability of acceptance at an LTPD = 0.05 is determined by using $\lambda_2 = (82)(0.05) = 4.1$. Accordingly, $P(A) \equiv P(X \leq 2) = 0.2238$.

TABLE 11.4   Determining values of c that bracket $\lambda_2/\lambda_1 = 5$

Acceptance number c	Value of $\lambda_1 = np_1$ at $P(A) = 0.95$	Value of $\lambda_2 = np_2$ at $P(A) = 0.1$	λ_2/λ_1
0	0.05	2.30	46.00
1	0.36	3.90	10.83
2	0.82	5.32	6.49
3	1.37	6.68	4.88

If we hold the consumer's risk at $\beta = 0.1$, then for $c = 2$, $np_2 = 5.32$, and $n = 107$. As a result, $\lambda_1 = (107)(0.01) = 1.07$, and the probability of acceptance at an AQL $= 0.01$ is $P(A) \equiv P(X \le 2) \approx 0.91$. The other two plans can be established by repeating the process with $c = 3$. The four plans are summarized in Table 11.5.

Of the four plans, the one that appears to be most off the mark with regard to the specified consumer's risk is $n = 82$ and $c = 2$. The other three, especially the last two, are close to the specified producer and consumer risks. The ultimate choice among the four is likely to be based on the circumstances of the situation.

11.3.2   Acceptance Sampling by Variables

The majority of acceptance sampling plans are by attributes for two main reasons. Inspection by attributes is very economical, and many quality characteristics are observable only as attributes. However, in some cases an actual physical measurement of the quality of a given product can be made. When acceptance is based on physical measurements, sampling is said to be by variables. When possible, sampling by variables is becoming more popular because a physical measurement is likely to provide more useful information about the quality of a product than sampling by attributes. Moreover, steeper OC curves can be achieved for the same sample size. But inspection by variables is likely to be more costly than inspection by attributes, primarily because acceptance criteria must be applied separately for each measurement of quality when sampling by variables.

In the simple case in which acceptance of the lot is based on the sample means, the measurement of quality is assumed to be a normally distributed random variable with known variance. Let α be the producer's risk and μ_α be the lot average for which the probability of acceptance is $1 - \alpha$. Similarly let

TABLE 11.5   Four sampling plans for $\alpha = 0.05$, $\beta = 0.1$, AQL $= 0.01$, and LTPD $= 0.05$

Sampling plan	Probability of acceptance at AQL $= 0.01$	Probability of acceptance at LTPD $= 0.05$
$n = 82$, $c = 2$	0.95	0.2238
$n = 107$, $c = 2$	0.91	0.10
$n = 137$, $c = 3$	0.95	0.09
$n = 134$, $c = 3$	0.95	0.10

β be the consumer's risk and μ_β be the lot average for which the probability of acceptance is β. That is, if a lot has mean μ_α, we want to accept that lot with probability $1 - \alpha$, and if it has a mean μ_β ($\mu_\alpha > \mu_\beta$) we want to accept the lot with probability β. Given α, β, μ_α, and μ_β, a sampling plan by variables is a sample size n and an acceptance value $\bar{x}_a$ such that when the observed value of the sample mean $\bar{X}$ exceeds $\bar{x}_a$ the lot will be accepted.

To determine $\bar{x}_a$ and n, consider the following. At the producer's risk

$$P(\bar{X} \leq \bar{x}_a) = \alpha$$

or

$$P\left(Z \leq \frac{\bar{x}_a - \mu_\alpha}{\sigma/\sqrt{n}}\right) = \alpha,$$

where

$$\frac{\bar{x}_a - \mu_\alpha}{\sigma/\sqrt{n}} = z_\alpha. \tag{11.14}$$

At the consumer's risk

$$P(\bar{X} > \bar{x}_a) = \beta$$

or

$$P\left(Z > \frac{\bar{x}_a - \mu_\beta}{\sigma/\sqrt{n}}\right) = \beta,$$

where

$$\frac{\bar{x}_a - \mu_\beta}{\sigma/\sqrt{n}} = z_{1-\beta}. \tag{11.15}$$

The equations given by (11.14) and (11.15) involve the desired unknowns $\bar{x}_a$ and n. Solving (11.14) and (11.15) for $\bar{x}_a$ we obtain

$$\bar{x}_a = \frac{\sigma}{\sqrt{n}} z_\alpha + \mu_\alpha \tag{11.16}$$

and

$$\bar{x}_a = \frac{\sigma}{\sqrt{n}} z_{1-\beta} + \mu_\beta. \tag{11.17}$$

Then by equating (11.16) and (11.17) and solving for n we have

$$n = \left[\frac{\sigma(z_{1-\beta} - z_\alpha)}{\mu_\alpha - \mu_\beta}\right]^2. \tag{11.18}$$

We use (11.18) to determine the sample size, then use either (11.16) or (11.17) to determine the acceptance value $\bar{x}_a$.

Example 11.3 The contractor on a high-rise office building is concerned about the compressive strength of the concrete to be used in the construction of the building. A process that prepares concrete with an average strength of 350 kilograms per square centimeter is good, and concrete purchased from such a process should be accepted 95 percent of the time. But a process that yields an average strength of 347 kilograms is not good, and concrete purchased from such a process ought to be rejected 90 percent of the time. If a cement manufacturer assures the contractor that the standard deviation of his process is no more than 5 kilograms per square centimeter, how many concrete specimens should the contractor test for strength, and what should be the acceptance value for the sample mean under the given conditions? Assume that the compressive strength of the concrete is normally distributed.

The producer and consumer risks are given as $\alpha = 0.05$ at $\mu_\alpha = 350$ and $\beta = 0.10$ at $\mu_\beta = 347$, respectively. For $\alpha = 0.05$ and $1 - \beta = 0.9$, the corresponding standard normal quantile values are $z_{0.05} = -1.645$ and $z_{0.9} = 1.282$. Then, using (11.18), the required sample size is

$$n = \left[\frac{5(1.282 + 1.645)}{350 - 347} \right]^2 = 24.$$

At the producer's risk (11.16)

$$\bar{x}_a = \frac{5}{\sqrt{24}} (-1.645) + 350 = 348.32,$$

and at the consumer's risk (11.17)

$$\bar{x}_a = \frac{5}{\sqrt{24}} (1.282) + 347 = 348.31.$$

For $\bar{x}_a = 348.32$ the sampling plan is to test the strength of 24 specimens of concrete from the process, and to accept the cement process as long as the mean strength of the 24 specimens is greater than 348.32 kilograms per square centimeter.

11.3.3   Systems of Sampling Plans

Since World War II, acceptance sampling plans have become standard procedures to ensure the quality of manufactured products, and a number of systems of acceptance sampling plans have been developed for this purpose. Three of the most widely used systems are MIL-STD-105D*, MIL-STD-414, and the Dodge–Romig Sampling Inspection Tables. Detailed information about these systems is available in [4], [5], and [1], respectively. The first two systems were developed for the Department of Defense and are applicable under a nonrectifying inspection procedure. MIL-STD-105D contains plans for sampling by attributes and MIL-STD-414 contains plans for sampling by variables. The Dodge–Romig sampling plans are based on a rectifying inspection program. They assume a known process percent defective, and the single sampling plans are indexed by LTPD for a consumer's risk of 0.10. All three systems are described in [3].

---

*Outside the United States this system is known as ABC-STD-105D.

References

1. H. F. Dodge and H. G. Romig, *Sampling inspection tables — Single and double sampling,* 2nd ed. Wiley, New York, 1959.
2. A. J. Duncan, *Quality control and industrial statistics,* 4th ed., Richard D. Irwin, Homewood, Ill., 1974.
3. E. L. Grant and R. S. Leavenworth, *Statistical quality control,* 4th ed., McGraw-Hill, New York, 1972.
4. *Military standard 105D, Sampling procedures and tables for inspection by attributes,* Superintendent of Documents, Government Printing Office, Washington, D.C., 1963.
5. *Military standard 414, Sampling procedures and tables for inspection by variables for percent defective,* Superintendent of Documents, Government Printing Office, Washington, D.C., 1957.

Exercises

11.1. A state water quality board selects five water specimens each week from a water supply and determines the average concentration of a toxic substance. The following are the average amounts in parts per million for twelve weeks.

Week	1	2	3	4	5	6	7	8	9	10	11	12
Sample mean	5.2	4.9	5.5	5.4	4.8	4.6	5.5	4.7	5.1	4.5	5.8	5.6

a. If the concentration average and standard deviation are known to be 5 and 0.5 ppm, respectively, determine 3σ control limits for the average concentration. For this reporting period, was there cause for alarm?

b. If an average concentration of 6 ppm is considered dangerous, how likely is such a result based on a sample of five water specimens if the true average concentration is 5 ppm?

c. Using the control limits in part a, what is the probability of detecting a shift in mean concentration from 5 ppm to 5.25 ppm?

11.2. Using the information in Exercise 11.1, determine 3σ control limits for the sample standard deviation.

11.3. The following are average breaking strengths based on periodic samples of six metal specimens.

Sample	1	2	3	4	5	6	7	8	9	10
Sample mean	498.6	508.3	484.6	505.7	491.7	495.4	482.6	515.2	510.8	503.7

The average breaking strength and standard deviation are known to be 500 and 20 pounds, respectively.

a. Determine 3σ control limits for sample mean breaking strength and graph the control chart. Are any of the sample means outside the control limits?

b. Determine the probability of failing to detect a shift in the true average breaking strength from 500 to 494 pounds.

c. Determine 3σ control limits for the sample standard deviation.

11.4. The data in Table 11.6 consist of 20 samples of four observations each on the diameters of ball bearings produced by a manufacturing process.

TABLE 11.6 Sample data for Exercise 11.4

Sample number	Sample values (in centimeters)			
1	4.01	4.03	3.98	4.04
2	3.97	3.99	3.99	4.02
3	4.06	4.05	3.97	4.02
4	3.96	3.98	4.07	4.03
5	3.98	3.99	3.99	4.00
6	4.01	4.02	3.96	3.99
7	3.95	3.98	4.02	4.03
8	4.03	4.00	3.96	4.04
9	4.07	3.96	3.98	4.05
10	3.98	3.97	4.02	4.04
11	3.92	4.03	4.05	3.99
12	3.97	4.05	4.04	4.01
13	4.04	4.04	3.96	3.99
14	4.03	4.00	4.02	4.05
15	3.95	3.96	3.95	4.02
16	4.05	4.09	4.07	4.02
17	3.98	4.06	4.04	4.03
18	4.01	4.02	4.00	3.97
19	4.02	4.01	4.05	3.99
20	3.99	3.99	4.01	4.00

a. Construct 3σ trial limits for $\overline{X}$ and S control charts.

b. If the process is found not to be in control based on some sample, recompute the trial limits.

11.5. Control charts for $\overline{X}$ and S are maintained on the amount poured in a container by a filling process. Based on 25 periodic samples, each sample consisting of five such containers, it is determined that $\overline{\overline{X}} = 400.2$ grams and $\overline{S} = 15.3$ grams.

a. If we assume the filling process is in control, what are the control limits for the sample mean and the sample standard deviation?

b. What is an estimate of the process standard deviation?

11.6. In Exercise 11.5, suppose each sample was based on the weights of six containers. How would this change your answers to parts a and b?

11.7. In a manufacturing process 100 units are randomly selected each day and inspected. The following is the number of defective units found on each of 25 days.

Day	1	2	3	4	5	6	7	8	9	10	11	12	13
Number of defectives	2	1	4	3	2	2	5	3	4	2	1	5	2

Day	14	15	16	17	18	19	20	21	22	23	24	25
Number of defectives	3	2	1	0	6	4	5	2	1	8	3	2

a. Based on this information, determine a p chart.

b. Revise your control limits if for some day the process is judged to be out of control.

c. If we assume the process is in control with a percent defective as determined in part b, what is the probability that on a given day the process will be judged to be out of control?

11.8. The percent defective of a manufacturing process is assumed to be 4%. The process is monitored daily by taking samples of $n = 80$ units. The process is stopped anytime five or more units are found to be defective in a sample. If the percent defective is really 5.5%, what is the probability of stopping the process?

11.9. Suppose the incoming quality of a large lot is 5% defective. An acceptance sampling plan calls for a random sample of 40 units and an acceptance number of 2 units.

a. What is the probability that the lot will be accepted?
b. If the incoming quality is really 6.25% defective, what is the probability that the lot will be accepted?

11.10. For Exercise 11.9, suppose the sample size is 80 units and the acceptance number is 4 units. How will this change affect your answers to parts a and b?

11.11. The incoming quality of a lot of $N = 20$ units is 10% defective. If there are no defective units in a random sample of 5 units, the lot will be accepted. What is the probability the lot will be accepted?

11.12. Graph and compare the operating characteristic curves for the sampling plans $n = 25$, $c = 1$; and $n = 50$, $c = 2$.

11.13. For the sampling plan $n = 25$, $c = 1$, use the OC curve to determine the LTPD for a consumer's risk of 0.05.

11.14. For the sampling plan $n = 50$, $c = 2$, use the OC curve to determine the AQL for a producer's risk of 0.05.

11.15. Determine the four sampling plans that bracket the producer and consumer risks of $\alpha = 0.05$ at AQL $= 0.02$ and $\beta = 0.1$ at LTPD $= 0.08$, respectively.

11.16. Determine the four sampling plans that bracket the producer and consumer risks of $\alpha = 0.10$ at AQL $= 0.01$ and $\beta = 0.1$ at LTPD $= 0.05$.

11.17. Many times a double sampling plan is utilized for acceptance sampling. Such a plan calls for a random sample of n_1 units to be selected from the lot of N units. If the number of defectives is no more than c_1 units, the lot is accepted; if more than $c_2 > c_1$ defective units are found, the lot is rejected. If the number of defectives in the first sample is more than c_1 but no more than c_2, another random sample of size n_2 is taken. The lot is accepted if the number of defectives from both samples does not exceed c_2; otherwise, the lot is rejected. Use this procedure to determine the following probabilities for the double sampling plan $N = 5000$, $n_1 = 50$, $n_2 = 80$, $c_1 = 0$, $c_2 = 3$ if the incoming quality of the lot is 2% defective.

a. Probability of accepting the lot based on the first sample.
b. Probability of rejecting the lot based on the first sample.
c. Probability of accepting the lot after the second sample.
d. Probability of rejecting the lot after the second sample.

11.18. A state agency is responsible for monitoring the concentration level of a certain chemical pollutant that had been dumped in large amounts in one of the state's largest rivers. The agency must decide from time to time when the concentration level is within safe limits to allow commercial fishing. The agency wants to determine a variables sampling plan so that when the true average concentration level is 5.6

ppm, the agency will decide 95 percent of the time to allow fishing. But the agency wants to prohibit fishing 99 percent of the time when the average concentration is as high as 6.0 ppm. If the standard deviation of the pollutant's concentration is no more than one part per million, determine the sampling plan. Assume the concentration of the pollutant is normally distributed.

11.19. A buyer of large quantities of yarn would like to develop a variables sampling plan for the breaking strength of the yarn. The yarn is acceptable to the buyer if its breaking strength exceeds 60 pounds. If the standard deviation of the yarn is known to be 8 pounds, and given $\alpha = 0.05$, $\beta = 0.05$, AQL = 0.05, and LTPD = 0.1, determine the sampling plan. Assume the strength of the yarn is normally distributed.

CHAPTER TWELVE

Design and Analysis of Statistical Experiments

12.1 Introduction

In Sections 9.6.3 and 9.6.4 we introduced some basic ideas about planning and acquiring experimental data to achieve maximum benefit from the application of statistical inference. In this chapter we will elaborate on the notion of statistically designed experiments and will extend some of the methods of Chapter 9 by introducing an important statistical technique known as analysis of variance.

12.2 Statistical Experiments

For any phenomenon in which uncertainty exists, the proper procedure for investigating the phenomenon is to experiment with it so that the features of interest may be identified. For example, we may wish to identify the optimum behavior of a system with respect to performance and cost under varying conditions. Thus we think of an experiment as the means by which the system will be observed under the conditions of interest so that its behavior may become known.

The most important element of an experiment, and one that is all too often overlooked, is the statement of the problem to be solved. One cannot hope to have a reasonable chance for success without some direction as to the purpose of the experiment. Once that is defined, it is necessary to identify the measurable variable or *response* to be studied and the potential *factor* or *factors* that may influence the variability of the response. The response is also known as the dependent variable; the factor is called the independent variable. It is assumed that the factor is under the control of the investigator. For example, in a service-providing facility, one has to be concerned with the number of servers available so that the customer's waiting time is not excessive. The response is the waiting time, and the factor is the number of available servers.

A *level* or a factor *treatment* is a value or condition of the factor under which the measurable response will be observed. For example, we may wish to observe the waiting time when a service facility has available two, four, or six servers at a time. If an experiment consists of several factors, a treatment is a combination of factor levels. For instance, we may wish to study the waiting time as a function of the number of servers and the time of day. Then a treatment is the combination of a particular number of servers at a particular time of day. The process by which treatments are selected is more or less dictated by the goals of the experiment. For preliminary experiments in which the overriding purpose is to isolate the principal factors, the investigator should choose the treatments with a fairly broad range in mind so as to obtain a workable knowledge of the mechanism under study. A more precise experiment can be conducted later for more specific findings.

An *experimental unit* is defined as the object (person or thing) that is capable of producing a measurement of the response variable after the application of a given treatment. The selection of the experimental unit or its size again rests with the investigator. For example, if a manufacturer of light bulbs wishes to compare the life of his or her bulbs with those of competing brands, then the bulbs selected for the experiment are the experimental units, and the number of different brands are the treatments. Or if we are interested in determining the concentration of a pollutant in a large body of water as a function of location, then the locations we select to measure the concentration are the treatments, and the relatively small surface area for each location is the experimental unit.

In an environment of uncertainty, experiments are usually comparative in the sense that, ideally, they measure and compare the responses of essentially identical experimental units after the units are exposed to treatments selected and applied by the investigator. All external factors that may influence the response must be controlled if not eliminated. However, the control of external factors cannot always be guaranteed. For example, practically any experiment involving some business activity will be interlocked with prevailing economic conditions that cannot be controlled. Such a departure from ideal experimental control calls for repetition of the experiment on a sample of experimental units to determine the random variation or *experimental error*. This is the extraneous variation in the response or the variation that cannot be attributed to a change of treatment. Then statistical inference is possible by comparing the experimental error to the average responses resulting from the application of different treatments.

In laboratory sciences ideal experiments can be carried out. But in the socioeconomic sciences, departures from ideal experimental conditions are commonplace because the environment does not permit sufficient control. For example, one may be concerned with the effect of an increase in the interest rate (treatment) on home construction activity (response) by home builders (experimental units). The treatments cannot be applied to the experimental units, nor can the response be measured in accordance with a planned experiment. One merely records the information as conditions change in the real world. Although to a purist this does not constitute a proper experiment, these types of studies are certainly worthy of consideration. The more general method of regression may be better suited for the analysis of such data than the methods to be examined in this chapter. Regression analysis will be examined in Chapters 13 and 14.

12.3 Statistical Designs

The process by which the observations of the response are to be measured is the thrust of a statistical design. In typical statistically designed experiments, experimental units must be selected impartially and assigned to treatments by a random process to remove possible systematic biases. As we have indicated in Chapter 9, the process of randomization not only protects against systematic bias in the assignment process but also tends to neutralize the effects of external factors not under the direct control of the investigator. Then the comparisons among treatments measure as closely as is practical the effect on the response due to the difference in the treatment.

Equally important in a statistically designed experiment is the concept of *replication*. As we have already noted, the purpose of replication is to measure experimental error. The magnitude of experimental error plays a very important role in decision-making about the possibility that differences among treatments are statistically discernible.

In designing statistical experiments, the primary concern is how to assign the experimental units to the treatments (or vice versa) to assure an impartial process. In this context, two basic concepts emerge. The assignment process should be based on a *completely randomized design* or on a *randomized complete block design*. Either one of these designs can be used in single-factor experiments or in experiments in which several factors will be investigated simultaneously. With a completely randomized design, the assignment of the treatments to the experimental units is done completely at random, and all experimental units are assumed to be homogeneous. Usually, a simple random procedure, such as the use of random numbers, is devised for the assignment process. The use of a completely randomized design implies that the conditions under which the response will be observed (other than those under the direct control of the investigator) are the same throughout the experiment. A completely randomized design should not be used in situations in which observations will be taken over potential factors such as time, space, or demographic effects unless these are legitimate parts of the experiment.

Many times, however, the investigator realizes that the entire experiment cannot be conducted in the same environment, primarily because not all of the experimental units are homogeneous. Therefore, one sorts experimental units into homogeneous *blocks* and assigns all treatments at random to the units of each block, thus creating what is known as a randomized complete block design. The word "complete" indicates that each block will contain all treatments, while the word "randomized" means the treatments will be assigned randomly to the homogeneous experimental units of each block.

The investigator recognizes the need for blocking by identifying potential elements of the experimental units that have not been included in the definition of a treatment but still may cause significant variation in the response. Many times these deal with time, spatial, or demographic effects. For example, if the experimental units are humans, then blocking should be tried for sex, age, health conditions, experience, and so on, as dictated by the experiment. If the experiment is to be conducted over a substantial period of time, then time should be viewed as a blocking variable. If the experimental data are to be collected from several locations or in batches, then locations or batches should be regarded as blocking variables. If several instruments are to be used in recording the data, then blocking the instruments should be considered, even if the instruments are all of the same model, and more so if they come from different manufacturers.

The need for blocking, therefore, is apparent. The more heterogeneous the experimental units are, the larger the experimental error will be, and the smaller the chance one will have of being able to detect real differences among the treatments. The reason for blocking is to account for and remove a source of variation on the response that is not of interest, thus increasing the sensitivity for detecting differences among treatments. On balance, therefore, the general principle of a statistical design is to minimize the experimental error by controlling extraneous variation so that the systematic variation in the response can be assessed.

12.4 Analysis of Single-Factor Experiments in a Completely Randomized Design

The simplest type of experiment compares the effects of $k \geq 2$ levels of a single factor on some response variable. The levels of the factor are the treatments, and if they are applied randomly to a set of virtually homogeneous experimental units, the experiment has a completely randomized design. This situation is a natural extension of the problem of comparing two population means in which the variances are unknown but are assumed to be equal. The two-sample t test discussed in Chapter 9 is based on a completely randomized design.

For $k \geq 2$ levels, we wish to test the null hypothesis

$$H_0: \mu_1 = \mu_2 = \cdots = \mu_k \tag{12.1}$$

against the alternative that some of the population means are not the same. If the null hypothesis can be rejected based on k independent samples, then the means of the k populations are not all the same, or the effect of the treatments on the response is statistically discernible. If the null hypothesis cannot be rejected, then any observed variation in the response is due only to random error and not due to a change in the treatment.

Many practical problems can be handled with a completely randomized, single-factor experiment. Whether slightly different amounts of residential ceiling insulation have an effect on energy consumption, whether the mean fill produced by machines in a filling process is the same, or whether exposure of salespersons to different training methods will result in different sales volumes are a few examples. In these cases the treatments are the specific amounts of insulation, the different machines, and the different training programs; the selected houses, filled containers, and salespersons are the respective experimental units. In the first case the treatments are quantitative since a well-defined scale (R rating) distinguishes them. In the last two cases the treatments are qualitative because they represent different things or subjects and thus lack numerical scales.

TABLE 12.1 Typical arrangement of sample data for a completely randomized single-factor experiment

		Treatment			
1	2	$\cdots$	j	$\cdots$	k
Y_{11}	Y_{12}	$\cdots$	Y_{1j}	$\cdots$	Y_{1k}
Y_{21}	Y_{22}	$\cdots$	Y_{2j}	$\cdots$	Y_{2k}
.	.		.		.
.	.		.		.
.	.		.		.
Y_{i1}	Y_{i2}	$\cdots$	Y_{ij}	$\cdots$	Y_{ik}
.	.		.		.
.	.		.		.
.	.		.		.
$Y_{n_1 1}$	$Y_{n_2 2}$	$\cdots$	$Y_{n_j j}$	$\cdots$	$Y_{n_k k}$

The requirement of essentially homogeneous experimental units can be illustrated with the first example. If the homes selected for the experiment are not essentially the same in size, do not have the same amount of wall insulation, have different qualities of weather stripping, and are located in different geographical areas, then differences in energy consumption could not possibly be assigned only to different ceiling insulations. Thus for a completely randomized design, the results will be ambiguous unless the experimental units are virtually homogeneous.

The *analysis of variance* technique provides the inferential procedure for testing the null hypothesis given by (12.1). To develop the analysis of variance method, let us analyze the insulation problem. Suppose we are interested in k different levels of ceiling insulation such that for the jth level we will observe the monthly energy consumption of the heating system in n_j different but very similar houses. We are assured that the homes selected are virtually homogeneous and that external factors are controlled to within practical limits. The sample information may be arranged in an array as given in Table 12.1, where the measurable response is the monthly kilowatt hours used by the heating system of each house.

It is assumed that each level of ceiling insulation represents a population from which a sample is obtained. It is also assumed that the distributions of the populations for each level of insulation are normal with equal variances. Accordingly, the columns in Table 12.1 represent k independent random samples of sizes n_j, $j = 1, 2, \ldots, k$. If the null hypothesis as given by (12.1) is true, then the observation Y_{ij} consists of the overall average energy usage of the heating systems for all k levels of ceiling insulation and a deviation from the average due to random error. If H_0 is false, then Y_{ij} is made up of the overall average plus the effect of the jth treatment plus the random error. The mathematical model for a single-factor completely randomized experiment is

$$Y_{ij} = \mu + \tau_j + \varepsilon_{ij} \qquad j = 1, 2, \ldots, k,$$

$$i = 1, 2, \ldots, n_j,$$

(12.2)

where Y_{ij} is the ith observation of the jth treatment, μ is the mean over all k populations, τ_j is the effect on the response due to the jth treatment, and ε_{ij}^* is the experimental error for the ith observation under the jth treatment.

It is assumed that the errors are independent normally distributed random variables with zero means and equal variances. In other words, $\varepsilon_{ij} \sim N(0, \sigma^2)$ for all i and j. The assumption on the τ_j's depends on how the investigator views the levels of the factor. If the investigator is interested in what happens to the response only for the particular levels of the factor that were selected, then $\tau_1, \tau_2, \ldots, \tau_k$ are considered to be fixed parameters such that

$$\sum_{j=1}^{k} n_j \tau_j = 0.$$

Then the model given by (12.2) is known as a *fixed effects model,* and statistical inferences about the treatment effects pertain only to the selected levels.

On the other hand, if the levels used in the experiment were selected at random from a population of possible levels, then $\tau_1, \tau_2, \ldots, \tau_k$ are independent random variables such that $\tau_j \sim N(0, \sigma_\tau^2)$ for all j. In this case model (12.2) is known as a *random effects model,* and statistical inferences about the levels of a factor pertain to the population of levels from which the ones used in the experiment were but a random sample.

In general, for quantitative factors it is usually desirable to pick fixed levels from the range of interest because a random selection is not likely to provide broad coverage for the range of interest. Interpolation within the selected fixed levels is also a safe practice for quantitative factors. When factors are qualitative, such as humans, locations, and batches, the particular subject, location, or batch chosen for the experiment is usually important only for what it can reveal about variability in the population of humans, locations, or batches.

For a fixed effects model, a null hypothesis equivalent to (12.1) is

$$H_0: \tau_j = 0, \qquad \text{for all } j. \tag{12.3}$$

The null hypothesis (12.3) states that there is no treatment effect on the response, which implies that the k population means are the same. As a result, each observation consists of the common mean and any deviation from the mean due to the inherent variation within each population.

For a random effects model, the null hypothesis consists of the statement that the variance among the τ_js (or the treatment effects) is zero; that is,

$$H_0: \sigma_\tau^2 = 0. \tag{12.4}$$

Then, assuming independence between the random errors and the random treatments,

$$Var(Y_{ij}) = \sigma^2 + \sigma_\tau^2.$$

---

*Rather than use a capital letter for the random variables ε_{ij}, we will adhere to tradition and use the lowercase Greek letter epsilon.

For the random effects model, it is of interest to make an assessment of how much of the variance in the observations is due to real differences in treatment means and how much is due to random errors about these means.

Our primary interest will be on a fixed effects model, but we will include the random effects case when necessary. Our approach to developing the analysis of variance technique will be largely intuitive. For a theoretical treatment of the subject, see [6].

12.4.1 Analysis of Variance for a Fixed Effects Model

Let μ_1, μ_2, ..., μ_k denote the k population means, and let μ be the mean for all populations. Define the jth treatment effect τ_j to be the deviation of the jth population mean μ_j from the overall mean μ. Thus

$$\tau_j = \mu_j - \mu, \quad j = 1, 2, ..., k.$$

In the same sense, the random error ε_{ij} corresponding to the observation Y_{ij} is the deviation of Y_{ij} from the jth mean μ_j, or

$$\varepsilon_{ij} = Y_{ij} - \mu_j, \quad j = 1, 2, ..., k,$$

$$i = 1, 2, ..., n_j.$$

Then the model (12.2) can be written as the identity

$$Y_{ij} = \mu + (\mu_j - \mu) + (Y_{ij} - \mu_j),$$

or

$$Y_{ij} - \mu = (\mu_j - \mu) + (Y_{ij} - \mu_j). \tag{12.5}$$

The identity given by (12.5) explicitly states that any deviation of an observation from the overall mean is due to two possible sources: deviation due to the difference in the treatment, and deviation due to random error. If the null hypothesis as given by (12.3) is to be rejected, the sample data must show that the total deviation due to the difference in the treatment is sufficiently greater than the deviation due to random error. Thus the analysis of variance technique is really an analysis of variation about means and is achieved by partitioning the total variation in the observations into components as specified by the mathematical model. This permits an appropriate statistic to be determined so that a decision regarding the hypothesis H_0: $\tau_j = 0$ can be made.

The parameters μ_1, μ_2, ..., μ_k and μ are unknown, but they can be estimated based on the observations of the k random samples. For the sample information given in Table 12.1, define the following:

$$T_{\cdot j} = \sum_{i=1}^{n_j} Y_{ij}, \quad j = 1, 2, ..., k,$$

$$\overline{Y}_{\cdot j} = T_{\cdot j}/n_j, \quad j = 1, 2, ..., k,$$

$$T_{\cdot \cdot} = \sum_{j=1}^{k} T_{\cdot j},$$

$$N = \sum_{j=1}^{k} n_j,$$

$$\overline{Y}_{..} = T_{..}/N.$$

Once again we are using the dot notation to indicate summation over the corresponding subscript. In particular, $T_{.j}$ is the sum of the n_j observations in the jth treatment, $\overline{Y}_{.j}$ is the sample mean of the jth treatment, $T_{..}$ is the sum of all N observations, and $\overline{Y}_{..}$ is the sample mean of all observations.

Substituting the statistics $\overline{Y}_{.j}$ and $\overline{Y}_{..}$ in (12.5) for the parameters μ_j and μ, respectively, we obtain the corresponding sample identity

$$Y_{ij} - \overline{Y}_{..} = (\overline{Y}_{.j} - \overline{Y}_{..}) + (Y_{ij} - \overline{Y}_{.j}). \tag{12.6}$$

The essence of the sample identity (12.6) is the partitioning of the deviation of an observation Y_{ij} from the overall sample average $\overline{Y}_{..}$ into two components: the deviation of the treatment sample mean $\overline{Y}_{.j}$ from $\overline{Y}_{..}$, and the deviation of Y_{ij} from its own treatment mean $\overline{Y}_{.j}$. Accordingly, we can argue logically that the larger the deviation between $\overline{Y}_{.j}$ and $\overline{Y}_{..}$, the more we are inclined to reject the null hypothesis (12.3).

To determine an appropriate test statistic, suppose we square both sides of (12.6) and sum over all i and j. Thus

$$\sum_{j=1}^{k} \sum_{i=1}^{n_j} (Y_{ij} - \overline{Y}_{..})^2 = \sum_{j=1}^{k} \sum_{i=1}^{n_j} (\overline{Y}_{.j} - \overline{Y}_{..})^2 + \sum_{j=1}^{k} \sum_{i=1}^{n_j} (Y_{ij} - \overline{Y}_{.j})^2$$

$$+ 2 \sum_{j=1}^{k} \sum_{i=1}^{n_j} (\overline{Y}_{.j} - \overline{Y}_{..}) (Y_{ij} - \overline{Y}_{.j}). \tag{12.7}$$

But

$$\sum_{j=1}^{k} \sum_{i=1}^{n_j} (\overline{Y}_{.j} - \overline{Y}_{..}) (Y_{ij} - \overline{Y}_{.j}) = \sum_{j=1}^{k} (\overline{Y}_{.j} - \overline{Y}_{..}) \left[\sum_{i=1}^{n_j} (Y_{ij} - \overline{Y}_{.j}) \right]$$

$$= \sum_{j=1}^{k} (\overline{Y}_{.j} - \overline{Y}_{..}) \left[\sum_{i=1}^{n_j} Y_{ij} - n_j \overline{Y}_{.j} \right]$$

$$= 0,$$

since $\sum_{i=1}^{n_j} Y_{ij} = T_{.j} = n_j \overline{Y}_{.j}$.

As a result, the equation

$$\sum_{j=1}^{k} \sum_{i=1}^{n_j} (Y_{ij} - \overline{Y}_{..})^2 = \sum_{j=1}^{k} \sum_{i=1}^{n_j} (\overline{Y}_{.j} - \overline{Y}_{..})^2 + \sum_{j=1}^{k} \sum_{i=1}^{n_j} (Y_{ij} - \overline{Y}_{.j})^2 \tag{12.8}$$

states that the total sum of the squared deviations about the overall mean is decomposed into the sum of the squared deviations of the treatment means about the overall mean, and the sum of the squared deviations of the observations about their own treatment means. Expression (12.8) is known as the fundamental equation of analysis of variance. The term on the left side of (12.8) is the *total sum of squares* and is denoted by SST. The middle sum of squares in (12.8) is the *treatment sum of squares,* denoted by SSTR. The last term is the *error sum of squares,* denoted by SSE. It follows therefore that

$$\text{SST} = \text{SSTR} + \text{SSE}. \tag{12.9}$$

SSE measures the amount of variation in the observations due to random error. If all observations within a treatment are the same and if this is true for all k treatments, then SSE $= 0$. Accordingly, the larger SSE is, the more of the variation in the observations is due to random error. SSTR measures the extent of the variation in the observations due to differences in the treatments. If all treatment means are the same, then SSTR $= 0$. Thus the larger SSTR is, the bigger is the difference between the treatment means and the overall mean.

It can be shown that under the null hypothesis $H_0: \tau_j = 0$ and the assumption that $\varepsilon_{ij} \sim N(0, \sigma^2)$, SSTR$/\sigma^2$ and SSE$/\sigma^2$ are two independent chi-square distributed random variables. Their degrees of freedom are determined from the breakdown of the total sum of squares. SST has $N - 1$ degrees of freedom because one degree of freedom is lost to the constraint that the sum of the deviations ($Y_{ij} - \overline{Y}_{..}$) over all j and i must be zero. The treatment sum of squares has $k - 1$ degrees of freedom because the constraint that $\Sigma_{j=1}^{k} n_j (\overline{Y}_{.j} - \overline{Y}_{..}) = 0$ is placed on the k deviations ($\overline{Y}_{.j} - \overline{Y}_{..}$). This constraint stems from the restriction that $\Sigma_{j=1}^{k} n_j \tau_j = 0$. Then, based on (12.9), the degrees of freedom for SSE will be the difference between the degrees of freedom for SST and SSTR,

$$\text{df(SSE)} = \text{df(SST)} - \text{df(SSTR)}$$

$$= N - 1 - (k - 1)$$

$$= N - k.$$

A sum of squares divided by its degrees of freedom yields what is known as a *mean square*. Accordingly, the treatment mean square is

$$\text{MSTR} = \text{SSTR}/(k - 1),$$

and the error mean square is

$$\text{MSE} = \text{SSE}/(N - k).$$

We can argue now that since SSTR$/\sigma^2$ and SSE$/\sigma^2$ are two independent chi-squares with $k - 1$ and $N - k$ degrees of freedom, respectively, then from Section 7.8, the ratio of their mean squares is F distributed with $k - 1$ and $N - k$ degrees of freedom. Such a ratio is the appropriate statistic to test the null hypothesis

$$H_0 : \tau_j = 0.$$

This can be verified by examining the expected values of the mean squares. It can be shown that

$$E(\text{MSE}) = \sigma^2$$

and

$$E(\text{MSTR}) = \sigma^2 + \frac{\sum\limits_{j=1}^{k} n_j \tau_j^2}{k - 1},$$

where σ^2 is the common error variance. As a result, the error mean square is an unbiased estimator of σ^2 regardless of whether the null hypothesis is true. On the other hand, if H_0 is true, $\tau_j = 0$ for all j, and $\Sigma n_j \tau_j^2 = 0$. Then $E(\text{MSTR}) = \sigma^2$; that is, under H_0, both MSE and MSTR are unbiased estimators of the error variance. But if the null hypothesis is not true, MSTR generally tends to be larger than MSE since the term $\Sigma n_j \tau_j^2$ will be positive. In other words, the larger the difference between the treatment means and the overall mean, the larger MSTR tends to be. But such an occurrence suggests that the k treatment means are not all the same, and thus the null hypothesis should be rejected. Accordingly, the null hypothesis is rejected whenever the mean square ratio

$$F = \frac{\sum\limits_{j=1}^{k} \sum\limits_{i=1}^{n_j} (\overline{Y}_{.j} - \overline{Y}_{..})^2 / (k - 1)}{\sum\limits_{j=1}^{k} \sum\limits_{i=1}^{n_j} (Y_{ij} - \overline{Y}_{.j})^2 / (N - k)} \tag{12.10}$$

is inside an upper tail critical region of size α.

The preceding discussion constitutes the analysis of variance technique for a single-factor, completely randomized experiment. The sources of variation, degrees of freedom, sums of squares, mean squares, and the F ratio are brought together to form what is known as the analysis of variance (ANOVA) table, given in Table 12.2.

Given the realizations y_{ij}, $j = 1, 2, \ldots, k$, $i = 1, 2, \ldots, n_j$, the computation of the quantities in Table 12.2 can be done easily using any standard statistical computer package. For hand computation, the sum of squares may be computed using the algebraically equivalent but computationally more convenient formulas

$$\text{SST} = \sum\limits_{j=1}^{k} \sum\limits_{i=1}^{n_j} (y_{ij} - \overline{y}_{..})^2 = \sum\limits_{j=1}^{k} \sum\limits_{i=1}^{n_j} y_{ij}^2 - \frac{T_{..}^2}{N},$$

$$\text{SSTR} = \sum\limits_{j=1}^{k} \sum\limits_{i=1}^{n_j} (\overline{y}_{.j} - \overline{y}_{..})^2 = \sum\limits_{j=1}^{k} \frac{T_{.j}^2}{n_j} - \frac{T_{..}^2}{N},$$

$$\text{SSE} = \text{SST} - \text{SSTR}.$$

It should be noted that the null hypothesis H_0: $\mu_1 = \mu_2$ for the two-sample case can also be handled with the analysis of variance method. In Chapter 13 we will show the relation between the F and Student's t statistics for $k = 2$.

Example 12.1 The data in Table 12.3 are the results of a completely randomized design in which the response is the kilowatt hours used by the heating systems

TABLE 12.2 Analysis of variance table for a single-factor completely randomized experiment

Source of variation	df	SS	MS	F statistic
Treatments	$k - 1$	$\Sigma\Sigma(\overline{Y}_{.j} - \overline{Y}_{..})^2$	$\Sigma\Sigma(\overline{Y}_{.j} - \overline{Y}_{..})^2/(k - 1)$	$F = \dfrac{\Sigma\Sigma(\overline{Y}_{.j} - \overline{Y}_{..})^2/(k - 1)}{\Sigma\Sigma(Y_{ij} - \overline{Y}_{.j})^2/(N - k)}$
Error	$N - k$	$\Sigma\Sigma(Y_{ij} - \overline{Y}_{.j})^2$	$\Sigma\Sigma(Y_{ij} - \overline{Y}_{.j})^2/(N - k)$	
Total	$N - 1$	$\Sigma\Sigma(Y_{ij} - \overline{Y}_{..})^2$		

TABLE 12.3 Heat used for five levels of insulation

		Thickness of ceiling insulation (inches)		
4	6	8	10	12
14.4	14.5	13.8	13.0	13.1
14.8	14.1	14.1	13.4	12.8
15.2	14.6	13.7	13.2	12.9
14.3	14.2	13.6		13.2
14.6		14.0		13.3
				12.7

(in hundreds of kilowatt hours) of very similar houses in a given month as a function of five levels of ceiling insulation (in inches). Based on this information, is there reason to believe that at least some of the average energy consumptions for the five levels of ceiling insulation are different? Assume a type I error α of 0.01.

We wish to test the null hypothesis that

$$H_0: \mu_1 = \mu_2 = \mu_3 = \mu_4 = \mu_5 = \mu,$$

or equivalently,

$$H_0: \tau_j = 0, \quad j = 1, 2, ..., 5.$$

The sample sizes are $n_1 = 5$, $n_2 = 4$, $n_3 = 5$, $n_4 = 3$, and $n_5 = 6$; so $N = 5 + 4 + \cdots + 6 = 23$. The treatment sums are $T_{.1} = 73.3$, $T_{.2} = 57.4$, $T_{.3} = 69.2$, $T_{.4} = 39.6$, and $T_{.5} = 78$. The overall sum is $T_{..} = 73.3 + 57.4 + \cdots + 78 = 317.5$. The sums of squares are as follows:

$$\text{SST} = 14.4^2 + 14.8^2 + \cdots + 12.7^2 - \frac{317.5^2}{23} = 11.05,$$

$$\text{SSTR} = \frac{73.3^2}{5} + \frac{57.4^2}{4} + \frac{69.2^2}{5} + \frac{39.6^2}{3} + \frac{78^2}{6} - \frac{317.5^2}{23} = 9.836,$$

$$\text{SSE} = 11.05 - 9.836 = 1.214.$$

We have collected the information into an analysis of variance table in Table 12.4. Since $f = 36.48 > f_{0.99, 4, 18} = 4.58$, the null hypothesis of no treatment effect is rejected. Accordingly, there is reason to believe that some of the average energy consumptions for the five levels of ceiling insulation are different.

TABLE 12.4   ANOVA table for Example 12.1

Source of variation	df	SS	MS	F value
Treatments	4	9.836	2.459	36.48
Error	18	1.214	0.0674	
Total	22	11.05	$f_{0.99, \, 4, \, 18} = 4.58$	

12.4.2   Scheffé's Method for Multiple Comparisons

Recall that the alternative hypothesis in analysis of variance does not specify which means are different. Rather it states that at least one is different, so rejection of the null hypothesis based on the F statistic cannot be used as a basis for accepting a particular alternative. For example, suppose the null hypothesis $H_0: \mu_1 = \mu_2 = \mu_3$ is rejected. It could mean that μ_3 is different, but μ_1 and μ_2 are the same. Or it could mean that all three means are different, and so on. It stands to reason, therefore, that an investigator needs more definitive analyses to explore statistically discernible differences among a number of population means.

Several methods have been proposed for this purpose. Among these are Tukey's studentized range procedure, Duncan's multiple range test, and Scheffé's method — see [5]. We will discuss only Scheffé's method for multiple comparisons because it has relatively few restrictions and is preferred by many when combinations of treatment means are to be compared. The Scheffé method is based on the formulation of a *contrast*, a comparison chosen by the investigator to represent a linear combination of any number of population means. A contrast is a general method of comparison that permits the investigator to determine, based on the sample evidence, whether the given contrast is statistically discernible.

A contrast, denoted by L, is defined to be

$$L = \sum_{j=1}^{k} c_j \mu_j, \tag{12.11}$$

where μ_j is the mean of the jth level and the c_j's are constants such that $\sum_{j=1}^{k} c_j = 0$. For example, $L = \mu_3 - \mu_4$ is a contrast with $c_1 = 1$ and $c_2 = -1$. This contrast is a comparison between μ_3 and μ_4. Another contrast is $L = 3\mu_1 - \mu_2 - \mu_3 - \mu_4$, with $c_1 = 3$, $c_2 = c_3 = c_4 = -1$. Such a contrast is a comparison between μ_1 and μ_2, μ_3, and μ_4. Thus Scheffé's method allows the investigator to choose the comparisons based on items of interest.

An unbiased estimator of L is given by

$$\hat{L} = \sum_{j=1}^{k} c_j \overline{Y}_{\cdot j}, \tag{12.12}$$

whose variance is estimated to be

$$s^2(\hat{L}) = \text{MSE} \sum_{j=1}^{k} \frac{c_j^2}{n_j}. \tag{12.13}$$

Scheffé showed (see [7]) that with probability $1 - \alpha$, all possible contrasts as defined by (12.11) are included in the set of intervals

$$\hat{L} - A s(\hat{L}) \leq L \leq \hat{L} + A s(\hat{L}), \tag{12.14}$$

where

$$A = \sqrt{(k - 1)f_{1-\alpha, k-1, N-k}}$$

and $\hat{L}$ and $s^2(\hat{L})$ are as defined by (12.12) and (12.13), respectively. If for some contrast L an interval as determined from (12.14) is found not to include zero, then the contrast is statistically discernible. In reality, therefore, for each contrast L we are testing the null hypothesis

$$H_0: L = 0.$$

The essence of the set of intervals as defined by (12.14) is that the confidence level of $100(1 - \alpha)$ percent is for *all* intervals. If we were to repeat an experiment many, many times, each time computing confidence intervals for all possible contrasts using (12.14), then in $100(1 - \alpha)$ percent of the repeats, all confidence intervals would be correct. That the confidence is $100(1 - \alpha)$ percent for *all* intervals is distinctly superior to determining, say, a $100(1 - \alpha)$ percent confidence interval for each pair of treatment means in which case the confidence level is only for each individual pair and not for the entire set.

Example 12.2 In Example 12.1, compare μ_4 against μ_5; μ_2, μ_3, and μ_4 against μ_5; μ_1 against μ_2; and μ_3 and μ_4 against μ_5, using Scheffé's method with $\alpha = 0.01$.

Although other comparisons involving various treatment combinations can be made, these comparisons seem reasonable if the objective is to sort the treatments into subgroups within which no discernible difference appears. For example, if there is no discernible difference between the average energy usage for 10 inches and 12 inches of ceiling insulation, it would be economically reasonable to use 10 inches of ceiling insulation rather than 12. The contrasts for the four comparisons are as follows:

$$L_1 = \mu_4 - \mu_5, \qquad L_2 = \mu_2 + \mu_3 + \mu_4 - 3\mu_5,$$

$$L_3 = \mu_1 - \mu_2, \qquad L_4 = 2\mu_5 - \mu_3 - \mu_4.$$

We will illustrate the computation of the confidence interval for L_2. Since $\bar{y}_{.2} = 14.35$, $\bar{y}_{.3} = 13.84$, $\bar{y}_{.4} = 13.2$, and $\bar{y}_{.5} = 13$,

$$\hat{L}_2 = 14.35 + 13.84 + 13.2 - (3)(13) = 2.39.$$

The estimated variance is

$$s^2(\hat{L}_2) = 0.0674 \left[\frac{1^2}{4} + \frac{1^2}{5} + \frac{1^2}{3} + \frac{(-3)^2}{6} \right] = 0.1539,$$

and

$$s(\hat{L}_2) = 0.3923.$$

Since $f_{0.99, 4, 18} = 4.58$, $A = \sqrt{(4)(4.58)} = 4.28$, so the confidence interval for L_2 is

$$2.39 \pm (4.28)(0.3923) = (0.7109, 4.0691).$$

Following the same procedure, we determine that the confidence intervals for the other contrasts are

$$L_1: \quad (-0.5857, 0.9857),$$

$$L_3: \quad (-0.4354, 1.0554),$$

$$L_4: \quad (-2.2572, 0.1772).$$

Notice that of the four confidence intervals for the contrasts of interest, only the one for L_2 does not include the value zero. Since the inclusion of the value zero in these confidence intervals is equivalent to lack of statistical significance in a two-sided test of differences in means, a comparison of the four intervals reveals that there is no discernible difference in the average energy consumption for eight, ten, or twelve inches of ceiling insulation. This conclusion is reached because contrasts L_1 and L_4 are not statistically discernible, but L_2 is. Since L_2 is the same as L_4 except that it contains μ_2 (six inches of insulation), based on the results of this experiment, it would appear that eight inches of ceiling insulation is economically optimal.

It should be noted that if the null hypothesis of equal means is rejected by way of the F statistic, then Scheffé's method will produce at least one contrast that is statistically discernible.

12.4.3   Residual Analysis and Effects of Violating Assumptions

Recall from Section 9.6.3 that, for different sample sizes, the effect of violating the equal-variance assumption when comparing two means can be substantial. Since the same assumption is made when k means are compared, we want to examine ways to detect this and discuss effects on inference when assumptions are violated.

A fairly simple but extremely useful way of detecting departures from the assumed model is based on an analysis of residuals. A *residual* is an estimate of the random error ε_{ij}. Since

$$\varepsilon_{ij} = Y_{ij} - \mu_j,$$

the corresponding residual, denoted by e_{ij}, is defined as

$$e_{ij} = y_{ij} - \bar{y}_{\cdot j}, \quad j = 1, 2, \ldots, k, \quad i = 1, 2, \ldots, n_j.$$

The residuals are not estimates in the classical sense of parameter estimation but are estimates of values of the unobservable random variables ε_{ij} based on the estimates $\bar{y}_{\cdot j}$ for the k population means.

If the assumption that the random errors have the same variances for all k levels is valid, then a plot of the residuals of each treatment should reveal no appreciable difference in the scatter of the residuals around zero. If the scatter

TABLE 12.5 Standardized residuals for Example 12.1

4	6	8	10	12
-1.00	0.58	-0.15	-0.77	0.39
0.54	-0.96	1.00	0.77	-0.77
2.08	0.96	-0.54	0	-0.39
-1.39	-0.58	-0.92		0.77
-0.23		0.62		1.16
				-1.16

is noticeably different for some treatments, then the variances may not be the same for all treatments. To normalize the scale for the magnitudes of the residuals, it is preferable to use the *standardized residuals* $e_{ij}/\sqrt{\text{MSE}}$. Then, since the assumption is made that the random errors are normally distributed, a standardized residual should rarely be outside the ± 3 range.

We will illustrate residual analysis with the data from Example 12.1. Since $\bar{y}_{.1} = 14.66$ and $\sqrt{\text{MSE}} = 0.2596$, the residuals for the first treatment are $14.4 - 14.66 = -0.26$, $14.8 - 14.66 = 0.14$, $15.2 - 14.66 = 0.54$, $14.3 - 14.66 = -0.36$, and $14.6 - 14.66 = -0.06$, and the corresponding standardized residuals are -1.00, 0.54, 2.08, -1.39, and -0.23. Following this procedure, we can determine all standardized residuals as in Table 12.5.

Figure 12.1 depicts the standardized residuals for each treatment. Other than that caused by one residual of the first treatment, no noticeable discrepancy appears in the scatter among the five treatments. Accordingly, the assumption that the variances for all five treatments are the same appears to be reasonable in this case. Formal procedures are also available for checking the assumption of equality among k variances. Two of the most widely used are Bartlett's test and Hartley's test. The reader is directed to [5] for details.

As we have commented in Chapter 9, the effect on inferences about means when the random errors are not normally distributed is minor so long as the departure from normality is not severe. Thus the F statistic in the analysis of variance procedure is largely robust to departures from normality. If the variances for all treatments are not equal, there is some upward adjustment in the size of the critical region for the F statistic in the fixed effects case; but as we have noted in Chapter 9, this effect can be minimized by using equal sample sizes for each treatment. In other words, the F statistic in the analysis of variance is also largely robust to unequal variances, so long as the treatment sample sizes are the same. Unfortunately, this result does not extend to the random effects case in which violation of the equal-variance assumption will usually have a considerable effect on inferences, even for equal sample sizes.

The most crucial assumption in the development of the analysis of variance procedure is that the random errors are independent. If the errors are interdependent, the actual size of the critical region may be substantially larger (five times or more) than the size as dictated by the selected probability of type I error. For a review of the consequences of violating assumptions in the analysis of variance, the reader is directed to [3].

FIGURE 12.1 Plot of the standardized residuals for the five treatments of Example 12.1

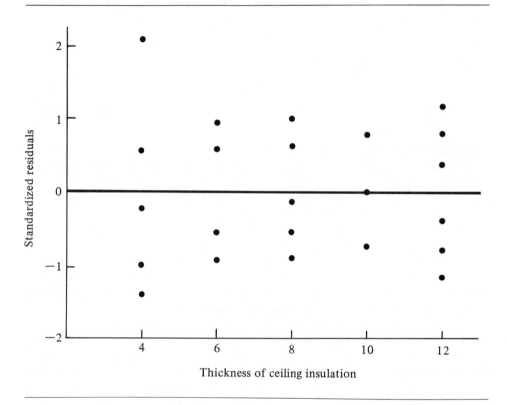

12.4.4   The Random Effects Case

We introduce the random effects case with the following brief discussion. For a thorough discussion of this case, [6] is suggested. For the random effects model, it is assumed that the levels used in the experiment were selected at random from a population of possible levels. It is further assumed that $\tau_j \sim N(0, \sigma_\tau^2)$, where σ_τ^2 is the variance of the random treatments τ_j. The decomposition of the total sum of squares and the analysis of variance is the same as in the fixed effects case for a single-factor experiment, but the expected value of the treatment mean square is now different. Given equal sample sizes n for all levels, it can be shown that

$$E(\text{MSE}) = \sigma^2,$$

and   (12.15)

$$E(\text{MSTR}) = \sigma^2 + n\sigma_\tau^2.$$

The appropriate rejection region is the same as before since a large ratio of MSTR to MSE would suggest that the null hypothesis H_0: $\sigma_\tau^2 = 0$ ought to be rejected.

TABLE 12.6 Content weights in a filling process

	Machine		
1	*2*	*3*	*4*
1.24	1.20	1.19	1.18
1.22	1.20	1.20	1.18
1.22	1.21	1.19	1.19
1.23	1.22	1.20	1.18
1.23	1.20	1.21	1.20

TABLE 12.7 ANOVA table for Example 12.3

Source of variation	df	SS	MS	*F value*
Treatments	3	0.004695	0.001565	20.87
Error	16	0.0012	0.000075	
Total	19	0.005895	$f_{0.95, \, 3, \, 16} = 3.24$	

Example 12.3 A canning plant uses a large number of machines for the filling process. Each machine is supposed to pour a specified weight of product into each container. The plant manager suspects too much variation in weight of the product poured among the machines. To check her suspicion, she selects four machines at random and weighs the contents of five randomly selected containers filled by each of the four machines. The results are given in Table 12.6. How much of the variance in the weights is attributed to differences among the machines?

First, let us perform an analysis of variance to determine whether $H_0: \sigma_\tau^2 = 0$ can be rejected. The machine totals are $T_{.1} = 6.14$, $T_{.2} = 6.03$, $T_{.3} = 5.99$, and $T_{.4} = 5.93$. The overall total is $T_{..} = 24.09$, and all sample sizes are $n = 5$. Then

$$\text{SST} = 1.24^2 + 1.22^2 + \cdots + 1.20^2 - \frac{24.09^2}{20} = 0.005895,$$

$$\text{SSTR} = \frac{6.14^2 + 6.03^2 + 5.99^2 + 5.93^2}{5} - \frac{24.09^2}{20} = 0.004695,$$

$$\text{SSE} = 0.005895 - 0.004695 = 0.0012.$$

The ANOVA table is given in Table 12.7. Since $f = 20.87 > f_{0.95, \, 3, \, 16} = 3.24$, the null hypothesis of no variation due to machines is rejected.

To estimate the variance in the weights and how much of it is attributed to differences among the machines, recall that for a random effects model

$$Var(Y_{ij}) = \sigma^2 + \sigma_\tau^2.$$

From (12.15), an estimate of σ^2 is MSE = 0.000075, and an estimate of $\sigma^2 + 5\sigma_\tau^2$ is MSTR = 0.001565. In other words,

$$0.000075 + 5s_\tau^2 = 0.001565$$

$$s_\tau^2 = \frac{0.001565 - 0.000075}{5}$$

$$= 0.000298$$

is an estimate of σ_τ^2. Then an estimate of the variance in the weight is

$$s^2(Y_{ij}) = 0.000075 + 0.000298$$

$$= 0.000373,$$

of which $0.000298/0.000373$, or 79.89%, stems from differences among machines.

12.5   Analysis of Single-Factor Experiments in a Randomized Complete Block Design

Recall that when the experimental units are not homogeneous, a potentially significant source of variation is introduced that usually can affect the inference about the factor of interest. In such cases it becomes necessary to use a randomized block design to remove the external source of variability, thereby increasing the sensitivity for detecting differences among the treatments of interest.

Example 12.4   The Environmental Protection Agency (EPA) annually rates every automobile available for purchase in the United States for fuel efficiency. It is well known, however, that the EPA ratings are based primarily on laboratory testing and thus tend to overestimate an automobile's actual fuel efficiency. An independent testing organization wants to determine whether a statistically discernible difference exists in the average fuel efficiency under actual road conditions for five different subcompacts that have the same EPA rating. The testing firm has access to a 400-mile course that includes both city and highway driving. Discuss the design issues for such an experiment.

It is clear that the treatments are the five automobiles, and the measurable response is the miles per gallon achieved over the 400-mile course. But what is the experimental unit? It has to be the person driving an automobile over the 400-mile course, but the testing organization is not likely to use only one driver for the entire experiment. Suppose four drivers are chosen for the experiment. Although the testing organization will adequately brief the drivers as to the purpose of the experiment, another source of possible variation has now been introduced. No matter how similar the drivers tend to be, there is still the potential of a driver effect. We can account for the driver effect by creating four blocks, one for each driver, so that the treatments within each block (the five automobiles) are applied to homogeneous experimental units (same driver). Now the question is how to go about assigning automobiles to drivers. The randomized design specifies that the assignment of treatments to experimental units within each block must be done at random. Thus, to assign the order in which the five automobiles will be driven by each driver, we devise a simple random process of selection. For example, the assignment might be made as in Table 12.8, which constitutes a randomized complete block design.

Let us now analyze a single-factor experiment in a randomized complete block design. It will be necessary to generalize first, but we will return to the fuel efficiency example to illustrate the computational steps. The observations of the experiment may be arranged in an array, as in Table 12.9.

Assuming k treatments and n blocks, the mathematical model for a single-factor randomized complete block design is

$$Y_{ij} = \mu + \beta_i + \tau_j + \varepsilon_{ij} \qquad i = 1, 2, ..., n, \qquad (12.16)$$

$$j = 1, 2, ..., k,$$

where Y_{ij} is the observation of the response in the ith block and under the jth treatment, μ is an overall mean, β_i is the effect on the response due to the ith block, τ_j is the effect due to the jth treatment, and ε_{ij} is the random error. As before, the errors are assumed to be independent random variables such that $\varepsilon_{ij} \sim N(0, \sigma^2)$ for all i and j. If both treatments and blocks are fixed effects, then the β_i's and τ_j's are fixed parameters representing deviations of block and treatment means from the overall mean, respectively. In other words,

$$\beta_i = \mu_{i\cdot} - \mu, \qquad i = 1, 2, ..., n, \qquad (12.17)$$

$$\tau_j = \mu_{\cdot j} - \mu, \qquad j = 1, 2, ..., k,$$

where $\mu_{i\cdot}$ and $\mu_{\cdot j}$ are population means for the ith block and the jth treatment, respectively.

As in the completely randomized design, we assume that the population variances for all treatments are the same. We must also assume that the treatment

TABLE 12.8 Randomized complete block design for Example 12.4

		Automobile				
	1	A_1	A_3	A_5	A_4	A_2
Driver	2	A_5	A_3	A_4	A_2	A_1
	3	A_4	A_1	A_5	A_3	A_2
	4	A_2	A_5	A_4	A_1	A_3

TABLE 12.9 Typical arrangement of observations for a single-factor randomized complete block design

		Treatment					
		1	2	$\cdots$	j	$\cdots$	k
	1	Y_{11}	Y_{12}	$\cdots$	Y_{1j}	$\cdots$	Y_{1k}
	2	Y_{21}	Y_{22}	$\cdots$	Y_{2j}	$\cdots$	Y_{2k}
	$\vdots$	$\vdots$	$\vdots$		$\vdots$		$\vdots$
Block	i	Y_{i1}	Y_{i2}	$\cdots$	Y_{ij}	$\cdots$	Y_{ik}
	$\vdots$	$\vdots$	$\vdots$		$\vdots$		$\vdots$
	n	Y_{n1}	Y_{n2}	$\cdots$	Y_{nj}	$\cdots$	Y_{nk}

effect on the response is the same for all blocks. In other words, the same conclusion about the treatment effect can be drawn for all blocks. When this occurs, treatments and blocks are said to be *noninteracting,* and their individual effects on the response are additive. The notion of *interaction* between two factors will be examined in the next section.

For a single-factor randomized complete block design, the primary purpose is to determine whether treatment differences are statistically discernible. That is, for the fixed effects case, we wish to test the null hypothesis

$$H_0: \tau_j = 0, \quad j = 1, 2, ..., k.$$

The reader may wonder about the block effect. By and large we really are not interested in whether the block effect is statistically discernible. All we want to do is isolate the block effect and remove it from the experimental error so as to increase the efficiency of detecting real differences among treatments, if they exist.

For the analysis of variance procedure, we may write the model given by (12.16) as

$$\varepsilon_{ij} = Y_{ij} - \mu - \beta_i - \tau_j. \tag{12.18}$$

Substituting (12.17) for β_i and τ_j in (12.18), we have

$$\varepsilon_{ij} = Y_{ij} - \mu - \mu_{i.} + \mu - \mu_{.j} + \mu. \tag{12.19}$$

Now substituting (12.17) for β_i and τ_j and (12.19) for ε_{ij} in (12.16) yields the desired identity

$$Y_{ij} - \mu = (\mu_{i.} - \mu) + (\mu_{.j} - \mu) + (Y_{ij} - \mu_{i.} - \mu_{.j} + \mu). \tag{12.20}$$

In other words, the deviation of an observation from the overall average is made up of three components — deviation due to blocks, deviation due to treatments, and deviation due to random error.

For the observations as arranged in Table 12.9, define the following statistics:

$$T_{i.} = \sum_{j=1}^{k} Y_{ij}, \quad \overline{Y}_{i.} = T_{i.}/k, \quad i = 1, 2, ..., n$$

$$T_{.j} = \sum_{i=1}^{n} Y_{ij}, \quad \overline{Y}_{.j} = T_{.j}/n, \quad j = 1, 2, ..., k$$

$$T_{..} = \sum_{i=1}^{n} \sum_{j=1}^{k} Y_{ij}, \quad \overline{Y}_{..} = T_{..}/nk.$$

Then the sample identity corresponding to (12.20) is

$$Y_{ij} - \overline{Y}_{..} = (\overline{Y}_{i.} - \overline{Y}_{..}) + (\overline{Y}_{.j} - \overline{Y}_{..}) + (Y_{ij} - \overline{Y}_{i.} - \overline{Y}_{.j} + \overline{Y}_{..}).$$

Squaring both sides and summing over i and j yields the relation

$$\sum_{i=1}^{n} \sum_{j=1}^{k} (Y_{ij} - \overline{Y}_{..})^2 = \sum_{i=1}^{n} \sum_{j=1}^{k} (\overline{Y}_{i.} - \overline{Y}_{..})^2 + \sum_{i=1}^{n} \sum_{j=1}^{k} (\overline{Y}_{.j} - \overline{Y}_{..})^2$$

$$+ \sum_{i=1}^{n} \sum_{j=1}^{k} (Y_{ij} - \overline{Y}_{i.} - \overline{Y}_{.j} + \overline{Y}_{..})^2,$$

where it can be shown that the three cross-product terms have reduced to zero. This equation is the fundamental equation for the analysis of variance, and it states that the total sum of squares (SST) is broken down into the block sum of squares (SSB), the treatment sum of squares (SSTR), and the error sum of squares (SSE).

Due to the restriction $\sum_{i=1}^{n} \sum_{j=1}^{k} (Y_{ij} - \overline{Y}_{..}) = 0$, the degrees of freedom for SST will be $nk - 1$. Similarly, because of the constraints $\sum_{i=1}^{n} (\overline{Y}_{i.} - \overline{Y}_{..}) = 0$ and $\sum_{j=1}^{k} (\overline{Y}_{.j} - \overline{Y}_{..}) = 0$, the degrees of freedom for SSB and SSTR will be $n - 1$ and $k - 1$, respectively. It follows that

$$df(SSE) = df(SST) - df(SSB) - df(SSTR)$$

$$= nk - 1 - (n - 1) - (k - 1)$$

$$= (n - 1)(k - 1).$$

It can be shown that under the assumptions of the model and the hypothesis $H_0: \tau_j = 0$, $SSTR/\sigma^2$ and SSE/σ^2 are two independent chi-square random variables with $k - 1$ and $(n - 1)(k - 1)$ degrees of freedom, respectively. It can also be shown that the expected values of the treatment and error mean squares are

$$E(MSE) = \sigma^2$$

and

$$E(MSTR) = \sigma^2 + \frac{n \sum_{j=1}^{k} \tau_j^2}{k - 1}.$$

Then, based on a previous argument, the appropriate test statistic is the ratio of the treatment and error mean squares, which is F distributed with $k - 1$ and $(n - 1)(k - 1)$ degrees of freedom. As before, an upper tail critical region of size α is suggested since a large ratio tends to imply that not all treatment means are the same. The analysis of variance is as given in Table 12.10.

We should note that a test for the block effect is possible by forming the ratio of MSB to MSE and comparing it to the upper tail critical region of an F distribution with $n - 1$ and $(n - 1)(k - 1)$ degrees of freedom. It really should not be an integral part of the analysis though. After all, one chooses a randomized complete block for a single-factor experiment to remove the potential effect of the extraneous source of variation. Whether such an effect is statistically discernible should not be of great concern.

TABLE 12.10   Analysis of variance table for a single-factor randomized complete block experiment

Source of variation	df	SS	MS	F statistic
Blocks	$n - 1$	$\Sigma\Sigma(\overline{Y}_{i\cdot} - \overline{Y}_{\cdot\cdot})^2$		
Treatments	$k - 1$	$\Sigma\Sigma(\overline{Y}_{\cdot j} - \overline{Y}_{\cdot\cdot})^2$	$\text{MSTR} = \text{SSTR}/(k - 1)$	$F = \dfrac{\text{MSTR}}{\text{MSE}}$
Error	$(n - 1)(k - 1)$	$\Sigma\Sigma(Y_{ij} - \overline{Y}_{i\cdot} - \overline{Y}_{\cdot j} + \overline{Y}_{\cdot\cdot})^2$	$\text{MSE} = \text{SSE}/(n - 1)(k - 1)$	
Total	$nk - 1$	$\Sigma\Sigma(Y_{ij} - \overline{Y}_{\cdot\cdot})^2$		

For hand computation it is preferable to use the following algebraically equivalent formulas to determine sums of squares.

$$\text{SST} = \sum_{i=1}^{n}\sum_{j=1}^{k} y_{ij}^2 - \frac{T_{\cdot\cdot}^2}{nk}$$

$$\text{SSB} = \frac{1}{k}\sum_{i=1}^{n} T_{i\cdot}^2 - \frac{T_{\cdot\cdot}^2}{nk}$$

$$\text{SSTR} = \frac{1}{n}\sum_{j=1}^{k} T_{\cdot j}^2 - \frac{T_{\cdot\cdot}^2}{nk}$$

$$\text{SSE} = \text{SST} - \text{SSB} - \text{SSTR}.$$

To illustrate the computational steps, suppose the results of the experiment described in Example 12.4 are as given in Table 12.11 (measurements are in miles per gallon over the 400-mile course). To test the null hypothesis

$$H_0: \tau_j = 0, \quad j = 1, 2, \ldots, 5,$$

the sums of squares are

$$\text{SST} = 33.6^2 + 36.9^2 + \cdots + 32.8^2 - \frac{672.4^2}{20} = 102.212,$$

$$\text{SSB} = \frac{156.1^2 + \cdots + 172.4^2}{5} - \frac{672.4^2}{20} = 41.676,$$

$$\text{SSTR} = \frac{139.5^2 + \cdots + 133.3^2}{4} - \frac{672.4^2}{20} = 38.092,$$

$$\text{SSE} = 102.212 - 41.676 - 38.092 = 22.444.$$

The ANOVA table is Table 12.12. Since $f = 5.09 > f_{0.95, 4, 12} = 3.26$, the null hypothesis of no treatment effect is rejected. There is reason to believe that the average fuel efficiencies of some of these automobiles are not the same.

The identification and removal of the effect of blocks from the total variation permits multiple comparisons to be made for the treatments, as discussed in

TABLE 12.11 Experimental data for Example 12.4

Driver	Automobile A_1	A_2	A_3	A_4	A_5	Totals
1	33.6	32.8	31.9	27.2	30.6	$T_{1.} = 156.1$
2	36.9	36.1	32.1	34.4	35.3	$T_{2.} = 174.8$
3	34.2	35.3	33.7	31.3	34.6	$T_{3.} = 169.1$
4	34.8	37.1	34.8	32.9	32.8	$T_{4.} = 172.4$

Totals $T_{.1} = 139.5$ $T_{.2} = 141.3$ $T_{.3} = 132.5$ $T_{.4} = 125.8$ $T_{.5} = 133.3$ $T_{..} = 672.4$

TABLE 12.12 ANOVA table for Example 12.4

Source of variation	df	SS	MS	F value
Blocks	3	41.676		
Treatments	4	38.092	9.523	5.09
Error	12	22.444	1.870	
Total	19	102.212	$f_{0.95, 4, 12} = 3.26$	

Section 12.4.2. Any number of contrasts may be defined and tested to determine whether they are statistically discernible by following the procedure outlined there. The only exception is that the quantity denoted by A in (12.14) is now given by

$$A = \sqrt{(k - 1)f_{1-\alpha,\ k-1,\ (n-1)(k-1)}}.$$

At times, the blocks are not fixed effects. That is, the blocks chosen for the experiment are selected at random from a population of possible blocks. If the treatments are fixed effects, the only difference from the previous case is in the assumption of β_i; i.e., $\beta_i \sim N(0, \sigma_\beta^2)$; but the analysis remains precisely the same, even for multiple comparisons for the treatments.

Aside from the assumption of independence, we have made two key assumptions for a randomized block design: that the variances for each treatment are the same, and that blocks and treatments do not interact. The presence of interaction between blocks and treatments implies that the treatment effect cannot be assessed over all blocks but must be described individually for each block. If indeed block and treatment effects are additive, the F statistic is relatively insensitive to the violation of the equal variance assumption. For equal variances, if there is interaction between blocks and treatments, the F statistic is negatively biased. That is, if the null hypothesis of no treatment difference is rejected, then we can be confident that treatment differences exist. But if the null hypothesis is not rejected, it may be due either to a negative bias (the presence of interaction) or to the absence of treatment differences. A procedure developed by Tukey and described in [4] can be used to test for interaction between blocks and treatments.

If both the equal variance and the additivity assumptions are violated, the F statistic for treatment differences is positively biased. In other words, if the null hypothesis of no treatment differences is rejected, it does not necessarily mean that treatment differences are statistically discernible. When there is sufficient concern about these assumptions, one should use a *conservative F test* developed by Geisser and Greenhouse (see [4]). The computational steps for the conservative F test are the same as in the conventional method we have described, except that the degrees of freedom for the treatment and error terms are now 1 and $n - 1$ instead of $k - 1$ and $(n - 1)(k - 1)$, respectively. If the null hypothesis is rejected by both conservative and conventional F tests, we can be confident that treatment differences are discernible. If both tests do not reject H_0, then we may proceed as if no treatment differences exist.

12.6 Factorial Experiments

Up to now we have concentrated on analyzing the effect of a single factor on the response variable. But in many practical situations we need to investigate simultaneously the effects of several factors on a response. A very efficient way to do this is to use a factorial experiment in which all levels of one factor are combined with all levels of every other factor to form the treatments. For example, in a two-factor factorial experiment in which one factor has three levels and the other has two, there will be $3 \times 2 = 6$ treatments. In other words, the given response will be observed under six different treatments.

With factorial experiments it is not only possible to evaluate the individual effects of the factors on the response, but also to determine the effect due to their interactions. The effect of a factor on a given response is simply the change in the response caused by a change in the level of the factor. But if the effect on the response of one factor is different at different levels of another factor, then the two factors are said to interact. The presence of interaction implies that the effect of the factors on the response is synergistic, and an additive model cannot be assumed.

To illustrate the interaction between two factors, consider the following. A large manufacturer of electronic components uses two ovens and two temperature settings in life testing a particular component. Four such components are selected from the same batch and are life tested according to the four combinations of ovens and temperature settings. The lifetimes of the components in hours are as follows:

	O_1	O_2
T_1	6.29	5.95
T_2	5.80	6.32

The treatments are the four possible combinations of oven and temperature setting: O_1T_1, O_1T_2, O_2T_1, and O_2T_2. The difference in the lifetimes for the treatments O_1T_2 and O_1T_1 represents an estimate of the effect on the lifetime of the components in the first oven from a change in the temperature setting. This estimate is seen to be $5.80 - 6.29 = -0.49$. The difference in the lifetimes for the treatments O_2T_2 and O_2T_1 is also an estimate of the temperature effect on the lifetime but now in the second oven. This difference is $6.32 - 5.95 = 0.37$. Since these two estimates are substantially different, the effect of temperature on the lifetime depends in which oven the component is placed. Thus, there is an interaction between oven and temperature setting. The same occurrence is also noted by estimating the oven effect at $T_1(5.95 - 6.29 = -0.34)$ and $T_2(6.32 - 5.80 = 0.52)$. These results are illustrated graphically in Figure 12.2 where the y axis represents the observations of the response, the x axis represents the levels of one factor, and plotted points represent each level of the other factor. If there were little interaction between oven and temperature setting, the lines on the graph would be nearly parallel.

The determination of whether individual effects or interactions are statistically discernible can be made only by statistical inference, not by using the preceding graphical analysis. We will examine a nonadditive model for a two-factor factorial experiment in a completely randomized design. Factorial experiments with more than two factors can be analyzed by extending the procedure we are about to examine.

In a factorial experiment involving two factors A and B with a and b levels, respectively, the number of treatments is $a \times b$. If we cannot assume an additive model (no interaction), a test to determine whether an interaction effect is statistically discernible is possible only if more than one observation of the response is taken for each treatment. This is because an estimate of the random error component cannot be determined unless the response is observed more than once for each treatment. That is, the assessment of random error variation is based on differences

FIGURE 12.2 Interacting effects

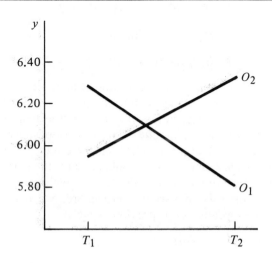

in the response observed under the same treatment. It is worthwhile to note that for a completely randomized design, the treatments must be applied to homogeneous experimental units no matter how many times the process is repeated.

Assuming n applications of the ab treatments, the nonadditive mathematical model for a two-factor factorial is

$$Y_{ijk} = \mu + \alpha_i + \beta_j + (\alpha\beta)_{ij} + \varepsilon_{ijk} \qquad i = 1, 2, \ldots, a, \qquad (12.21)$$

$$j = 1, 2, \ldots, b,$$

$$k = 1, 2, \ldots, n,$$

where Y_{ijk} is the kth observation of the response for the (i, j) treatment, μ is the overall mean, α_i is the main effect due to the ith level of A, β_j is the main effect due to the jth level of B, $(\alpha\beta)_{ij}$ is the interaction effect for the ith level of A and jth level of B, and ε_{ijk} is the kth random error in the (i, j) treatment. As before, we assume that the population variances for each of the ab treatments are equal, and that the random errors are independent normally distributed random variables with zero means and common variance σ^2.

If the factors A and B are assumed to be fixed effects, then α_i, β_j, and $(\alpha\beta)_{ij}$ are fixed parameters such that

$$\sum_{i=1}^{a} \alpha_i = \sum_{j=1}^{b} \beta_j = 0$$

and

$$\sum_{i=1}^{a} (\alpha\beta)_{ij} = \sum_{j=1}^{b} (\alpha\beta)_{ij} = 0.$$

The following hypotheses are of interest:

1. $H_0 : (\alpha\beta)_{ij} = 0$ for all i and j,

2. $H_0 : \alpha_i = 0$ for all i,

3. $H_0 : \beta_j = 0$ for all j.

The last two hypotheses involve the *main* (individual) effects of factors A and B, and the first hypothesis pertains to the possible interaction between A and B. If a strong interaction exists between A and B, the tests for a main effect due to A or B may not be meaningful. This is true because two factors can interact in such a way (opposite direction) that the effect balances out over one or both factors. Such a balancing process would preclude the detection of significant main effects based on a comparison of the factor level means.

To develop the analysis of variance procedure, we may write the model (12.21) in terms of deviations, as in previous cases.

$$Y_{ijk} - \mu = (\mu_{i..} - \mu) + (\mu_{.j.} - \mu)$$

$$+ (\mu_{ij.} - \mu_{i..} - \mu_{.j.} + \mu) + (Y_{ijk} - \mu_{ij.}), \qquad (12.22)$$

TABLE 12.13 Typical arrangement of observations for a two-factor factorial design with n observations per treatment

		A	
	Level 1	Level i	Level a
B Level 1	$Y_{111} \cdots Y_{11k} \cdots Y_{11n}$ $\cdots$	$Y_{i11} \cdots Y_{i1k} \cdots Y_{i1n}$ $\cdots$	$Y_{a11} \cdots Y_{a1k} \cdots Y_{a1n}$
Level j	$Y_{1j1} \cdots Y_{1jk} \cdots Y_{1jn}$ $\cdots$	$Y_{ij1} \cdots Y_{ijk} \cdots Y_{ijn}$ $\cdots$	$Y_{aj1} \cdots Y_{ajk} \cdots Y_{ajn}$
Level b	$Y_{1b1} \cdots Y_{1bk} \cdots Y_{1bn}$ $\cdots$	$Y_{ib1} \cdots Y_{ibk} \cdots Y_{ibn}$ $\cdots$	$Y_{ab1} \cdots Y_{abk} \cdots Y_{abn}$

where $\mu_{i\cdot\cdot}$ is the true mean of the ith level of A, $\mu_{\cdot j\cdot}$ is the true mean of the jth level of B, and $\mu_{ij\cdot}$ is the true mean of the (i, j) treatment. Thus the identity given by (12.22) states that the deviation of an observation from the overall average is made up of four components: deviation due to the main effect of A, deviation due to the main effect of B, deviation due to the interaction effect of A and B, and deviation due to random error.

The observations of a two-factor factorial in a completely randomized experiment may be arranged as in Table 12.13. From this we define the following statistics:

$$T_{i\cdot\cdot} = \sum_{j=1}^{b} \sum_{k=1}^{n} Y_{ijk}, \qquad T_{\cdot j\cdot} = \sum_{i=1}^{a} \sum_{k=1}^{n} Y_{ijk}, \qquad T_{\cdot\cdot k} = \sum_{i=1}^{a} \sum_{j=1}^{b} Y_{ijk},$$

$$\overline{Y}_{i\cdot\cdot} = T_{i\cdot\cdot}/nb, \qquad \overline{Y}_{\cdot j\cdot} = T_{\cdot j\cdot}/na, \qquad \overline{Y}_{\cdot\cdot k} = T_{\cdot\cdot k}/ab,$$

$$T_{ij\cdot} = \sum_{k=1}^{n} Y_{ijk}, \qquad \overline{Y}_{ij\cdot} = T_{ij\cdot}/n,$$

$$T_{\cdots} = \sum_{i=1}^{a} \sum_{j=1}^{b} \sum_{k=1}^{n} Y_{ijk}, \qquad \overline{Y}_{\cdots} = T_{\cdots}/nab.$$

Notice that $T_{i\cdot\cdot}$ ($T_{\cdot j\cdot}$) is the sum of all observations in the ith (jth) level of A (B), and $T_{\cdot\cdot k}$ is the sum of all observations in the kth replication. Similarly, $T_{ij\cdot}$ is the sum of all observations in the (i, j) treatment. Corresponding definitions for the sample means should be apparent.

Replacing the parameters in (12.22) with their corresponding estimators, we have

$$(Y_{ijk} - \overline{Y}_{\cdots}) = (\overline{Y}_{i\cdot\cdot} - \overline{Y}_{\cdots}) + (\overline{Y}_{\cdot j\cdot} - \overline{Y}_{\cdots})$$

$$+ (\overline{Y}_{ij\cdot} - \overline{Y}_{i\cdot\cdot} - \overline{Y}_{\cdot j\cdot} + \overline{Y}_{\cdots}) + (Y_{ijk} - \overline{Y}_{ij\cdot}).$$

If the preceding sample identity is squared and then summed over i, j, and k, all terms involving cross-products reduce to zero, and the result would be

$$\sum_i \sum_j \sum_k (Y_{ijk} - \overline{Y}_{...})^2 = nb \sum_i (\overline{Y}_{i..} - \overline{Y}_{...})^2 + na \sum_j (\overline{Y}_{.j.} - \overline{Y}_{...})^2$$

$$+ n \sum_i \sum_j (\overline{Y}_{ij.} - \overline{Y}_{i..} - \overline{Y}_{.j.} + \overline{Y}_{...})^2 + \sum_i \sum_j \sum_k (Y_{ijk} - \overline{Y}_{ij.})^2. \quad (12.23)$$

In other words, the total sum of squares is broken down into the sum of squares due to factor A (SSA), the sum of squares due to B (SSB), the sum of squares due to the interaction of A and B (SSAB), and the error sum of squares (SSE).

We may also write the model (12.21) in terms of the deviation due to treatments and the deviation due to random error. That is,

$$(Y_{ijk} - \mu) = (\mu_{ij} - \mu) + (Y_{ijk} - \mu_{ij}). \quad (12.24)$$

In this form, the deviation due to treatments encompasses the effects due to A, B, and the interaction AB. Substituting in (12.24) the corresponding statistics, we have

$$(Y_{ijk} - \overline{Y}_{...}) = (\overline{Y}_{ij.} - \overline{Y}_{...}) + (Y_{ijk} - \overline{Y}_{ij.}),$$

which, when squared and summed over i, j, and k, yields

$$\sum_i \sum_j \sum_k (Y_{ijk} - \overline{Y}_{...})^2 = n \sum_i \sum_j (\overline{Y}_{ij.} - \overline{Y}_{...})^2 + \sum_i \sum_j \sum_k (Y_{ijk} - \overline{Y}_{ij.})^2,$$

or

$$\text{SST} = \text{SSTR} + \text{SSE}. \quad (12.25)$$

Then it follows from (12.23) that

$$\text{SSTR} = \text{SSA} + \text{SSB} + \text{SSAB}. \quad (12.26)$$

It can be shown that, based on (12.23), the decomposition of the degrees of freedom is as follows:

$$\text{df(SST)} = \text{df(SSA)} + \text{df(SSB)} + \text{df(SSAB)} + \text{df(SSE)},$$

or

$$(nab - 1) = (a - 1) + (b - 1) + (a - 1)(b - 1) + ab(n - 1).$$

For the assumptions of the model and the hypotheses of interest, SSA/σ^2, SSB/σ^2, SSAB/σ^2, and SSE/σ^2 are independent chi-square random variables with $(a - 1)$, $(b - 1)$, $(a - 1)(b - 1)$, and $ab(n - 1)$ degrees of freedom, respectively. Accordingly, the test statistics for the main and interaction effects are the ratios of the corresponding mean squares to the error mean square, and are F distributed. As before, an upper tail critical region of size α is appropriate in each case. The preceding result can be seen to hold by examining the expected values of the mean squares. For the fixed effects case, the expected mean squares are as follows:

$$E(\text{MSE}) = \sigma^2,$$

$$E(\text{MSA}) = \sigma^2 + nb \frac{\sum \alpha_i^2}{a - 1},$$

$$E(\text{MSB}) = \sigma^2 + na \frac{\sum \beta_j^2}{b - 1},$$

$$E(\text{MSAB}) = \sigma^2 + n \frac{\sum \sum (\alpha\beta)_{ij}^2}{(a - 1)(b - 1)}.$$

If no interaction exists between A and B — that is, if $(\alpha\beta)_{ij} = 0$ for all i and j — then MSAB and MSE have the same expectation, and the effects are additive. But if the ratio MSAB/MSE is sufficiently large, it would suggest a statistically discernible interaction between A and B, and the null hypothesis should therefore be rejected. Similarly, if $\alpha_i = 0$ for all i, MSA and MSE have identical expectations, and there is no main effect due to A. But a large ratio of MSA to MSE tends to imply that the main effect due to A is statistically discernible. The same argument holds for the main effect of B.

The analysis of variance for a two-factor factorial design is summarized in Table 12.14. Although we have provided computational formulas in the table for each source of variation, the usual practice for hand computation is to compute SST from the formula in Table 12.14 and SSTR from the formula

$$\text{SSTR} = \frac{1}{n} \sum_i \sum_j T_{ij\cdot}^2 - \frac{T_{\cdots}^2}{nab}.$$

Then we can determine SSE using (12.25). In turn, we compute SSA and SSB using the formulas in Table 12.14, and determine SSAB based on (12.26).

Example 12.5 An investigation was carried out to determine whether appreciable differences can be found in average starting salaries for accounting graduates

TABLE 12.14 ANOVA table for a two-factor factorial completely randomized experiment

Source of variation	df	SS	MS	*F statistic*
Factor A	$a - 1$	$\frac{1}{nb} \sum_i T_{i\cdots}^2 - \frac{T_{\cdots}^2}{nab}$	SSA/$(a - 1)$	MSA/MSE
Factor B	$b - 1$	$\frac{1}{na} \sum_j T_{\cdot j\cdot}^2 - \frac{T_{\cdots}^2}{nab}$	SSB/$(b - 1)$	MSB/MSE
Interaction AB	$(a - 1)(b - 1)$	$\frac{1}{n} \sum_i \sum_j T_{ij\cdot}^2 - \frac{1}{nb} \sum_i T_{i\cdots}^2 - \frac{1}{na} \sum_j T_{\cdot j\cdot}^2 + \frac{T_{\cdots}^2}{nab}$	SSAB/$(a - 1)(b - 1)$	MSAB/MSE
Error	$ab(n - 1)$	$\sum_i \sum_j \sum_k Y_{ijk}^2 - \frac{1}{n} \sum_i \sum_j T_{ij\cdot}^2$	SSE/$ab(n - 1)$	
Total	$nab - 1$	$\sum_i \sum_j \sum_k Y_{ijk}^2 - \frac{T_{\cdots}^2}{nab}$		

TABLE 12.15   Starting salaries for accounting graduates (thousands of dollars)

	Northeast	Midwest	West	Totals
Females	15.2	14.9	16.2	
	16.8	16.2	15.9	
	15.5	15.6	16.8	
	14.9	15.3	15.8	
	$T_{11\cdot} = 62.4$	$T_{21\cdot} = 62.0$	$T_{31\cdot} = 64.7$	$T_{\cdot1\cdot} = 189.1$
Males	18.1	17.8	18.4	
	16.3	18.2	16.8	
	17.2	18.1	17.5	
	17.9	17.6	18.7	
	$T_{12\cdot} = 69.5$	$T_{22\cdot} = 71.7$	$T_{32\cdot} = 71.4$	$T_{\cdot2\cdot} = 212.6$
Totals	$T_{1\cdot\cdot} = 131.9$	$T_{2\cdot\cdot} = 133.7$	$T_{3\cdot\cdot} = 136.1$	$T_{\cdots} = 401.7$

based on sex, location of employment, or the interaction of the two. Of interest were large metropolitan areas in the Northeast, Midwest, and West. It was felt that a factorial arrangement in a completely randomized design would be sufficient. It was decided to use the starting salaries of four persons for each of the six treatment combinations. To assure homogeneous experimental units, the persons selected were as similar in background as possible. They were relatively the same age and had virtually the same grade-point average; none of them had any prior professional experience; and all had graduated from comparable universities. Based on the sample information in Table 12.15, determine which effects are statistically discernible.

The various sums of interest are given in the table. Then

$$SST = 15.2^2 + 16.8^2 + \cdots + 18.7^2 - \frac{401.7^2}{24} = 32.8563,$$

$$SSTR = \frac{62.4^2 + 69.5^2 + \cdots + 71.4^2}{4} - \frac{401.7^2}{24} = 24.7838,$$

$$SSE = 32.8563 - 24.7838 = 8.0725.$$

Similarly,

$$SS(SEX) = \frac{189.1^2 + 212.6^2}{12} - \frac{401.7^2}{24} = 23.0104,$$

$$SS(LOC) = \frac{131.9^2 + 133.7^2 + 136.1^2}{8} - \frac{401.7^2}{24} = 1.11.$$

Thus

$$SS(LOC \times SEX) = 24.7838 - 23.0104 - 1.11 = 0.6634.$$

The analysis of variance table is Table 12.16. We conclude that based on this information, the only statistically discernible effect on the starting salaries is from the sex of the graduate.

TABLE 12.16 ANOVA table for Example 12.5

Source of variation	df	SS	MS	F value
Location	2	1.11	0.555	1.24
Sex	1	23.0104	23.0104	51.31
Location × sex	2	0.6634	0.3317	0.74
Error	18	8.0725	0.4485	
Total	23	32.8563	$f_{0.99, 1, 18} = 8.29; f_{0.99, 2, 18} = 6.01$	

TABLE 12.17 Expected mean squares for a two-factor factorial: Random effects or mixed effects model

Source	Random effects (A and B random) EMS	F statistic	Mixed effects (A fixed, B random) EMS	F statistic
A	$\sigma^2 + n\sigma_{\alpha\beta}^2 + nb\sigma_\alpha^2$	MSA/MSAB	$\sigma^2 + n\sigma_{\alpha\beta}^2 + nb\dfrac{\Sigma\,\alpha_i^2}{(a-1)}$	MSA/MSAB
B	$\sigma^2 + n\sigma_{\alpha\beta}^2 + na\sigma_\beta^2$	MSB/MSAB	$\sigma^2 + na\sigma_\beta^2$	MSB/MSE
AB	$\sigma^2 + n\sigma_{\alpha\beta}^2$	MSAB/MSE	$\sigma^2 + n\sigma_{\alpha\beta}^2$	MSAB/MSE
Error	σ^2		σ^2	

It should be noted that Scheffé's method for comparing factor level means extends to a factorial experiment in a straightforward manner. A residual analysis for the levels of each factor may also be carried out to check, among other things, the assumption of equal variances. The residuals are determined using the relation

$$e_{ijk} = y_{ijk} - \bar{y}_{ij}.$$

In the cases we have examined up to now, the error mean square was always used as the denominator in the F ratio. However, for statistical experiments involving two or more factors, this does not always hold. The appropriate F statistic for an analysis of variance depends directly on the expected mean squares of the sources of variation, which in turn depend on whether the corresponding effects are regarded as fixed or random.

For two-factor factorials, three distinct situations arise: (a) the levels of both factors are fixed effects; (b) the levels of both factors are random effects; or (c) the levels of one factor are fixed, while those of the other are random. We have already discussed the first possibility. For the remaining two, the expected mean squares for the random effects model and the mixed effects model are given in Table 12.17.

Based on the material of this chapter, the procedure we have used to construct the test statistic is to compare two mean squares that, under the null hypothesis, have the same expectation, and under the alternative hypothesis, the numerator mean square has a larger expectation than the denominator mean square. If the null hypothesis is true, the statistic follows an F distribution with appropriate degrees of freedom. With this in mind, the indicated mean square ratios in Table 12.17 should now be apparent. For example, consider the random effects case and, in particular, the null hypothesis of no variation among all possible levels of A; that is, H_0: $\sigma_\alpha^2 = 0$. If H_0 is true, $E(MSA) = \sigma^2 + n\sigma_{\alpha\beta}^2$, where $\sigma_{\alpha\beta}^2$ denotes the variance due to the interaction between A and B. But this expectation is the same only to $E(MSAB)$ and not to $E(MSE)$ under H_0. On the other hand, if H_0 is false, $E(MSA)$ is larger than $E(MSAB)$. Accordingly, the appropriate test statistic for H_0 is $MSA/MSAB$.

It should be remembered that in factorial experiments, the error mean square will be the denominator in the mean square ratio for all main and interaction effects only if the levels of all factors are fixed effects. Thus, in the design phase of a statistical experiment, the selection of factor levels is extremely important because it has a direct bearing on the analysis.

References

1. W. G. Cochran and G. M. Cox, *Experimental designs,* 2nd ed., Wiley, New York, 1957.
2. R. C. Hicks, *Fundamental concepts in the design of experiments,* 2nd ed., Holt, Rinehart and Winston, New York, 1973.
3. R. L. Horton, *The general linear model,* McGraw-Hill, New York, 1978.
4. R. E. Kirk, *Experimental design: Procedures for the behavioral sciences,* Brooks/Cole, Belmont, Calif., 1968.
5. J. Neter and W. Wasserman, *Applied linear statistical models,* Richard D. Irwin, Homewood, Ill., 1974.
6. H. Scheffé, *Analysis of variance,* Wiley, New York, 1953.
7. H. Scheffé, *A method for judging all contrasts in the analysis of variance,* Biometrika **40** (1953), 87–104.

Exercises

12.1. You have been given the responsibility of investigating the effect that different arrangements of the 40-hour work week would have on the average productivity rate in a large plant. Specifically, you want to compare 5-day week, 4-day week, and $3\frac{1}{3}$-day week configurations. Describe your statistical design in detail. Be sure to identify treatments, experimental units, and other important factors for carrying out this investigation.

12.2. Accident statistics indicate that about two-thirds of automobile fatalities in the United States are caused by drunken drivers. You have been hired to investigate the degree that alcohol impairs one's ability to perform routine functions in driving an automobile. Fully describe a statistical design to accomplish this task and indicate how this experiment should be carried out.

12.3. An insurance company wants to determine whether there are discernible differences in the average number of days patients suffering from the same illness stay at an area's four major hospitals. The company is also interested in determining any differences among male and female patients. Fully describe a statistical design to accomplish this objective. Be sure to identify the nature of each factor as either a fixed or a random effect, to write the model, and to state the hypotheses to be tested.

12.4. A filling operation consists of three identical machines that are set to pour a specified amount of a product into equal-sized containers. Random samples are taken from the machines periodically to check for the equality of the average amounts poured by each machine. For a particular time period, the data in Table 12.18 were recorded.

TABLE 12.18 Sample data for Exercise 12.4

A	Machine B	C
16	18	19
15	19	20
15	19	18
14	20	20
	19	19
	19	

a. Compute $y_{ij} - \bar{y}_{..}$ and verify that the sum of these deviations over all i and j is zero.
b. Estimate τ_j for all j, and thus verify that the sum of $n_j(\bar{y}_{.j} - \bar{y}_{..})$ over all j is zero.
c. Compute each of the three sums of squares given in Expression 12.8 directly, to verify that SST = SSTR + SSE.
d. Are there any statistically discernible differences in the average amounts poured by the three machines? Use $\alpha = 0.05$.

12.5. In Exercise 12.4, suppose you divide each observation by 10. Show whether this operation has any effect on your answers to part c and part d.

12.6. Set up contrasts of your choice for Exercise 12.4 and use Scheffé's method to determine whether they are statistically discernible.

12.7. An independent testing laboratory is asked to compare the durability of four different brands of golf balls. The laboratory sets up an experiment in which eight balls from each manufacturer are randomly selected and subjected to a machine set to hit the ball with a constant force. The measurement of interest is the number of times each ball is hit before its outside cover cracks. The information in Table 12.19 is obtained.

TABLE 12.19 Sample data for Exercise 12.7

A	Brand B	C	D
205	242	237	212
229	253	259	244
238	226	265	229
214	219	229	272
242	251	218	255
225	212	262	233
209	224	242	224
204	247	234	245

a. Is there reason to believe the average durability differs for these four brands? Use $\alpha = 0.05$.

b. Is there reason to doubt the assumption of equal error variances?

12.8. To determine whether there are differences in the average yields of three varieties of corn, a large homogeneous farm area is divided into three equal-sized plots. Each plot is then divided into five equal subplots and planted with one variety of corn. At harvest time the measurement of interest is the yield in bushels per acre. Table 12.20 is a partial analysis of variance table for this problem.

TABLE 12.20   Partial ANOVA table for Exercise 12.8

Source	df	SS	MS	F value
Treatments		64		
Error				
Total		100		

a. Write the model for this problem.

b. Are you satisfied with the assumptions? Comment.

c. State the null hypothesis to be tested.

d. Complete the ANOVA table and determine whether the null hypothesis can be rejected at the $\alpha = 0.01$ level.

12.9. We wish to determine whether the amount of carbon used in the manufacture of steel has an effect on the tensile strength of the steel. Five different percentages of carbon are investigated: 0.2%, 0.3%, 0.4%, 0.5%, and 0.6%. For each percentage of carbon, five steel specimens are randomly selected from the same batch and their strengths are measured. The information in Table 12.21 is obtained where the strength is in kilograms per square centimeter.

TABLE 12.21   Sample data for Exercise 12.9

		Carbon content		
0.2%	0.3%	0.4%	0.5%	0.6%
1240	1420	1480	1610	1700
1350	1510	1470	1590	1790
1390	1410	1520	1580	1740
1280	1530	1540	1630	1810
1320	1470	1510	1560	1730

a. Based on this information, determine whether the percentage of carbon has a statistically discernible effect on the strength of steel. Use $\alpha = 0.01$.

b. If the answer to part a is affirmative, set up some relevant contrasts and test for their statistical significance.

12.10. In Exercise 12.9, is there reason to doubt the assumption of equal variances?

12.11. A number of company presidents were randomly sampled from four distinct geographical areas in the United States to determine whether area has an effect on the annual salaries of company presidents. The annual salaries in Table 12.22 were observed. With the information given, provide an argument for or against whether one should utilize the analysis of variance technique to determine if area has an effect on annual salaries. Be sure to give substantive support in either case.

TABLE 12.22 Sample data for Exercise 12.11 (thousands of dollars)

| | | Area | |
Northeast	Midwest	Southeast	West
140	93	78	85
125	135	112	72
95	68	57	97
110	53	97	105
59	115	52	62

12.12. In a large plant, we wish to determine whether different workers with the same skill level have any effect on the number of units that are expected to be produced in a fixed period of time. An experiment is conducted in which five workers are randomly selected, and the number of units produced by each worker for six equal-length time periods is recorded as in Table 12.23.

TABLE 12.23 Sample data for Exercise 12.12

| | | Worker | | |
1	2	3	4	5
45	52	39	57	48
47	55	37	49	44
43	58	46	52	55
48	49	45	50	53
50	47	42	48	49
44	57	41	55	52

a. Write the model for this problem and explain each term in the model.
b. State the null hypothesis to be tested.
c. Determine whether the null hypothesis can be rejected at the $\alpha = 0.05$ level.
d. How much of the variance in the number of units produced is attributed to differences among the workers?

12.13. Since the increase in the price of gasoline, several devices have been developed that purport to increase the mileage of automobiles with these devices installed in their carburetors. A testing organization has selected three of the most popular devices for testing. The organization would like to compare these with the standard carburetors to determine if there is any appreciable increase in mileage with the devices. The organization has selected five types of automobiles for the experiment. To control variation, it plans to use the same driver for the entire experiment.

a. Outline the specific plan to carry out this experiment.
b. Suppose the data in Table 12.24 are observed. Write the model and state the

TABLE 12.24 Sample data for Exercise 12.13 (miles per gallon)

Auto	Standard carburetor	Device A	Device B	Device C
1	18.2	18.9	19.1	20.4
2	27.4	27.9	28.1	29.9
3	35.2	34.9	35.8	38.2
4	14.8	15.2	14.9	17.3
5	25.4	24.8	25.6	26.9

null hypothesis to be tested. Can the hypothesis be rejected at the $\alpha = 0.05$ level?

c. If you rejected the null hypothesis in part b, set up at least two relevant contrasts and test for their statistical significance.

12.14. In Exercise 12.13, suppose you had not considered the automobile as a viable source of the variation in the observed mileage. Show whether this omission would have any effect on your answer to part b.

12.15. Burning cigarettes produce appreciable quantities of carbon monoxide. When cigarette smoke is inhaled, carbon monoxide combines with hemoglobin to form carboxy-hemoglobin. In a recent study,* the researchers wanted to determine whether an appreciable concentration of carboxyhemoglobin reduces the exercise tolerance of patients suffering from chronic bronchitis and emphysema. Seven** such patients were selected and, in a controlled environment, they were asked to walk for 12 minutes, breathing one of four gas mixtures: air, oxygen, air plus carbon monoxide (CO), or oxygen plus carbon monoxide. The amount of carbon monoxide breathed was sufficient to raise the carboxyhemoglobin concentration of each subject by 9 percent. To control the intake of carbon monoxide, all smokers in the group of seven were asked to stop smoking 12 hours prior to the experiment. The data in Table 12.25 represent the distances walked by the subjects under each condition in 12 minutes.

TABLE 12.25   Sample data for Exercise 12.15 (in meters)

Subject			Gas mixture	
	Air	Oxygen	Air + CO	Oxygen + CO
1	835	874	750	854
2	787	827	755	829
3	724	738	698	726
4	336	378	210	279
5	252	315	168	336
6	560	672	558	642
7	336	341	260	336

a. Write the model for this problem.

b. Can the null hypothesis of no gas mixture effect on the distance walked in twelve minutes be rejected at the $\alpha = 0.05$ level?

c. Perform a conservative F test for the null hypothesis of no gas mixture effect. Is your conclusion different from that in part b?

d. If the answer to part b is yes, set up some pertinent contrasts and use Scheffé's method to determine whether they are statistically discernible.

12.16. We wish to determine whether there are appreciable differences in the average prices among four major supermarkets in a given city. From the regularly bought brand items, ten are randomly selected and their unit prices are observed at each supermarket. The information in Table 12.26 is obtained.

a. Write the model for this problem.

b. State an appropriate null hypothesis and determine whether it can be rejected at the $\alpha = 0.01$ level.

*P. M. A. Calverly, R. J. E. Leggett, and D. C. Flenley, *Carbon monoxide and exercise tolerance in chronic bronchitis and emphysema*, Brit. Med. J. **283** (1981), 877–880.
**Fifteen subjects were in the actual study.

TABLE 12.26 Sample data for Exercise 12.16 (in dollars)

Item	A	Supermarket B	C	D
1	3.29	3.42	3.27	3.35
2	0.59	0.65	0.59	0.60
3	1.25	1.29	1.25	1.27
4	4.35	4.59	4.29	4.49
5	0.89	0.95	0.89	0.89
6	1.85	1.79	1.89	1.89
7	0.95	0.89	0.89	0.90
8	0.75	0.79	0.69	0.79
9	2.35	2.35	2.39	2.39
10	1.49	1.55	1.55	1.49

c. Determine all residuals and plot the residuals for each treatment and each block. Comment on your results.

12.17. In the illustration discussed in Section 12.6, suppose twelve electronic components are randomly selected from the same batch, and groups of three are assigned to the four combinations of oven and temperature setting. The lifetimes of the components are observed to be as given in Table 12.27.

TABLE 12.27 Sample data for Exercise 12.17 (in hours)

	O_1	O_2
T_1	6.29	5.95
	6.38	6.05
	6.25	5.89
T_2	5.80	6.32
	5.92	6.44
	5.78	6.29

a. Write the appropriate model for this problem.
b. State the hypotheses to be tested.
c. Determine the analysis of variance table and draw appropriate conclusions. Use $\alpha = 0.05$.

12.18. In Exercise 12.3, suppose the information in Table 12.28 was obtained for the randomly selected patients suffering from the same illness.

TABLE 12.28 Sample data for Exercise 12.18. Length of hospitalization in days at four hospitals

	Hospital A	*Hospital* B	*Hospital* C	*Hospital* D
Males	7	9	10	6
	10	9	8	7
	8	12	12	6
	11	14	13	9
Females	9	11	13	8
	12	12	11	9
	12	14	14	8
	11	13	14	10

a. Determine which are the statistically discernible effects at the $\alpha = 0.01$ level.
b. Determine all residuals and plot the residuals for each hospital. What conclusions can you draw?

12.19. The objective of an agricultural experiment was to determine whether appreciable differences occurred in the yield of wheat among four varieties and among three types of fertilizers. For the experiment, a large farm area was found whose soil conditions were nearly homogeneous. The farm was divided into 12 equal plots for the 12 combinations of wheat variety and fertilizer type. To measure the experimental error, each plot was divided into 4 subplots, and all subplots within a main plot received the same treatment. The three kinds of fertilizer were randomly selected from a relatively large number of types of fertilizer, but interest does not extend beyond the four varieties of wheat selected for the experiment. At harvest time, the yields in Table 12.29 were observed.

TABLE 12.29 Sample data for Exercise 12.19 (bushels per acre)

| Fertilizer | Wheat Variety | | | |
	A	B	C	D
1	35	45	24	55
	26	39	23	48
	38	39	36	39
	20	43	29	49
2	55	64	58	68
	44	57	74	61
	68	62	49	60
	64	61	69	75
3	97	93	89	82
	89	91	98	78
	92	82	85	89
	99	98	87	92

a. Write the appropriate model for this problem.
b. State the hypotheses to be tested.
c. Determine the analysis of variance table and draw appropriate conclusions. Use $\alpha = 0.05$.

12.20. In Exercise 12.19, how would your answer to part c change if

a. the varieties were assumed to be a random effect, and the types of fertilizer were assumed to be a fixed effect?
b. both were assumed to be fixed effects?
c. both were assumed to be random effects?

CHAPTER THIRTEEN

Regression Analysis: The Simple Linear Model

13.1 Introduction

In the last chapter we developed the basic criteria for the statistical design of experiments. In this chapter we will examine the quantitative associations among a number of variables, which in statistical terminology is known as *regression analysis*.

Although statistically designed experiments are being implemented in many disciplines, the precision of balance that is usually required precludes using these designs in many situations. To investigate the simultaneous effect of several factors based on analysis of variance techniques requires the assumption that data are taken in balanced arrays and that proper randomization procedures are exercised. Obviously, this is desirable if it can be accomplished, but it is often impractical. In reality, what the experimenter is usually faced with is a mass of data, which typically is not expected to have been observed under tightly controlled conditions and which rarely contains any real replicates for an appropriate assessment of the experimental error. Under these conditions, the more general methods of least squares and regression analysis, not analysis of variance, are appropriate.

Our general purpose here is to provide the basic concepts and methodology to extract from masses of data the main features of an inconspicuous relationship. Specifically, we want to examine techniques that will allow us to fit an equation of some type to a given set of data for the purpose of obtaining a reasonably accurate prediction equation that usually is empirical and augments a theoretical model that is not available. We will assume the existence of a set of n measurements $y_1, y_2, ..., y_n$ of a response variable Y, each of the measurements having been observed under a set of experimental conditions $(x_1, x_2, ..., x_k)$ that represent values of k predictor variables. Of interest is the determination of a simple mathematical function, such as a polynomial, that can reasonably account for the behavior of the response variable, given values for the predictor variables.

Note that the equation determined may very well have some limitations for physical interpretation. However, in an empirical environment, it will be extremely useful if it can provide adequate predictive capability for the response within a prescribed region of the predictor variables.

Although we find no fault with the usual designations of dependent and independent variables for Y and the x's, respectively, we prefer the designations of *response* and *predictor* variables because in regression we can only *associate* an observed Y to a predictor x; we cannot establish a cause-and-effect relationship between Y and the x's. Some examples will give an insight into why the confirmation of a cause-and-effect relationship is beyond the power of regression analysis. Obviously a relationship exists between height and weight in humans, but does such a relationship imply, for example, that we can change someone's height by either increasing or decreasing weight? There is also a relationship between the amount of natural gas consumed in a metropolitan area and the average atmospheric temperature, but does this mean that we can raise the temperature by simply reducing the amount of natural gas consumed? Some relationship may occur between a particular economic factor and a business cycle, but does this imply that the economic factor "causes" the business cycle?

The essence of these illustrations is that regression analyses uncover only an association between the response variable and the predictor variables instead of detecting a cause-and-effect relationship. Causation implies that a change in the x's will cause a corresponding change in the response variable. For example, when heat is applied to metal, the metal will expand. There is no doubt that the establishment of a cause-and-effect relationship is very important. Unfortunately, it cannot usually be done based purely on statistical analyses unless an extremely tightly controlled experiment is performed. An example that has been in the limelight recently is the relation between smoking and lung cancer. The evidence appears to be overwhelming that intensive cigarette smoking (predictor) is statistically associated with a higher incidence of lung cancer (response). The tobacco industry counters these findings by insisting that no causal relationship has been established.

Our approach in this chapter as well as in the next will rest entirely on establishing the degree of association among variables without regard to the notion of causation. In this chapter we will examine the essentials of regression analysis for the model with a single predictor variable. In Chapter 14 we will take up what is known as the *general linear model* in which a given response is assumed to be a function of several predictor variables.

13.2 The Meaning of Regression and Basic Assumptions

If regression methods are to be useful in a practical environment, we must understand their meaning and the assumptions under which they have been developed. Regression techniques provide legitimate means of establishing associations between variables of interest in which the relation is usually not causal. The word "regression" was first used in this context by Francis Galton (1822–1911) in his biological studies of inheritance. In these studies, it was noted that the average characteristics of the next generation of a particular group tended to move in the direction of the average characteristics of the general population rather than toward the average characteristics of the previous generation of that group. This tendency was referred to as a regression toward the population mean.

Basically, regression has two meanings. One stems from the joint probability distribution of two random variables; the other is empirical and stems from the need to fit some assumed function to a set of data. To illustrate the first meaning, let us try to predict the annual salary of a college graduate, given the number of years since graduation. Let X be the number of years, and let Y be the annual salary. It should be obvious that for a given value x, it is impossible to predict exactly the annual salary of a particular person. However, it is possible to predict the average salary of individuals who have been out of college x years. In other words, for each value x, there is a distribution of annual incomes, and what we are seeking is the mean of that distribution, given x. The graph of the conditional mean $E(Y|x)$ as a function of x is called the *curve of regression* of Y on X. Thus if $f(x, y)$ is the joint probability density function of X and Y, and if $f(y|x)$ is the conditional density function of Y given x, the curve of regression is defined to be

$$E(Y|x) = \int_{-\infty}^{\infty} yf(y|x)\, dy.$$

Example 13.1   Let the joint probability density function be defined by

$$f(x, y) = \begin{cases} 2x & 0 < x < y < 1, \\ 0 & \text{elsewhere.} \end{cases}$$

Determine the curve of regression of Y on X.

Since

$$f(y|x) = f(x, y)/f_X(x),$$

then

$$f_X(x) = \int_Y f(x, y)\, dy = \int_x^1 2x\, dy = 2x(1 - x),$$

and

$$f(y|x) = \frac{2x}{2x(1 - x)} = \frac{1}{1 - x}.$$

As a result, the curve of regression is

$$E(Y|x) = \int_x^1 (1 - x)^{-1} y\, dy = (1 + x)/2,$$

which is a straight line with slope and intercept equal to 1/2.

The second meaning of regression is much more practical than the first. Here we realize that we do not have the necessary ingredients to determine the curve of regression as illustrated by Example 13.1. However, given a set of typical data, we are willing to assume a functional form for the curve of regression and then attempt to fit that function to the data. In these situations the response variable is a random variable whose values are observed by selecting values of the predictor variables in a desired range. The predictor variables are therefore not regarded as random variables. Rather, they are a set of fixed values representing points of observation for the response variable. The assumed regression model should be relatively simple and should contain few parameters. An extremely useful procedure for the initial selection when there is a single predictor variable is to plot the response variable against the predictor variable. If this graph reveals a linear trend, a linear regression model should be assumed. If curvature is apparent, a quadratic or a higher order model ought to be fitted to the data.

Once the model is selected, the task is to determine estimates for the parameters of the model. A widely accepted technique for this purpose is the *least squares* (LS) *method*. This method finds estimates for the parameters in the selected equation by minimizing the sum of the squared deviations of the observed values of the response variable from those predicted by the equation. These values are known as the least squares estimates (LSE) of the parameters. Least squares estimators possess certain desirable properties, but the following assumptions must be made to determine them.

1. The correct form of regression equation has been selected. This implies that whatever variability in the response variable cannot be accounted for by the equation is due to random error. For example, we know that the distance d that an object travels in time t is given by the relation

$$d = \beta_0 + \beta_1 t,$$

where β_1 is the average velocity and β_0 is the position of the object at $t = 0$. If we could not measure d precisely for a given value of t, but we observed a value

$$y = d + \varepsilon,$$

where ε is the random error, the correct form of the regression equation has been selected, and the problem is that of estimating β_0 and β_1. However, the problem is rarely that simple.

For example, if we are interested in predicting the amount of ozone in the upper atmosphere as a function of concentration levels of chemical constituents and time of day, the selected equation would be primarily a conjecture. The error can no longer be regarded as purely random because it may very well contain systematic variation due to modeling error. Some values of the response variable given by the prediction equation will be biased since the estimates of the parameters are themselves biased.

2. The observed data are typical in the sense that they represent a cross-section of an environment about which the investigator wishes to generalize. If the investigator knows that the data are not typical, the typical behavior of the mechanism would be beyond his or her reach from that data.

3. The observed values of the response variable are statistically uncorrelated. Each observed value is assumed to be made up of a true value and a random component. The random component consists of an unobservable random variable called the random error. Then the covariance between any two observations Y_i and Y_j, or between the corresponding random errors ε_i and ε_j, is zero for all $i \neq j$.

4. For all $i = 1, 2, \ldots, n$, the mean of ε_i is zero and the variance of ε_i is σ^2. σ^2 is called the *error variance* and is usually unknown. Since the predictor variables are not random variables, the variance of Y_i is also σ^2 for all i and thus independent of the point of observation. If the constant variance assumption for the observations of the response variable cannot hold, the more general weighted least squares method is usually employed. This topic will be considered in some detail in Chapter 14.

5. The points of observation or the values of the predictor variables are fixed or selected in advance and are measured without error. In many practical situations, both conditions may not hold. Fortunately, the least squares procedure remains valid provided that the errors in the x values are small when compared to the random errors and provided they do not depend on the parameters of the model.

In a final comment on the assumptions of the LS procedure, we will consider only linear least squares, where the word "linear" means that the selected model is linear in the parameters. The phrase "linear in the parameters" means that no parameter in the model appears as an exponent or is multiplied by or divided by another parameter. For example, the models

$$Y = \beta_0 + \beta_1 x + \varepsilon,$$

$$Y = \beta_0 + \beta_1 x + \beta_2 x^2 + \varepsilon,$$

$$Y = \beta_0 + \beta_1 \ln(x) + \varepsilon,$$

$$Y = \beta_0 + \beta_1 x_1 + \beta_2 x_2 + \beta_3 x_1 x_2 + \varepsilon$$

are linear in the parameters β_0, β_1, β_2, and β_3, but the model

$$Y = \beta_0 \exp(\beta_1 x) + \varepsilon$$

is not because the parameter β_1 appears as an exponent.

13.3 Least Squares Estimation for the Simple Linear Model

In this section we will examine least squares estimation for the simple linear model in which there is a single predictor variable, and the regression equation is assumed to be a linear function. For example, university students learn rather quickly that the better their grade point averages (GPA), the better their chances of landing good jobs upon graduation. Suppose the data in Table 13.1 represent the grade point averages of 15 recent graduates and their starting annual salaries.

Here the response variable is the starting salary and the potential predictor variable is the grade point average. The grade point averages were selected to reflect a fairly broad range. We want to determine a regression equation for

TABLE 13.1 Sample data for a simple linear model (thousands of dollars)

GPA	*Starting salary*
2.95	18.5
3.20	20.0
3.40	21.1
3.60	22.4
3.20	21.2
2.85	15.0
3.10	18.0
2.85	18.8
3.05	15.7
2.70	14.4
2.75	15.5
3.10	17.2
3.15	19.0
2.95	17.2
2.75	16.8

average starting salary as a function of grade point average. Since a single predictor variable has been proposed, plotting the data would be helpful in the initial selection of a regression model. The graph of starting salaries against grade point averages is given in Figure 13.1. It should be noted that the graph in Figure 13.1 was produced by a statistical computer package known as "Minitab." Although not as sophisticated as, say, SAS, Minitab is extremely easy to use and is highly recommended for preliminary regression analyses, among other applications.

Although this plot contains much scatter,* a linear trend is apparent. Accordingly, we will assume a model of the form

$$Y_i = \beta_0 + \beta_1 x_i + \varepsilon_i \qquad i = 1, 2, \ldots, n, \tag{13.1}$$

where Y_i is the ith observation of the response variable corresponding to the ith value x_i of the predictor variable; ε_i is the unobservable random error associated with Y_i; and β_0 and β_1 are unknown parameters representing the intercept and slope, respectively. Expression (13.1) is known as the *simple linear model* because it is linear in the parameters and a linear function of a single predictor variable.

Each observation Y_i is a random variable and is the sum of two components, the nonrandom term $\beta_0 + \beta_1 x_i$, and the random component ε_i. If ε_i were zero, the observation Y_i would fall precisely on the regression line $\beta_0 + \beta_1 x_i$. Thus ε_i is the vertical distance from the observation to the regression line. Since we assume that

$$E(\varepsilon_i) = 0, \quad Var(\varepsilon_i) = \sigma^2 \qquad i = 1, 2, \ldots, n,$$

and

$$Cov(\varepsilon_i, \varepsilon_j) = 0 \qquad i \neq j;$$

---

*For this reason, such a graph is known as a scatter plot.

FIGURE 13.1 Starting salary versus grade point average

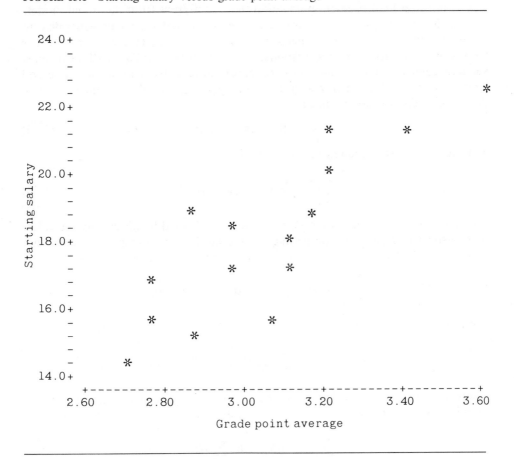

then

$$E(Y_i) = E(\beta_0 + \beta_1 x_i + \varepsilon_i) = \beta_0 + \beta_1 x_i,$$

$$Cov(Y_i, Y_j) = \sigma^2 \quad i \neq j,$$

and

$$Var(Y_i) = Var(\beta_0 + \beta_1 x_i + \varepsilon_i) = Var(\varepsilon_i) = \sigma^2.$$

The last result stems from the fact that the variance of a random variable is location invariant; in this case the location shift is provided by the nonrandom term $\beta_0 + \beta_1 x_i$. In real terms, therefore, we are assuming that for each specific grade point average x, there is a probability distribution of starting salaries whose mean is a linear function of the value x and whose variance is the same for all x. The model as given by (13.1) should be regarded only as an initial selection for the functional form of the curve of regression. Based on appropriate analyses that we will examine later, it may be necessary to make adjustments, and these may result in a final prediction equation that is different from the initial model.

To determine the least squares estimates of β_0 and β_1, let us generalize to a data set consisting of the n pairs (x_1, y_1), (x_2, y_2), ..., (x_n, y_n), where the y values are realizations of the response random variables. The method of least squares considers the deviation of the observation Y_i from its mean value and determines the values of β_0 and β_1 that minimize the sum of the squares of such deviations. The ith deviation or error is

$$\varepsilon_i = Y_i - (\beta_0 + \beta_1 x_i), \tag{13.2}$$

and the sum of the squares of the errors is

$$\sum_{i=1}^{n} \varepsilon_i^2 = \sum_{i=1}^{n} (Y_i - \beta_0 - \beta_1 x_i)^2. \tag{13.3}$$

The least squares estimators of β_0 and β_1 are determined by differentiating (13.3) with respect to β_0 and β_1 and setting the partial derivatives equal to zero. That is,

$$\frac{\partial \sum \varepsilon_i^2}{\partial \beta_0} = -2 \sum (Y_i - B_0 - B_1 x_i) = 0,$$

and

$$\frac{\partial \sum \varepsilon_i^2}{\partial \beta_1} = -2 \sum x_i(Y_i - B_0 - B_1 x_i) = 0,$$

where B_0 and B_1 are the least squares estimators* of β_0 and β_1, respectively. Simplifying and distributing the sums in these equations we obtain

$$\sum_{i=1}^{n} Y_i = nB_0 + B_1 \sum_{i=1}^{n} x_i$$

and

$$(13.4)$$

$$\sum_{i=1}^{n} x_i Y_i = B_0 \sum_{i=1}^{n} x_i + B_1 \sum_{i=1}^{n} x_i^2.$$

The two equations given by (13.4) are known as the *normal equations*.

Given the realizations $y_1, y_2, ..., y_n$, we can solve these equations for the least squares estimates b_0 and b_1. If we divide both sides of the first equation by n we obtain

$$\frac{\sum y_i}{n} = b_0 + b_1 \frac{\sum x_i}{n};$$

---

*Many authors choose to designate least squares estimators with lower case italic letters. To maintain consistency of notation with previous chapters, we will designate a least squares estimator with an upper case italic letter and reserve the lower case for the LS estimate.

then the least squares estimate of β_0 is

$$b_0 = \frac{\sum\limits_{i=1}^{n} y_i}{n} - b_1 \frac{\sum\limits_{i=1}^{n} x_i}{n} = \bar{y} - b_1 \bar{x}. \tag{13.5}$$

Substituting for b_0 in the second equation of (13.4), we obtain

$$\sum x_i y_i = \left(\frac{\sum y_i}{n} - b_1 \frac{\sum x_i}{n} \right) \sum x_i + b_1 \sum x_i^2,$$

which, after solving for b_1, reduces to

$$b_1 = \frac{\sum\limits_{i=1}^{n} x_i y_i - \dfrac{\left(\sum\limits_{i=1}^{n} x_i \right)\left(\sum\limits_{i=1}^{n} y_i \right)}{n}}{\sum\limits_{i=1}^{n} x_i^2 - \dfrac{\left(\sum\limits_{i=1}^{n} x_i \right)^2}{n}} = \frac{\sum\limits_{i=1}^{n} (x_i - \bar{x})(y_i - \bar{y})}{\sum\limits_{i=1}^{n} (x_i - \bar{x})^2}. \tag{13.6}$$

The values given by (13.5) and (13.6) are the ones that minimize the sum of the squares of the errors.

Given the least squares estimators B_0 and B_1 of the intercept and slope, respectively, the estimated regression line for model (13.1) is

$$\hat{Y}_i = B_0 + B_1 x_i \tag{13.7}$$

where $\hat{Y}_i$ is the estimator for the mean of the observation Y_i that corresponds to the value x_i of the predictor variable. Notice that if we substitute (13.5) for B_0 in (13.7), we obtain an alternative form for the estimated regression line given by

$$\hat{Y}_i = \bar{Y} - B_1 \bar{x} + B_1 x_i$$

$$= \bar{Y} + B_1(x_i - \bar{x}). \tag{13.8}$$

Based on (13.2), the difference between the realization y_i and the estimated value $\hat{y}_i$ is an estimate of the corresponding error. This estimate is known as the ith residual and is denoted by

$$e_i = y_i - \hat{y}_i. \tag{13.9}$$

We note again that the residuals are not estimates in the classical sense of (fixed) parameter estimation. Rather, they are estimates of values of the unobservable random variables ε_i, which are determined from the estimated regression line. The residuals $e_1, e_2, \ldots, e_n$ are very important because they provide a wealth of information on what may be missing from the estimated regression model. Details for this will come later. At this time we will illustrate the computational steps for determining the estimated regression line for the simple linear model using the salary data. Our purpose here is only to acquaint the reader with the computational procedure. Otherwise we would urge the use of a statistical computer package. A computer printout based on the salary data will be presented later.

In Table 13.2, we include the basic computations necessary to determine the least squares estimates of the intercept and slope. The last four columns of this table are not necessary for the determination of b_0 and b_1, but they will be used later in another context.

Using (13.5) and (13.6), the least squares estimate of the slope is

$$b_1 = \frac{830.425 - \dfrac{(45.6)(270.8)}{15}}{139.51 - \dfrac{(45.6)^2}{15}} = 8.12,$$

and the least squares estimate of the intercept is

$$b_0 = \frac{270.8}{15} - (8.12)\frac{45.6}{15} = -6.63.$$

Accordingly, the estimated regression equation is

$$\hat{y}_i = -6.63 + 8.12\, x_i. \tag{13.10}$$

Let us attempt to interpret this equation. The values $\hat{y}_i$ are estimates for the means of the probability distributions of starting salaries corresponding to the

TABLE 13.2 Basic computations to determine the least squares estimates b_0 and b_1 (based on the salary data in Table 13.1)

GPA x_i	Salary y_i	$x_i y_i$	x_i^2	y_i^2	Estimated salary $\hat{y}_i$	Residual $y_i - \hat{y}_i$	Squared residual $(y_i - \hat{y}_i)^2$
2.95	18.5	54.575	8.7025	342.25	17.32	1.18	1.3924
3.20	20.0	64.000	10.2400	400.00	19.35	0.65	0.4225
3.40	21.1	71.740	11.5600	445.21	20.98	0.12	0.0144
3.60	22.4	80.640	12.9600	501.76	22.60	-0.20	0.0400
3.20	21.2	67.840	10.2400	449.44	19.35	1.85	3.4225
2.85	15.0	42.750	8.1225	225.00	16.51	-1.51	2.2801
3.10	18.0	55.800	9.6100	324.00	18.54	-0.54	0.2916
2.85	18.8	53.580	8.1225	353.44	16.51	2.29	5.2441
3.05	15.7	47.885	9.3025	246.49	18.13	-2.43	5.9049
2.70	14.4	38.880	7.2900	207.36	15.29	-0.89	0.7921
2.75	15.5	42.625	7.5625	240.25	15.70	-0.20	0.0400
3.10	17.2	53.320	9.6100	295.84	18.54	-1.34	1.7956
3.15	19.0	59.850	9.9225	361.00	18.95	0.05	0.0025
2.95	17.2	50.740	8.7025	295.84	17.32	-0.12	0.0144
2.75	16.8	46.200	7.5625	282.24	15.70	1.10	1.2100
Totals 45.6	270.8	830.425	139.5100	4970.12	270.79	0.01	22.8671

grade point averages x_i. A negative intercept is bothersome because, for example, if $x = 0.5$, $\hat{y} = -2.57$, which is absurd. But the grade point averages in this data set range from 2.70 to 3.60, so whatever validity the estimated regression equation has in predicting average starting salaries, it holds for values of x in the range 2.70 to 3.60. In practice, one often wishes to predict the response beyond the range of x values from which the estimated regression equation is derived. If a value of x is relatively close to this range, the prediction still has some validity. Otherwise it must be viewed with extreme care because the estimated regression equation may not be appropriate over a wider range of values for the predictor variable.

The interpretation of the estimated value of the slope is straightforward. The estimated increase in the average starting salary for each whole unit increase in the grade point average is 8,120 dollars.

The third column from the right in Table 13.2 contains the estimated average salaries for each grade point average as determined by (13.10). For example, if $x = 2.95$ the estimated average starting salary is $\hat{y} = -6.63 + 8.12(2.95) = 17.32$ thousand dollars. Since the corresponding observed value is 18.5, by (13.9), $e = 18.5 - 17.32 = 1.18$ is the residual at $x = 2.95$. In other words, the residual value 1.18 is the vertical distance from the realization 18.5 to the point on the estimated regression line at $x = 2.95$. The other residuals are determined in the same manner and have similar meanings. Figure 13.2 illustrates the residuals as vertical distances from the estimated regression equation. Since a residual represents the amount by which an estimated value fails to predict the mean of the cor-

FIGURE 13.2 Residuals as vertical distances from the estimated regression equation

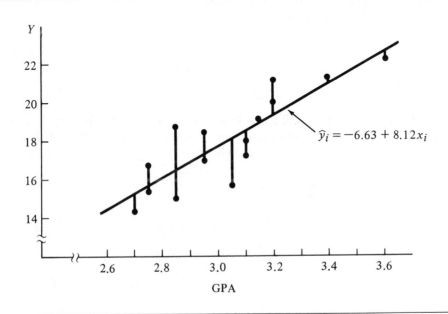

$$\hat{y}_i = -6.63 + 8.12x_i$$

GPA

responding random observation, the larger the magnitudes of the residuals are, the larger the effect of the random component in the model tends to be.

Recall that the variance σ^2 of the response variable is the same as the error variance and is constant for all values of the predictor variable. Since σ^2 is usually unknown, an estimate of it can be determined from the least squares estimates b_0 and b_1. Since each $\hat{y}_i$ estimates the mean of Y_i, the difference $y_i - \hat{y}_i$ represents the deviation of Y_i from its mean. The sum of the squares of such differences divided by an appropriate constant is the way one determines a variance. But these differences are the residuals. It follows, therefore, that the sum of the squares of the residuals divided by an appropriate constant is an estimate of σ^2. The appropriate constant is $n - 2$ because two degrees of freedom are lost in having to estimate the two parameters β_0 and β_1 prior to determining $\hat{y}_i$. The estimate of σ^2 is denoted by s^2 and given by

$$s^2 = \frac{\sum_{i=1}^{n} (y_i - \hat{y}_i)^2}{n - 2} = \frac{\sum_{i=1}^{n} e_i^2}{n - 2}. \tag{13.11}$$

The estimate s^2 is known as the *residual variance,* or MSE, and the positive square root s is called the *residual standard deviation.* For the starting salary example, the residual variance is $s^2 = 22.8671/13 = 1.759$. The residual variance s^2 is an absolute measure of how well the estimated regression line fits the means of the observed response variables. In general, therefore, the smaller the value s^2, the better the fit. It can be shown that the estimator S^2 is an unbiased estimator of σ^2 provided that the form of the regression model is correct. Otherwise S^2 estimates σ^2 plus a component that is the bias due to model error.

When a regression line is determined by the method of least squares, a number of properties emerge. Some of these are as follows:

1. $\sum_{i=1}^{n} e_i = 0.$

2. $\sum_{i=1}^{n} y_i = \sum_{i=1}^{n} \hat{y}_i.$

3. $\sum_{i=1}^{n} x_i e_i = 0.$

We will show Property 1 and leave Properties 2 and 3 to the reader. It should be noted that Property 2 follows from the first equation in (13.4), and Property 3 is obtained from the second normal equation. For Property 1,

$$\sum_{i=1}^{n} e_i = \sum_{i=1}^{n} (y_i - \hat{y}_i)$$

$$= \sum (y_i - b_0 - b_1 x_i)$$

$$= \sum y_i - nb_0 - b_1 \sum x_i$$

$$= n\bar{y} - n(\bar{y} - b_1 \bar{x}) - nb_1 \bar{x}$$

$$= 0.$$

That the residuals do not add exactly to zero for the example in Table 13.2 is due to rounding error. Moreover, since LS estimates are determined by minimizing the sum of the squares of the errors, for this example the minimum value is 22.8671.

13.4 Maximum Likelihood Estimation for the Simple Linear Model

We can use the principle of maximum likelihood to estimate the unknown parameters in the simple linear model given by (13.1). Recall that least squares estimates were determined without having to specify the probability distribution of the random errors ε_i. If we are willing to assume that the ε_i are independent normally distributed random variables with mean zero and variance σ^2 for all $i = 1, 2, ..., n$, it is possible to determine maximum likelihood estimates of β_0, β_1, and σ^2. That is, if in addition to the previous assumptions we specify that $\varepsilon_i \sim N(0, \sigma^2)$ for all $i = 1, 2, ..., n$, then each Y_i is also normally distributed with mean $\beta_0 + \beta_1 x_i$ and variance σ^2, since it is a linear function of a normally distributed random variable. The maximum likelihood estimates are determined by maximizing the likelihood function given by

$$L(y_1, y_2, ..., y_n; \beta_0, \beta_1, \sigma^2) = \frac{1}{\sqrt{2\pi}\,\sigma} \exp\left[-\frac{1}{2\sigma^2}(y_1 - \beta_0 - \beta_1 x_1)^2\right]$$

$$\cdots \frac{1}{\sqrt{2\pi}\,\sigma} \exp\left[-\frac{1}{2\sigma^2}(y_n - \beta_0 - \beta_1 x_n)^2\right]$$

$$= \left(\frac{1}{\sqrt{2\pi}\,\sigma}\right)^n \exp\left[-\frac{1}{2\sigma^2}\sum_{i=1}^{n}(y_i - \beta_0 - \beta_1 x_i)^2\right],$$

where

$$\ln[L(\beta_0, \beta_1, \sigma^2)] = -\frac{n}{2}\ln(2\pi) - \frac{n}{2}\ln(\sigma^2) - \frac{1}{2\sigma^2}\sum(y_i - \beta_0 - \beta_1 x_i)^2.$$

Taking partial derivatives with respect to β_0, β_1, and σ^2 and equating them to zero, we can show that the maximum likelihood estimates of β_0 and β_1 are identical to the least squares estimates given by (13.5) and (13.6), respectively, and the maximum likelihood estimate of σ^2 is

$$\hat{\sigma}^2 = \frac{\sum\limits_{i=1}^{n}(y_i - \hat{y}_i)^2}{n}. \tag{13.12}$$

The maximum likelihood estimator of σ^2 is biased, but for large n, the difference between it and the least squares estimator is negligible.

The reader may wonder why the need to even bother with the maximum likelihood estimators since they are the same as the least squares estimators.

One of the reasons is that maximum likelihood estimators possess the desirable properties of consistency, sufficiency, and minimum variance. In addition, they provide the necessary means to develop inference criteria for β_0 and β_1.

The assumption that the errors are normally distributed is justifiable because the error component in the model is usually a composite effect representing many small but random disturbances that are independent of the predictor variable and are due to factors not included in the model. At any rate, departure from normality is usually not serious for large n.

13.5   General Properties of Least Squares Estimators

In this section we will develop some general properties of least squares estimators and then look at criteria that would allow us to construct confidence intervals and perform tests of hypotheses for the regression parameters β_0 and β_1. In addition, we will examine the estimation of the mean response for a given x and the prediction of a particular Y for a given x. To a large extent the treatment in this section will be theoretical.

Consider unbiased estimators of β_0 and β_1 that are linear functions of the observations Y_1, Y_2, ..., Y_n. If among these unbiased estimators of β_0 and β_1 there exist estimators whose variances are smaller than those of any other unbiased estimators of β_0 and β_1, then these are the *best linear unbiased estimators* (BLUE) of β_0 and β_1. The following theorem, usually known as the Gauss–Markoff theorem, guarantees that the least squares estimators of β_0 and β_1 are the BLUE for β_0 and β_1.

Theorem 13.1   Let the assumptions for the model $Y_i = \beta_0 + \beta_1 x_i + \varepsilon_i$ be the same as those required for the least squares estimation of β_0 and β_1. Then the least squares estimators B_0 and B_1 are the best linear unbiased estimators of β_0 and β_1.

While the proof of Theorem 13.1 is beyond the scope of this text, we will show that B_0 and B_1 are linear combinations of the observations Y_1, Y_2, ..., Y_n. This will permit us to show that

$$E(B_1) = \beta_1$$

and

$$Var(B_1) = \frac{\sigma^2}{\sum\limits_{i=1}^{n} (x_i - \bar{x})^2}, \tag{13.13}$$

while

$$E(B_0) = \beta_0$$

and

$$Var(B_0) = \frac{\sigma^2 \sum\limits_{i=1}^{n} x_i^2}{n \sum\limits_{i=1}^{n} (x_i - \bar{x})^2}. \tag{13.14}$$

To show that B_1 is a linear combination of Y_1, Y_2, ..., Y_n, recall the second expression of (13.6). We want to show first that

$$\sum_{i=1}^{n} (x_i - \bar{x})(Y_i - \bar{Y}) = \sum_{i=1}^{n} (x_i - \bar{x})Y_i.$$

This is true since

$$\sum (x_i - \bar{x})(Y_i - \bar{Y}) = \sum (x_i - \bar{x})Y_i - \bar{Y} \sum (x_i - \bar{x});$$

but $\Sigma(x_i - \bar{x}) = 0$, and

$$\sum (x_i - \bar{x})(Y_i - \bar{Y}) = \sum (x_i - \bar{x})Y_i.$$

Accordingly,

$$B_1 = \frac{\displaystyle\sum_{i=1}^{n} (x_i - \bar{x})Y_i}{\displaystyle\sum_{i=1}^{n} (x_i - \bar{x})^2},$$

where the x_i are fixed since they are values of the nonrandom predictor variable.

Let

$$c_i = \frac{x_i - \bar{x}}{\displaystyle\sum_{i=1}^{n} (x_i - \bar{x})^2}, \tag{13.15}$$

where the c_i's are fixed quantities since the x_i's are fixed. Then the estimator B_1 is expressed as

$$B_1 = \sum_{i=1}^{n} c_i Y_i,$$

which is seen to be a linear combination of the observations Y_1, Y_2, ..., Y_n.

To show that B_1 is an unbiased estimator of β_1, we have

$$E(B_1) = E\left(\sum_{i=1}^{n} c_i Y_i \right)$$

$$= \sum c_i E(Y_i)$$

$$= \sum c_i (\beta_0 + \beta_1 x_i)$$

$$= \beta_0 \sum_{i=1}^{n} c_i + \beta_1 \sum_{i=1}^{n} c_i x_i.$$

But

$$\sum_{i=1}^{n} c_i = \frac{\displaystyle\sum_{i=1}^{n} (x_i - \bar{x})}{\displaystyle\sum_{i=1}^{n} (x_i - \bar{x})^2} = 0,$$

and

$$\sum_{i=1}^{n} c_i x_i = \frac{\sum_{i=1}^{n} (x_i - \bar{x})x_i}{\sum_{i=1}^{n} (x_i - \bar{x})^2} = \frac{\sum (x_i - \bar{x})(x_i - \bar{x})}{\sum (x_i - \bar{x})^2} = 1.$$

Thus

$$E(B_1) = \beta_1.$$

Since by assumption the observations Y_i are pairwise uncorrelated, $Cov(Y_i, Y_j) = 0$, $i \neq j$. Then using the second part of Theorem 6.1, we show that the variance of B_1 is as given by (13.13). Thus we have

$$
\begin{aligned}
Var(B_1) &= Var\left(\sum_{i=1}^{n} c_i Y_i\right) \\
&= \sum c_i^2 Var(Y_i) \\
&= \sum c_i^2 \sigma^2 \\
&= \sigma^2 \sum c_i^2 \\
&= \sigma^2 \sum_{i=1}^{n} \left[\frac{(x_i - \bar{x})}{\sum (x_i - \bar{x})^2}\right]^2 \\
&= \sigma^2 \left\{ \sum (x_i - \bar{x})^2 \bigg/ \left[\sum (x_i - \bar{x})^2\right]^2 \right\} \\
&= \frac{\sigma^2}{\sum_{i=1}^{n} (x_i - \bar{x})^2}.
\end{aligned}
$$

The square root of $Var(B_1)$ is the standard deviation* of the least squares estimator of the slope and is given by

$$s.d.(B_1) = \frac{\sigma}{\left[\sum (x_i - \bar{x})^2\right]^{1/2}}.$$

Since the error standard deviation σ is usually unknown, we can obtain an estimate of $s.d.(B_1)$ by replacing σ with the residual standard deviation s as determined from (13.11). Thus an estimate of the standard deviation of B_1 is

$$s(B_1)** = \frac{s}{\left[\sum_{i=1}^{n} (x_i - \bar{x})^2\right]^{1/2}}. \tag{13.16}$$

*Also known as the standard error.
**We will use the convenient notation $s^2(T)$ and $s(T)$ to denote the estimated variance and standard deviation, respectively, of an estimator T.

Let us turn our attention now to the least squares estimator of the unknown intercept β_0. Since the least squares estimator is

$$B_0 = \bar{Y} - B_1\bar{x},$$

and since the least squares estimator of the slope is a linear combination of the observations $Y_1, Y_2, ..., Y_n$, then B_0 is also a linear combination of the observations. To show that B_0 is an unbiased estimator of β_0, we have

$$E(B_0) = E(\bar{Y} - B_1\bar{x})$$

$$= \frac{\sum\limits_{i=1}^{n} E(Y_i)}{n} - \bar{x}\,E(B_1)$$

$$= \frac{\sum (\beta_0 + \beta_1 x_i)}{n} - \beta_1\bar{x}$$

$$= \frac{n\beta_0 + \beta_1 \sum x_i}{n} - \beta_1\bar{x}$$

$$= \beta_0 + \beta_1\bar{x} - \beta_1\bar{x}$$

$$= \beta_0.$$

To show that $Var(B_0)$ is as given by (13.14), we will once again use the second part of Theorem 6.1 and the fact that B_0 and B_1 are linear combinations of uncorrelated random variables. Since $B_0 = \bar{Y} - B_1\bar{x}$,

$$Var(B_0) = Var(\bar{Y} - B_1\bar{x})$$

$$= Var\left(\frac{\sum Y_i}{n} - \bar{x}\sum c_i Y_i\right)$$

$$= Var\left[\sum_{i=1}^{n} \left(\frac{Y_i}{n} - \bar{x}c_i Y_i\right)\right]$$

$$= Var\left[\sum \left(\frac{1}{n} - \bar{x}c_i\right)Y_i\right]$$

$$= \sum \left(\frac{1}{n} - \bar{x}c_i\right)^2 Var(Y_i)$$

$$= \sigma^2 \sum \left(\frac{1}{n^2} - \frac{2\bar{x}c_i}{n} + \bar{x}^2 c_i^2\right)$$

$$= \sigma^2 \left(\frac{1}{n} - \frac{2\bar{x}}{n}\sum c_i + \bar{x}^2 \sum c_i^2\right).$$

Substituting (13.15) for c_i and remembering that $\Sigma c_i = 0$, we have

$$Var(B_0) = \sigma^2 \left\{ \frac{1}{n} + \bar{x}^2 \sum_{i=1}^{n} \frac{(x_i - \bar{x})^2}{\left[\sum_{i=1}^{n} (x_i - \bar{x})^2 \right]^2} \right\}$$

$$= \sigma^2 \left[\frac{1}{n} + \frac{\bar{x}^2}{\sum (x_i - \bar{x})^2} \right].$$

Finally, substituting $\bar{x}^2 = (\Sigma x_i)^2/n^2$, we obtain

$$Var(B_0) = \sigma^2 \left[\frac{1}{n} + \frac{\left(\sum x_i \right)^2}{n^2 \sum (x_i - \bar{x})^2} \right]$$

$$= \sigma^2 \left[\frac{n \sum (x_i - \bar{x})^2 + \left(\sum x_i \right)^2}{n^2 \sum (x_i - \bar{x})^2} \right]$$

$$= \frac{\sigma^2 \sum_{i=1}^{n} x_i^2}{n \sum_{i=1}^{n} (x_i - \bar{x})^2}.$$

Then an estimate of the standard deviation of B_0 is

$$s(B_0) = s \left[\frac{\sum_{i=1}^{n} x_i^2}{n \sum_{i=1}^{n} (x_i - \bar{x})^2} \right]^{1/2}. \tag{13.17}$$

It is of interest to note that the variances of B_0 and B_1 are functions of the values x_i at which the response variable is observed. In particular, for the slope estimator B_1, $Var(B_1)$ is minimized when $\Sigma(x_i - \bar{x})^2$ is maximized. But $\Sigma(x_i - \bar{x})^2$ is maximized when the distance between the values x_i is the greatest. This occurs when we choose to observe the response only at the two extreme values of the range of the predictor variable. That is, if the regression model is truly linear, then we should take $n/2$ observations at one extreme and $n/2$ at the other to have the best possible efficiency for estimating the slope of the straight line. This is logical since only two points are necessary to define a straight line. In practice, however, we are not likely to know for a fact that the regression function is linear, so it would not be prudent to select the extremes of the range of x as observation points and minimize the variance of the slope estimator. A safe alternative is to space the observation points equally throughout the range of interest for the predictor variable.

For the simple linear model, the estimated regression line given by (13.7) permits the determination of an estimate for the mean of the response variable at a specific value of the predictor variable. Let x_p be the particular value at which we wish to estimate the mean of the response variable Y_p. Then the estimate is $\hat{y}_p = b_0 + b_1 x_p$. For the same set of x values, there will be sample-to-sample variation in the estimator $\hat{Y}_p$ since there is sample-to-sample variation in the least squares estimators B_0 and B_1. This is seen to be true for the starting salary example because one is not expected to produce the same estimated regression line if another set of students with the same GPAs as the first was selected.

Of interest now is the determination of the mean and variance of $\hat{Y}_p$. $\hat{Y}_p$ is an unbiased estimator of the mean of Y_p since

$$E(\hat{Y}_p) = E(B_0 + B_1 x_p) = \beta_0 + \beta_1 x_p = E(Y_p).$$

To determine the variance of $\hat{Y}_p$, we will use the same technique as the one for the variance of B_0. Using (13.8), we have

$$Var(\hat{Y}_p) = Var[\bar{Y} + B_1(x_p - \bar{x})]$$

$$= Var\left[\frac{\sum Y_i}{n} + (x_p - \bar{x})\sum c_i Y_i\right]$$

$$= Var\left\{\sum_{i=1}^{n}\left[\frac{1}{n} + c_i(x_p - \bar{x})\right]Y_i\right\}$$

$$= \sum\left[\frac{1}{n} + c_i(x_p - \bar{x})\right]^2 Var(Y_i)$$

$$= \sigma^2\left[\frac{1}{n} + \frac{2(x_p - \bar{x})}{n}\sum c_i + (x_p - \bar{x})^2 \sum c_i^2\right]$$

$$= \sigma^2\left[\frac{1}{n} + \frac{(x_p - \bar{x})^2}{\sum(x_i - \bar{x})^2}\right]. \tag{13.18}$$

It follows that an estimate of the standard deviation of $\hat{Y}_p$ is given by

$$s(\hat{Y}_p) = s\left[\frac{1}{n} + \frac{(x_p - \bar{x})^2}{\sum(x_i - \bar{x})^2}\right]^{1/2}. \tag{13.19}$$

Instead of estimating the mean of Y_p at x_p, suppose we wish to predict a particular value of Y_p that we would observe if we imposed the value x_p for the predictor variable. For example, given the estimated regression equation, what starting salary would we predict for a particular student with a known GPA? Even though we are dealing with an individual student, it would be reasonable to predict the average starting salary for the given GPA. Thus whether we wish to estimate the mean of Y_p or a particular value of Y_p at x_p, the estimated value is the same and is given by (13.7). But it stands to reason that the variance of the prediction for the latter case would have to be larger because it has to account not only for the sample-to-sample variation of $\hat{Y}_p$ but also for the inherent variation of the probability distribution of Y_p. Assuming that the predicted value of Y_p at x_p is independent of the sample that yielded the estimated regression line, the covariance of Y_p and $\hat{Y}_p$ is zero. Then

$$Var(\hat{Y}_{\text{part}}) = Var(Y_p) + Var(\hat{Y}_p)$$

$$= \sigma^2 + \sigma^2 \left[\frac{1}{n} + \frac{(x_p - \bar{x})^2}{\sum (x_i - \bar{x})^2} \right]$$

$$= \sigma^2 \left[1 + \frac{1}{n} + \frac{(x_p - \bar{x})^2}{\sum (x_i - \bar{x})^2} \right], \tag{13.20}$$

where $\hat{Y}_{\text{part}}$ denotes the particular prediction for Y_p at x_p. It follows from previous discussion that an estimate of the standard deviation of $\hat{Y}_{\text{part}}$ is given by

$$s(\hat{Y}_{\text{part}}) = s \left[1 + \frac{1}{n} + \frac{(x_p - \bar{x})^2}{\sum (x_i - \bar{x})^2} \right]^{1/2}. \tag{13.21}$$

Using the starting salary data and Table 13.2, we now illustrate the computation of the variances and standard deviations of the least squares estimators B_1 and B_0. Since

$$\sum (x_i - \bar{x})^2 = \sum x_i^2 - \left(\sum x_i \right)^2 / n = 0.886$$

and $s^2 = 1.759$,

$$s^2(B_1) = \frac{1.759}{0.886} = 1.985,$$

and

$$s(B_1) = 1.409.$$

Similarly

$$s^2(B_0) = \frac{(1.759)(139.51)}{(15)(0.886)} = 18.465$$

and

$$s(B_0) = 4.297.$$

Continuing with this example, suppose we wish to estimate the mean of the distribution of starting salaries when the GPA is $x_p = 3.25$. Notice that this value is not one of the x values that produced the estimated regression line, but it certainly is within their range. From (13.10) and (13.18), the estimated mean and variance for $x_p = 3.25$ are

$$\hat{y}_p = -6.63 \pm 8.12(3.25) = 19.76$$

and

$$s^2(\hat{Y}_p) = 1.759 \left[\frac{1}{15} + \frac{(3.25 - 3.04)^2}{0.886} \right] = 0.205,$$

respectively. Thus the estimated standard deviation is $\sqrt{0.205} = 0.453$ thousand dollars. If we wish to predict the actual starting salary for a particular student with a GPA of 3.25, the estimated value would still be 19.76 thousand dollars, but the estimated variance would be

$$1.759 \left[1 + \frac{1}{15} + \frac{(3.25 - 3.04)^2}{0.886} \right] = 1.964,$$

or a standard deviation of 1.401 thousand dollars.

So far in this section we have determined the means and variances of the estimators B_0, B_1, $\hat{Y}_p$ and $\hat{Y}_{\text{part}}$, but we have yet to develop their sampling distributions. To do this, it is necessary to assume the normal theory case of the last section in which the distribution of each random error ε_i was assumed to be normal with mean zero and variance σ^2 for all $i = 1, 2, ..., n$. Then the observations $Y_1, Y_2, ..., Y_n$ are independent, normally distributed random variables with means $\beta_0 + \beta_1 x_i$ and a common variance σ^2, for $i = 1, 2, ..., n$.

To determine the sampling distribution of the slope estimator B_1 under the normal theory case, we need only recall that B_1 is a linear combination of normally distributed random variables, and thus is itself a normally distributed random variable with mean β_1 and variance as given by (13.13). By recalling the definition of a Student's t random variable, one can show that the distribution of the quantity

$$(B_1 - \beta_1)/s(B_1)$$

is Student's t with $n - 2$ degrees of freedom. The estimator B_0 is also a linear combination of normally distributed random variables. Thus B_0 is also normally distributed with mean β_0 and variance given by (13.14). Moreover, it can be shown that the quantity

$$(B_0 - \beta_0)/s(B_0)$$

is a Student's t random variable with $n - 2$ degrees of freedom. As we will see in the next section, these results permit statistical inferences to be made about the unknown parameters β_0 and β_1.

Under the normal theory case, the estimator $\hat{Y}_p = B_0 + B_1 x_p$ of the mean of Y_p at x_p is also normally distributed with mean $E(Y_p)$ and variance as given by (13.18) since it is a linear combination of normally distributed random variables. Then the distribution of

$$[\hat{Y}_p - E(Y_p)]/s(\hat{Y}_p)$$

is Student's t with, once again, $n - 2$ degrees of freedom. A similar result is also obtained for the prediction $\hat{Y}_{\text{part}}$ for a particular response Y_p at x_p. The $n - 2$ degrees of freedom for the preceding quantities should be understandable because the determination of the estimated regression line requires estimation of the two regression parameters β_0 and β_1.

13.6   Statistical Inference for the Simple Linear Model

In the last section we examined the theoretical properties of estimators for the simple linear model. In this section we use these properties to perform a regression analysis. That is, we develop confidence intervals and tests of hypotheses for the quantities of interest in this model.

The key parameter of the simple linear model

$$Y_i = \beta_0 + \beta_1 x_i + \varepsilon_i$$

has to be the slope β_1. If the response Y is linearly related to the predictor variable x, the slope β_1 has to be different from zero. Otherwise there is no linear relationship between Y and x. A natural inferential procedure for β_1 is to construct a $100(1 - \alpha)\%$ confidence interval for β_1. If this interval does not contain the value zero, it would be reasonable to conclude that β_1 is different from zero and that Y and x are, to some degree, linearly related.

Recall that under the normal theory case, the random variable $(B_1 - \beta_1)/s(B_1)$ is Student's t distributed with $n - 2$ degrees of freedom. Then

$$P[B_1 - t_{1-\alpha/2, \, n-2}s(B_1) < \beta_1 < B_1 + t_{1-\alpha/2, \, n-2}s(B_1)] = 1 - \alpha,$$

or the probability of the random interval $[B_1 - t_{1-\alpha/2, \, n-2}s(B_1), \; B_1 + t_{1-\alpha/2, \, n-2}s(B_1)]$ containing the true slope β_1 is $1 - \alpha$. Replacing the least squares estimator B_1 by its estimate given by (13.6), a $100(1 - \alpha)\%$ confidence interval for β_1 is

$$b_1 \pm t_{1-\alpha/2, \, n-2}s(B_1),$$

where the estimated standard deviation $s(B_1)$ is given by (13.16). For illustration, recall the estimated regression line $\hat{y}_i = -6.63 + 8.12x_i$ for the starting salary data. Since $b_1 = 8.12$ and $s(B_1) = 1.409$, then a 95% confidence interval for β_1 is

$$8.12 \pm (2.160)(1.409) = (5.08, 11.16),$$

where $t_{0.975, \, 13} = 2.160$. The interpretation of this interval is as follows. Suppose repeated samples of size n of the response variable are taken for the same values of x that produced the estimated line $\hat{y}_i = -6.63 + 8.12x_i$, and each time a 95% confidence interval is constructed for β_1. Then 95% of these intervals would contain the true value of the slope β_1.

Consider testing the null hypothesis

$$H_0: \beta_1 = \beta_{1_0}$$

against the alternative

$$H_1: \beta_1 \neq \beta_{1_0}$$

where β_{1_0} is the claimed value of the unknown slope β_1. Under H_0, the statistic

$$T = \frac{B_1 - \beta_{1_0}}{s(B_1)}$$

has a Student's t distribution with $n - 2$ degrees of freedom. Thus for a given size of type I error, the decision regarding H_0 can be made easily based on the sample evidence. Note that one-sided alternative hypotheses are also possible.

As was the case in previous situations, any claimed value for β_1 that is contained in the corresponding confidence interval would cause a failure to reject H_0. Usually the claimed value is zero; that is, the null hypothesis states there is no linear association between x and Y. Then the value of the test statistic is

$$t = b_1/s(B_1).$$

For illustration, consider testing the null hypothesis

$$H_0: \beta_1 = 0$$

against the alternative

$$H_1: \beta_1 > 0$$

for the starting salary versus GPA example. We have selected a one-sided alternative hypothesis because common sense dictates that if there is a linear relationship between GPA and starting salary, the slope should be positive. Say $\alpha = 0.01$; then $t_{0.99,\ 13} = 2.650$, and

$$t = 8.12/1.409 = 5.76.$$

The null hypothesis of zero slope is rejected. This result, along with the confidence interval for β_1, does suggest that the average starting salary is linearly influenced by the grade point average.

A confidence interval for the intercept parameter β_0 can also be constructed in a similar manner. Since $(B_0 - \beta_0)/s(B_0) \sim$ Student's t with $n - 2$ degrees of freedom,

$$P[B_0 - t_{1-\alpha/2,\ n-2}s(B_0) < \beta_0 < B_0 + t_{1-\alpha/2,\ n-2}s(B_0)] = 1 - \alpha$$

is a random interval for β_0 with probability $1 - \alpha$. It follows that a $100(1 - \alpha)\%$ confidence interval for β_0 is

$$b_0 \pm t_{1-\alpha/2,\ n-2}s(B_0)$$

where b_0 is the least squares estimate, and $s(B_0)$ is the estimated standard deviation. Using the starting salary example, a 99% confidence interval for β_0 is

$$-6.63 \pm (3.012)(4.297) = (-19.57, 6.31).$$

The reader should be aware that the meaning of such an interval for this particular example is not at all apparent since the regression model is meaningless if the grade point average $x = 0$. Generally, inferences about the intercept should be avoided altogether unless there is data for the response at $x = 0$.

We now consider interval estimation of the mean of Y_p at x_p. Recall that under the normal theory case, the estimator $\hat{Y}_p = B_0 + B_1x_p$ is normally distributed with mean $E(Y_p)$ and variance as given by (13.18), and the sampling distribution of $[\hat{Y}_p - E(Y_p)]/s(\hat{Y}_p)$ is Student's t with $n - 2$ degrees of freedom. Then the probability of the random interval

$$\hat{Y}_p - t_{1-\alpha/2,\, n-2} s(\hat{Y}_p) < E(Y_p) < \hat{Y}_p + t_{1-\alpha/2,\, n-2} s(\hat{Y}_p)$$

is $1 - \alpha$, and a $100(1 - \alpha)\%$ confidence interval for $E(Y_p)$ is

$$\hat{y}_p \pm t_{1-\alpha/2,\, n-2} s(\hat{Y}_p).$$

In the starting salary example, suppose we wish to construct a 95% confidence interval for the mean of Y_p at $x_p = 2.80$. The estimated value is

$$\hat{y}_p = -6.63 + 8.12(2.80) = 16.11$$

and the estimated standard deviation is

$$s(\hat{Y}_p) = \left\{ 1.759 \left[\frac{1}{15} + \frac{(2.80 - 3.04)^2}{0.886} \right] \right\}^{1/2} = 0.481.$$

Since $t_{0.975,\, 13} = 2.160$, a 95% confidence interval for $E(Y_p)$ is

$$16.11 \pm (2.160)(0.481) = (15.07, 17.15).$$

Following this procedure, we determine 95% confidence intervals for $E(Y_p)$ at various other values of the predictor variable. The results are summarized in Table 13.3.

To illustrate the nature of these confidence intervals as compared to values of the predictor variable, we graph the estimated regression line, then plot the upper and lower limits of each interval against x_p. The result is illustrated in Figure 13.3. Notice that the upper and lower limits form two hyperbolas about the estimated regression line. The vertical distance from each curve to the regression line is shortest at the point $\bar{x} = 3.04$ and increases symmetrically in both directions away from $\bar{x}$ at an increasing rate. Simply put, the preceding results indicate that the prediction of $E(Y_p)$ is more reliable (smaller variance) around the middle of the x values that produced the estimated regression equation than at the extremes of the range of x.

TABLE 13.3   Confidence intervals for mean starting salaries

x_p	$\hat{y}_p$	$s(\hat{Y}_p)$	95% confidence interval
2.60	14.48	0.708	(12.95, 16.01)
2.70	15.29	0.589	(14.02, 16.56)
2.80	16.11	0.481	(15.07, 17.15)
2.90	16.92	0.395	(16.07, 17.77)
3.00	17.73	0.347	(16.98, 18.48)
3.10	18.54	0.353	(17.78, 19.30)
3.20	19.35	0.410	(18.46, 20.24)
3.30	20.17	0.501	(19.09, 21.25)
3.40	20.98	0.612	(19.66, 22.30)
3.50	21.79	0.733	(20.21, 23.37)
3.60	22.60	0.860	(20.74, 24.46)

FIGURE 13.3 Confidence intervals and the estimated regression line

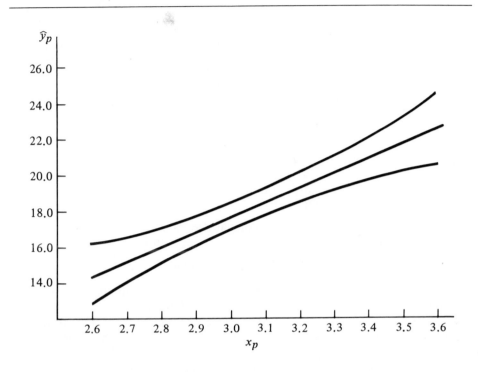

Recall that a user may be more interested in predicting a particular response for a given x than in estimating the mean response at the x value. While the predicted value would be the same in either case, the variability of the estimate relative to the particular response is decidedly larger than that for the mean response. Since under the normal theory case the quantity $[\hat{Y}_{\text{part}} - Y_p]/s(\hat{Y}_{\text{part}})$ is a Student's t random variable with $n - 2$ degrees of freedom, then for a given α,

$$P[\hat{Y}_{\text{part}} - t_{1-\alpha/2,\,n-2}s(\hat{Y}_{\text{part}}) < Y_p < \hat{Y}_{\text{part}} + t_{1-\alpha/2,\,n-2}s(\hat{Y}_{\text{part}})] = 1 - \alpha.$$

Based on this result, we can determine what is usually called a *prediction interval* for the observation Y_p. A prediction interval is analogous to a confidence interval. A $100(1 - \alpha)\%$ prediction interval for a particular observation Y_p is

$$\hat{y}_{\text{part}} \pm t_{1-\alpha/2,\,n-2}s(\hat{Y}_{\text{part}}).$$

Let us construct a 95% prediction interval for the starting salary of a particular graduating senior whose grade point average is 2.80. The predicted value would be the same as for the mean response,

$$\hat{y}_{\text{part}} = -6.63 + 8.12(2.80) = 16.11;$$

TABLE 13.4 Prediction intervals for individual starting salaries

x_p	$\hat{y}_{\text{part}}$	$s(\hat{Y}_{\text{part}})$	95% prediction interval
2.60	14.48	1.503	(11.23, 17.73)
2.80	16.11	1.411	(13.06, 19.16)
2.90	16.92	1.384	(13.93, 19.91)
3.00	17.73	1.371	(14.77, 20.69)
3.30	20.17	1.418	(17.11, 23.23)
3.50	21.79	1.515	(18.52, 25.06)

but the estimated standard deviation is

$$s(\hat{Y}_{\text{part}}) = \left\{ 1.759 \left[1 + \frac{1}{15} + \frac{(2.80 - 3.04)^2}{0.886} \right] \right\}^{1/2} = 1.411,$$

which is quite a bit larger than the comparable value of 0.481 for $\hat{Y}_p$. Then a 95% prediction interval for Y_p is

$$16.11 \pm (2.160)(1.411) = (13.06, 19.16).$$

In Table 13.4 we provide 95% prediction intervals for observations of the response corresponding to the values of x in Table 13.3 that were not part of the original set that produced the estimated regression equation. As expected, prediction intervals for individual observations of the response are much wider than the corresponding confidence intervals for the mean response.

Since regression analysis has been based on the normal theory case, it is appropriate to comment on the inference consequences when the probability distributions of the random errors are not normal. If the deviation from normality is not extreme, the sampling distributions of the estimators will be approximately normal and will approach normality as the sample size increases. Under these conditions, the Student's t distribution remains largely robust and provides close approximations to the stated confidence levels.

13.7 The Use of Analysis of Variance

Regression analysis for the simple linear model also encompasses the application of the analysis of variance technique discussed in Chapter 12. In substance, the analysis of variance technique provides only an alternative approach to that of Section 13.6 for testing the null hypothesis that the slope is zero. However, it permits an innate understanding of the problem and therefore is especially useful for the analysis of more complicated models, which will be taken up later.

Recall that the analysis of variance technique partitions the total variation of the observations into its component parts as prescribed by the assumed model. In essence, for the simple linear model, the total variation is the sum of two components: that which is due to the nonrandom term $\beta_1 x$, and that which is due to the random error ε. Since the objective is for the estimated regression line to account for as much as possible of the total variation, the contribution of the term $\beta_1 x$ must be substantial. Such a result would imply that the response and predictor variables are linearly related. If $\beta_1 = 0$, there is no linear association between x and Y.

To develop the analysis of variance approach, we follow the procedure established in Chapter 12. Consider the deviation of the observation Y_i from the mean of the observations $\overline{Y}$. For the moment assume that all observations Y_i are the same. Then the slope β_1 must be zero, $\varepsilon_i = 0$, and $Y_i = \overline{Y}$ for all i. On the other hand, if the magnitude of the deviation $Y_i - \overline{Y}$ is greater than zero, it must be attributed to the components of the model.

To the deviation

$$Y_i - \overline{Y}$$

suppose we add and subtract the estimator $\hat{Y}_i$ for the mean of Y_i as determined from the regression equation. Then

$$Y_i - \overline{Y} = Y_i - \overline{Y} + \hat{Y}_i - \hat{Y}_i$$

$$= \hat{Y}_i - \overline{Y} + Y_i - \hat{Y}_i.$$

Thus the total deviation of the observation Y_i around the mean $\overline{Y}$ is the sum of the deviation of the estimated mean response $\hat{Y}_i$ from $\overline{Y}$ and the deviation of Y_i from $\hat{Y}_i$. Notice that the last difference is the estimator for the ith residual, which represents the vertical distance from the observed response to the corresponding point on the estimated regression line. The deviations $Y_i - \hat{Y}_i$ represent the contribution of the error component to the total variation. Recall that $\hat{Y}_i$ estimates the mean of Y_i at x_i. If the predictor variable has no linear effect on the response, then $\hat{Y}_i$ is virtually the same as $\overline{Y}$ for all i. That is, $\beta_1 = 0$, and the least squares estimator of β_0 is $\overline{Y}$. It follows that if the magnitude of the deviation $\hat{Y}_i - \overline{Y}$ is great, then a linear effect of x on Y ($\beta_1 \neq 0$) is implied.

To proceed with the analysis of variance approach, we take the identity

$$Y_i - \overline{Y} = \hat{Y}_i - \overline{Y} + Y_i - \hat{Y}_i,$$

square both sides and sum over all observations $i = 1, 2, ..., n$. Then we have

$$\sum_{i=1}^{n} (Y_i - \overline{Y})^2 = \sum_{i=1}^{n} (\hat{Y}_i - \overline{Y})^2 + \sum_{i=1}^{n} (Y_i - \hat{Y}_i)^2 + 2 \sum_{i=1}^{n} (\hat{Y}_i - \overline{Y})(Y_i - \hat{Y}_i).$$

To show that the cross-product term is zero, let us rewrite the last sum as

$$\sum (\hat{Y}_i - \overline{Y})(Y_i - \hat{Y}_i) = \sum [\hat{Y}_i(Y_i - \hat{Y}_i) - \overline{Y}(Y_i - \hat{Y}_i)]$$

$$= \sum \hat{Y}_i(Y_i - \hat{Y}_i) - \overline{Y} \sum (Y_i - \hat{Y}_i).$$

The second sum is zero from Property 1 of the estimated regression line as discussed in Section 13.3. The first sum may be written as

$$\sum \hat{Y}_i (Y_i - \hat{Y}_i) = \sum \hat{Y}_i e_i$$

$$= \sum (B_0 + B_1 x_i) e_i$$

$$= B_0 \sum e_i + B_1 \sum x_i e_i$$

$$= 0,$$

Since Σe_i and $\Sigma x_i e_i$ are both zero from Properties 1 and 3, respectively. Thus the fundamental equation of regression analysis is

$$\sum_{i=1}^{n} (Y_i - \overline{Y})^2 = \sum_{i=1}^{n} (\hat{Y}_i - \overline{Y})^2 + \sum_{i=1}^{n} (Y_i - \hat{Y}_i)^2. \tag{13.22}$$

Adhering to the terminology of Chapter 12, the term $\Sigma(Y_i - \overline{Y})^2$ is the total sum of squares (SST); it accounts for the total variation of the observations Y_i about their mean without regard to the predictor variable. The components of SST are the error sum of squares SSE $= \Sigma(Y_i - \hat{Y}_i)^2$ and the *regression sum of squares* SSR $= \Sigma(\hat{Y}_i - \overline{Y})^2$. SSE accounts for the variation of the observations from the estimated regression line. If all observations fell on the estimated line, all residuals would be zero and SSE $= 0$. It follows that the larger SSE is, the larger is the contribution of the error component to the variation of the observations, or the larger is the uncertainty when the response is estimated by using the regression equation. On the other hand, SSR represents the variation of the observations that is attributed to the linear effect of x on Y. If the slope of the estimated regression line is zero, then SSR $= 0$. Thus the larger the proportion SSR is of SST, the more the linear term $\beta_1 x$ accounts for the variation in the observations.

We now turn to the degrees of freedom associated with each term in (13.22). Recall the definition of the number of degrees of freedom associated with a sum of squares given in Chapter 12. For SST there are $n - 1$ degrees of freedom since one degree of freedom is lost due to the linear constraint $\Sigma(Y_i - \overline{Y}) = 0$ among the observations Y_i. Notice that SSE is the numerator in Expression (13.11) for the computation of the residual variance, so the degrees of freedom for SSE will be $n - 2$.* Since the degrees of freedom are additive,

$$\text{df(SSR)} = \text{df(SST)} - \text{df(SSE)},$$

and SSR has a single degree of freedom. As we will observe later when we deal with more complicated models, the degrees of freedom for SSR will always be equal to the number of regression parameters in the model, not counting β_0.

For analysis of variance, we now seek a statistic to test the null hypothesis

$$H_0: \beta_1 = 0$$

against the alternative

$$H_1: \beta_1 \neq 0.$$

---

*Actually the two degrees of freedom lost are due to the two linear constraints given by Properties 1 and 3 in Section 13.3.

H_0 is usually known as the hypothesis of no linear regression between x and Y. If we assume the normal theory case, then under the null hypothesis the observations Y_i are n independently distributed normal random variables with the same mean $\mu = \beta_0$ and the same variance σ^2. It can therefore be shown that SSR/σ^2 and SSE/σ^2 are two independent chi-square distributed random variables with 1 and $n - 2$ degrees of freedom, respectively. Then from Theorem 7.8, the random variable

$$F = \frac{\dfrac{SSR/\sigma^2}{1}}{\dfrac{SSE/\sigma^2}{n-2}} = \frac{SSR/1}{SSE/(n-2)} = MSR/MSE \tag{13.23}$$

is F distributed with 1 and $n - 2$ degrees of freedom, where the error mean square is the same as the residual variance.

Let us use our intuition to arrive at the appropriate rejection region for H_0 as suggested by (13.23). Based on a given set of data, a large value for MSE relative to MSR would imply a poor fit and would suggest the absence of a linear association between x and Y. But a relatively small value for MSE would imply that a considerable portion of the variation in the observations is attributable to the linear effect of x on Y. It follows, therefore, that the null hypothesis of no linear regression between x and Y should be rejected as long as a value of (13.23) is relatively large. Otherwise, the experimental evidence does not support the rejection of H_0. On a more theoretical basis, it can be shown that

$$E(MSR) = \sigma^2 + \beta_1^2 \sum (x_i - \bar{x})^2$$

and

$$E(MSE) = \sigma^2.$$

Then if H_0 is true, the expected value of MSR is also σ^2. But if $\beta_1 \neq 0$, $E(MSR)$ is greater than σ^2 since the term $\beta_1^2 \Sigma(x_i - \bar{x})^2$ is positive. Therefore, the appropriate statistic is as given by (13.23) with the upper tail of the F distribution serving as the critical region. That is, for a given size of type I error α, the null hypothesis of no linear regression is rejected when a value of $F = MSR/MSE$ is inside the upper-tail critical region of an F distribution with 1 and $n - 2$ degrees of freedom. The analysis of variance (ANOVA) table for the simple linear model is Table 13.5.

To compute the sums of squares in Table 13.5, we have

$$SST = \sum (y_i - \bar{y})^2 = \sum y_i^2 - \frac{\left(\sum y_i\right)^2}{n},$$

$$SSE = \sum (y_i - \hat{y}_i)^2 = \sum e_i^2,$$

where $y_1, y_2, \ldots, y_n$ are the realizations of the observations and $e_1, e_2, \ldots, e_n$ are the corresponding residuals. Then $SSR = SST - SSE$, or it may be computed

TABLE 13.5 ANOVA table for the simple linear model

Source of variation	df	SS	MS	F statistic
Regression	1	$\sum (\hat{Y}_i - \overline{Y})^2$	$\sum (\hat{Y}_i - \overline{Y})^2/1$	
				$\dfrac{\sum (\hat{Y}_i - \overline{Y})^2/1}{\sum (Y_i - \hat{Y}_i)^2/(n-2)}$
Error	$n-2$	$\sum (Y_i - \hat{Y}_i)^2$	$\sum (Y_i - \hat{Y}_i)^2/(n-2)$	
Total	$n-1$	$\sum (Y_i - \overline{Y})^2$		

directly. Since the estimated regression line is

$$\hat{y}_i = \overline{y} + b_1(x_i - \overline{x})$$

or

$$\hat{y}_i - \overline{y} = b_1(x_i - \overline{x}),$$

squaring and summing both sides over all $i = 1, 2, ..., n$ yields

$$\text{SSR} = \sum (\hat{y}_i - \overline{y})^2 = b_1^2 \sum (x_i - \overline{x})^2. \tag{13.24}$$

For illustration, recall again the starting salary problem. Say we want to test the null hypothesis that there is no linear regression between starting salary and GPA against the alternative that there is, with $\alpha = 0.01$. Using Table 13.2, we compute the following quantities:

$$\text{SST} = 4970.12 - \frac{(270.8)^2}{15} = 81.2773,$$

$$\text{SSE} = 22.8671,$$

$$\text{SSR} = 81.2773 - 22.8671 = 58.4102.$$

For $n = 15$ the ANOVA table is as in Table 13.6. Since $f = 33.21 > f_{0.99, 1, 13} = 9.07$, the null hypothesis of no linear regression is rejected, and we conclude that the average starting salary is linearly influenced by the grade point average.

As one would expect, there is a relationship between the preceding F statistic

TABLE 13.6 ANOVA table for starting salaries

Source of variation	df	SS	MS	F value
Regression	1	58.4102	58.4102	
				33.21
Error	13	22.8671	1.759	
Total	14	81.2773		$f_{0.99, 1, 13} = 9.07$

with 1 and $n - 2$ degrees of freedom and the corresponding Student's t statistic (see Section 13.6) for a two-sided alternative hypothesis. The relationship can be established by the following. Since

$$SSR = B_1^2 \sum (x_i - \bar{x})^2$$

and

$$s^2(B_1) = MSE \Big/ \sum (x_i - \bar{x})^2,$$

then

$$F = \frac{MSR}{MSE} = \frac{B_1^2 \sum (x_1 - \bar{x})^2/1}{s^2(B_1) \sum (x_i - \bar{x})^2} = [B_1/s(B_1)]^2.$$

Accordingly, if a random variable is F distributed with 1 and $n - 2$ degrees of freedom, then

$$F = T^2,$$

where T is a Student's t random variable with $n - 2$ degrees of freedom. The relation between the quantile values is

$$f_{1-\alpha, 1, n-2} = t^2_{1-\alpha/2, n-2}. \tag{13.25}$$

So far we have examined ways for testing the null hypothesis of no linear regression between x and Y. Now we discuss a useful numerical quantity that is a relative measure of the degree of linear association between x and Y. What we are looking for is a quantity that measures the proportion of the total variation of the observations about their mean that is attributed to the estimated regression line. Since SST represents the total variation about the mean and SSR measures the portion that is attributed to the linear effect of x on Y, an appropriate relative measure is

$$r^2 = \frac{SSR}{SST} = \frac{SST - SSE}{SST} = 1 - \frac{SSE}{SST}. \tag{13.26}$$

r^2 is called the *coefficient of determination*. Its range is always the interval $0 \leq r^2 \leq 1$ since $0 \leq SSE \leq SST$. Ideally, we would like to have $r^2 = 1$ because then SSE $= 0$, and all of the variation in the observations is explained by the linear presence of x in the regression equation. Thus the closer r^2 is to one, the higher is the degree of linear association between x and Y. To illustrate, the coefficient of determination for the starting salary example is

$$r^2 = 1 - \frac{22.8671}{81.2773} = 0.7187.$$

Therefore, the linear presence of the GPA in the regression model accounts for 71.87 percent of the total variation in the observed starting salaries.

Because r^2 has been misinterpreted, we should comment on what r^2 does not measure. r^2 does *not* measure the validity of the assumed regression model.

That is, r^2 cannot verify that the true regression equation between x and Y is strictly linear. All it can measure is how much of the total variation is explained by the estimated regression equation. In reality, the true regression model between x and Y may very well contain nonlinear terms in x, or other predictor variables, or both. Such issues will be examined in Chapter 14.

Now we would like to provide a sample computer printout for the linear regression analysis of the salary data. The list of available statistical computer packages includes SAS, SPSS, BMDP, and Minitab. The printout in Figure 13.4 was generated by Minitab. Notice that the printout includes the estimated regression coefficients, their standard deviations, the T test for zero slope, the residual standard deviation (or the standard deviation of Y about the regression line), the

FIGURE 13.4   Sample computer printout for linear regression analysis (starting salary data)

```
THE REGRESSION EQUATION IS
Y = - 6.63 + 8.12 X1

                                                    ST. DEV.        T-RATIO =
             COLUMN           COEFFICIENT           OF COEF.        COEF/S.D.
             -                 - 6.627              4.298            -1.54
X1           C2                  8.118              1.409             5.76

THE ST. DEV. OF Y ABOUT REGRESSION LINE IS
S = 1.327
WITH ( 15- 2) = 13 DEGREES OF FREEDOM

R-SQUARED = 71.8 PERCENT

ANALYSIS OF VARIANCE
   DUE TO          DF           SS            MS=SS/DF
REGRESSION         1         58.393          58.393
RESIDUAL          13         22.880           1.760
TOTAL             14         81.274

           X1         Y       PRED. Y      ST.DEV.
ROW        C2         C1       VALUE      PRED. Y    RESIDUAL    ST.RES.
  1       2.95      18.500    17.323       0.365      1.177       0.92
  2       3.20      20.000    19.352       0.410      0.648       0.51
  3       3.40      21.100    20.976       0.612      0.124       0.11
  4       3.60      22.400    22.600       0.860     -0.200      -0.20
  5       3.20      21.200    19.352       0.410      1.848       1.46
  6       2.85      15.000    16.511       0.435     -1.511      -1.21
  7       3.10      18.000    18.540       0.353     -0.540      -0.42
  8       2.85      18.800    16.511       0.435      2.289       1.83
  9       3.05      15.700    18.134       0.343     -2.434      -1.90
 10       2.70      14.400    15.293       0.589     -0.893      -0.75
 11       2.75      15.500    15.699       0.533     -0.199      -0.16
 12       3.10      17.200    18.540       0.353     -1.340      -1.05
 13       3.15      19.000    18.946       0.376      0.054       0.04
 14       2.95      17.200    17.323       0.365     -0.123      -0.10
 15       2.75      16.800    15.699       0.533      1.101       0.91
```

r^2 value, the sums of squares and mean squares for the analysis of variance, and the standardized residuals as defined in Chapter 12.

13.8   Linear Correlation

In Section 6.4 we defined the correlation coefficient ρ given by (6.14) as a measure of linear association between the random variables X and Y. In this section we will examine the sample correlation coefficient in the context of regression analysis.

Throughout the discussion of regression analysis, we have assumed the availability of a random sample of responses $Y_1, Y_2, ..., Y_n$, corresponding to n fixed values $x_1, x_2, ..., x_n$ of a predictor variable. To define the sample correlation coefficient, we assume that both X and Y are random variables. Let the joint distribution of X and Y be bivariate normal (see Section 6.8), and let (X_1, Y_1), $(X_2, Y_2), ..., (X_n, Y_n)$ be a random sample of size n from this distribution. Then it can be shown that the maximum likelihood estimator of ρ — called the *sample correlation coefficient* — is given by

$$r^*(X, Y) = \frac{\sum_{i=1}^{n} (X_i - \overline{X})(Y_i - \overline{Y})}{\left[\sum_{i=1}^{n} (X_i - \overline{X})^2\right]^{1/2} \left[\sum_{i=1}^{n} (Y_i - \overline{Y})^2\right]^{1/2}}. \tag{13.27}$$

After some algebra we can determine an equivalent expression of the form

$$r(X, Y) = \frac{\sum X_i Y_i - \dfrac{\left(\sum X_i\right)\left(\sum Y_i\right)}{n}}{\left[\sum X_i^2 - \dfrac{\left(\sum X_i\right)^2}{n}\right]^{1/2} \left[\sum Y_i^2 - \dfrac{\left(\sum Y_i\right)^2}{n}\right]^{1/2}}. \tag{13.28}$$

Like the parameter ρ, r falls in the range $-1 \leqslant r \leqslant 1$ and measures the linear relationship between X and Y, whether X is used to predict Y or vice versa. Based on a random sample, a value of $r = -1$ indicates a perfect negative linear relation between X and Y, while a value of $r = 1$ indicates a perfect positive linear association of X and Y. If $r = 0$, then there is no linear relationship between X and Y. Typical scatter plots are illustrated for some values of r in Figure 13.5.

Because various unjustifiable interpretations of r have surfaced, it is imperative for the reader to understand that r by itself can neither prove nor disprove causation between X and Y even if $r = \pm 1$. As we have indicated earlier in this chapter, the manifestation of a cause-and-effect relationship is possible only

*We will adhere to tradition and use a lower case r.

FIGURE 13.5 Typical scatter plots for some values of *r*

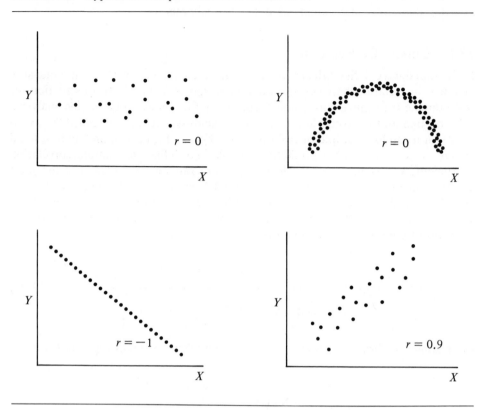

through understanding the natural relationship between *X* and *Y*, and should not be implied by merely producing a strong correlation between *X* and *Y*.

While in regression analysis we assume the *x* values are fixed, the sample correlation coefficient as defined by (13.27) or (13.28) is still an estimator of ρ. Since *r* measures the degree of linear association between *x* and *Y* and since B_1 is the corresponding least squares estimator of the slope in the assumed linear model between *x* and *Y*, then *r* and B_1 must be related. Using the second equation of (13.6) and (13.27), we can show that the least squares estimate of the slope and the corresponding value of the sample correlation coefficient are related by

$$b_1 = \left[\frac{\sum (y_i - \bar{y})^2}{\sum (x_i - \bar{x})^2} \right]^{1/2} r. \tag{13.29}$$

Notice that if $r = 0$, $b_1 = 0$ and vice versa. Moreover, the sign of b_1 is always the same as the sign of *r*. Finally, the square of the sample correlation coefficient is the coefficient of determination. That is, if r^2 and b_1 are known, then *r* and its sign are known. It follows, therefore, that not only can *r* measure the degree of linear association between two variables, but a function of *r* can be used as a measure of the goodness of fit for an estimated regression equation.

13.9 Time Series and Autocorrelation

In the preceding sections of this chapter, we have examined regression and correlation analyses based on a random sample of the response variable *Y*. In many situations, such as in business and economics, the response variable is measured periodically over time. For example, we may choose to examine the unemployment rate for the previous 24 months, or we may observe the quarterly sales volume of some company and compare it to the corresponding sales volume for the entire industry during the previous twelve quarters. Since in both of these examples the observations are recorded sequentially over time, they form what is known as a *time series*.

Although regression methods can be useful in analyzing time series data, the observations of *Y* in a time series cannot be regarded as representing a random sample. In fact, they may be correlated with each other. For example, the movement in the unemployment rate for this month is likely to be related to the movement in the rate that is observed for next month. Thus some of the assumptions that were necessary for the development of inferential procedures are not likely to hold for time series data.

In this context we wish to consider a useful inferential procedure known as the Durbin–Watson statistic for determining whether the errors in a simple linear model* are correlated over time. Errors of the same regression model that are correlated as functions of time are said to be *serially correlated* or *autocorrelated*. Before we discuss the Durbin–Watson procedure, we will briefly mention the usual components of time series data.

13.9.1 Components of a Time Series

The fluctuations of the response variable in an economic time series are usually assigned to four different causes (components): trend variation *T*, seasonal variation *S*, cyclical variation *C*, and random variation *R*. *Trend variation* is the long-term movement in *Y*. For example, auto production in the United States has exhibited an upward trend during the past 50 years, but this does not necessarily mean that auto production increased every year during this period. Thus trend reflects the general movement of *Y* over a long period of time. *Seasonal variation* represents the movement of *Y* that recurs during specific periods within a year. For example, retail sales tend to be higher during the fourth quarter and lower during the first quarter of a given year. The *cyclical variation* depicts the movement of *Y* that is repeated over time periods that are usually longer than a year. Cyclical movements are often related to prevailing economic conditions. For example, the number of housing starts in the United States decreased during the recession of 1974–75, increased during the recovery period of 1976–79, and decreased again during the recession of 1981–82. *Random variation* in a time series is the fluctuation of *Y* that cannot be assigned to an identifiable cause. Therefore, the total fluctuation in *Y* over time is assigned to systematic variation (trend, seasonal, and cyclical) and to random variation.

By assuming how these components are related, we can formulate a time

---

*This procedure can also be used for the general linear model, which is discussed in Chapter 14.

series model that will help us separate these components and make forecasts about Y. Time series models are usually additive of the form

$$Y = T + S + C + R$$

or multiplicative of the form

$$Y = T \times S \times C \times R.$$

For an additive model we assume that the four components are independent of one another, while for a multiplicative model we assume that they are related. Suggested references for thorough treatments of time series analyses are [1] and [4].

13.9.2   The Durbin–Watson Statistic

In this section we will concentrate on the detection of autocorrelated errors and a discussion of remedial measures. One reason for autocorrelation is that important predictor variables may have been left out of the regression model. For example, we mentioned that auto production has generally increased over the last 50 years. If we assume some regression model with time as the only predictor variable, we would no doubt find correlation among the errors. But during the same period, there has been an increase in the population as well as an upward movement in the economic well-being of the people in the United States. When predictor variables such as these are positively correlated with auto production but are left out of the regression model, then errors will tend to be positively autocorrelated since they also reflect the effects of missing predictor variables. This type of autocorrelation is in appearance only and can be eliminated by including the omitted variables in the regression model.

In economic time series, autocorrelation may also be present because successive residuals tend to be positively correlated. That is, large negative residuals are followed by large negative residuals, and large positive residuals are followed by large positive residuals. This type of autocorrelation is usually the pure kind that is in need of some adjustment. We will concentrate on this type and discuss remedial measures, such as transformation of the data to correct for it.

Recall that by Assumption 3 in Section 13.2 the covariance between the random errors ε_i and ε_j is zero for all $i \neq j$. Although this assumption is not necessary to determine least squares estimators, its violation affects the inferential properties of these estimators. When autocorrelation is present, the regression analysis is affected in three ways.

1. The LS estimators, though still unbiased, no longer have minimum variance.
2. The estimates $s^2(B_i)$ may seriously underestimate the variances of the LS estimators B_i.
3. Confidence intervals and tests of hypotheses involving either the Student's t or the F distribution are no longer theoretically valid.

Suppose, for instance, the data below represent the sales Y of some company in millions of dollars and the sales x, also in millions of dollars, for the entire industry during the past 16 quarters, where the data have been adjusted for inflation.

t	1	2	3	4	5	6	7	8
x_t	270.36	258.38	254.96	259.70	265.40	274.98	281.86	285.78
Y_t	44.84	42.97	41.98	42.75	43.95	45.65	46.87	47.35

t	9	10	11	12	13	14	15	16
x_t	290.58	290.18	296.72	292.32	301.72	305.42	314.96	321.10
Y_t	48.13	47.95	49.10	48.52	50.22	51.15	52.78	53.91

A plot of Y against x reveals a linear trend, which suggests that the company's share of the market is being maintained. Assume the simple linear model as given by (13.1). The Minitab computer printout is given in Figure 13.6.

FIGURE 13.6 Linear regression analysis (market share data)

```
THE REGRESSION EQUATION IS
Y = - 2.97 + 0.177 X1
```

	COLUMN	COEFFICIENT	ST. DEV. OF COEF.	T-RATIO = COEF/S.D.
	—	-2.9716	0.7023	-4.23
X1	C2	0.176510	0.002456	71.86

```
THE ST. DEV. OF Y ABOUT REGRESSION LINE IS
S = 0.1919
WITH ( 16 - 2) = 14 DEGREES OF FREEDOM

R-SQUARED = 99.7 PERCENT

ANALYSIS OF VARIANCE
```

DUE TO	DF	SS	MS = SS/DF
REGRESSION	1	190.2330	190.2330
RESIDUAL	14	0.5157	0.0368
TOTAL	15	190.7487	

ROW	X1 C2	Y C1	PRED. Y VALUE	ST.DEV. PRED. Y	RESIDUAL	ST.RES.
1	270	44.8400	44.7497	0.0604	0.0903	0.50
2	258	42.9699	42.6350	0.0816	0.3349	1.93
3	255	41.9800	42.0314	0.0886	-0.0515	-0.30
4	260	42.7499	42.8680	0.0790	-0.1181	-0.68
5	265	43.9499	43.8742	0.0684	0.0758	0.42
6	275	45.6500	45.5651	0.0542	0.0848	0.46
7	282	46.8699	46.7795	0.0487	0.0904	0.49
8	286	47.3499	47.4714	0.0480	-0.1215	-0.65
9	291	48.1299	48.3187	0.0497	-0.1887	-1.02
10	290	47.9499	48.2481	0.0495	-0.2981	-1.61
11	297	49.0999	49.4025	0.0556	-0.3025	-1.65
12	292	48.5200	48.6258	0.0510	-0.1059	-0.57
13	302	50.2199	50.2850	0.0627	-0.0651	-0.36
14	305	51.1500	50.9381	0.0689	0.2119	1.18
15	315	52.7800	52.6220	0.0873	0.1579	0.92
16	321	53.9100	53.7058	0.1002	0.2042	1.25

Notice that the model seems to fit the data very well since $r^2 = 0.997$, and the null hypothesis of zero slope is rejected at almost any α level. The estimated standard deviations of B_0 and B_1 are small, especially for the slope estimator. But let us plot the standardized residuals against time, as in Figure 13.7. Notice that residuals of the same sign occur in clusters. For example, residuals 5–7 are positive, 8–13 are negative, and 14–16 are positive. This type of pattern is characteristic when errors are autocorrelated.

The Durbin–Watson statistic is a more formal approach to plotting residuals for the detection of autocorrelated errors. It is based on the assumption that the errors ε_t in the regression model

$$Y_t = \beta_0 + \beta_1 x_t + \varepsilon_t \tag{13.30}$$

form a first-order autoregressive series given by

$$\varepsilon_t = \rho \varepsilon_{t-1} + \eta_t \qquad t \geq 2, \tag{13.31}$$

where $|\rho| < 1$ is the slope of the line through the origin, and η_t is the pure random error that is uncorrelated with any other component. The term η_t is

FIGURE 13.7 Standardized residuals versus time for the sales example

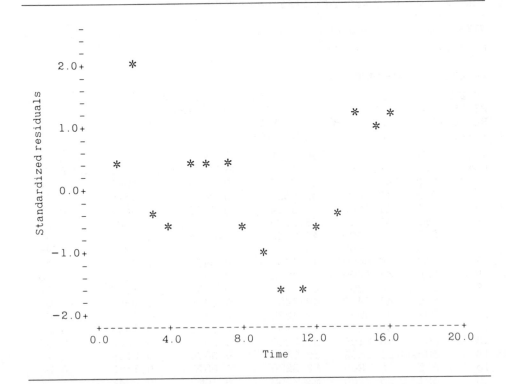

often called *white noise*. We should note that (13.31) is an *autoregressive model* because the predictor variable ε_{t-1} is a time-lagged term of the response variable ε_t. Although the correlation structure among the errors may be more complex than is implied by (13.31), a first-order autoregressive model is a reasonable approximation since often the autocorrelation between ε_t and ε_{t+p} diminishes rapidly as the distance between the time points t and $t + p$ increases.

For the model given by (13.31), we wish to use the Durbin–Watson statistic to test the null hypothesis

$$H_0: \rho = 0$$

against the alternative

$$H_1: \rho > 0.$$

Notice that H_1 is an upper one-sided alternative hypothesis because economic time series often exhibit positive autocorrelation. The Durbin–Watson statistic is based on the residuals that result after determining the estimated regression equation for (13.30). A value of this statistic is computed from the expression

$$d = \frac{\sum_{t=2}^{n} (e_t - e_{t-1})^2}{\sum_{t=1}^{n} e_t^2}, \tag{13.32}$$

where the residual $e_t = y_t - \hat{y}_t$.

If the errors are positively autocorrelated, then adjacent errors are likely to be of the same magnitude. Thus small differences between adjacent residuals would suggest that ρ is greater than zero, but when the differences are small, the numerator in (13.32) will also be small. Accordingly, the null hypothesis of zero autocorrelation is rejected whenever d is a relatively small value.

Durbin and Watson tabulated lower and upper bounds d_L and d_U, respectively, for testing H_0. In Table K in the Appendix the bounds d_L and d_U are given for $\alpha = 0.05$ and 0.01 as functions of the sample size n and the number of predictor variables k in the regression model. Given the bounds d_L and d_U, the decision for H_0 is as follows.

    a. If $d < d_L$, reject H_0,

    b. If $d > d_U$, cannot reject H_0,

    c. If $d_L < d < d_U$, the test is inconclusive.

We should point out that a test for negative autocorrelation ($H_1: \rho < 0$) is also possible with the Durbin–Watson statistic. In this case the value of the statistic is $4 - d$, where d is computed according to (13.32). The decision procedure is the same as before with $4 - d$ being compared to d_L or d_U. In either case if the test is inconclusive, the suggested remedy is to take more observations.

For the example, we compute d by first determining the differences $e_t - e_{t-1}$, using the column of residuals as given in the computer printout. These differences are as follows:

t	2	3	4	5	6
$e_t - e_{t-1}$	0.2446	-0.3864	-0.0666	0.1939	0.0090

t	7	8	9	10	11
$e_t - e_{t-1}$	0.0056	-0.2119	-0.0672	-0.1094	-0.0044

t	12	13	14	15	16
$e_t - e_{t-1}$	0.1966	0.0408	0.2770	-0.0540	0.0463

Using (13.32) we obtain

$$d = 0.434789/0.5157 = 0.843.$$

Say $\alpha = 0.05$; then for the simple linear model (13.30) and $n = 16$, the bounds are $d_L = 1.10$ and $d_U = 1.37$. Since $d < d_L$, we reject the null hypothesis and conclude that there is reason to believe the errors in (13.30) are autocorrelated.

13.9.3 Removal of Autocorrelation by Transforming the Data

When the null hypothesis of zero autocorrelation is rejected, the estimated regression equation should be adjusted to compensate for the presence of autocorrelated errors. We will try an approach for removing autocorrelation that is due to Cochrane and Orcutt.* It is based on an iterative method that involves transformation of the response and predictor variables in the original regression model.

For the model given by (13.30), consider the transformation

$$Y'_t = Y_t - \rho Y_{t-1}. \tag{13.33}$$

Substituting in (13.33) for Y_t and Y_{t-1} according to (13.30), we determine that

$$Y'_t = (\beta_0 + \beta_1 x_t + \varepsilon_t) - \rho(\beta_0 + \beta_1 x_{t-1} + \varepsilon_{t-1})$$
$$= \beta_0(1 - \rho) + \beta_1(x_t - \rho x_{t-1}) + (\varepsilon_t - \rho \varepsilon_{t-1}).$$

But from (13.31)

$$\varepsilon_t - \rho \varepsilon_{t-1} = \eta_t$$

---

*D. Cochrane and G. H. Orcutt, *Application of least squares regression to relationships containing autocorrelated error terms*, J. Amer. Statistical Assoc. **44** (1949), 32–61.

where η_t are uncorrelated random errors. Then

$$Y'_t = \beta_0(1 - \rho) + \beta_1(x_t - \rho x_{t-1}) + \eta_t,$$

or

$$Y'_t = \beta'_0 + \beta'_1 x'_t + \eta_t, \tag{13.34}$$

where $\beta'_0 = \beta_0(1 - \rho)$, $\beta'_1 = \beta_1$, and $x'_t = x_t - \rho x_{t-1}$. Accordingly, the errors in the transformed simple linear model (13.34) are uncorrelated, and this model satisfies the standard assumptions.

Notice that the transformed observations $Y'_t = Y_t - \rho Y_{t-1}$ and $x'_t = x_t - \rho x_{t-1}$ are functions of the unknown autocorrelation ρ, so before we fit the transformed model, we must determine an estimate of ρ. This can be done by using the residuals obtained from the original estimated regression equation to compute the LS estimate of the slope ρ in the first-order autoregressive model given by (13.31). Since this model assumes a zero intercept, the LS estimate r of the slope ρ based on the discussion in Section 13.3 is

$$r = \frac{\sum\limits_{t=2}^{n} e_{t-1} e_t}{\sum\limits_{t=1}^{n} e_t^2}, \tag{13.35}$$

and the transformed values are

$$y'_t = y_t - r y_{t-1}, \tag{13.36}$$

$$x'_t = x_t - r x_{t-1}.$$

Given the transformed values for the response and predictor variables, the iterative procedure is to determine the estimated regression equation for the transformed model and then recompute the Durbin–Watson statistic. If the null hypothesis of zero autocorrelation cannot be rejected, the procedure is terminated. Otherwise, the procedure is repeated until H_0 cannot be rejected. It is suggested that alternative procedures be sought if more than one iteration is required.

To illustrate, the LS estimate of ρ for the sales example is

$$r = 0.2734/0.5157 = 0.53,$$

and the transformed values are as follows:

t	2	3	4	5	6	7	8	9
x'_t	115.09	118.02	124.57	127.76	134.32	136.12	136.39	139.12
Y'_t	19.20	19.21	20.50	21.29	22.36	22.68	22.51	23.03

t	10	11	12	13	14	15	16
x'_t	136.17	142.92	135.06	146.79	145.51	153.09	154.17
Y'_t	22.44	23.69	22.50	24.50	24.53	25.67	25.94

FIGURE 13.8   Linear regression analysis after transformation of data for autocorrelation

---

```
THE REGRESSION EQUATION IS
Y = -1.52 + 0.177 X1
```

COLUMN	COEFFICIENT	ST. DEV. OF COEF.	T-RATIO = COEF/S.D.
—	-1.5178	0.5176	-2.93
X1 C2	0.177407	0.003784	46.88

```
THE ST. DEV. OF Y ABOUT REGRESSION LINE IS
S = 0.1627
WITH ( 15 - 2) = 13 DEGREES OF FREEDOM
R-SQUARED = 99.4 PERCENT

ANALYSIS OF VARIANCE
```

DUE TO	DF	SS	MS = SS/DF
REGRESSION	1	58.16086	58.16086
RESIDUAL	13	0.34401	0.02646
TOTAL	14	58.50485	

```
DURBIN-WATSON STATISTIC = 1.61
```

The computer printout using Minitab* for the transformed model is Figure 13.8. Notice that the printout also includes the value $d = 1.61$ for the Durbin–Watson statistic; Minitab provides this value as part of the printout. For $n = 15$ and $\alpha = 0.05$, we obtain the bounds $d_L = 1.08$ and $d_U = 1.36$ from Table K. Since $d > d_U$, we cannot reject the null hypothesis of zero autocorrelation.

We now need to write the estimated regression equation in terms of the original variables and adjust the estimated standard deviations of B_0 and B_1 to reflect the removal of autocorrelated errors. Since $\beta_0' = \beta_0(1 - \rho)$ and $\beta_1' = \beta_1$, the LS estimates of β_0 and β_1 are

$$b_0 = \frac{b_0'}{(1 - r)} = \frac{-1.5178}{(1 - 0.53)} = -3.2294,$$

and

$$b_1 = b_1' = 0.1774.$$

For the estimators B_0' and B_1' we note from the computer printout in Figure 13.8 that their estimated standard deviations are $s(B_0') = 0.5176$ and $s(B_1') = 0.003784$. Then for the estimated standard deviations of B_0 and B_1, we have

$$s(B_0) = s\left[\frac{B_0'}{(1 - r)}\right] = s(B_0')/(1 - r) = 1.1013,$$

$$s(B_1) = s(B_1') = 0.003784.$$

*A portion of the printout involving predictor and response variable values, residuals, etc., has been deleted.

TABLE 13.7 Summary information for the sales data

Original estimated equation	Final estimated equation
$\hat{y}_t = -2.9716 + 0.1765x_t$	$\hat{y}_t = -3.2294 + 0.1774x_t$
$s(B_0) = 0.7023, \quad s(B_1) = 0.002456$	$s(B_0) = 1.1013, \quad s(B_1) = 0.003784$
$\text{MSE} = 0.0368$	$\text{MSE} = 0.0265$
$r^2 = 0.997$	$r^2 = 0.994$

We summarize pertinent information for the original and final estimated regression equations for the sales data in Table 13.7. Notice that although the change in the estimated values for the coefficients is slight, there has been a considerable increase in the estimated standard deviations of B_0 and B_1, and especially for B_1. But the residual variance (MSE) has actually decreased. In this example the autocorrelation apparently was not strong enough to cause substantive differences for inference. When it is, drastic differences are likely to be noted.

13.10 Matrix Approach for the Simple Linear Model

The use of matrix algebra provides a convenient means of regression analysis of linear models, especially those with more than a single predictor variable. We will illustrate the use of matrix algebra by examining the simple linear model. For a brief review of the essentials of matrix algebra, the reader is directed to the appendix to this chapter.

For the n pairs $(x_1, Y_1), (x_2, Y_2), \ldots, (x_n, Y_n)$, assume the simple linear model

$$Y_i = \beta_0 + \beta_1 x_i + \varepsilon_i \qquad i = 1, 2, \ldots, n.$$

In other words,

$$Y_1 = \beta_0 + \beta_1 x_1 + \varepsilon_1$$

$$Y_2 = \beta_0 + \beta_1 x_2 + \varepsilon_2$$

$$\vdots$$

$$Y_n = \beta_0 + \beta_1 x_n + \varepsilon_n$$

are n linear equations in which $Y_1, Y_2, \ldots, Y_n$ are the observations of the response at the corresponding fixed values $x_1, x_2, \ldots, x_n$ of the predictor variable, $\varepsilon_1, \varepsilon_2, \ldots, \varepsilon_n$ are unobservable random errors, and β_0 and β_1 are parameters to be estimated. If we define the matrices

$$\mathbf{Y} = \begin{bmatrix} Y_1 \\ Y_2 \\ \vdots \\ Y_n \end{bmatrix} \qquad \mathbf{X} = \begin{bmatrix} 1 & x_1 \\ 1 & x_2 \\ \vdots & \vdots \\ 1 & x_n \end{bmatrix} \qquad \boldsymbol{\beta} = \begin{bmatrix} \beta_0 \\ \beta_1 \end{bmatrix} \qquad \boldsymbol{\varepsilon} = \begin{bmatrix} \varepsilon_1 \\ \varepsilon_2 \\ \vdots \\ \varepsilon_n \end{bmatrix},$$

then

$$\begin{bmatrix} Y_1 \\ Y_2 \\ \vdots \\ Y_n \end{bmatrix} = \begin{bmatrix} 1 & x_1 \\ 1 & x_2 \\ \vdots & \vdots \\ 1 & x_n \end{bmatrix} \begin{bmatrix} \beta_0 \\ \beta_1 \end{bmatrix} + \begin{bmatrix} \varepsilon_1 \\ \varepsilon_2 \\ \vdots \\ \varepsilon_n \end{bmatrix} = \begin{bmatrix} \beta_0 + \beta_1 x_1 + \varepsilon_1 \\ \beta_0 + \beta_1 x_2 + \varepsilon_2 \\ \vdots \\ \beta_0 + \beta_1 x_n + \varepsilon_n \end{bmatrix}.$$

As a result, the simple linear model may be expressed in the matrix form

$$\mathbf{Y} = \mathbf{X}\boldsymbol{\beta} + \boldsymbol{\varepsilon}. \tag{13.37}$$

If we assume the normal theory case, then $\boldsymbol{\varepsilon}$ is a vector of independent normal random variables such that

$$E(\boldsymbol{\varepsilon}) = \mathbf{0},$$

$$Var(\boldsymbol{\varepsilon}) = \sigma^2 \mathbf{I}$$

where σ^2 is the common error variance and $\mathbf{I}$ is the corresponding identity matrix.

Now consider the least squares estimation of β_0 and β_1. Recall the normal equations as given by (13.4). Since

$$\mathbf{X'X} = \begin{bmatrix} 1 & 1 & \cdots & 1 \\ x_1 & x_2 & \cdots & x_n \end{bmatrix} \begin{bmatrix} 1 & x_1 \\ 1 & x_2 \\ \vdots & \vdots \\ 1 & x_n \end{bmatrix} = \begin{bmatrix} n & \Sigma x_i \\ \Sigma x_i & \Sigma x_i^2 \end{bmatrix} \tag{13.38}$$

and

$$\mathbf{X'Y} = \begin{bmatrix} 1 & 1 & \cdots & 1 \\ x_1 & x_2 & \cdots & x_n \end{bmatrix} \begin{bmatrix} Y_1 \\ Y_2 \\ \vdots \\ Y_n \end{bmatrix} = \begin{bmatrix} \Sigma Y_i \\ \Sigma x_i Y_i \end{bmatrix}, \tag{13.39}$$

then

$$(\mathbf{X'X})\mathbf{B} = \begin{bmatrix} n & \Sigma x_i \\ \Sigma x_i & \Sigma x_i^2 \end{bmatrix} \begin{bmatrix} B_0 \\ B_1 \end{bmatrix} = \begin{bmatrix} nB_0 + B_1 \Sigma x_i \\ B_0 \Sigma x_i + B_1 \Sigma x_i^2 \end{bmatrix} = \begin{bmatrix} \Sigma Y_i \\ \Sigma x_i Y_i \end{bmatrix} = \mathbf{X'Y}.$$

Therefore, the normal equations in matrix form are

$$(\mathbf{X'X})\mathbf{B} = \mathbf{X'Y}, \tag{13.40}$$

where

$$\mathbf{B} = \begin{bmatrix} B_0 \\ B_1 \end{bmatrix}$$

is the vector containing the least squares estimators B_0 and B_1.

If we assume that the square matrix $\mathbf{X'X}$ has an inverse, then in (13.40)

$$(\mathbf{X'X})^{-1}(\mathbf{X'X})\mathbf{B} = (\mathbf{X'X})^{-1}\mathbf{X'Y},$$

or

$$\mathbf{IB} = (\mathbf{X'X})^{-1}\mathbf{X'Y},$$

and

$$\mathbf{B} = (\mathbf{X'X})^{-1}\mathbf{X'Y} \tag{13.41}$$

is the matrix expression for determining the least squares estimators B_0 and B_1.

Using the starting salary data, we illustrate that expression (13.41) yields the same least squares estimates for β_0 and β_1 that we have previously determined. The vector $\mathbf{Y}$ of starting salaries and the matrix $\mathbf{X}$ of corresponding grade point averages are

$$\mathbf{Y} = \begin{bmatrix} 18.5 \\ 20.0 \\ 21.1 \\ \vdots \\ 16.8 \end{bmatrix}, \qquad \mathbf{X} = \begin{bmatrix} 1 & 2.95 \\ 1 & 3.20 \\ 1 & 3.40 \\ \vdots & \vdots \\ 1 & 2.75 \end{bmatrix}.$$

The reader should note that the ones in the first column of $\mathbf{X}$ represent the intercept β_0 as defined by the assumed simple linear model. Proceeding with the computation, we have

$$(\mathbf{X'X}) = \begin{bmatrix} 1 & 1 & \cdots & 1 \\ 2.95 & 3.20 & \cdots & 2.75 \end{bmatrix} \begin{bmatrix} 1 & 2.95 \\ 1 & 3.20 \\ \vdots & \vdots \\ 1 & 2.75 \end{bmatrix} = \begin{bmatrix} 15 & 45.6 \\ 45.6 & 139.51 \end{bmatrix}$$

and

$$\mathbf{X'Y} = \begin{bmatrix} 1 & 1 & \cdots & 1 \\ 2.95 & 3.20 & \cdots & 2.75 \end{bmatrix} \begin{bmatrix} 18.5 \\ 20.0 \\ \vdots \\ 16.8 \end{bmatrix} = \begin{bmatrix} 270.8 \\ 830.425 \end{bmatrix}.$$

The inverse of the 2×2 matrix can be determined to be

$$(\mathbf{X'X})^{-1} = \frac{1}{13.29} \begin{bmatrix} 139.51 & -45.6 \\ -45.6 & 15 \end{bmatrix}.$$

To avoid possibly substantial roundoff error, it is best not to divide each element of $(\mathbf{X'X})^{-1}$ by the denominator value of 13.29 until after the product $(\mathbf{X'X})^{-1}\mathbf{X'Y}$ has been determined. Then from (13.41), the least squares estimates are

$$(\mathbf{X'X})^{-1}\mathbf{X'Y} = \frac{1}{13.29} \begin{bmatrix} 139.51 & -45.6 \\ -45.6 & 15 \end{bmatrix} \begin{bmatrix} 270.8 \\ 830.425 \end{bmatrix}$$

$$= \frac{1}{13.29} \begin{bmatrix} -88.072 \\ 107.895 \end{bmatrix} = \begin{bmatrix} -6.6269 \\ 8.1185 \end{bmatrix},$$

or $b_0 = -6.6269$ and $b_1 = 8.1185$. When rounded to two significant digits, these values are the same as those we obtained earlier.

References

1. G. E. P. Box and G. M. Jenkins, *Time series analysis: Forecasting and control,* 2nd ed., Holden–Day, San Francisco, 1977.
2. S. Chatterjee and B. Price, *Regression analysis by example,* Wiley, New York, 1977.
3. N. R. Draper and H. Smith, *Applied regression analysis,* 2nd ed., Wiley, New York, 1981.
4. C. R. Nelson, *Applied time series analysis for managerial forecasting,* Holden–Day, San Francisco, 1977.
5. J. Neter and W. Wasserman, *Applied linear statistical models,* Richard D. Irwin, Homewood, Ill., 1974.

Exercises

13.1. Comment on causation in the following documented associations.

    a. In 12 of 15 recent years, the stock market has gone up when the aggregate major league baseball average has gone down, and vice versa.

    b. Since the first Super Bowl in 1967, the stock market went up every year in which the team that won the Super Bowl came originally from the old National Football League, and went down every year in which the Super Bowl champion was a team from the old American Football League.

13.2. Which of the following are linear models?

    a. $Y = \beta \sin(x) + \varepsilon$
    b. $Y = \beta_1 \sin(\beta_2 x) + \varepsilon$
    c. $Y = \beta_0 + \beta_1 x_1^2 x_2 + \beta_2 x_2^3 + \varepsilon$
    d. $Y = \beta_0 + \beta_1^2 x + \varepsilon$

13.3. Given the linear model $Y_i = \beta x_i + \varepsilon_i$, $i = 1, 2, ..., n$, assume that $E(\varepsilon_i) = 0$, $Var(\varepsilon_i) = \sigma^2$ for all i, and $Cov(\varepsilon_i, \varepsilon_j) = 0$ for all $i \neq j$.

    a. Determine the least squares estimator B of β.

    b. Determine whether B is an unbiased estimator of β, and show that $Var(B) = \sigma^2/\Sigma x_i^2$.

13.4. A typical residential house was selected by the local power company to develop an empirical model for energy consumption (in kilowatts per day) as a function of average daily temperature during the winter months. For fifteen days the following information was obtained.

Temperature (°C)	0	8	7.5	13,5	14	8.5	4.5	−11
Energy usage	70	57	60	63	57	66	67	107

Temperature (°C)	−7.5	−8.5	1.5	0.5	2	−6	−4
Energy usage	96	88	80	64	79	82	97

    a. Graph the data. Is a linear association suggested?

    b. For a simple linear model, determine the estimated regression equation and plot the line on your graph in part a.

    c. Interpret the estimated regression coefficients.

    d. What would you recommend to the power company to improve the empirical model?

13.5. An insurance company wants to determine the extent of the relationship between family income x and amount of life insurance Y on the head of the household. Based on a random sample of eighteen families the following information was obtained (in thousands of dollars).

Income	45	20	40	40	47	30	25	20	15
Life insurance	70	50	60	50	90	55	55	35	40
Income	35	40	55	50	60	15	30	35	45
Life insurance	65	75	105	110	120	30	40	65	80

Repeat all parts of Exercise 13.4.

13.6. Given the estimated regression equation for Exercise 13.4,

    a. compute the residuals.
    b. verify that Properties 2 and 3 of Section 13.3 hold.
    c. determine the residual variance.
    d. compute estimates of the standard deviations of B_0 and B_1.
    e. determine a 95% confidence interval estimate for the true slope.
    f. determine whether a linear relationship between average atmospheric temperature and energy usage is statistically discernible at the $\alpha = 0.05$ level.
    g. For each atmospheric temperature, compute 95% confidence interval estimates for the mean energy usage, and graph the intervals against the estimated regression line.

13.7. Repeat all parts of Exercise 13.6 for the estimated regression equation in Exercise 13.5.

13.8. Referring to Exercise 13.4, estimate individual energy consumptions for temperatures of -10, -8, -5, -2, 1, 4, 7, 10, and 13, and determine 95% prediction intervals for your estimates.

13.9. Referring to Exercise 13.5, estimate individual amounts of life insurance for the annual incomes of 18, 28, 38, 48, and 58, and determine 95% prediction intervals for the estimates.

13.10. Using the data from Exercises 13.4 and 13.5,

    a. perform an analysis of variance for each data set and determine whether the null hypothesis of no linear regression can be rejected at the $\alpha = 0.05$ level.
    b. compare your results in part a with those obtained in part f of Exercise 13.6, and comment on the relation between the value of the F statistic computed here with that of the T statistic determined in part f of Exercise 13.6.
    c. compute the coefficients of determination and explain their meaning. Can we conclude that the true regression equations between temperature and energy usage or between annual income and amount of life insurance are strictly linear?

13.11. The following data are the heights X and the weights Y of a random sample of ten female employees of a large company.

Height (inches)	68	67	65	68	64	67	66	65	64	66
Weight (lbs)	119	118	129	135	123	140	125	132	118	130

    a. Graph the data.
    b. Compute the sample correlation coefficient and comment on any apparent linearity between height and weight.

13.12. The following data* represent the power generated daily in thousands of megawatts by a regional utility for the month of August 1980 and the atmospheric temperature in degrees Fahrenheit as recorded at 11 A.M. in a central location.

Temperature	99	99	99	99	99	96	96	97	97
Power	153.4	141.0	143.1	156.8	158.7	158.5	158.7	159.6	148.3

Temperature	97	99	94	91	97	96	85	79	76
Power	137.8	160.0	154.0	142.2	149.4	147.9	114.2	94.7	112.5

Temperature	84	90	76	78	81	90	93	90	96
Power	123.6	131.1	119.4	111.9	103.5	103.7	125.4	129.0	135.6

Temperature	98	95	95	95
Power	142.3	142.5	128.9	124.3

a. Graph the data.

b. Compute the sample correlation coefficient and comment on any apparent linearity between temperature and amount of power generated.

13.13. Suppose it is known that the curve of regression between a response Y and a predictor variable x is linear. To estimate the regression equation, $n/2$ observations of Y will be made at the lower extreme of the range of x and $n/2$ observations will be made at the upper extreme of x. The extreme values of x have been scaled to -1 and $+1$ for convenience.

a. Use equation (13.18) to determine the range for the variance of a mean response at any point x_p of x inside the interval $(-1, 1)$.

b. Use equation (13.20) to determine a similar expression for the variance of a particular response.

c. Assume the following observations have been recorded.

x	-1	-1	-1	-1	-1	1	1	1	1	1
Y	10	12	9	13	8	20	17	23	24	19

Use matrix algebra to determine least squares estimates for the slope and intercept.

13.14. Assume the following information on gross annual income x and percent taxes paid Y is from a random sample of fourteen federal income tax returns.

Gross income (thousand $)	25.6	42.2	57.6	98.8	10.4	30.1	40.0
Percent taxes paid	15.4	16.8	19.7	21.7	10.8	15.2	18.9

Gross income (thousand $)	29.3	16.1	18.0	88.2	34.0	22.1	70.0
Percent taxes paid	15.9	12.0	14.1	21.1	17.6	14.8	21.6

*Courtesy of K. L. Fugett.

a. Graph the data. Is a linear association suggested?

b. Assuming a linear fit, estimate the regression equation and plot the line on your graph for part a.

c. Perform an analysis of variance, determine the coefficient of determination, and comment on whether you believe the estimated regression equation provides adequate prediction. Use $\alpha = 0.05$.

d. Predict the average percent taxes paid for people with gross incomes of 15 and 85 thousand dollars and determine estimates of their standard deviations.

13.15. A plant manager wishes to determine whether there is a linear relation between the number of units Y assembled by the operators of an assembly line and the length of time x before a break. Based on a random sample of operators from the assembly line, the following information is observed.

Time length (hours)	1	2	3	4
Units assembled	25, 29, 23, 31	55, 65, 63, 59	73, 75, 74, 71	90, 88, 91, 87

a. Graph the data and comment on your result.

b. Estimate a linear regression equation using matrix algebra.

c. Determine whether a linear relationship is statistically discernible at the $\alpha = 0.01$ level.

d. Determine a 95% confidence interval for the slope.

13.16. The following data depict the percentage of population with four or more years of college x and the infant mortality rate per 1,000 births Y for a sample of fifteen states.*

x	19.4	12.3	13.7	11.0	11.5	16.8	11.8	12.8
Y	12.0	15.4	16.0	14.2	17.9	11.9	14.2	12.7
x	15.3	11.8	11.7	10.4	17.5	15.6	16.1	
Y	13.8	15.8	13.7	17.6	10.1	10.1	12.1	

a. Graph the data and compute the sample correlation coefficient.

b. Fit a linear regression function with the mortality rate as the response and the population percentage with four or more years of college as the predictor. Interpret the estimated regression coefficient for the slope.

c. Is the linear regression statistically discernible at the $\alpha = 0.05$ level? How would you explain any linear association between these two quantities?

13.17 The data** in Table 13.8 consist of annual information on the relative price of alcohol x and the per capita consumption in liters of absolute alcohol Y for the period 1948–1967 in Ontario.

a. Graph the data and compute the sample correlation coefficient.

b. Use analysis of variance to determine whether the linear regression between relative price and per capita consumption is statistically discernible at the $\alpha = 0.01$ level.

Hammond almanac, 1981.

R. E. Popham, W. Schmidt, and J. de Lint, *The prevention of alcoholism: Epidemiological studies of the effects of government control measures,* Brit. J. of Addiction **70 (1975), 125–144.

TABLE 13.8 Sample data for Exercise 13.17

Year	Relative price	Per capita consumption
1948	0.057	7.09
1949	0.058	7.18
1950	0.055	7.23
1951	0.052	7.23
1952	0.051	7.32
1953	0.055	7.64
1954	0.056	7.73
1955	0.047	7.55
1956	0.045	7.91
1957	0.044	7.86
1958	0.043	7.96
1959	0.043	7.77
1960	0.043	8.14
1961	0.043	8.14
1962	0.041	8.23
1963	0.040	8.46
1964	0.039	8.73
1965	0.038	8.77
1966	0.039	9.18
1967	0.035	8.91

13.18. A study was conducted to determine the relationship between years of experience x and annual salary Y for a particular profession in a geographical region. A random sample of seventeen persons in this profession was selected and the following information obtained.

Years of experience	13	16	30	2	8	31	19	20	1
Current annual salary (thousand $)	26.1	33.2	36.1	16.5	26.4	36.4	33.8	36.5	16.9

Years of experience	4	27	25	7	15	13	6	10
Current annual salary (thousand $)	19.8	36.0	36.5	21.4	31.0	31.4	19.1	24.6

a. Graph the data and based on your graph, comment on whether a linear fit should be sufficient.
b. Fit a linear model and interpret the estimated regression coefficients.
c. Can the null hypothesis of zero slope be rejected at the $\alpha = 0.01$ level?
d. Estimate the average salary for someone in this profession with twelve years of experience and compute a 99% confidence interval about this value.
e. Determine the residuals and graph them against the corresponding years of experience. Do you detect something unusual? Explain.

13.19. The following data represent the gross national product x and the personal consumption expenditures Y in billions of 1972 dollars for the years 1960–1980.*

Year	1960	1961	1962	1963	1964	1965	1966
x	737.2	756.6	800.3	832.5	876.4	929.3	984.8
Y	452.0	461.4	482.0	500.5	528.0	557.5	585.7

*Economic report of the president, February 1982.

Year	1967	1968	1969	1970	1971	1972	1973
x	1,011.4	1,058.1	1,087.6	1,085.6	1,122.4	1,185.9	1,255.0
Y	602.7	634.4	657.9	672.1	696.8	737.1	768.5

Year	1974	1975	1976	1977	1978	1979	1980
x	1,248.0	1,233.9	1,300.4	1,371.7	1,436.9	1,483.0	1,480.7
Y	763.6	780.2	823.7	863.9	904.8	930.9	935.1

a. Fit a linear model and interpret the estimated regression coefficients.

b. Plot the standardized residuals against time. Can you detect a pattern?

c. Compute the Durbin–Watson statistic and determine whether the errors are positively autocorrelated. Use $\alpha = 0.05$.

d. If positive autocorrelation is statistically discernible, adjust the estimated regression equation by transforming the data.

13.20. The following data represent corporate profits by inventory valuation and capital consumption adjustments x and corporate profits tax liability Y in billions of dollars for the years 1960–1980.* Repeat all parts of Exercise 13.19.

Year	1960	1961	1962	1963	1964	1965	1966
x	47.6	48.6	56.6	62.1	69.2	80.0	85.1
Y	22.7	22.8	24.0	26.2	28.0	30.9	33.7

Year	1967	1968	1969	1970	1971	1972	1973
x	82.4	89.1	85.1	71.4	83.2	96.6	108.3
Y	32.5	39.2	39.5	34.2	37.5	41.6	49.0

Year	1974	1975	1976	1977	1978	1979	1980
x	94.9	110.5	138.1	164.7	185.5	196.8	182.7
Y	51.6	50.6	63.8	72.6	83.0	87.6	82.3

APPENDIX

Brief Review of Matrix Algebra

A matrix is a rectangular array of elements arranged in rows and columns. For example,

$$
\mathbf{X} = \begin{bmatrix}
x_{11} & x_{12} & \cdots & x_{1j} & \cdots & x_{1n} \\
x_{21} & x_{22} & \cdots & x_{2j} & \cdots & x_{2n} \\
\vdots & \vdots & & \vdots & & \vdots \\
x_{i1} & x_{i2} & \cdots & x_{ij} & \cdots & x_{in} \\
\vdots & \vdots & & \vdots & & \vdots \\
x_{m1} & x_{m2} & \cdots & x_{mj} & \cdots & x_{mn}
\end{bmatrix}
$$

is a matrix containing m rows and n columns. The entries x_{ij}, $i = 1, 2, \ldots, m$,

Economic report of the president, February 1982.

$j = 1, 2, ..., n$, are the elements of the matrix $\mathbf{X}$. The first subscript (i) identifies the row position of the element, and the second (j) identifies the column position. The matrix $\mathbf{X}$ with m rows and n columns is known as a matrix of order (or dimension) m by n. Usually a matrix is denoted by a boldface capital letter with the corresponding lower case letter designating an element. It is common practice to use the shorthand notation

$$\mathbf{X} = [x_{ij}], \quad i = 1, 2, ..., m, \quad j = 1, 2, ..., n$$

to designate the matrix $\mathbf{X}$ of dimension $m \times n$.

A matrix containing only one column is known as a *column vector,* and a matrix with only one row is a *row vector.* The matrices

$$\mathbf{Y} = \begin{bmatrix} y_1 \\ y_2 \\ \vdots \\ y_n \end{bmatrix} \qquad \mathbf{Z}' = [z_1 \quad z_2 \quad \cdots \quad z_n]$$

are examples of column and row vectors, respectively; $\mathbf{Y}$ is an $n \times 1$ column vector, and $\mathbf{Z}'$ is a $1 \times n$ row vector. The reason for the prime symbol on the row vector $\mathbf{Z}'$ will be explained shortly. Since a column or row vector has only one column or one row, it is necessary to use only one subscript to identify the position of the elements.

A matrix containing the same number of columns as rows is known as a *square matrix.*

$$\mathbf{A} = \begin{bmatrix} 3 & -2 & 1 \\ 0 & 2 & 4 \\ -3 & 1 & 5 \end{bmatrix} \qquad \mathbf{B} = \begin{bmatrix} 10 & -3 \\ 2 & 1 \end{bmatrix}$$

are examples of square matrices. $\mathbf{A}$ is a 3×3 square matrix, and $\mathbf{B}$ is a 2×2 square matrix.

Interchanging corresponding rows and columns of an $m \times n$ matrix $\mathbf{X}$ results in a new matrix, denoted by $\mathbf{X}'$, of dimension $n \times m$ and called the *transpose* of $\mathbf{X}$. For example, given the matrix

$$\mathbf{X} = \begin{bmatrix} 2 & -3 & 0 \\ 1 & 5 & -12 \end{bmatrix},$$

the transpose of $\mathbf{X}$ is the matrix whose first column is the same as the first row of $\mathbf{X}$ and whose second column is the same as the second row of $\mathbf{X}$,

$$\mathbf{X}' = \begin{bmatrix} 2 & 1 \\ -3 & 5 \\ 0 & -12 \end{bmatrix}.$$

In general, given

$$\mathbf{X} = [x_{ij}], \quad i = 1, 2, ..., m, \quad j = 1, 2, ..., n,$$

we have

$$\mathbf{X}' = [x_{ji}], \quad j = 1, 2, ..., n, \quad i = 1, 2, ..., m.$$

In other words, the element in the ith row and jth column of **X** is found in the jth row and ith column of the transpose matrix **X′**. It follows that the transpose of a column vector is a row vector, and the transpose of a row vector is a column vector. For this reason it is customary to use the prime symbol to denote a row vector.

Two matrices are said to be equal if and only if their corresponding elements are equal. Thus a necessary condition for two matrices to be equal is that they have the same dimension. For example, the two matrices

$$\mathbf{A} = \begin{bmatrix} a_{11} & a_{12} \\ a_{21} & a_{22} \\ a_{31} & a_{32} \end{bmatrix} \quad \mathbf{B} = \begin{bmatrix} -2 & 0 \\ 5 & 6 \\ 12 & -5 \end{bmatrix}$$

are equal if

$$\begin{aligned} a_{11} &= -2 & a_{12} &= 0 \\ a_{21} &= 5 & a_{22} &= 6 \\ a_{31} &= 12 & a_{32} &= -5. \end{aligned}$$

Addition or subtraction of two matrices is possible only when their dimensions are the same. The sum (difference) of two matrices is a matrix whose elements are the sums (differences) of the corresponding elements of the two matrices. For example, given

$$\mathbf{A} = \begin{bmatrix} -2 & 5 \\ 3 & 8 \end{bmatrix}, \quad \mathbf{B} = \begin{bmatrix} 4 & -3 \\ 2 & -6 \end{bmatrix},$$

$$\mathbf{A} + \mathbf{B} = \begin{bmatrix} -2+4 & 5-3 \\ 3+2 & 8-6 \end{bmatrix} = \begin{bmatrix} 2 & 2 \\ 5 & 2 \end{bmatrix},$$

$$\mathbf{A} - \mathbf{B} = \begin{bmatrix} -2-4 & 5-(-3) \\ 3-2 & 8-(-6) \end{bmatrix} = \begin{bmatrix} -6 & 8 \\ 1 & 14 \end{bmatrix}.$$

Given two matrices **A** and **B**, the product matrix **AB** is defined if and only if the number of columns of **A** is equal to the number of rows of **B**. Then if **A** is $m \times n$ and **B** is $n \times p$, the product **AB** is a matrix of dimension $m \times p$ whose element in the ith row and jth column is equal to the sum of the products of the elements in the ith row of **A** and the jth column of **B**. If

$$\mathbf{A} = \begin{bmatrix} 1 & -2 \\ -3 & 4 \\ 0 & -1 \end{bmatrix}, \quad \mathbf{B} = \begin{bmatrix} -2 & 1 \\ 4 & 3 \end{bmatrix},$$

$$\mathbf{AB} = \begin{bmatrix} 1 & -2 \\ -3 & 4 \\ 0 & -1 \end{bmatrix} \begin{bmatrix} -2 & 1 \\ 4 & 3 \end{bmatrix} = \begin{bmatrix} (1)(-2)+(-2)(4) & (1)(1)+(-2)(3) \\ (-3)(-2)+(4)(4) & (-3)(1)+(4)(3) \\ (0)(-2)+(-1)(4) & (0)(1)+(-1)(3) \end{bmatrix}$$

$$= \begin{bmatrix} -10 & -5 \\ 22 & 9 \\ -4 & -3 \end{bmatrix}.$$

Notice that for this pair of matrices, the product **BA** is not defined; matrix multiplication is not in general commutative. It is also of interest to note that if **Y** is an $n \times 1$ column vector and **Y'** is a $1 \times n$ row vector, then **Y'Y** is a scalar and **YY'** is a square matrix of dimension n. A *scalar* is any number from the real line $(-\infty, \infty)$. The multiplication of a matrix by a scalar yields a matrix whose elements are the products of the corresponding original elements and the scalar quantity. For example, given

$$\mathbf{A} = \begin{bmatrix} -2 & 1 & -2 \\ 3 & 4 & 1 \end{bmatrix},$$

$$-5\mathbf{A} = \begin{bmatrix} (-5)(-2) & (-5)(1) & (-5)(-2) \\ (-5)(3) & (-5)(4) & (-5)(1) \end{bmatrix} = \begin{bmatrix} 10 & -5 & 10 \\ -15 & -20 & -5 \end{bmatrix}.$$

Certain special matrices are worthy of mention. A square matrix of dimension n that has zeros for elements everywhere except down the main diagonal,* where all elements are equal to one, is called the *identity matrix* of order n. For example,

$$\mathbf{I} = \begin{bmatrix} 1 & 0 \\ 0 & 1 \end{bmatrix} \qquad \mathbf{I} = \begin{bmatrix} 1 & 0 & 0 \\ 0 & 1 & 0 \\ 0 & 0 & 1 \end{bmatrix}$$

are identity matrices of orders 2 and 3, respectively. In multiplication of appropriate square matrices, the identity matrix plays the same role as the number 1 in multiplication involving scalars. That is, given any matrix **A**, the product of the corresponding identity matrix and **A** yields **A** as long as there is compatibility for multiplication. Thus

$$\mathbf{IA} = \mathbf{AI} = \mathbf{A}.$$

A square matrix **A** is said to be *symmetric* if it is equal to its transpose. Given any square matrix **A**, if $\mathbf{A} = \mathbf{A'}$, then **A** is symmetric. For example,

$$\mathbf{A} = \begin{bmatrix} 2 & 1 & -2 \\ 1 & 4 & 3 \\ -2 & 3 & 1 \end{bmatrix}$$

is a symmetric matrix. Notice that the elements in the triangle below the main diagonal are correspondingly identical to the elements in the triangle above the main diagonal. If an $m \times n$ matrix **A** is premultiplied by its transpose matrix, the product matrix will be symmetric. Thus **A'A** is a symmetric matrix of order n. For example, given

$$\mathbf{A} = \begin{bmatrix} 2 & 1 \\ 1 & 4 \\ 3 & 2 \end{bmatrix}, \qquad \mathbf{A'} = \begin{bmatrix} 2 & 1 & 3 \\ 1 & 4 & 2 \end{bmatrix},$$

$$\mathbf{A'A} = \begin{bmatrix} 2 & 1 & 3 \\ 1 & 4 & 2 \end{bmatrix} \begin{bmatrix} 2 & 1 \\ 1 & 4 \\ 3 & 2 \end{bmatrix} = \begin{bmatrix} 14 & 12 \\ 12 & 21 \end{bmatrix}.$$

---

*The main diagonal contains the elements whose row and column positions are the same.

A *diagonal matrix* is any square matrix whose elements outside the main diagonal are all zero.

$$\mathbf{A} = \begin{bmatrix} 4 & 0 & 0 \\ 0 & 3 & 0 \\ 0 & 0 & 7 \end{bmatrix}$$

is a diagonal matrix. It should be apparent that an identity matrix is a special case of a diagonal matrix.

A zero vector is any column vector whose elements are all zero,

$$\mathbf{0} = \begin{bmatrix} 0 \\ 0 \\ 0 \\ 0 \end{bmatrix}$$

is a 4×1 zero vector.

We now define an important concept in matrix algebra known as the inverse of a square matrix. Let $\mathbf{A}$ be a square matrix of order n. If there exists a matrix denoted by $\mathbf{A}^{-1}$ such that

$$\mathbf{A}^{-1}\mathbf{A} = \mathbf{A}\mathbf{A}^{-1} = \mathbf{I}$$

where $\mathbf{I}$ is the corresponding identity matrix, then $\mathbf{A}^{-1}$ is the *unique inverse matrix* of $\mathbf{A}$. If a square matrix has an inverse, the matrix is said to be *nonsingular;* otherwise it is known as a *singular* matrix.

For each square matrix, we are able to define and compute a scalar quantity known as the *determinant* of the matrix. The value of the determinant of a square matrix is the deciding factor for whether or not the matrix has an inverse. Let $\mathbf{A}$ be any square matrix. If the determinant of $\mathbf{A}$, denoted by det($\mathbf{A}$), is not equal to zero, there exists an inverse matrix for $\mathbf{A}$. If det($\mathbf{A}$) = 0, $\mathbf{A}$ is singular. The notion of an inverse matrix is analogous to the multiplicative inverse in the algebra of scalars.

We will illustrate finding inverse matrices only for the 2×2 case. In general, let

$$\mathbf{A} = \begin{bmatrix} a_{11} & a_{12} \\ a_{21} & a_{22} \end{bmatrix}$$

be any 2×2 matrix. The determinant of $\mathbf{A}$ is defined by

$$\det(\mathbf{A}) = a_{11}\,a_{22} - a_{12}\,a_{21}$$

and the inverse matrix of $\mathbf{A}$ can be shown to be

$$\mathbf{A}^{-1} = \begin{bmatrix} \dfrac{a_{22}}{\det(\mathbf{A})} & -\dfrac{a_{12}}{\det(\mathbf{A})} \\ -\dfrac{a_{21}}{\det(\mathbf{A})} & \dfrac{a_{11}}{\det(\mathbf{A})} \end{bmatrix}$$

For example, given

$$A = \begin{bmatrix} 2 & 3 \\ -1 & 1 \end{bmatrix},$$

$$\det(A) = (2)(1) - (-1)(3) = 5,$$

and

$$A^{-1} = \begin{bmatrix} 1/5 & -3/5 \\ 1/5 & 2/5 \end{bmatrix}$$

is the inverse matrix of **A**. This result is easily verified since

$$A^{-1}A = \begin{bmatrix} 1/5 & -3/5 \\ 1/5 & 2/5 \end{bmatrix} \begin{bmatrix} 2 & 3 \\ -1 & 1 \end{bmatrix} = AA^{-1}$$

$$= \begin{bmatrix} 2 & 3 \\ -1 & 1 \end{bmatrix} \begin{bmatrix} 1/5 & -3/5 \\ 1/5 & 2/5 \end{bmatrix} = \begin{bmatrix} 1 & 0 \\ 0 & 1 \end{bmatrix}.$$

Finally, it should be noted that the inverse of any diagonal matrix is also a diagonal matrix whose elements on the main diagonal are the reciprocals of the elements on the main diagonal of the original matrix. For example, given that

$$A = \begin{bmatrix} 9 & 0 & 0 \\ 0 & 5 & 0 \\ 0 & 0 & 10 \end{bmatrix},$$

$$A^{-1} = \begin{bmatrix} 1/9 & 0 & 0 \\ 0 & 1/5 & 0 \\ 0 & 0 & 1/10 \end{bmatrix}.$$

CHAPTER FOURTEEN

Regression Analysis: The General Linear Model

14.1 Introduction

In Chapter 13 we examined the essentials of regression analysis for the simple linear model. In this chapter we will extend these concepts to the general linear model in which a given response is considered to be a function of several predictor variables. In discussing this model we will look at ways to determine the best set of predictor variables to include in the regression equation. We will also provide a detailed discussion of analysis of residuals, weighted least squares, and indicator variables with ample illustrations. Throughout this chapter we will rely on the Minitab and SAS (see [6]) computer statistical packages. We will assume that these or comparable computer packages are available to the reader. For a more theoretical treatment of the topics in this chapter, the reader is referred to [4].

14.2 The General Linear Model

Let $x_1, x_2, \ldots, x_k$ be k predictor variables that may have some influence on a response Y, and assume the model to be of the form

$$Y_i = \beta_0 + \beta_1 x_{i1} + \beta_2 x_{i2} + \cdots + \beta_k x_{ik} + \varepsilon_i, \qquad i = 1, 2, \ldots, n, \qquad (14.1)$$

where Y_i is the ith observation of the response having been observed under the fixed values $x_{i1}, x_{i2}, \ldots, x_{ik}$ of the predictor variables, ε_i is the unobservable random error associated with Y_i, and $\beta_0, \beta_1, \ldots, \beta_k$ are $m = k + 1$ unknown linear parameters. Equation (14.1) is called the *general linear model* and gives rise to what is known as *multiple linear regression*.

Assuming the normal theory case, the observations Y_i are independent normally distributed random variables such that

$$E(Y_i) = \beta_0 + \beta_1 x_{i1} + \cdots + \beta_k x_{ik},$$

$$Var(Y_i) = \sigma^2, \qquad i = 1, 2, \ldots, n.$$

Thus the random errors ε_i are independent $N(0, \sigma^2)$. The general linear model defines a hyperplane regression equation in which the parameter β_0 is the value of the mean response when all predictor variables are set to zero. The parameter β_j, $j = 1, 2, ..., k$, represents the change in the average response for each unit change in the corresponding predictor variable x_j, when all other predictor variables are held constant. In this sense β_j represents the partial effect of x_j on the response.

The only functional restriction placed on the general linear model is that it be linear in the unknown parameters; the model is not restricted with regard to the nature of the predictor variables. Many interesting special cases therefore arise, some of which are worthy of mention. The model as given by (14.1) implies that the effects of the predictor variables $x_1, x_2, ..., x_k$ on the response are additive, so the assumed regression equation is a linear function of the predictor variables. Such an equation is called a *first order model*. It is possible, however, for two or more of the predictor variables to interact; that is, the effect of one predictor on the response depends on the particular value of the other predictor. When this occurs, the effects are not additive because of the presence in the model of a cross-product term to represent the interaction effect. For example, consider a model containing two predictor variables that interact. The model is

$$Y_i = \beta_0 + \beta_1 x_{i1} + \beta_2 x_{i2} + \beta_3 x_{i1} x_{i2} + \varepsilon_i, \tag{14.2}$$

where the cross-product term $\beta_3 x_{i1} x_{i2}$ reflects the interaction between x_1 and x_2. If we define

$$x_{i3} = x_{i1} x_{i2}, \qquad i = 1, 2, ..., n,$$

then (14.2) can be written in the form of the general linear model (14.1) and thus is a special case of it. Note that for this special case the meaning of β_1 and β_2 is not the same as previously given. The partial derivative of the mean response with respect to x_1 (or with respect to x_2) represents the effect on the average response per unit change in x_1 (x_2) when x_2 (x_1) is held fixed. The partial derivatives are

$$\frac{\partial E(Y)}{\partial x_1} = \beta_1 + \beta_3 x_2$$

$$\frac{\partial E(Y)}{\partial x_2} = \beta_2 + \beta_3 x_1.$$

Another interesting case arises when in (14.1) we let

$$x_{ij} = x_i^j, \qquad i = 1, 2, ..., n, \quad j = 1, 2, ..., k.$$

Then the general linear model specializes to

$$Y_i = \beta_0 + \beta_1 x_i + \beta_2 x_i^2 + \cdots + \beta_k x_i^k + \varepsilon_i, \tag{14.3}$$

which is known as the *curvilinear model*. In this case we assume the average response is a polynomial function of degree k of a single predictor variable.

Therefore, the assumed regression equation for the mean response remains linear in the parameters, but it is a nonlinear function of the predictor variable. It is worthwhile to note that in this case what is usually sought is the degree k that best fits a given random sample of responses.

To adequately describe a given response variable, it sometimes becomes necessary to include linear, quadratic, and interaction terms in the assumed model. For example, for two predictor variables the model would be

$$Y_i = \beta_0 + \beta_1 x_{i1} + \beta_2 x_{i2} + \beta_3 x_{i1}^2 + \beta_4 x_{i2}^2 + \beta_5 x_{i1} x_{i2} + \varepsilon_i. \tag{14.4}$$

By defining new predictor variables for the quadratic and interaction terms in the same manner as before, (14.4) is also a special case of the general linear model. This type of model is known as a complete *second order equation* and defines various surfaces for the average response as a nonlinear function of the predictor variables x_1 and x_2. For $k \geq 2$ distinct predictor variables, a complete second order regression equation consists of a constant term, k linear terms, k quadratic terms, and $k(k - 1)/2$ interaction terms.

We now return to the general linear model as given by (14.1) to obtain least squares estimators for the parameters and to develop regression techniques for this model. All special cases previously mentioned as well as many others that have not been specifically cited are included in the subsequent discussion. Our treatment will be based on matrix algebra, which greatly facilitates the presentation.

Given a random sample of observations $Y_1, Y_2, ..., Y_n$ at observation points $x_{11}, x_{12}, ..., x_{1k}, x_{21}, x_{22}, ..., x_{2k}, ..., x_{n1}, x_{n2}, ..., x_{nk}$, respectively, the following n equations result based on the general linear model:

$$Y_1 = \beta_0 + \beta_1 x_{11} + \beta_2 x_{12} + \cdots + \beta_k x_{1k} + \varepsilon_1$$

$$Y_2 = \beta_0 + \beta_1 x_{21} + \beta_2 x_{22} + \cdots + \beta_k x_{2k} + \varepsilon_2$$

$$\vdots$$

$$Y_n = \beta_0 + \beta_1 x_{n1} + \beta_2 x_{n2} + \cdots + \beta_k x_{nk} + \varepsilon_n.$$

As a result, the general linear model may also be expressed in matrix form as

$$\mathbf{Y} = \mathbf{X}\boldsymbol{\beta} + \boldsymbol{\varepsilon}, \tag{14.5}$$

where

$$\mathbf{Y} = \begin{bmatrix} Y_1 \\ Y_2 \\ \vdots \\ Y_n \end{bmatrix}, \quad \mathbf{X} = \begin{bmatrix} 1 & x_{11} & x_{12} & \cdots & x_{1k} \\ 1 & x_{21} & x_{22} & \cdots & x_{2k} \\ \vdots & \vdots & \vdots & & \vdots \\ 1 & x_{n1} & x_{n2} & \cdots & x_{nk} \end{bmatrix}, \quad \boldsymbol{\beta} = \begin{bmatrix} \beta_0 \\ \beta_1 \\ \vdots \\ \beta_k \end{bmatrix}, \quad \boldsymbol{\varepsilon} = \begin{bmatrix} \varepsilon_1 \\ \varepsilon_2 \\ \vdots \\ \varepsilon_n \end{bmatrix}.$$

The reader will have no difficulty recognizing that (14.5) is exactly identical to the matrix form of the simple linear model (13.37) except that now $\mathbf{X}$ is an $n \times m$ matrix of values for the predictor variables and $\boldsymbol{\beta}$ is an $m \times 1$ vector of unknown parameters, while $\mathbf{Y}$ and $\boldsymbol{\varepsilon}$ remain $n \times 1$ vectors of response observations and associated random errors, respectively.

Under the normal theory case

$$\mathbf{Y} \sim N(\mathbf{X}\boldsymbol{\beta}, \sigma^2 \mathbf{I}),$$

$$\boldsymbol{\varepsilon} \sim N(\mathbf{0}, \sigma^2 \mathbf{I}),$$

where

$$Var(\mathbf{Y}) = Var(\boldsymbol{\varepsilon}) = \sigma^2 \mathbf{I}.$$

Thus $\mathbf{Y}$ and $\boldsymbol{\varepsilon}$ are vectors of independent normally distributed random variables.

For least squares estimation of the parameters, the normal equations take the same form as (13.40) or

$$(\mathbf{X}'\mathbf{X})\mathbf{B} = \mathbf{X}'\mathbf{Y}$$

where now $(\mathbf{X}'\mathbf{X})$ is an $m \times m$ matrix and $\mathbf{B}$ is an $m \times 1$ vector containing the least squares estimators $B_0, B_1, ..., B_k$. If $(\mathbf{X}'\mathbf{X})$ has an inverse, the solution for the vector $\mathbf{B}$ is given by

$$\mathbf{B} = (\mathbf{X}'\mathbf{X})^{-1}\mathbf{X}'\mathbf{Y}.$$

Hence the estimated regression equation is

$$\hat{\mathbf{Y}} = \mathbf{X}\mathbf{B}, \tag{14.6}$$

where the $n \times 1$ vector $\hat{\mathbf{Y}}$ contains the estimated values for the average response corresponding to the n observation points of the predictor variables. The difference between the vectors $\mathbf{Y}$ and $\hat{\mathbf{Y}}$ yields the vector of residuals.

It can be shown that properties of the least squares estimators $B_0, B_1, ..., B_k$ are extensions of those in the simple linear model. That is, under the normal theory case they are also the maximum likelihood estimators such that the following hold:

1. Each B_j is normally distributed with mean $E(B_j) = \beta_j, j = 0, 1, 2, ..., k$, and variance $Var(B_j) = c_{(j+1)}\sigma^2, j = 0, 1, 2, ..., k$, where $c_{(j+1)}$ is the $(j+1)$st diagonal element of $(\mathbf{X}'\mathbf{X})^{-1}$.
2. $Cov(B_i, B_j) = c_{(i+1), (j+1)}\sigma^2, i \neq j = 0, 1, 2, ..., k$, where $c_{(i+1), (j+1)}$ is the element of $(\mathbf{X}'\mathbf{X})^{-1}$ in the $(i+1)$st row and the $(j+1)$st column, for $i \neq j$.

An unbiased estimator of the error variance is

$$S^2 = \frac{\mathbf{Y}'\mathbf{Y} - \mathbf{B}'\mathbf{X}'\mathbf{Y}}{n - m}, \tag{14.7}$$

where the numerator in (14.7) is nothing more than the sum of the squares of the residuals. Notice that the denominator of (14.7) is the number of observations less the number of parameters in the model, which for the general linear model is $m = k + 1$. It follows, therefore, that an estimate of $Var(B_j)$ is

$$s^2(B_j) = c_{(j+1)}s^2, \qquad j = 0, 1, 2, ..., k,$$

where $c_{(j+1)}$ is as previously defined.

From the preceding results one can deduce that the quantity

$$(B_j - \beta_j)/s(B_j), \qquad j = 0, 1, 2, \ldots, k,$$

is a Student's t random variable with $n - m$ degrees of freedom. Then a $100(1 - \alpha)\%$ confidence interval for the parameter β_j is

$$b_j \pm t_{1-\alpha/2,\, n-m} s(B_j), \qquad j = 0, 1, 2, \ldots, k, \tag{14.8}$$

and an appropriate statistic to test the null hypothesis

$$H_0: \beta_j = 0$$

against either a two-sided or a one-sided alternative is the familiar Student's t,

$$T = B_j/s(B_j), \qquad j = 0, 1, 2, \ldots, k,$$

with $n - m$ degrees of freedom.

Now we turn our attention to the analysis of variance technique to test the null hypothesis

$$H_0: \beta_1 = \beta_2 = \cdots = \beta_k = 0$$

against the alternative

$$H_1: \beta_j \neq 0 \quad \text{for some } j = 1, 2, \ldots, k.$$

Since H_0 states that all regression parameters except the constant term are zero, this implies that there is no relationship as specified by the assumed model between the response and the set of predictor variables. The reader is cautioned, however, that even if H_0 is rejected, it does not necessarily mean that the estimated regression equation is useful for making predictions. Further analyses are necessary before a judgment can be rendered on the usefulnes of a regression equation.

Following the same argument for the general linear model as that for the simple linear model in Section 13.7, one can show that the total sum of squares is partitioned into the sum of squares of regression and the sum of squares of error. Using matrix notation, SST, SSR, and SSE are defined in Table 14.1.

The total degrees of freedom remain the same at $n - 1$, but the error degrees of freedom are now $n - m$. The degrees of freedom for regression are $(n - 1) - (n - m) = m - 1 = k$, since $m = k + 1$. The residual variance, or $\mathrm{SSE}/(n - m)$, is the error mean square, and $\mathrm{SSR}/(m - 1)$ is the regression mean square. Under the null hypothesis the appropriate test statistic is

$$F = \mathrm{MSR}/\mathrm{MSE},$$

which is F distributed with $m - 1$ and $n - m$ degrees of freedom. We can argue as before that if a value of this statistic is sufficiently large, then a considerable portion of the variation in the observations is attributable to the regression of Y on the predictor variables as defined by the model. Thus the null hypothesis is rejected so long as the computed value is inside an upper tail critical region of size α. The analysis of variance table for the general linear model is given in Table 14.1.

TABLE 14.1   ANOVA table for the general linear model

Source of variation	Degrees of freedom	Sums of squares	Mean squares	F statistic
Regression	$k = m - 1$	$\mathbf{B'X'Y} - \dfrac{(\Sigma Y_i)^2}{n}$	$SSR/(m-1)$	$\dfrac{SSR/(m-1)}{SSE/(n-m)}$
Error	$n - m$	$\mathbf{Y'Y} - \mathbf{B'X'Y}$	$SSE/(n-m)$	
Total	$n - 1$	$\mathbf{Y'Y} - \dfrac{(\Sigma Y_i)^2}{n}$		

For the general linear model the notion of the coefficient of determination extends to produce what is known as the *multiple correlation coefficient* or the *coefficient of multiple determination*. The multiple correlation coefficient is defined by

$$R^2 = \frac{SSR}{SST} = 1 - \frac{SSE}{SST}, \tag{14.9}$$

and like r^2 measures the proportion of the total variation of the observations about their mean attributable to the estimated regression equation. In other words, R^2 is a relative measure of how much all the terms in the regression equation that involve predictor variables explain the variation of the observations. As in the simple linear model, $0 \leqslant R^2 \leqslant 1$, and the larger R^2 is, the more of the total variation in the response can be explained by the terms in the model. R^2 by itself cannot validate the assumed model, nor does a large value for R^2 necessarily imply that the estimated regression equation is appropriate for prediction.

Suppose we wish to predict the average response when the k predictor variables assume the specific values $x_1, x_2, \ldots, x_k$, respectively. In matrix notation, let

$$\mathbf{X}_p' = [1 \; x_1 \; x_2 \cdots x_k]$$

be a row vector identifying the coordinates at which the prediction is to be made. Then the estimated mean response is

$$\hat{Y}_p = \mathbf{X}_p' \mathbf{B}$$
$$= B_0 + B_1 x_1 + B_2 x_2 + \cdots + B_k x_k. \tag{14.10}$$

Given (14.10), one can show that

$$Var(\hat{Y}_p) = \sigma^2 \mathbf{X}_p'(\mathbf{X'X})^{-1}\mathbf{X}_p.$$

Thus an estimate of $Var(\hat{Y}_p)$ is

$$s^2(\hat{Y}_p) = s^2 \mathbf{X}_p'(\mathbf{X'X})^{-1}\mathbf{X}_p, \tag{14.11}$$

where s^2 is the residual variance and $\mathbf{X}$ is the original matrix of x values that produced the estimated regression equation. Under the normal theory case a

$100(1 - \alpha)\%$ confidence interval for the average response at $x_1, x_2, ..., x_k$ is

$$\hat{y}_p \pm t_{1-\alpha/2, \, n-m} s(\hat{Y}_p). \tag{14.12}$$

If we want to estimate a particular response at $x_1, x_2, ..., x_k$, the prediction would still be as given by (14.10), but the variance is now

$$Var(\hat{Y}_{\text{part}}) = \sigma^2 [1 + \mathbf{X}_p'(\mathbf{X}'\mathbf{X})^{-1}\mathbf{X}_p].$$

It follows that a $100(1 - \alpha)\%$ prediction interval for the true response at $x_1, x_2, ..., x_k$ is

$$\hat{y}_{\text{part}} \pm t_{1-\alpha/2, \, n-m} s(\hat{Y}_{\text{part}}), \tag{14.13}$$

where

$$s^2(\hat{Y}_{\text{part}}) = s^2 [1 + \mathbf{X}_p'(\mathbf{X}'\mathbf{X})^{-1}\mathbf{X}_p].$$

Example 14.1   N. H. Prater* developed a regression equation to estimate gasoline yield as a function of the distillation properties of a given crude oil. Four predictor variables were identified: crude oil gravity, °API (x_1); crude oil vapor pressure, psi (x_2); crude oil ASTM 10% point, °F (x_3); and gasoline ASTM end point, °F (x_4). The first two measure the gravity and vapor pressure of a given crude. The crude oil ASTM 10% point is the temperature at which a certain amount of liquid has been vaporized, and the gasoline end point is the temperature at which all of the liquid has vaporized. The response was the gasoline produced as a percentage of crude. The objective was to determine a regression equation for the gasoline yield as a linear function of the distillation properties of a given crude $x_1, x_2,$ x_3 and the desired gasoline end point x_4. The laboratory data obtained by Prater are presented in Table 14.2.

We will use these data to illustrate the techniques we have developed for multiple linear regression using SAS. We will also consider this example as it pertains to a particular problem one can encounter in multiple linear regression, known as *multicollinearity*. It should be noted that several authors have used the Prater data since its publication in 1956 to illustrate aspects of the general linear model. Among these, Daniel and Wood [2] developed a substantively different regression equation from Prater's.

Using an option of SAS called GLM, we fit the linear model

$$Y = \beta_0 + \beta_1 x_1 + \beta_2 x_2 + \beta_3 x_3 + \beta_4 x_4 + \varepsilon.$$

The computer output is given in Figure 14.1. Notice that at the bottom of the figure are five columns of information. The first column on the left identifies the predictor variables in the model, including the constant term. The second column gives the least squares estimates, the third gives the Student's t value for testing the null hypothesis that the parameter is zero, the fourth column gives the

*N. H. Prater, *Estimate gasoline yields from crudes*, Petroleum Refiner **35** (1956), 236–238. Table reproduced with permission from Petroleum Refiner (later Hydrocarbon Processing), May 1956.

TABLE 14.2 Sample data for Example 14.1

Observation	Y	x_1	x_2	x_3	x_4
1	6.9	38.4	6.1	220	235
2	14.4	40.3	4.8	231	307
3	7.4	40.0	6.1	217	212
4	8.5	31.8	0.2	316	365
5	8.0	40.8	3.5	210	218
6	2.8	41.3	1.8	267	235
7	5.0	38.1	1.2	274	285
8	12.2	50.8	8.6	190	205
9	10.0	32.2	5.2	236	267
10	15.2	38.4	6.1	220	300
11	26.8	40.3	4.8	231	367
12	14.0	32.2	2.4	284	351
13	14.7	31.8	0.2	316	379
14	6.4	41.3	1.8	267	275
15	17.6	38.1	1.2	274	365
16	22.3	50.8	8.6	190	275
17	24.8	32.2	5.2	236	360
18	26.0	38.4	6.1	220	365
19	34.9	40.3	4.8	231	395
20	18.2	40.0	6.1	217	272
21	23.2	32.2	2.4	284	424
22	18.0	31.8	0.2	316	428
23	13.1	40.8	3.5	210	273
24	16.1	41.3	1.8	267	358
25	32.1	38.1	1.2	274	444
26	34.7	50.8	8.6	190	345
27	31.7	32.2	5.2	236	402
28	33.6	38.4	6.1	220	410
29	30.4	40.0	6.1	217	340
30	26.6	40.8	3.5	210	347
31	27.8	41.3	1.8	267	416
32	45.7	50.8	8.6	190	407

probability (*p*-value) of observing a Student's *t* value that large or larger in magnitude, and the fifth column gives the standard deviations (errors) for the least squares estimates. Thus the estimated regression equation (rounded off to two places) is

$$\hat{y} = -6.82 + 0.23x_1 + 0.55x_2 - 0.15x_3 + 0.15x_4.$$

At the top of the figure we find the ANOVA table, with df(SSR) = 4, SSR = 3429.27, MSR = 857.32, df(SSE) = 27, SSE = 134.80, MSE = 4.99, df(SST) = 31, and SST = 3564.08. The computed *F* value for testing the null hypothesis

$$H_0: \beta_1 = \beta_2 = \beta_3 = \beta_4 = 0$$

is 171.71, and the probability of observing a value that large or larger is found immediately to the right of it. Underneath the *p*-value is the residual standard

FIGURE 14.1 Computer output for linear regression of Y on x_1, x_2, x_3, and x_4 for the Prater data

DEPENDENT VARIABLE: Y

SOURCE	DF	SUM OF SQUARES	MEAN SQUARE	F VALUE	PR > F	R-SQUARE	C.V.
MODEL	4	3429.27322460	857.31830615	171.71	0.0001	0.962177	11.3658
ERROR	27	134.80396290	4.99273937		STD DEV		Y MEAN
CORRECTED TOTAL	31	3564.07718750			2.23444386		19.65937500

SOURCE	DF	TYPE I SS	F VALUE	PR > F	DF	TYPE IV SS	F VALUE	PR > F
X1	1	216.25576661	43.31	0.0001	1	25.81557060	5.17	0.0311
X2	1	309.85082754	62.06	0.0001	1	11.19716648	2.24	0.1458
X3	1	29.21431690	5.85	0.0226	1	130.67556799	26.17	0.0001
X4	1	2873.95231355	575.63	0.0001	1	2873.95231355	575.63	0.0001

PARAMETER	ESTIMATE	T FOR H0: PARAMETER=0	PR > |T|	STD ERROR OF ESTIMATE
INTERCEPT	-6.82077407	-0.67	0.5062	10.12315182
X1	0.22724595	2.27	0.0311	0.09993664
X2	0.55372621	1.50	0.1458	0.36975194
X3	-0.14953562	-5.12	0.0001	0.02922920
X4	0.15465009	23.99	0.0001	0.00644584

deviation, $s = 2.23$. The multiple correlation coefficient is 0.9622, which means that over 96% of the total variation of the observations about their mean is explained by the four predictor variables in the regression equation.

At the extreme upper right hand corner of the figure we find the coefficient of variation, which was defined in Chapter 3. Here the value of the CV is the ratio of the residual standard deviation to the mean of the observations. Since in this case $s = 2.23$ and $\bar{y} = 19.66$, CV $= 11.37\%$. In regression analysis it is highly desirable for the residual standard deviation to be a small fraction of the mean of the observations because this usually implies that much of the variation in the response has been explained by the predictor variables in the regression equation. We will elaborate on the information at the middle of the figure in the next section.

Based on the preceding analysis, there is little doubt that linear regression between gasoline yield and the four predictor variables is statistically discernible. The null hypothesis that all regression coefficients (except the constant term) are zero is certainly rejected, and the value of the multiple correlation coefficient is relatively high at 0.9622. There is reason for concern, however, about the usefulness of the regression equation as given. For example, the standard deviations of the least squares estimators for β_0 and β_2 are large, suggesting that x_2 and possibly other predictor variables may not have much effect on the gasoline yield. In subsequent sections we will be examining appropriate procedures to determine the best regression equation for a given set of predictor variables. Among other examples we will from time to time use the data of Example 14.1.

14.3   The Extra Sum of Squares Principle

The inclusion of a predictor variable in a regression model does not necessarily imply that the variable has a substantive effect on the given response. That is, when a set of predictor variables is identified by an investigator, it indicates the *potential* of the variables to explain the variation in the response. It remains to be seen whether some actually do.

The appropriate procedure for finding the individual effects of predictor variables is based on the *Extra Sum of Squares Principle*. This principle allows us to determine the reduction in the error sum of squares when an additional regression coefficient for some function of a predictor variable is introduced into the regression equation. Two important things are worth remembering: (1) The total sum of squares always remains the same no matter how many terms are introduced in the regression model. (2) The error sum of squares always decreases (however slightly) as more terms are added to the model.

Since the regression sum of squares is the difference between SST and SSE, SSR is bound to increase as more terms are added to the model. A logical strategy in multiple linear regression is to add not just any terms to the model but only terms that significantly increase the regression sum of squares and thus significantly reduce the error sum of squares. As an example, in the simple linear model SSR is the extra sum of squares due to the inclusion of the linear term $\beta_1 x$ in the model. In other words, SSR represents the reduction in the error sum of squares when a linear effect of the predictor variable is added to the original model

$$Y_i = \beta_0 + \varepsilon_i.$$

To illustrate the Extra Sum of Squares Principle, let us use as potential predictor variables only x_2 and x_3 from the Prater data and fit all possible regressions of gasoline yield for these two predictors. There will be three regression equations; one each will involve x_2 and x_3 individually, and the third will contain both x_2 and x_3. The estimated regression equations and analysis of variance tables are given in Table 14.3. Notice that we use the notation $SSR(x_2)$, $SSR(x_2, x_3)$, $SSE(x_2, x_3)$, to denote that these sums of squares are functions of the indicated predictor variables in the regression equation and their corresponding least squares coefficients.

Let us examine the results in Table 14.3. As we have said before, for the given 32 observations of the response the total sum of squares is $SST = 3564.08$ no matter how many predictor variables are included in the model. For the regression of Y on x_2, $SSR(x_2) = 525.74$ is the reduction in the error sum of

TABLE 14.3 Estimated regression equations and ANOVA tables for gasoline yield involving x_2 and/or x_3

(a) $\hat{y} = 13.09 + 1.57x_2$

Source of variation	df	SS	MS	F value
Regression	1	$SSR(x_2) = 525.74$	$MSR(x_2) = 525.74$	5.19
Error	30	$SSE(x_2) = 3038.34$	$MSE(x_2) = 101.28$	
Total	31	$SST = 3564.08$	$f_{0.95, 1, 30} = 4.17$	

(b) $\hat{y} = 41.39 - 0.09x_3$

Source of variation	df	SS	MS	F value
Regression	1	$SSR(x_3) = 353.70$	$MSR(x_3) = 353.70$	3.31
Error	30	$SSE(x_3) = 3210.38$	$MSE(x_3) = 107.01$	
Total	31	$SST = 3564.08$	$f_{0.95, 1, 30} = 4.17$	

(c) $\hat{y} = -2.52 + 2.26x_2 + 0.05x_3$

Source of variation	df	SS	MS	F value
Regression	2	$SSR(x_2, x_3) = 547.49$	$MSR(x_2, x_3) = 273.74$	2.63
Error	29	$SSE(x_2, x_3) = 3016.59$	$MSE(x_2, x_3) = 104.02$	
Total	31	$SST = 3564.08$	$f_{0.95, 2, 29} = 3.33$	

squares when the term $\beta_2 x_2$ is added to the model $Y_i = \beta_0 + \varepsilon_i$. In other words, if we fit the model $Y_i = \beta_0 + \varepsilon_i$, one assumes that the only source of variation in Y_i is random error; the estimated regression line is simply $\hat{Y}_i = \bar{Y}$. When the term $\beta_2 x_2$ is added to the model, some of the total variation is then explained by the presence of x_2. That is precisely what $\text{SSR}(x_2) = 525.74$ represents. $\text{SSR}(x_2) = 525.74$ is the extra sum of squares removed from SSE when the term $\beta_2 x_2$ is added to the model. Using the same argument for the regression of Y on x_3, $\text{SSR}(x_3) = 353.70$ is the extra sum of squares removed from the error when the term $\beta_3 x_3$ is added to the model $Y_i = \beta_0 + \varepsilon_i$. In either case, if the reduction in the error sum of squares is substantial, the null hypothesis of zero value for the corresponding regression coefficient is rejected. Notice that for the regression of Y on x_2, $H_0: \beta_2 = 0$ is rejected (f value $= 5.19 > f_{0.95,1,30} = 4.17$), but for the regression of Y on x_3, $H_0: \beta_3 = 0$ cannot be rejected.

Now let us turn our attention to the regression of Y on x_2 and x_3. What we want to determine is the reduction in the error sum of squares when the term $\beta_3 x_3$ is added to the model that already contains the constant term β_0 and the term $\beta_2 x_2$, or the reduction in SSE when the term $\beta_2 x_2$ is introduced to the model that contains β_0 and $\beta_3 x_3$. Notice in Model c of Table 14.3 that the error sum of squares when both x_2 and x_3 are included in the regression model is $\text{SSE}(x_2, x_3) = 3016.59$. But when only x_2 is in the model, $\text{SSE}(x_2) = 3038.34$. The difference between $\text{SSE}(x_2)$ and $\text{SSE}(x_2, x_3)$ must therefore be the extra sum of squares due to the inclusion of the term $\beta_3 x_3$ in the model that already contains the terms β_0 and $\beta_2 x_2$. We will label this difference $\text{SSR}(x_3 \mid x_2)$. Thus

$$\text{SSR}(x_3 \mid x_2) = \text{SSE}(x_2) - \text{SSE}(x_2, x_3) \qquad (14.14)$$

$$= 3038.34 - 3016.59$$

$$= 21.75$$

is the additional reduction in the error sum of squares when x_3 is introduced to the model in the presence of x_2.

Since a reduction in the error sum of squares means a corresponding increase in the regression sum of squares,

$$\text{SSR}(x_2, x_3) = \text{SSR}(x_3 \mid x_2) + \text{SSR}(x_2) \qquad (14.15)$$

$$= 21.75 + 525.74$$

$$= 547.49.$$

The regression sum of squares when both x_2 and x_3 are in the model is broken down into two components, each with a single degree of freedom: $\text{SSR}(x_3 \mid x_2)$, which reflects the contribution of x_3 when added to the model $Y = \beta_0 + \beta_2 x_2 + \varepsilon$, and $\text{SSR}(x_2)$, which measures the contribution of x_2 when added to the model $Y = \beta_0 + \varepsilon$.

It can be shown that $\text{SSR}(x_3 \mid x_2)$ and $\text{SSR}(x_2)$ are independent chi-square random variables, each with one degree of freedom. A comparison can then be made between the mean square of $\text{SSR}(x_3 \mid x_2)$, or that of $\text{SSR}(x_2)$, and the mean square of error, $\text{MSE}(x_2, x_3)$, by way of the F statistic. This test is known as a

TABLE 14.4 Expanded ANOVA table for the regression of Y on x_2 and x_3

Source of variation	df	SS	MS	F value
Regression	2	$SSR(x_2, x_3) = 547.49$	$MSR(x_2, x_3) = 273.74$	2.63
x_2	1	$SSR(x_2) = 525.74$	$MSR(x_2) = 525.74$	5.05
$x_3 \mid x_2$	1	$SSR(x_3 \mid x_2) = 21.75$	$MSR(x_3 \mid x_2) = 21.75$	0.2
Error	29	$SSE(x_2, x_3) = 3016.59$	$MSE(x_2, x_3) = 104.02$	
Total	31	$SST = 3564.08$	$f_{0.95, 2, 29} = 3.33; f_{0.95, 1, 29} = 4.18$	

partial F test on a predictor variable. In reality, the partial F test determines whether the contribution of a regression coefficient is large enough to warrant its inclusion in the model, given that other terms that do not involve the coefficient are already in the model. In a sense, therefore, we are attempting to pass judgment on the individual effect of the corresponding predictor variable on a given response. The expanded ANOVA table for the regression of Y on x_2 and x_3, including the partial F tests, is given in Table 14.4. Notice that the inclusion of the term $\beta_2 x_2$ in the model $Y = \beta_0 + \varepsilon$ is beneficial, while the inclusion of $\beta_3 x_3$ in $Y = \beta_0 + \beta_2 X_2 + \varepsilon$ is not.

Throughout the preceding discussion we assumed the term $\beta_3 x_3$ was added last to the model involving both x_2 and x_3. It is possible, however, to perform partial F tests for each regression coefficient as if the corresponding predictor variable were last to be added to the model. In this manner the individual effects of each predictor variable in the presence of others can be ascertained. In our example what we would like to determine is the contribution of the term $\beta_2 x_2$ when the model already contains β_0 and $\beta_3 x_3$.

Proceeding as before, the error sum of squares when both x_2 and x_3 are in the model is $SSE(x_2, x_3) = 3016.59$. But when only x_3 is in the model, $SSE(x_3) = 3210.38$. Thus the reduction in the error sum of squares when the term $\beta_2 x_2$ is added to the model containing β_0 and $\beta_3 x_3$ is

$$SSR(x_2 \mid x_3) = SSE(x_3) - SSE(x_2, x_3) \tag{14.16}$$

$$= 3210.38 - 3016.59$$

$$= 193.79.$$

Then the regression sum of squares when both x_2 and x_3 are in the model is the sum of the two components,

$$SSR(x_2, x_3) = SSR(x_2 \mid x_3) + SSR(x_3) \tag{14.17}$$

$$= 193.79 + 353.70$$

$$= 547.49,$$

with each component having a single degree of freedom. An important consequence of all this is that both $SSR(x_2 \mid x_3) = 193.79$ and $SSR(x_3 \mid x_2) = 21.75$ are smaller

TABLE 14.5 Expanded ANOVA table for regression of Y on x_2 and x_3

Source of variation	df	SS	MS	F value
Regression	2	$SSR(x_2, x_3) = 547.49$	$MSR(x_2, x_3) = 273.74$	2.63
x_3	1	$SSR(x_3) = 353.70$	$MSR(x_3) = 353.70$	3.40
$x_2 \mid x_3$	1	$SSR(x_2 \mid x_3) = 193.79$	$MSR(x_2 \mid x_3) = 193.79$	1.86
Error	29	$SSE(x_2, x_3) = 3016.59$	$MSE(x_2, x_3) = 104.02$	
Total	31	$SST = 3564.08$	$f_{0.95, 2, 29} = 3.33; f_{0.95, 1, 29} = 4.18$	

than $SSR(x_2) = 525.74$ and $SSR(x_3) = 353.70$, respectively. The reason for this is the subject of the next section.

To determine the partial F tests for the regression due to x_3, or due to x_2 given x_3, another version of Table 14.4 is now possible. This is given in Table 14.5. Notice that a comparison of the results of Tables 14.4 and 14.5 shows disagreement on the effect of x_2 on gasoline yield. Whereas the simple linear regression of Y on x_2 is statistically discernible ($f = 5.19$), the regression of Y on x_2 given the presence of x_3 is not ($f = 1.86$). We will elaborate further on this occurrence in the next section.

The Extra Sum of Squares Principle extends in a straightforward manner to apply the basic idea to any number of predictor variables. For example, say we have the three predictor variables x_1, x_2, and x_3. We can define the reduction in the error sum of squares when one of these is added to the model that already contains the other two as follows:

$$SSR(x_3 \mid x_1, x_2) = SSE(x_1, x_2) - SSE(x_1, x_2, x_3), \tag{14.18}$$

$$SSR(x_2 \mid x_1, x_3) = SSE(x_1, x_3) - SSE(x_1, x_2, x_3), \tag{14.19}$$

$$SSR(x_1 \mid x_2, x_3) = SSE(x_2, x_3) - SSE(x_1, x_2, x_3). \tag{14.20}$$

To develop expressions similar to (14.15) or (14.17), we deduce from (14.14) that

$$SSR(x_2 \mid x_1) = SSE(x_1) - SSE(x_1, x_2),$$

or

$$SSE(x_1, x_2) = SSE(x_1) - SSR(x_2 \mid x_1). \tag{14.21}$$

Now when only x_1 is in the model, by definition

$$SSE(x_1) = SST - SSR(x_1);$$

but when all three variables are in the model,

$$SST = SSR(x_1, x_2, x_3) + SSE(x_1, x_2, x_3).$$

Then
$$\text{SSE}(x_1) = \text{SSR}(x_1, x_2, x_3) + \text{SSE}(x_1, x_2, x_3) - \text{SSR}(x_1),$$

and substituting for $\text{SSE}(x_1)$ in (14.21), we obtain

$$\text{SSE}(x_1, x_2) = \text{SSR}(x_1, x_2, x_3) + \text{SSE}(x_1, x_2, x_3)$$
$$- \text{SSR}(x_1) - \text{SSR}(x_2 \mid x_1). \quad (14.22)$$

Substituting (14.22) for $\text{SSE}(x_1, x_2)$ in (14.18) yields the desired result

$$\text{SSR}(x_3 \mid x_1, x_2) = \text{SSR}(x_1, x_2, x_3) - \text{SSR}(x_1) - \text{SSR}(x_2 \mid x_1), \quad (14.23)$$

or

$$\text{SSR}(x_1, x_2, x_3) = \text{SSR}(x_1) + \text{SSR}(x_2 \mid x_1) + \text{SSR}(x_3 \mid x_1, x_2). \quad (14.24)$$

The sum of squares of regression when all three variables are in the model has three components, each with a single degree of freedom. $\text{SSR}(x_1)$ measures the contribution (reduction in the error sum of squares) of x_1 when x_1 is added to the model $Y = \beta_0 + \varepsilon$; $\text{SSR}(x_2 \mid x_1)$ represents the contribution of x_2 when x_2 is added to the model $Y = \beta_0 + \beta_1 x_1 + \varepsilon$; and $\text{SSR}(x_3 \mid x_1, x_2)$ is the contribution of x_3 when x_3 is added to the model $Y = \beta_0 + \beta_1 x_1 + \beta_2 x_2 + \varepsilon$.

Using (14.19) or (14.20) and following the same procedure, results similar to (14.24) can be established as follows:

$$\text{SSR}(x_1, x_2, x_3) = \text{SSR}(x_1) + \text{SSR}(x_3 \mid x_1) + \text{SSR}(x_2 \mid x_1, x_3), \quad (14.25)$$

$$\text{SSR}(x_1, x_2, x_3) = \text{SSR}(x_2) + \text{SSR}(x_3 \mid x_2) + \text{SSR}(x_1 \mid x_2, x_3). \quad (14.26)$$

These results permit partial F tests to be made on each regression coefficient as though its predictor variable was the last to be included in the model. In other words, with the partial F tests we can determine whether the individual effect of a predictor variable in the presence of others is statistically discernible. It should be noted that by interchanging the order of entry to the model for the predictor variables, it is possible to identify other relationships similar to (14.24)–(14.26). For example,

$$\text{SSR}(x_1, x_2, x_3) = \text{SSR}(x_2) + \text{SSR}(x_1 \mid x_2) + \text{SSR}(x_3 \mid x_2, x_1)$$

is yet another breakdown of $\text{SSR}(x_1, x_2, x_3)$. As the number of predictor variables increases, the number of possible breakdowns becomes extremely large.

For the analysis of the Prater data as given in the last section, we are now in a position to explain the information at the middle portion of Figure 14.1. The reader will note two columns identified as "Type I SS" and "Type IV SS." The Type I SS are the four components of $\text{SSR}(x_1, x_2, x_3, x_4)$ such that

$$\text{SSR}(x_1, x_2, x_3, x_4) = \text{SSR}(x_1) + \text{SSR}(x_2 \mid x_1)$$
$$+ \text{SSR}(x_3 \mid x_1, x_2) + \text{SSR}(x_4 \mid x_1, x_2, x_3).$$

Each component has one degree of freedom and is the reduction in the error sum of squares when the identified variable is added to the model. The order of entry to the model for the variables is the same as the order in which the predictor variables were identified by the user, so

$$\text{SSR}(x_1) = 216.26,$$

$$\text{SSR}(x_2 \mid x_1) = 309.85,$$

$$\text{SSR}(x_3 \mid x_1, x_2) = 29.21,$$

$$\text{SSR}(x_4 \mid x_1, x_2, x_3) = 2873.95.$$

The two columns immediately to the right of the "Type I SS" column give the values of the partial F tests and the corresponding p-values for each of the four components. From these it is apparent that the individual effect of each regression coefficient in the presence of other terms in the model is statistically discernible.

The Type IV SS represents the reduction in the error sum of squares due to the addition of the identified predictor variable to the model, given that all other predictor variables are already in the model. For the example the components are

$$\text{SSR}(x_1 \mid x_2, x_3, x_4) = 25.82,$$

$$\text{SSR}(x_2 \mid x_1, x_3, x_4) = 11.20,$$

$$\text{SSR}(x_3 \mid x_1, x_2, x_4) = 130.68,$$

$$\text{SSR}(x_4 \mid x_1, x_2, x_3) = 2873.95.$$

Notice that there is no theoretical reason that these four components should sum to $\text{SSR}(x_1, x_2, x_3, x_4)$.

Based on the partial F values for these components, some discrepancy is apparent between these results and those from Type I SS. For example, the contribution of x_2 in the presence of only x_1 is statistically discernible, but the contribution of x_2 in the presence of x_1, x_3, and x_4 is not.

14.4   The Problem of Multicollinearity

One is very likely to reach wrong conclusions with a casual approach to the application of regression analysis without an appreciation of the problems that can be encountered. In the last section we noted several discrepancies that may arise in multiple linear regression. Such discrepancies provide useful information for identifying problems that need further attention. The approach to regression analysis should never be simply to maximize the multiple correlation coefficient without due consideration of the estimated regression coefficients and their standard deviations, or of checking the underlying assumptions of regression analysis.

A frequent problem in multiple linear regression is that some of the predictor variables are correlated. If the correlation is slight, the consequences are rather minor. However, if two or more predictor variables are severely correlated, the regression results are ambiguous, especially with regard to the values of the estimated regression coefficients. A very high correlation between two or more predictor variables usually constitutes what is called *multicollinearity*. The problem of multicollinearity is often difficult to detect because it stems from deficient data. This is the price we pay at times when we cannot statistically design experiments and take data in balanced arrays, as discussed in Chapter 12.

Recall that the prediction equation, although it may not be physically precise, should be a viable, if empirical, means of predicting the average response given a condition of the predictor variables. Multicollinearity does not preclude a good fit, nor does it prevent the response from being adequately predicted within the range of the observations. It does severely affect the least squares estimates because under multicollinearity they tend to be less than precise for the individual effects of predictor variables. That is, when two or more predictor variables are collinear, the estimated regression coefficients do not measure individual effects on the response. Rather they reflect a partial effect on the response subject to whatever other correlated predictor variables happen to be in the regression equation.

To appreciate the nature of multicollinearity, we will first illustrate a situation in which multicollinearity does not exist. Consider a regression model with two predictor variables. If the simple correlation coefficient between the two variables is exactly zero, the two variables are said to be *orthogonal*.* With orthogonal predictor variables the individual effect of one variable on a given response is measured totally independently of the individual effect of the other variable on the same response. Whether one or both of the predictor variables are in the regression equation, the least squares estimates will not change in value.

Example 14.2 To illustrate orthogonal effects, examine the (limited) data in Table 14.6, which consists of the apparent temperature Y (how warm it actually feels) as a function of air temperature x_1 and relative humidity x_2.

The reader will have no trouble verifying that the simple correlation coefficient between x_1 and x_2 is exactly zero. Now let us fit the three models $Y = \beta_0 +$

TABLE 14.6 Sample data for Example 14.2

$Y(°F)$	$x_1(°F)$	$x_2(\%)$
66	70	20
72	75	20
77	80	20
67	70	30
73	75	30
78	80	30
68	70	40
74	75	40
79	80	40

Source: National Weather Service.

*One of the primary reasons for statistically designing experiments is to acquire orthogonal factors. For many experiments that use analysis of variance, the factors are orthogonal.

TABLE 14.7 Estimated regression equations and ANOVA tables for apparent temperature, involving x_1 and/or x_2

$$\hat{y} = -9.83 + 1.10x_1$$

Source of variation	df	SS	MS	F value
Regression	1	$SSR(x_1) = 181.5$	$MSR(x_1) = 181.5$	195.46
Error	7	$SSE(x_1) = 6.5$	$MSE(x_1) = 0.9286$	
Total	8	$SST = 188.0$	$f_{0.95, 1, 7} = 5.59$	

$$\hat{y} = 69.67 + 0.10x_2$$

Source of variation	df	SS	MS	F value
Regression	1	$SSR(x_2) = 6.0$	$MSR(x_2) = 6.0$	0.23
Error	7	$SSE(x_2) = 182.0$	$MSE(x_2) = 26.0$	
Total	8	$SST = 188.0$	$f_{0.95, 1, 7} = 5.59$	

$$\hat{y} = 12.83 + 1.10x_1 + 0.10x_2$$

Source of variation	df	SS	MS	F value
Regression	2	$SSR(x_1, x_2) = 187.5$	$MSR(x_1, x_2) = 93.75$	1125.0
x_1	1	$SSR(x_1) = 181.5$	$MSR(x_1) = 181.5$	2178.0
$x_2 \mid x_1$	1	$SSR(x_2 \mid x_1) = 6.0$	$MSR(x_2 \mid x_1) = 6.0$	72.0
Error	6	$SSE(x_1, x_2) = 0.5$	$MSE(x_1, x_2) = 0.0833$	
Total	8	$SST = 188.0$	$f_{0.95, 2, 6} = 5.14, f_{0.95, 1, 6} = 5.99$	

$\beta_1 x_1 + \varepsilon$, $Y = \beta_0 + \beta_2 x_2 + \varepsilon$, and $Y = \beta_0 + \beta_1 x_1 + \beta_2 x_2 + \varepsilon$. The relevant information is contained in Table 14.7.

Notice that the estimated regression coefficients for x_1 and x_2 are 1.10 and 0.10, respectively, regardless whether one or both of the predictor variables are in the regression equation. Thus, for each degree increase in the air temperature the apparent temperature increases by 1.10 degrees, and for each percentage point increase in relative humidity the apparent temperature increases by 0.10 degrees.* Notice further that

$$SSR(x_2 \mid x_1) = SSR(x_2),$$

$$SSR(x_1, x_2) = SSR(x_1) + SSR(x_2).$$

*The reader should not generalize from these results because of the limited range of the data.

The preceding results are precisely what one expects when predictor variables are orthogonal and multicollinearity does not exist.

Now let us return to the Prater data and the regressions involving x_2 or x_3 as given in Table 14.3 and show that there is reason to suspect the existence of collinearity between x_2 and x_3. First, notice that the estimated regression coefficient for x_2 is 1.57 when only x_2 is in the regression equation but jumps to 2.26 when x_3 is added. Similarly, the coefficient of x_3 is -0.09 for the straight line model, but it changes sign and becomes 0.05 when x_2 is also included in the regression equation. Second, it is clear that the reduction in the error sum of squares due to x_3 when x_2 is present in the model, $SSR(x_3 \mid x_2) = 21.75$, is much less than that when only x_3 is in the model, $SSR(x_3) = 353.70$. The apparently strong correlation between x_2 and x_3 has drastically reduced the individual effect of x_3 upon the response in the presence of x_2. The same comment can be made about the effect of x_2 since it is statistically discernible in the absence of x_3 — $SSR(x_2) = 525.74$, $f = 5.19$ — but is substantially diminished when x_3 is present — $SSR(x_2 \mid x_3) = 193.79$.

To show the strong correlation between x_2 and x_3, let us determine the correlation matrix for all four predictor variables of the Prater data. This matrix contains all possible pairwise correlation coefficients and can easily be determined for a given set of variables by using a computer package.* The correlation matrix for x_1, x_2, x_3, and x_4 is as follows:

$$
\begin{array}{c c c c c}
 & x_1 & x_2 & x_3 & x_4 \\
x_1 & \begin{bmatrix} 1.00 \\ 0.62 \\ -0.70 \\ -0.32 \end{bmatrix} & \begin{matrix} 0.62 \\ 1.00 \\ -0.91 \\ -0.30 \end{matrix} & \begin{matrix} -0.70 \\ -0.91 \\ 1.00 \\ 0.41 \end{matrix} & \begin{matrix} -0.32 \\ -0.30 \\ 0.41 \\ 1.00 \end{matrix} \\
x_2 \\
x_3 \\
x_4
\end{array}
$$

Notice that all diagonal elements equal one since each variable is perfectly linearly correlated with itself. The elements outside the diagonal are the values of the simple correlation coefficients. For example, $r_{12} = 0.62$ is the correlation coefficient between x_1 and x_2. It follows, therefore, that the value $r_{23} = -0.91$ is close enough to -1 to suggest a strong linear association between x_2 and x_3. This result is predictable if one visually inspects the data as given in Example 14.1. Notice that as the crude oil vapor pressure x_2 increases, the ASTM 10% point x_3 decreases, and vice versa. These results provide just cause to suspect the presence of multicollinearity in this example.

What can be done when multicollinearity is uncovered? One approach has been to add observation points for the collinear variables, which tends to lessen the severity of the correlation. But such observation points may not be readily available. For the gasoline data, for example, the types of crude oil that may break the strong linearity between x_2 and x_3 may not exist. A second approach is simply to delete one or more of the collinear variables, thereby reducing the variability of the estimated regression coefficients of the remaining variables.

*For SAS, PROC CORR would be appropriate.

More formal approaches have been developed to remedy multicollinearity problems, including principal components regression and ridge regression. These topics are beyond the scope of this book; the reader is directed to [1] and [3] for details.

We illustrate the second approach to remedy multicollinearity by examining the regressions in which either x_2 or x_3 is deleted. For comparison we also consider the regression of gasoline yield involving only the ASTM 10% point (x_3) and gasoline end point (x_4). Without any further discussion, these three regressions are believed to be the candidates for the "best" linear regression equation for the Prater data. The relevant information is contained in Table 14.8.

On balance, it appears that the regression of Y on only x_3 and x_4 is better than the other two models. In Model b, the standard deviation of the least squares estimator for the constant term is much too large, and the standard deviation of the coefficient of x_1 is nearly half that value. For Model a, $R^2 = 0.9255$, whereas for Model c, $R^2 = 0.9521$, a value that is extremely close to the R^2 value when all four predictor variables are in the regression equation. Moreover, the standard deviations of the estimated regression coefficients are relatively better in Model c than in Model a. Ultimately, key physical factors, such as logical consistency of the estimated regression coefficients, are likely to dictate the final choice.

14.5   Determination of the Best Set of Predictor Variables

A very important problem in regression analysis is to determine which of the predictor variables in the original list ought to be included in the regression model. More often than not, an investigator will decide on an initial list of predictor variables that is likely to contain the most important factors for the given response. What is needed is a way of determining from the initial list of predictor variables those that appear to be best for accounting for the change in the average response, and thus will yield a prediction equation that is representative of the conditions under which the data were collected. The word "best" should not be interpreted as having a theoretical connotation of optimality. Rather, it should be viewed as the means by which the salient features of the problem are isolated so that a meaningful analysis can be carried out.

Let k be the number of potential predictor variables in the initial list; the number of terms in the full linear model, including the constant term, is $m = k + 1$. A procedure that is highly recommended for determining the best set of predictor variables to include in the regression equation is to compute and compare all possible 2^k regression equations. With this process there will be one equation that contains none of the predictor variables ($\hat{Y} = \overline{Y}$), k equations each containing one predictor variable, $k(k - 1)/2$ equations each using two variables, and so on. The procedure provides the investigator with the opportunity to evaluate and compare all regression equations, and a best equation should emerge based on the investigation of all apparent discrepancies. Since computing capability is abundant today, the determination of all possible regression equations is the best approach even if k is as large as nine or ten.

When k is larger the determination and evaluation of all possible regressions may not be practical. For such cases, *variable selection techniques* have been

TABLE 14.8   Candidates for the best regression equation for the Prater data

(a) Regression of Y on x_1, x_2, x_4

Variable	Estimated regression coefficient	Estimated standard deviation	t value
Constant	− 53.899	5.8135	− 9.27
x_1	0.422	0.1273	3.32
x_2	2.154	0.2716	7.93
x_4	0.144	0.0084	17.10

$R^2 = 0.9255$ $t_{0.975,\,28} = 2.048$

ANOVA

Source	df	SS	MS	F value
Regression	3	3298.60	1099.53	115.97
x_1	1	216.26	216.26	22.81
$x_2 \mid x_1$	1	309.85	309.85	32.68
$x_4 \mid x_1, x_2$	1	2772.49	2772.49	292.41
Error	28	265.48	9.48	
Total	31	3564.08	$f_{0.95,\,3,\,28} = 2.95;\ f_{0.95,\,1,\,28} \doteq 4.20$	

(b) Regression of Y on x_1, x_3, x_4

Variable	Estimated regression coefficient	Estimated standard deviation	t value
Constant	4.032	7.2233	0.56
x_1	0.222	0.1021	2.17
x_3	− 0.187	0.0159	− 11.72
x_4	0.157	0.0065	24.22

$R^2 = 0.959$ $t_{0.975,\,28} = 2.048$

ANOVA

Source	df	SS	MS	F value
Regression	3	3418.08	1139.38	218.51
x_1	1	216.26	216.26	41.47
$x_3 \mid x_1$	1	142.08	142.08	27.25
$x_4 \mid x_1, x_3$	1	3059.74	3059.74	586.79
Error	28	146.00	5.21	
Total	31	3564.08	$f_{0.95,\,3,\,28} = 2.95;\ f_{0.95,\,1,\,28} = 4.20$	

(continued)

TABLE 14.8 (continued)

(c) Regression of Y on x_3, x_4

Variable	Estimated regression coefficient	Estimated standard deviation	t value
Constant	18.468	3.0090	6.14
x_3	−0.209	0.0127	−16.43
x_4	0.156	0.0069	22.73

$$R^2 = 0.9521 \qquad t_{0.975,\,29} = 2.045$$

ANOVA

Source	df	SS	MS	F value
Regression	2	3393.47	1696.73	228.41
x_3	1	353.70	353.70	60.12
$x_4 \mid x_3$	1	3039.77	3039.77	516.69
Error	29	170.61	5.88	
Total	31	3564.08	$f_{0.95,\,2,\,29} = 3.33$; $f_{0.95,\,1,\,29} = 4.18$	

developed that can provide the user with useful information without having to evaluate all possible regressions. These techniques have some drawbacks, however, and should not be regarded as equals to the evaluation of all possible regressions. Whereas the variable selection procedures give reliable results when multicollinearity is not a problem, they often produce conflicting results for collinear data. Thus one should not use variable selection methods if multicollinearity is suspected. The usual variable selection technique uses a *stepwise regression* procedure to determine the best regression equation. There are two main versions of this technique: forward selection and backward elimination.

The forward selection procedure begins with the equation that contains no predictor variables. The first variable to be included in the equation is the one that produces the greatest reduction in the error sum of squares. This is the predictor variable with the highest simple correlation coefficient with the given response. Based on a test of hypothesis, if the regression coefficient of this variable is different from zero, the variable is retained in the equation, and a search begins for a second variable. The second variable to enter the equation is the one that effects the greatest reduction in the error sum of squares, given the presence of the first variable.* This is the variable with the highest correlation with the response after the response has been adjusted for the effect of the first variable. If statistical significance is discernible for the regression coefficient of the second variable, the variable is retained and a search begins for a third predictor variable. The process continues in this manner until statistical significance is not discernible for the coefficient of the last variable that has entered the equation.

*Thus difficulties can arise when data are collinear.

The backward elimination procedure begins with the regression equation containing all predictor variables. Then it eliminates one at a time the least important variables based on their contribution to the reduction of the error sum of squares. For example, the first variable deleted is the one that effects the smallest reduction in the error sum of squares, given the presence of the other variables. The procedure is terminated when all of the variables remaining in the equation have coefficients whose significance is statistically discernible.

The forward selection procedure has been modified so that the possibility of deleting a variable is considered at each stage. This modification produces what is usually identified in computer packages as a stepwise regression procedure. With this method a predictor variable that has entered the regression equation at an earlier stage may be removed at a later stage. The decision process is once again based on the reduction in the error sum of squares and partial F tests and depends on the particular mix of variables that happen to be in the regression equation.

With the development of highly sophisticated computer packages, several other techniques have become available, but the common feature remains the concept of reducing (or increasing) the error sum of squares when a variable enters (or is removed from) the regression, given the presence of other variables. For well-behaved data, stepwise regression and backward elimination procedures usually yield the same results. If the results differ, it is often a good indication to take a closer look at the problem and consider additional analyses.

To evaluate and compare regression equations, especially in the context of all possible regressions, one needs effective criteria. Two of the most useful criteria are the error mean square (MSE) and the C_p criterion. For proper balance, we will also discuss the multiple correlation coefficient R^2.

1. *The error mean square criterion.* Recall that the error mean square is the same as the residual variance. Since MSE is the sum of the squares of the residuals divided by the degrees of freedom for SSE, MSE does take into account the number of parameters in the model through the degrees of freedom. Whereas the sum of squares of error cannot increase if more variables are allowed into the model, the error mean square can, if the reduction in SSE is so small that it cannot offset the loss of additional degrees of freedom. For example, recall Table 14.3, and in particular Models a and c. Notice that $SSE(x_2) = 3038.34$ is greater than $SSE(x_2, x_3) = 3016.59$, but $MSE(x_2) = 101.28$ is less than $MSE(x_2, x_3) = 104.02$. With the MSE criterion one determines the set of predictor variables that either minimizes MSE or nearly minimizes it to the point where the introduction of additional variables to the regression equation is not warranted.

2. *The C_p criterion.* Recall that the residual variance S^2 is an unbiased estimator of the error variance σ^2 only when the correct form has been chosen for the regression model. Otherwise one can show that

$$E(S^2) = \sigma^2 + \frac{\sum_{i=1}^{n} A_i^2}{(n-p)} \qquad (14.27)$$

where p is the number of terms in the model, including the constant term, and

$$A_i = E(Y_i) - E(\hat{Y}_i)$$

is the bias.

We assume that the regression equation that contains all k predictor variables has been carefully chosen so that MSE $\equiv S^2$ is an unbiased estimator of σ^2. But for any regression equation which contains only a subset of the k predictor variables, it is possible that $A_i \neq 0$, and predictions of the response based on the estimated regression equation may be biased. To evaluate the performance of such an estimated regression equation for prediction, we should consider the error mean square of a predicted value rather than the variance. The standardized total error mean square defined by

$$\Gamma_p = \frac{1}{\sigma^2} \sum_{i=1}^{n} \text{MSE}(\hat{Y}_i)$$

$$= \frac{1}{\sigma^2} \left[\sum_{i=1}^{n} A_i^2 + \sum_{i=1}^{n} Var(\hat{Y}_i) \right] \tag{14.28}$$

has been proposed as an appropriate criterion of goodness of fit for an estimated regression equation containing p terms. The quantity Γ_p accounts for the bias component in $\hat{Y}_i$, since some predictor variables are not included, and the variance in $\hat{Y}_i$ for all n observations of the response. What we seek now is an estimator for Γ_p.

It can be shown that

$$\sum_{i=1}^{n} Var(\hat{Y}_i) = p\sigma^2,$$

which implies that the total variance of prediction increases as the number of terms in the regression equation increases. Substitution in (14.28) yields

$$\Gamma_p = \frac{1}{\sigma^2} \sum_{i=1}^{n} A_i^2 + p. \tag{14.29}$$

Since for a regression equation that contains p terms

$$\text{SSE}_p = (n - p)S_p^2,$$

we have

$$E(\text{SSE}_p) = (n - p)E(S_p^2)$$

$$= (n - p) \left[\sigma^2 + \frac{\sum A_i^2}{(n - p)} \right]$$

$$= (n - p)\sigma^2 + \sum A_i^2,$$

or

$$\sum A_i^2 = E(\text{SSE}_p) - (n - p)\sigma^2.$$

Substituting in (14.29), we obtain

$$\Gamma_p = \frac{E(\text{SSE}_p) - (n - p)\sigma^2}{\sigma^2} + p$$

$$= \frac{E(\text{SSE}_p)}{\sigma^2} - (n - p) + p$$

$$= \frac{E(\text{SSE}_p)}{\sigma^2} - (n - 2p).$$

Since SSE_p is an estimator of $E(\text{SSE}_p)$ and S_k^2 is an estimator of σ^2, an estimator of Γ_p is the statistic

$$C_p = \frac{\text{SSE}_p}{S_k^2} - (n - 2p). \tag{14.30}$$

Notice that SSE_p is the error sum of squares for the regression equation containing p terms, and that $S_k^2 = \text{MSE}(x_1, x_2, \ldots, x_k)$ is the estimator of σ^2 based on all k predictor variables.

The desirable values for C_p for goodness of fit of a regression equation containing p terms are those that are very close to p. This stems from the fact that if the bias of a p-term regression equation is negligible, $\Sigma A_i^2 \approx 0$ and $E(\text{SSE}_p) = (n - p)\sigma^2$. Under this condition the expected value of the statistic C_p is

$$E(C_p \mid A_i = 0) = \frac{(n - p)\sigma^2}{\sigma^2} - (n - 2p)$$

$$= p.$$

Thus when all possible regressions are determined, a value of C_p is computed in each case. Regressions that have C_p values close to p are deemed desirable.

It may actually be beneficial to accept a small bias in prediction by deleting a few predictor variables, even if their nonzero regression coefficients are statistically discernible. This is especially true if the regression coefficients of the new model are estimated with smaller variances. Moreover, since the total variance of prediction increases as more variables are added to the regression model, it may also be advantageous to delete a few variables to lower the average error of prediction.

In addition to MSE and C_p, some thought should be given to the multiple correlation coefficient R^2 for evaluating regression equations. Since R^2 varies inversely with the error sum of squares, R^2 will increase as more variables are added to the regression model, and R^2 will be at its maximum when all predictor variables are in the regression equation. The reason for using R^2 as a criterion therefore is not to find that set of variables that maximizes R^2 but to determine the point beyond which adding more variables is not desirable because the increase in R^2 is only minimal.

To provide an illustration of all possible regressions and their comparisons on the preceding criteria, we once again turn to the Prater data. Table 14.9

TABLE 14.9   All possible regressions for the Prater data

Predictor variables in the model	b_0	b_1	b_2	b_3	b_4
x_1	1.264	0.469			
x_2	13.087		1.572		
x_3	41.389			-0.090	
x_4	-16.662				0.019
x_1, x_2	12.256	0.025	1.539		
x_1, x_3	35.174	0.096		-0.080	
x_1, x_4	-64.951	1.009			0.136
x_2, x_3	-2.524		2.257	0.053	
x_2, x_4	-37.808		2.677		0.139
x_3, x_4	18.468			-0.209	0.156
x_1, x_2, x_3	-11.013	0.125	2.278	0.067	
x_1, x_2, x_4	-53.899	0.422	2.154		0.144
x_1, x_3, x_4	4.032	0.222		-0.187	0.157
x_2, x_3, x_4	8.562		0.523	-0.175	0.154
x_1, x_2, x_3, x_4	-6.821	0.227	0.554	-0.150	0.155

contains the least squares estimates of the coefficients for each regression (other than the trivial $\hat{y}_i = \bar{y} = 19.66$), and Table 14.10 identifies the corresponding values of SSE, MSE, C_p, and R^2.

The error mean square when all four predictor variables are in the regression model is $MSE(x_1, x_2, x_3, x_4) = 4.99$. Thus, for example, to determine the value of C_p for the regression of Y on x_1, x_3, and x_4 we have $SSE(x_1, x_3, x_4) = 146.00$, $p = 4$, $n = 32$, and

$$C_p = \frac{146}{4.99} - (32 - 8) = 5.26.$$

TABLE 14.10   Goodness of fit criteria for all possible regressions for the Prater data

Predictor variables	R^2	SSE	MSE	C_p
x_1	0.0607	3347.82	111.59	642.91
x_2	0.1475	3038.34	101.28	580.89
x_3	0.0992	3210.38	107.01	615.36
x_4	0.5063	1759.69	58.66	324.64
x_1, x_2	0.1476	3037.97	104.76	582.81
x_1, x_3	0.1005	3205.74	110.54	616.43
x_1, x_4	0.7582	861.95	29.72	146.74
x_2, x_3	0.1536	3016.59	104.02	578.53
x_2, x_4	0.8962	369.87	12.75	48.12
x_3, x_4	0.9521	170.61	5.88	8.19
x_1, x_2, x_3	0.1558	3008.76	107.46	578.96
x_1, x_2, x_4	0.9255	265.48	9.48	29.20
x_1, x_3, x_4	0.9590	146.00	5.21	5.26
x_2, x_3, x_4	0.9549	160.62	5.74	8.19
x_1, x_2, x_3, x_4	0.9622	134.80	4.99	5.00

Taking into account both MSE and C_p, it appears that the best prediction equation for gasoline yield should be selected from the regressions involving (x_3, x_4), (x_1, x_3, x_4), (x_2, x_3, x_4), and (x_1, x_2, x_3, x_4). The last one is not particularly appealing since the estimates of the regression coefficients for the constant term and x_2 have standard deviations that are too large. Although the regression equation involving x_2, x_3, and x_4 has nearly optimal MSE and C_p values, it lacks satisfactory precision in the estimate of the coefficient of x_2 since $b_2 = 0.523$, with $s(B_2) = 0.396$. The same can be said about the regression involving x_1, x_3, and x_4 for the estimates of β_0 and the coefficient of x_1 (see Model b in Table 14.8). Accordingly, we accept a slight bias in prediction and conclude that the regression equation containing x_3 and x_4 is best for predicting gasoline yield in the range of the observations.

We now outline the steps involved in a stepwise regression procedure:

1. The procedure begins by determining k simple linear regression equations. The F statistic

$$F = \text{MSR}(x_i)/\text{MSE}(x_i)$$

   is computed for each $i = 1, 2, \ldots, k$ variables. If the largest F value exceeds a predetermined level of statistical significance, the corresponding variable is the first to be included in the regression. Otherwise the best equation is $\hat{Y} = \overline{Y}$. This process is the same as determining the predictor variable that is most highly correlated with the response.

2. Suppose variable x_3 enters the regression equation in step 1. Now the stepwise procedure calculates all equations with two variables, including x_3. For each case the value of the partial F statistic

$$F = \text{MSR}(x_i \mid x_3)/\text{MSE}(x_i, x_3)$$

   is computed to determine whether $H_0: \beta_i = 0$ can be rejected in the presence of x_3. If the largest F value is sufficient for statistical significance, the corresponding second variable is added to the equation.

3. Suppose x_1 is added to the equation in step 2. The procedure continues by examining whether any of the other variables already in the equation should be dropped; in this case it would be x_3. The value of the partial F statistic

$$F = \text{MSR}(x_3 \mid x_1)/\text{MSE}(x_1, x_3)$$

   is computed and compared to the predetermined level for significance. If the effect of x_3 given x_1 is now not statistically discernible, x_3 is dropped from the equation; otherwise it is retained. At later stages there will be a number of these partial F tests for all the variables that were added earlier. The variable that may be deleted is the one for which the F value is smallest.

4. Suppose x_3 is retained. At this point the regression equation includes x_1 and x_3. The stepwise process continues by examining which of the remaining variables is a candidate for inclusion in the model. Then it examines whether any of the included variables should now be dropped. The process terminates

when no other predictor variables can be added or deleted from the regression model.

It is left as an exercise to the reader to use the gasoline yield data with whatever variable selection options are available to him or her and compare the results.

14.6 Analysis of Residuals

In the last section we examined ways to determine a "best" regression equation under the circumstances prescribed by the data set. A very effective way of detecting possible deficiencies in a model is to perform a residual analysis. No other single thing is more important in regression analysis than the analysis of the residuals. The well-known economist Paul A. Samuelson remarked: "To the scientific forecaster I say, 'Always study your residuals.' "

As noted in Chapter 12, a residual analysis uncovers violations of the assumptions or model deficiencies. We will examine three common deficiencies: The regression equation may not be linear in the predictor variables; the error variance σ^2 may not be constant; and one or more influential predictor variables may not have been included in the model. We will also look at the problem of *outlier* observations, observations whose values are out of line with the rest of the data.

Recall that the ith residual e_i is the numerical difference between the observed value y_i and the corresponding estimated value $\hat{y}_i$, for $i = 1, 2, ..., n$. The residual e_i is regarded as an estimate of the unobservable true error ε_i. The error mean square is the variance of the residuals, which is an estimate of σ^2.

In substance, residual analysis means an analysis of graphs of the residuals. If the regression equation has been correctly defined and no deficiencies exist, then a plot of the residuals against either the estimated values $\hat{y}_i$ or the corresponding values of each predictor variable in the equation should reveal no pattern. That is, there should be no relationship between the residuals and the fitted values or between the residuals and the values of predictor variables. If there is, some deficiency in the regression equation is suggested. To detect problem areas through a residual analysis it is once again preferred to use the standardized residuals. Since the mean of the residuals is zero,

$$e_{i_s} = e_i/s$$

defines the ith standardized residual, where s is the residual standard deviation ($\sqrt{\text{MSE}}$). It should be noted that if the sample size n is fairly large, the distribution of the standardized residuals should be well approximated by a standard normal. In fact, many have suggested that any noticeable departure from normality in the distribution of the residuals may indicate model deficiency.

To determine whether or not the regression model is linear in the predictor variables, we plot the residuals against corresponding values for each predictor variable in the equation. To determine whether or not the error variance is constant, the standardized residuals are plotted against the corresponding estimated values of the response. And to determine whether a potentially important variable ought to have been included in the regression model, the residuals are plotted against the values of the variable. If the estimated regression equation is practically free of any deficiencies or violations of assumptions, then the standardized residuals tend to fall within a horizontal band centered around zero, with no systematic tendencies to be positive or negative, and rarely outside the ± 3 range. Any significant deviation from this behavior would suggest a problem.

Figure 14.2 depicts typical residual plots (a) when a quadratic effect of a predictor variable is present and ought to be included in the model; (b) when

FIGURE 14.2 Typical residual plots for (a) presence of a quadratic effect, (b) nonconstant error variance, and (c) linear effect of an omitted variable

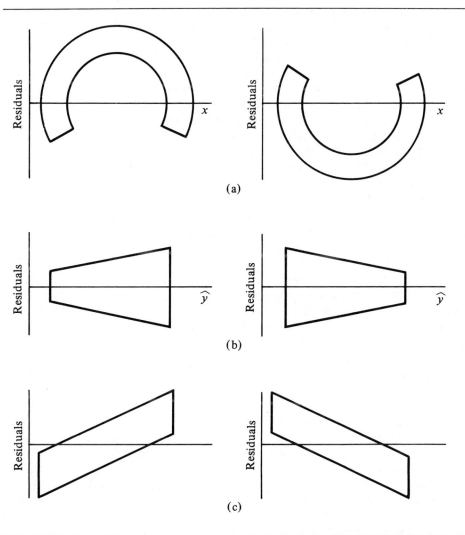

the error variance is not constant and weighted least squares ought to be used to estimate the regression coefficients; and (c) when an omitted variable shows strong (linear) association with the residuals and ought to be included in the regression model. We can elaborate further on these three cases. If the regression equation contains only a linear effect of a predictor variable x, when in reality a statistically discernible quadratic effect exists, then the plot of the standardized residuals versus x would be a U-shaped (or inverted U-shaped) curve. Under a quadratic effect, the residuals corresponding to the extreme values of x tend to be large and positive (negative), and the residuals for mid-range values of x tend to be small but negative (positive). By including a quadratic term of x in the model, the predictive performance of the resulting regression equation is usually improved considerably over the previous equation. Higher-order effects can also be detected in the same manner.

If a residual plot reveals a wedge-shaped figure, then the assumption of a constant error variance may not hold. In other words, if there is a tendency for the standardized residuals to increase or decrease with increasing fitted values, the error variance may not be constant. This gives rise to what is called a *heteroscedastic model*. To remedy the situation one resorts to *weighted least squares,* where the weights are inversely proportional to the variance of the errors. Thus instead of attempting to determine estimates of regression coefficients by minimizing the sum of the squares of the errors, we now determine the set for which the weighted sum of squares of the errors is a minimum. The essence of using weighted least squares in a heteroscedastic situation is to estimate the regression coefficients with smaller deviations and obtain a better fit.

If the standardized residuals, when plotted against a variable that is not part of the regression equation but under which the response may have been observed, reveal a linear (or higher-order) trend, then, as we noted in Chapter 13, the errors can no longer be regarded as independent of this variable. This type of variable usually turns out to be a demographic or a time-related effect. For example, for many experiments in which the data are observed over a significant time span, an investigator may initially decide not to include time as a potential predictor variable. But if the residuals reveal a systematic pattern when plotted against time, the time variable ought to be introduced into the regression equation.

Residual plots also help in dealing with extreme observations or outliers. Extreme observations usually have residuals that are large relative to those of the other observations. The standardized residual value of an outlier observation will usually be well beyond the ± 3 range. Outliers can create a difficult situation in a regression equation because they have a disproportionate effect on the estimated values of the regression coefficients. Recall that an assumption in least squares estimation is that the data set is typical of the situation for which we are attempting to identify a good prediction equation. Therefore, the removal of any one observation from the data set should have virtually no effect on the performance of the regression equation. This is precisely the reason why an outlier observation can only be removed with extreme care. A logical method that has been suggested is to remove an outlier only if there is corroborated evidence that the outlier is a mistake due to a cause such as instrument malfunction.

TABLE 14.11 Sample data for Example 14.3

Y	x_1	x_2
13.59	87	80
15.71	78	95
15.97	81	106
20.21	65	115
24.64	51	128
21.25	62	128
18.94	70	115
14.85	91	92
15.18	94	93
16.30	100	111
15.93	102	116
16.45	82	117
19.02	74	127
18.16	85	133
18.57	86	135
17.01	90	136
18.03	93	140
19.22	81	142
21.12	72	148
23.32	60	150

In the absence of such evidence, the outlier observation may actually be supplying unique information about the response that may be vital to the experiment.

The following two examples illustrate cases (a) and (c) in Figure 14.2. The case involving nonconstant variance will be discussed in Section 14.8.

Example 14.3 A manufacturing firm wishes to predict the manufacturing unit cost Y of one of its products as a function of fluctuating production rate x_1 and material and labor costs x_2. Data were collected over a 20-month span during which production rate and material and labor costs fluctuated widely. The production rate was measured as a percentage of rated capacity, and an appropriate index was used to reflect material and labor costs. The observations are listed in Table 14.11. Determine the best regression equation to predict unit cost.

First we assume a linear regression model involving x_1 and x_2. Estimates and other relevant information are given in Table 14.12. Everything appears to be quite good. The estimates make sense (negative value for the coefficient of x_1 and positive value for that of x_2), the standard deviations are small, the R^2 value is relatively high, and all effects are statistically discernible. The temptation would be to conclude that we have determined a good prediction equation, but a plot of the standardized residuals versus x_1 reveals a definite quadratic pattern in the top half of Figure 14.3. No pattern is apparent for x_2.

The residual plot for x_1 implies that we should include a quadratic term in x_1 in the regression model. Thus we fit the model

$$Y = \beta_0 + \beta_1 x_1 + \beta_2 x_2 + \beta_3 x_1^2 + \varepsilon$$

and obtain the results in Table 14.13.

TABLE 14.12 Regression analysis for Example 14.3

Regression of Y on x_1 and x_2

Variable	Estimated regression coefficient	Estimated standard deviation	t value
Constant	20.2800	2.1300	9.54
x_1	−0.1377	0.0159	−8.69
x_2	0.0742	0.0110	6.77

$R^2 = 0.914$ $t_{0.975,\ 17} = 2.11$

ANOVA

Source	df	SS	MS	F value
Regression	2	144.39	72.19	90.24
x_1	1	107.72	107.72	134.65
$x_2 \mid x_1$	1	36.67	36.67	45.84
Error	17	13.59	0.80	
Total	19	157.98	$f_{0.95,\ 2,\ 17} = 3.59;\ f_{0.95,\ 1,\ 17} = 4.45$	

TABLE 14.13 Revised regression analysis for Example 14.3

Regression of Y on x_1, x_2, and x_1^2

Variable	Estimated regression coefficient	Estimated standard deviation	t value
Constant	41.550000	3.050000	13.64
x_1	−0.700300	0.076200	−9.20
x_2	0.073400	0.005400	13.68
x_1^2	0.003624	0.000488	7.43

$R^2 = 0.981$ $t_{0.975,\ 16} = 2.12$

ANOVA

Source	df	SS	MS	F value
Regression	3	154.92	51.640	270.37
x_1	1	107.72	107.72	563.98
$x_2 \mid x_1$	1	36.66	36.66	191.94
$x_1^2 \mid x_1, x_2$	1	10.54	10.54	55.18
Error	16	3.06	0.191	
Total	19	157.98	$f_{0.95,\ 3,\ 16} = 3.24;\ f_{0.95,\ 1,\ 16} = 4.49$	

FIGURE 14.3 Standardized residual plots for Example 14.3

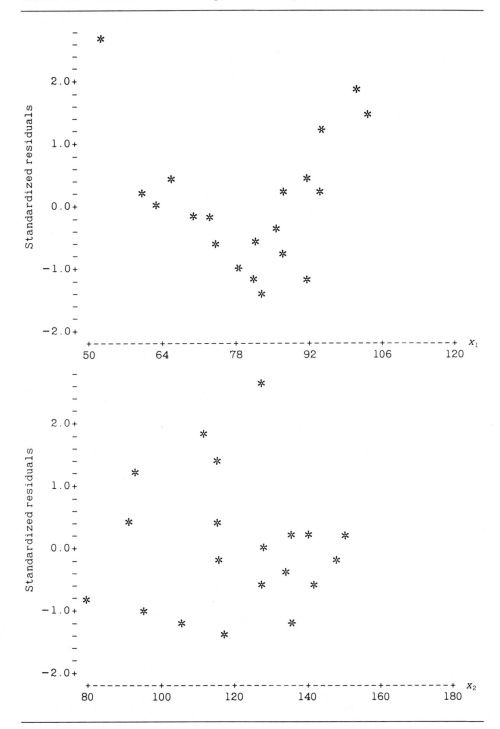

FIGURE 14.4   Standardized residual plots for the revised regression equation in Example 14.3

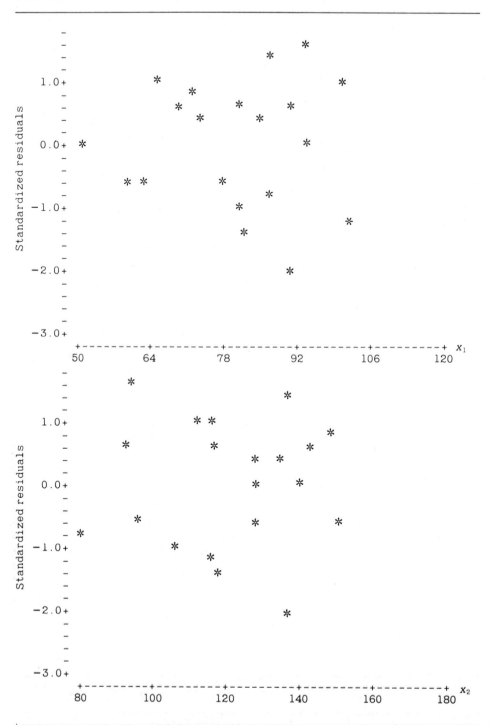

TABLE 14.14 Augmented data for the starting salary example

Y	x_1 (GPA)	x_2 (Age)
18.5	2.95	22
20.0	3.20	23
21.1	3.40	23
22.4	3.60	23
21.2	3.20	27
15.0	2.85	22
18.0	3.10	25
18.8	2.85	28
15.7	3.05	23
14.4	2.70	22
15.5	2.75	28
17.2	3.10	22
19.0	3.15	26
17.2	2.95	23
16.8	2.75	26

A comparison with the earlier results reveals that the inclusion of a quadratic effect in x_1 has greatly improved the estimated regression equation. For example, the regression coefficients of x_1 and x_2 are estimated with better precision than before, and the value of R^2 has increased to 0.981. Moreover, the new residual plot versus x_1 — see Figure 14.4 — shows no discernible pattern.

Example 14.4 Recall the example of starting salary versus grade point average that we used throughout Chapter 13. Perhaps the reader has wondered whether there might be other potential predictor variables. Suppose we had also recorded the age of each student in the sample. Since a company may reward some experience that an older graduate might have, it is possible that the age of a graduate might influence the average starting salary. The data are augmented as given in Table 14.14.

When we plot the standardized residuals of the estimated regression equation $\hat{y} = -6.63 + 8.12x_1$ against the corresponding values of x_2, given in Figure 14.5, an upward linear trend emerges. We therefore include the linear effect of x_2 in the regression model and fit

$$Y = \beta_0 + \beta_1 x_1 + \beta_2 x_2 + \varepsilon.$$

The new results are given in Table 14.15. Since the constant term and the coefficient of x_1 are now estimated with better precision, and the value of R^2 has increased appreciably, the inclusion of x_2 has yielded a better prediction equation.

14.7 Curvilinear Regression

In Section 14.2 we noted that the curvilinear model given by (14.3), or one that contains interaction terms such as (14.4), is a special case of the general linear

FIGURE 14.5 Standardized residuals versus age in Example 14.4

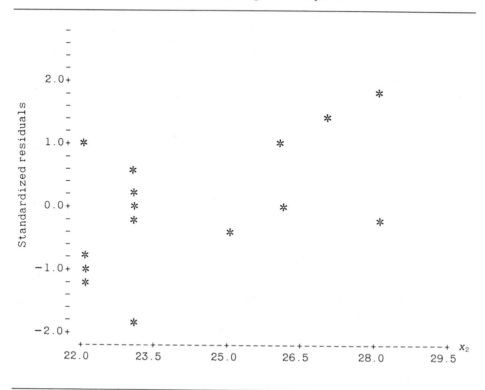

TABLE 14.15 Regression analysis for Example 14.4

Variable	Estimated regression coefficient	Estimated standard deviation	t value
Constant	-16.880	5.470	-3.05
x_1	8.740	1.220	7.16
x_2	0.338	0.137	2.47

$R^2 = 0.813$		$t_{0.975,\ 12} = 2.179$

ANOVA

Source	df	SS	MS	F value
Regression	2	66.10	33.05	26.23
x_1	1	58.40	58.40	46.35
$x_2 \mid x_1$	1	7.70	7.70	6.11
Error	12	15.17	1.26	
Total	14	81.27	$f_{0.95,\ 2,\ 12} = 3.89;\ f_{0.95,\ 1,\ 12} = 4.75$	

model. In fact, we illustrated in Example 14.3 how the quadratic effect of a predictor variable can improve the predictive capability of the regression equation. In this section we will elaborate further on these types of models.

If a single predictor variable x has been identified and a plot of the observed responses versus the values of x reveals curvature, then a polynomial in x of some degree ought to be used to approximate the true curve of regression. For example, a cubic model in x is given by

$$Y_i = \beta_0 + \beta_1 x_i + \beta_{11} x_i^2 + \beta_{111} x_i^3 + \varepsilon_i,$$

where β_1 is called the *linear coefficient*, β_{11} the *quadratic coefficient*, and β_{111} the *cubic coefficient*. To maintain tradition we have altered the notation for these regression coefficients slightly to reflect the pattern of the corresponding power of x.

As we noted before, what we seek with a polynomial is to find the degree that best fits the given data. Accordingly, we are interested in testing hypotheses such as, for example, H_0: $\beta_{11} = 0$ or H_0: $\beta_{111} = 0$. Using this approach we are able to determine the most appropriate polynomial to estimate the average response. However, the reader is cautioned that what is usually sought and preferred is a relatively low-order polynomial. One should refrain from using high powers of the predictor variable because what often happens then is the fitting of the random peaks and valleys in the data. In other words, one can always find a polynomial model of sufficiently high degree to fit the data perfectly, since a regression equation in one variable of degree $n - 1$ will go through all n values of the response.

Many times a complete second-order model containing linear, quadratic, and interaction terms provides excellent functional approximation to a usually complex and unknown response function. For example, a complete second-order model in two variables is

$$Y_i = \beta_0 + \beta_1 x_{i1} + \beta_2 x_{i2} + \beta_{11} x_{i1}^2 + \beta_{22} x_{i2}^2 + \beta_{12} x_{i1} x_{i2} + \varepsilon_i,$$

where β_1 and β_2 are the linear coefficients, β_{11} and β_{22} are the quadratic coefficients, and β_{12} is the interaction coefficient. For this model the matrix $\mathbf{X}$ and parameter vector $\boldsymbol{\beta}$ in the matrix equation

$$\mathbf{Y} = \mathbf{X}\boldsymbol{\beta} + \boldsymbol{\varepsilon}$$

are

$$\mathbf{X} = \begin{bmatrix} 1 & x_{11} & x_{12} & x_{11}^2 & x_{12}^2 & x_{11}x_{12} \\ 1 & x_{21} & x_{22} & x_{21}^2 & x_{22}^2 & x_{21}x_{22} \\ \vdots & \vdots & \vdots & \vdots & \vdots & \vdots \\ 1 & x_{n1} & x_{n2} & x_{n1}^2 & x_{n2}^2 & x_{n1}x_{n2} \end{bmatrix} \qquad \boldsymbol{\beta} = \begin{bmatrix} \beta_0 \\ \beta_1 \\ \vdots \\ \beta_{12} \end{bmatrix}.$$

We illustrate both a polynomial model in one variable and a complete second-order model with the following two examples.

TABLE 14.16 Sample data for Example 14.5

Y (units)	x (dollars)
360	8.8
305	9.7
230	9.9
242	10.3
180	11.0
172	12.5
121	13.2
83	14.8
122	15.8
91	17.4
105	18.2

FIGURE 14.6 Graph of demand versus unit price for Example 14.5

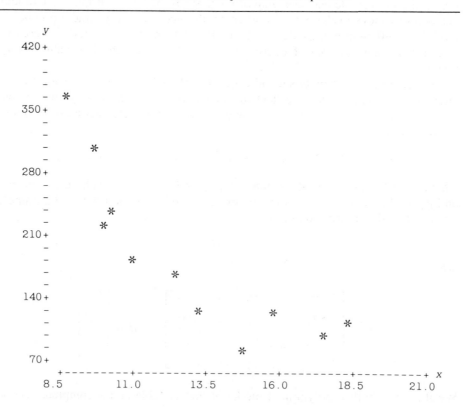

FIGURE 14.7 Computer printout for Example 14.5

```
THE REGRESSION EQUATION IS
Y = 497. - 24.4 X1
```

	COLUMN	COEFFICIENT	ST. DEV. OF COEF.	T-RATIO = COEF/S.D.
	—	497.15	60.85	8.17
X1	C2	-24.419	4.594	-5.32

```
THE ST. DEV. OF Y ABOUT REGRESSION LINE IS
S = 47.53
WITH ( 11- 2) =  9 DEGREES OF FREEDOM

R-SQUARED = 75.8 PERCENT
```

```
ANALYSIS OF VARIANCE
```

DUE TO	DF	SS	MS = SS/DF
REGRESSION	1	63815	63815
RESIDUAL	9	20330	2259
TOTAL	10	84145	

Example 14.5 Demand for a product is changing because of a rapid change in its unit price. Suppose the demand Y for the product is observed in a particular geographic region over a fairly wide price range x. Given the data in Table 14.16, determine the degree of a polynomial that best fits this data.

Since there is only one predictor variable, the first thing to do is to plot the demand against the unit price. Figure 14.6 reveals a distinct curvature, which suggests that at least a quadratic model ought to be attempted.

To illustrate that the curvature would be detected, suppose we assume a simple linear model. Figure 14.7 is the Minitab computer printout, and the resulting standardized residuals are plotted against price in Figure 14.8. The need for a quadratic effect in x is rather apparent.

The printout for a quadratic model is in Figure 14.9. As expected, there is a considerable improvement in prediction over the estimated regression equation for the simple linear model. Notice that Minitab also provides the "Type I SS." That is, across the entries identified by "C2" and "C3" one finds $SSR(x) = 63,814.5$ and $SSR(x^2 \mid x) = 14,961.4$, respectively.

Although not given, a plot of the standardized residuals versus price for the quadratic model reveals no noticeable pattern. Moreover, no appreciable improvement is obtained if higher-order terms are added to the model. A quadratic estimated regression equation is best for predicting demand for this product as a function of unit price.

Example 14.6 In Example 14.2 we considered the linear regression of the apparent temperature Y on air temperature x_1 and relative humidity x_2 for a limited range

FIGURE 14.8   Standardized residuals versus unit price for a simple linear model in Example 14.5

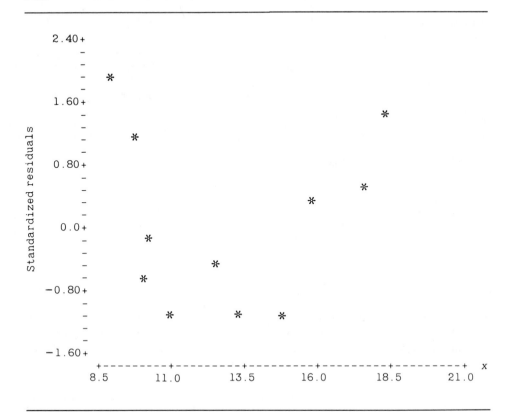

of x_1 and x_2. For the expanded data set given in Table 14.17 we want to fit and analyze a complete second-order regression equation.

Based on everyone's experience with the weather, it should be apparent that air temperature and relative humidity have to interact with regard to the apparent temperature. For example, how warm it feels when the air temperature is 90° and the relative humidity is 10% is significantly different from when the relative humidity is, say, 70%. The results in Table 14.18 are obtained when a complete second-order model is assumed.

The effect of each term in the model on the apparent temperature is statistically discernible, the regression coefficients are estimated with reasonably good accuracy, and the R^2 value is quite high. Thus the estimated complete second-order regression equation is adequate for prediction.

FIGURE 14.9 Revised printout for Example 14.5.

```
THE REGRESSION EQUATION IS
Y =  1330. - 155. X1 + 4.87 X2
```

	COLUMN	COEFFICIENT	ST. DEV. OF COEF.	T-RATIO = COEF/S.D.
	—	1330.4	179.6	7.41
X1	C2	-155.47	27.87	-5.58
X2	C3	4.866	1.031	4.72

```
THE ST. DEV. OF Y ABOUT REGRESSION LINE IS
S = 25.91
WITH ( 11- 3) =  8 DEGREES OF FREEDOM

R-SQUARED = 93.6 PERCENT
```

ANALYSIS OF VARIANCE

DUE TO	DF	SS	MS = SS/DF
REGRESSION	2	78775.8	39387.9
RESIDUAL	8	5368.8	671.1
TOTAL	10	84144.7	

```
FURTHER ANALYSIS OF VARIANCE
SS EXPLAINED BY EACH VARIABLE WHEN ENTERED IN THE ORDER GIVEN
```

DUE TO	DF	SS
REGRESSION	2	78775.8
C2	1	63814.5
C3	1	14961.4

TABLE 14.17 Sample data for Example 14.6

x_2 \ x_1	70°	75	80	85	90	95
0%	64	69	73	78	83	87
10	65	70	75	80	85	90
20	66	72	77	82	87	93
30	67	73	78	84	90	96
40	68	74	79	86	93	101
50	69	75	81	88	96	107
60	70	76	82	90	100	114
70	70	77	85	93	106	124
80	71	78	86	97	113	136

TABLE 14.18   Regression analysis for Example 14.6

Regression of Y on x_1, x_2, x_1^2, x_2^2, and $x_1 x_2$

Variable	Estimated regression coefficient	Estimated standard deviation	t value
Constant	175.3300	36.11000	4.86
x_1	-3.1689	0.87580	-3.62
x_2	-1.4351	0.13210	-10.87
x_1^2	0.0236	0.00530	4.46
x_2^2	0.0017	0.00056	3.07
$x_1 x_2$	0.0188	0.00150	12.56

$R^2 = 0.977$ $t_{0.975,\,48} = 2.01$

ANOVA

Source	df	SS	MS	F value
Regression	5	11,966.71	2393.34	407.20
Linear effect of x_1	1	8536.13	8536.13	1452.32
Linear effect of x_2	1	2330.71	2330.71	396.54
$x_1^2 \mid x_1, x_2$	1	116.68	116.68	19.85
$x_2^2 \mid x_1, x_2, x_1^2$	1	55.41	55.41	9.43
Interaction of x_1, x_2	1	927.78	927.78	157.85
Error	48	282.12	5.88	
Total	53	12,248.83	$f_{0.95,\,5,\,48} = 2.42$; $f_{0.95,\,1,\,48} = 4.04$	

14.8   Weighted Least Squares

A key assumption in least squares estimation is that the variance of each random error is the same. Recall from Section 14.6 that if the standardized residuals tend to increase or decrease with increasing estimated values of the response, the error variance can no longer be regarded as being constant. The proper remedy for such a situation is to apply *weighted* (as opposed to ordinary) least squares, in which estimates for the regression coefficients are determined by minimizing the weighted sum of the squares of the errors. If one were to use ordinary least squares estimation in a nonconstant error variance situation, the regression coefficients would not be estimated with the same precision.

Before we work some examples, let us briefly examine the key theoretical aspects of weighted least squares estimation. As in ordinary least squares, we assume that for the general linear model

$$\mathbf{Y} = \mathbf{X}\boldsymbol{\beta} + \boldsymbol{\varepsilon},$$

$\boldsymbol{\varepsilon}$ is an unobservable vector of random errors such that

$$E(\boldsymbol{\varepsilon}) = \mathbf{0},$$

and the variance-covariance matrix is

$$E(\boldsymbol{\varepsilon}\boldsymbol{\varepsilon}') = \mathbf{Q}.$$

The matrix $\mathbf{Q}$ is such that the diagonal element q_{ii} is the variance of ε_i, and q_{ij} is the covariance between ε_i and ε_j for all $i \neq j$. $\mathbf{Q}$ must be nonsingular; in fact, $\mathbf{Q}^{-1}$ is called the matrix of weights and is the one that is specified by the investigator. That is, weights are assigned to each observation of the response in accordance with some information about the corresponding error variance. There are some procedures available to users to determine the weights. These will be illustrated later.

Estimates of the regression coefficients are determined by minimizing the weighted sum of squares of the errors given by

$$\boldsymbol{\varepsilon}'\mathbf{Q}^{-1}\boldsymbol{\varepsilon} = (\mathbf{Y} - \mathbf{X}\boldsymbol{\beta})'\mathbf{Q}^{-1}(\mathbf{Y} - \mathbf{X}\boldsymbol{\beta}).$$

One can show that the normal equations in matrix form are

$$\mathbf{X}'\mathbf{Q}^{-1}\mathbf{X}\mathbf{B} = \mathbf{X}'\mathbf{Q}^{-1}\mathbf{Y}.$$

If the inverse matrix $(\mathbf{X}'\mathbf{Q}^{-1}\mathbf{X})^{-1}$ exists, the weighted least squares estimators are determined by

$$\mathbf{B} = (\mathbf{X}'\mathbf{Q}^{-1}\mathbf{X})^{-1}\mathbf{X}'\mathbf{Q}^{-1}\mathbf{Y}. \tag{14.31}$$

It is worthwhile to note that ordinary least squares is a special case of weighted least squares. That is, if $\mathbf{Q} = \sigma^2\mathbf{I}$, then it is relatively easy to show that (14.31) reduces to the familiar expression

$$\mathbf{B} = (\mathbf{X}'\mathbf{X})^{-1}\mathbf{X}'\mathbf{Y}.$$

The definition of the matrix $\mathbf{Q}$ implies a covariance structure among the random errors. In practice this structure is difficult to identify. The simplest application of weighted least squares estimation is to assume that $\mathbf{Q}$ is a diagonal matrix of the form

$$\mathbf{Q} = \begin{bmatrix} \sigma_1^2 & & & \\ & \sigma_2^2 & & \mathbf{0} \\ & & \cdot & \\ & & & \cdot \\ \mathbf{0} & & & \cdot \\ & & & & \sigma_n^2 \end{bmatrix},$$

where σ_i^2 is the variance of ε_i. Then

$$\mathbf{Q}^{-1} = \begin{bmatrix} 1/\sigma_1^2 & & & \\ & 1/\sigma_2^2 & & \mathbf{0} \\ & & \cdot & \\ & & & \cdot \\ \mathbf{0} & & & \cdot \\ & & & & 1/\sigma_n^2 \end{bmatrix}.$$

Therefore, the random errors are assumed independent, but some (if not all) of their variances may be different.

Let us now examine some situations in which the assumption of constant error variance is likely to be violated if ordinary least squares are used. A frequent practice in the acquisition of experimental data is to take several measurements of the response at each observation point and compute the average of the measurements at each point. The primary reason for this procedure is to stabilize the variability of the individual observations. Under this procedure the response turns out to be an average. Since the standard deviation of an average is proportional to the square root of the sample size on which the average is based, the variation of $\overline{Y}_i$, and thus ε_i, is σ^2/n_i, where σ^2 is the common error variance and n_i is the sample size relative to $\overline{Y}_i$. The preceding lead to a weighted least squares estimation procedure in which the inverse of matrix $\mathbf{Q}$ is given by

$$
\mathbf{Q}^{-1} = \frac{1}{\sigma^2}
\begin{bmatrix}
n_1 & & & \\
& n_2 & & \mathbf{0} \\
& & \cdot & \\
& & & \cdot \\
\mathbf{0} & & & \cdot \\
& & & & n_n
\end{bmatrix}.
$$

The weights are the individual sample sizes $n_1, n_2, \ldots, n_n$ for the n observation points. The logic here is simple enough; averages based on a larger number of observations should have more weight in the determination of the estimates than those based on fewer observations.

Example 14.7   A company has instituted an inspection program in which units of a product are visually inspected in a line process to detect defective units. Management knows that line speed will affect the number of defectives found. A batch of units of sufficient size is selected and is submitted to a 100 percent inspection to determine the total number of defectives. Then the batch is run through the line a variable number of times at each of eight line speeds. For each line speed x, the average number $\overline{Y}$ of defective units that went undetected is computed. The data in Table 14.19 are compiled, where the last column represents the individual sample sizes. Determine and compare simple regressions of $\overline{Y}$ on x based on ordinary and weighted least squares.

TABLE 14.19   Sample data for Example 14.7

$\overline{Y}$	x(ft/min)	n
0.50	10	14
4.67	20	3
6.25	30	25
10.00	40	2
13.50	50	3
13.70	60	22
17.50	70	5
23.00	80	2

TABLE 14.20 Ordinary least squares estimates and ANOVA table for Example 14.7

Variable	Estimated regression coefficient	Estimated standard deviation	t value
Constant	-2.1190	0.9490	-2.23
x	0.2946	0.0188	15.68

$r^2 = 0.976$ $\qquad\qquad t_{0.975,\,6} = 2.447$

ANOVA

Source	df	SS	MS	F value
Regression	1	364.62	364.62	246.36
Error	6	8.89	1.48	
Total	7	373.51	$f_{0.95,\,1,\,6} = 5.99$	

For ordinary least squares, we disregard the variable sample sizes and proceed as usual. The results are given in Table 14.20. For the weighted least squares we illustrate the computation of the estimates. Since the weights are the sample sizes,

$$\mathbf{Q}^{-1} = \frac{1}{\sigma^2} \begin{bmatrix} 14 & & & \\ & 3 & & \mathbf{0} \\ & & \ddots & \\ & & & \ddots \\ \mathbf{0} & & & 2 \end{bmatrix},$$

and

$$\mathbf{X'Q}^{-1}\mathbf{X} = \begin{bmatrix} 1 & 1 & \cdots & 1 \\ 10 & 20 & \cdots & 80 \end{bmatrix}\frac{1}{\sigma^2} \begin{bmatrix} 14 & & & & \\ & 3 & & & \\ & & \ddots & & \\ & & & \ddots & \\ & & & & 2 \end{bmatrix} \begin{bmatrix} 1 & 10 \\ 1 & 20 \\ \cdot & \cdot \\ \cdot & \cdot \\ \cdot & \cdot \\ 1 & 80 \end{bmatrix}$$

$$= \frac{1}{\sigma^2} \begin{bmatrix} 76 & 3010 \\ 3010 & 152{,}300 \end{bmatrix}.$$

Moreover,

$$(\mathbf{X'Q}^{-1}\mathbf{X})^{-1} = \sigma^2 \begin{bmatrix} 0.06056388 & -0.00119696 \\ -0.00119696 & 0.00003022 \end{bmatrix}.$$

Then, using (14.31), the weighted least squares estimates are

$$
\begin{bmatrix} b_0 \\ b_1 \end{bmatrix} = \sigma^2 \begin{bmatrix} 0.06056388 & -0.00119696 \\ -0.00119696 & 0.00003022 \end{bmatrix} \begin{bmatrix} 1 & 1 & \cdots & 1 \\ 10 & 20 & \cdots & 80 \end{bmatrix}
$$

$$
\frac{1}{\sigma^2} \begin{bmatrix} 14 & & & & 0 \\ & 3 & & & \\ & & \cdot & & \\ & & & \cdot & \\ 0 & & & & \cdot \\ & & & & 2 \end{bmatrix} \begin{bmatrix} 0.5 \\ 4.67 \\ \cdot \\ \cdot \\ \cdot \\ 23.0 \end{bmatrix} = \begin{bmatrix} -2.0540 \\ 0.2753 \end{bmatrix}.
$$

The results of the weighted regression analysis are given in Table 14.21.

A comparison of the results based on ordinary and weighted least squares reveals a slight improvement in the precision of the weighted least squares estimates, as well as a slight increase in the value of r^2. It should be noted that if the individual sample sizes are not appreciably different, results based on ordinary or weighted least squares are likely to be very similar.

In Example 14.7 a nonconstant error variance was imposed in advance because the recorded observations of the response were averages based on variable sample sizes. More often that not, however, lack of a constant error variance has to be determined empirically. We have already indicated that a plot of the standardized residuals versus the estimated responses aids considerably in the detection of heteroscedasticity. But for problems in which repeated observations of the response are available at the same observation point, it is preferred to

TABLE 14.21 Weighted least squares estimates and ANOVA table for Example 14.7

Variable	Estimated regression coefficient	Estimated standard deviation	t value
Constant	−2.0540	0.6990	−2.94
x	0.2753	0.0156	17.63

$r^2 = 0.981$ $\qquad\qquad t_{0.975, 6} = 2.447$

ANOVA

Source	df	SS	MS	F value
Regression	1	2508.66	2508.66	310.86
Error	6	48.43	8.07	
Total	7	2557.09*	$f_{0.95, 1, 6} = 5.99$	

*The sums of squares are different from before because now they are functions of the imposed weights.

record the actual observations rather than averages and to use the observations to detect a nonconstant error variance. For these types of problems, the plot of the obervations versus the values of the predictor variable will reveal a nonconstant variance, if one exists. The following example illustrates this problem.

Example 14.8 Ozone variability in the upper atmosphere has received wide attention recently, especially in man's impact on climate. Ozone is a form of oxygen found in varying amounts in the upper atmosphere. It is an important constituent in the earth's atmosphere because it blocks ultraviolet radiation from the sun. The data in Table 14.22 depict recorded ozone Y in millibars and ozone partial pressure x in each altitude layer, where each layer is approximately one kilometer in height. The layers have been scaled for convenience from -7 to $+7$. Determine whether the error variance can be regarded as constant.

A plot of the recorded ozone versus layer, Figure 14.10, reveals that the error variance cannot be regarded as constant because the variability of ozone

TABLE 14.22 Sample data for Example 14.8

Layer	Ozone	Layer	Ozone
-7.00	53.8	-1.00	102.8
-7.00	53.3	-1.00	96.9
-7.00	54.8	-1.00	98.2
-7.00	54.6	0.0	98.9
-7.00	53.7	0.0	96.1
-7.00	55.2	0.0	99.6
-7.00	55.7	0.0	91.4
-7.00	54.1	1.00	101.1
-6.00	63.8	1.00	94.6
-6.00	64.2	1.00	95.9
-6.00	66.9	2.00	92.3
-6.00	67.2	2.00	96.6
-6.00	65.4	2.00	98.5
-6.00	67.3	3.00	93.6
-5.00	71.8	3.00	86.2
-5.00	73.2	3.00	87.9
-5.00	75.6	3.00	89.5
-5.00	76.2	4.00	74.8
-5.00	72.7	4.00	82.3
-4.00	79.4	4.00	76.9
-4.00	81.1	4.00	81.2
-4.00	85.2	5.00	73.6
-4.00	83.0	5.00	65.4
-4.00	84.1	5.00	67.1
-4.00	82.8	6.00	60.2
-3.00	90.3	6.00	54.9
-3.00	84.2	6.00	50.8
-3.00	88.3	7.00	44.7
-3.00	86.0	7.00	38.5
-2.00	93.2		
-2.00	97.4		
-2.00	98.3		

FIGURE 14.10   Graph of ozone versus altitude layer in Example 14.8

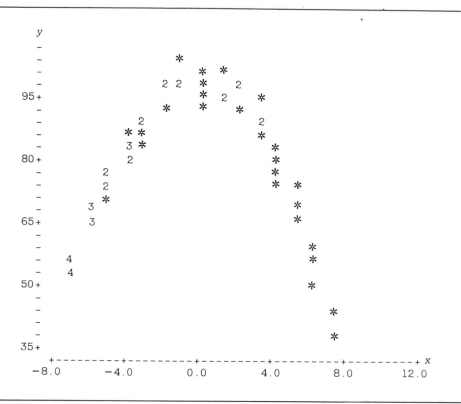

increases as the layer increases. Figure 14.10 also suggests that the appropriate model to use is a quadratic equation.

In a situation such as this in which repeats exist at several observation points, the weights are determined by computing the variance of the response measurements at each observation point. Then each weight is the reciprocal of the corresponding variance. For example, if y_{ij} denotes the ith measurement of ozone at the jth layer, the sample variance at the jth layer is

$$s_j^2 = \sum_{j=1}^{n_j} (y_{ij} - \bar{y}_{.j})^2/(n_j - 1),$$

and the corresponding weight is $w_j = 1/s_{.j}^2$. To illustrate, consider the observations at $x = 0$. These are 98.9, 96.1, 99.6, and 91.4. Then $n_j = 4$, $\bar{y}_{.j} = 96.5$, $s_j^2 = 13.8467$, and $w_j = 1/13.8467 = 0.0722$. Following this procedure, the weights for each layer work out to be as given in Table 14.23.

Using these weights and fitting a quadratic model, the results in Table 14.24 are obtained for the ozone data. It is apparent that a quadratic regression equation based on weighted least squares is quite adequate to describe the variability of the average amount of ozone as a function of altitude.

TABLE 14.23 Weights for Example 14.8

Layer	Weight	Layer	Weight
-7	1.4956	1	0.0845
-6	0.4119	2	0.0991
-5	0.2755	3	0.0997
-4	0.2304	4	0.0797
-3	0.1411	5	0.0534
-2	0.1349	6	0.0450
-1	0.1041	7	0.0520
0	0.0722		

TABLE 14.24 Weighted least squares estimates and ANOVA table for Example 14.8

Variable	Estimated regression coefficient	Estimated standard deviation	t value
Constant	96.7590	0.6367	151.98
x	-0.5585	0.1266	-4.41
x^2	-0.9495	0.0238	-39.83

$R^2 = 0.9817$ $\qquad$ $t_{0.975,\ 58} = 2.00$

ANOVA

Source	df	SS	MS	F value
Regression	2	4082.33	2041.17	1556.30
Linear effect	1	2001.11	2001.11	1525.78
Quadratic effect	1	2081.22	2081.22	1586.82
Error	58	76.07	1.31	
Total	60	4158.40		

$f_{0.95,\ 2,\ 58} = 3.15;\ f_{0.95,\ 1,\ 58} = 4.00$

More often than not, repeated observations do not exist, but data are collected by natural groups that may, a priori, suggest different error variances for each group. What is usually done in such cases is to assume that the variance of the jth group is $c_j^2 \sigma^2$, where c_j is unique to the jth group, but σ^2 is common for all groups. Usually the c_j's are unknown, but they can be estimated by first determining a residual variance for each group, say s_j^2, based on the residuals of the group. The residuals are obtained by fitting a general linear model using ordinary least squares. Then an estimate of c_j is s_j/s, where s is the overall residual standard deviation based on ordinary least squares, and s_j is the residual standard deviation for the jth group. The weight for the jth group, then, is $w_j = 1/c_j^2 = s^2/s_j^2$.

14.9 Indicator Variables

In nearly all of the problems we have considered up to now, the predictor variables used in regression equations have been quantitative in the sense that they assumed values from a well-defined numerical scale. For many variables, however, such as geographic location, marital status, urban or rural, for or against, a well-defined scale is not apparent. Since such qualitative variables are important factors in many situations, we now examine a way of quantifying the levels of a qualitative predictor variable for regression analysis. We consider what are commonly referred to as *indicator* or *dummy variables*. Each of these variables is assigned the values 0 and 1.

For illustration, consider the murder rate for contiguous states, for which data are found in Exercise 14.16 at the end of this chapter. In particular, suppose we want to regress the murder rate on the percentage of urban population in a state for the states in Regions 1 and 5 only. The regression model will be a function of the quantitative variable x_1 (percentage of urban population) and one qualitative predictor variable representing the two regions of interest.

Since there are only two regions, our inclination is to define two indicator variables x_2 and x_3 such that

$$x_2 = \begin{cases} 1 & \text{if a state is in Region 1,} \\ 0 & \text{otherwise,} \end{cases}$$

$$x_3 = \begin{cases} 1 & \text{if a state is in Region 5,} \\ 0 & \text{otherwise.} \end{cases}$$

Then, to determine a single regression equation for both regions, we would fit the model

$$Y = \beta_0 + \beta_1 x_1 + \beta_2 x_2 + \beta_3 x_3 + \varepsilon.$$

But if this were done, the matrix $\mathbf{X'X}$ would not have an inverse. An easy way out of this dilemma is to drop one of the two indicator variables and use only one, say x_2, where as before

$$x_2 = \begin{cases} 1 & \text{if a state is in Region 1,} \\ 0 & \text{otherwise.} \end{cases}$$

In other words, either a state is in Region 1 ($x_2 = 1$) or it is in Region 5 ($x_2 = 0$). In general, if a qualitative variable has m levels, it can be represented by $m - 1$ indicator variables, each assigned the values 0 and 1.

Let us return to the murder rate problem for Regions 1 and 5. There are several ways of approaching the development of a regression model. We may pool the information from both regions and fit the simple linear model

$$Y = \beta_0 + \beta_1 x_1 + \varepsilon,$$

ignoring regional differences. Or we may determine separate regression equations for the regions, each with different estimates for the regression coefficients. The choice must be made carefully. We really must decide whether each of these two regions is distinct with regard to murder rate, or whether a common relationship exists. If the former is true and a pooled model is fitted, it is likely that the

TABLE 14.25   Pooled and separate regression models for the murder rate example

Pooled regression model

Variable	Estimated regression coefficient	Estimated standard deviation	t value
Constant	7.0350	4.2300	1.66
x_1	−0.0094	0.0673	−0.14

$n = 12$	$r^2 = 0.002$	$t_{0.975, 10} = 2.228$

Regression model for Region 1

Variable	Estimated regression coefficient	Estimated standard deviation	t value
Constant	0.4170	0.8020	0.52
x_1	0.0404	0.0118	3.41

$n = 6$	$r^2 = 0.745$	$t_{0.975, 4} = 2.776$

Regression model for Region 5

Variable	Estimated regression coefficient	Estimated standard deviation	t value
Constant	7.4400	3.9500	1.88
x_1	0.0439	0.0686	0.64

$n = 6$	$r^2 = 0.093$	$t_{0.975, 4} = 2.776$

murder rate in one region will be overestimated while it is underestimated in the other region. If a common relationship exists, separate regression equations are not necessary.

Let us now compare the results based on pooled and separate regression equations for Regions 1 and 5, using the percentage of urban population as the only predictor variable. These are as given in Table 14.25.

A comparison of the estimated regression equations for each region reveals estimates for the respective slopes that are essentially the same, but the estimates of the intercepts are appreciably different. Notice also that the pooled regression equation exhibits the least desirable properties. In fact, with the pooled equation the rates for the states in Region 1 are overestimated and those of states in Region 5 are underestimated with only one exception. Apparently, therefore, regional differences for the response exist and should not be disregarded.

To incorporate regional differences within one model, let us use the single indicator variable x_2 as previously defined; the model becomes

$$Y = \beta_0 + \beta_1 x_1 + \beta_2 x_2 + \varepsilon. \tag{14.32}$$

To interpret the regression coefficients, consider the states of Region 5. Since for these states $x_2 = 0$, the curve of regression is assumed to be

$$E(Y) = \beta_0 + \beta_1 x_1,$$

which is a straight line equation with slope β_1 and intercept β_0. For states in Region 1, $x_2 = 1$, and the mean response becomes

$$E(Y) = \beta_0 + \beta_1 x_1 + \beta_2$$

$$= (\beta_0 + \beta_2) + \beta_1 x_1,$$

which is also a straight line equation with the same slope, β_1, but with a different intercept, $\beta_0 + \beta_2$. Then the model given by (14.32) depicts the average response as a linear function of x_1 with the same slope for both regions but different intercepts. The parameter β_2 represents a differential effect between the intercepts of the two regions. The vector **Y** and matrix **X** for fitting the model (14.32) are

$$Y = \begin{bmatrix} 4.2 \\ 2.4 \\ 3.1 \\ 3.2 \\ 3.9 \\ 1.4 \\ 10.2 \\ 11.7 \\ 10.6 \\ 11.9 \\ 9.0 \\ 6.0 \end{bmatrix} \quad X = \begin{bmatrix} 1 & 77.6 & 1 \\ 1 & 50.8 & 1 \\ 1 & 84.6 & 1 \\ 1 & 56.4 & 1 \\ 1 & 87.1 & 1 \\ 1 & 32.2 & 1 \\ 1 & 80.5 & 0 \\ 1 & 60.3 & 0 \\ 1 & 45.0 & 0 \\ 1 & 47.6 & 0 \\ 1 & 63.1 & 0 \\ 1 & 39.0 & 0 \end{bmatrix}$$

The regression results are given in Table 14.26.

Based on these results, regional differences are statistically discernible. Thus, this regression equation is superior to that of the pooled model in which regional differences were disregarded. In particular, the two regions have the same estimate of the slope (0.0416), but intercepts of 7.58 for Region 5 and $7.58 - 7.23 = 0.35$ for Region 1. Generally, therefore, if it can be assumed that the slope is the same, it is better to use a model with an indicator variable rather than a pooled model. Moreover, the indicator variable model is also better than using separate regression models because with the former more degrees of freedom are available for the error than with the latter. Accordingly, β_0 and β_2 are estimated with better precision, as is the case with the example.

What if the slope is not the same? This can be handled by introducing to the model an interaction term for the quantitative variable x_1 and the indicator

TABLE 14.26 Regression analysis for the murder rate example

Variable	Estimated regression coefficient	Estimated standard deviation	t value
Constant	7.5800	1.6400	4.62
x_1	0.0416	0.0269	1.54
x_2	-7.2340	0.9520	-7.60
$n = 12$	$R^2 = 0.865$	$t_{0.975,\,9} = 2.262$	

variable x_2. The assumed model becomes

$$Y = \beta_0 + \beta_1 x_1 + \beta_2 x_2 + \beta_{12} x_1 x_2 + \varepsilon. \tag{14.33}$$

For states in Region 5, $x_2 = 0$. Then $x_1 x_2 = 0$, and the average response for this region is

$$E(Y) = \beta_0 + \beta_1 x_1.$$

For states in Region 1, $x_2 = 1$, and $x_1 x_2 = x_1$. The mean response for this region is

$$E(Y) = \beta_0 + \beta_1 x_1 + \beta_2 + \beta_{12} x_1$$
$$= (\beta_0 + \beta_2) + (\beta_1 + \beta_{12}) x_1.$$

Notice that the regression coefficient of x_2 is the differential effect between the intercepts of the two regions, and the regression coefficient of the cross-product $x_1 x_2$ is the differential effect between the slopes of the two regions. Therefore, assuming that a statistically discernible interaction exists between x_1 and x_2, one can obtain the estimated regression equations for each region by using model (14.33).

Finally, we examine the problem in which a qualitative variable has more than two levels. This case requires the use of more than one indicator variable in the regression model. For illustration, let us continue with the murder rate problem in a comparison among the states of Regions 1, 5, and 7. Since three levels of a qualitative variable are identified, we define two indicator variables as follows:

$$x_2 = \begin{cases} 1 & \text{if a state is in Region 1,} \\ 0 & \text{otherwise,} \end{cases}$$

$$x_3 = \begin{cases} 1 & \text{if a state is in Region 5,} \\ 0 & \text{otherwise.} \end{cases}$$

This arrangement yields the same number of possible combinations of the values of x_2 and x_3 as there are levels of the qualitative variable. These are $x_2 = 1$, $x_3 = 0$; $x_2 = 0$, $x_3 = 1$; and $x_2 = x_3 = 0$. They represent states in Regions 1, 5, and 7, respectively.

If we assume equal slopes for the three regions, the model is

$$Y = \beta_0 + \beta_1 x_1 + \beta_2 x_2 + \beta_3 x_3 + \varepsilon.$$

For states in Region 7, $x_2 = 0$ and $x_3 = 0$, so the mean response becomes

$$E(Y) = \beta_0 + \beta_1 x_1,$$

which is a straight line equation with slope β_1 and intercept β_0. For states in Region 5, $x_2 = 0$ and $x_3 = 1$. Accordingly, the curve of regression is

$$E(Y) = \beta_0 + \beta_1 x_1 + \beta_3$$
$$= (\beta_0 + \beta_3) + \beta_1 x_1,$$

where β_3 represents the change in the intercept of Region 5 over that of Region

7. Similarly, when $x_2 = 1$ and $x_3 = 0$, the mean response is

$$E(Y) = \beta_0 + \beta_1 x_1 + \beta_2$$
$$= (\beta_0 + \beta_2) + \beta_1 x_1,$$

where now β_2 is the change in the intercept of Region 1 over that of Region 7. It follows that both β_2 and β_3 represent differential effects for the intercepts of Regions 1 and 5, respectively, relative to the intercept of Region 7.

The case in which the slopes cannot be assumed equal should now be apparent. That is, we assume a model of the form

$$Y = \beta_0 + \beta_1 x_1 + \beta_2 x_2 + \beta_3 x_3 + \beta_{12} x_1 x_2 + \beta_{13} x_1 x_3 + \varepsilon, \quad (14.34)$$

where β_{12} and β_{13} are the regression coefficients for the interactions involving the quantitative variable x_1 and each of the two indicator variables x_2 and x_3.

Example 14.9   In a certain locality, five residential houses that were recently sold were selected at random from each of three distinct neighborhoods (A, B, and C) in the city, and the selling price Y was compared to the property valuation x_1 as determined by the local real estate assessor's office. The data are given in Table 14.27, where selling price and property valuation are in thousands of dollars. Using indicator variables, fit a linear regression equation and determine whether the slopes for all three neighborhoods are the same.

Since there are three neighborhoods, we define two indicator variables x_2 and x_3 such that

$$x_2 = \begin{cases} 1 & \text{if a house is in neighborhood B,} \\ 0 & \text{otherwise,} \end{cases}$$

$$x_3 = \begin{cases} 1 & \text{if a house is in neighborhood C,} \\ 0 & \text{otherwise.} \end{cases}$$

For the model (14.34) the vector **Y** and matrix **X** are

$$\mathbf{Y} = \begin{bmatrix} 42.5 \\ 36.8 \\ 42.6 \\ 41.2 \\ 48.6 \\ 75.2 \\ 83.4 \\ 83.3 \\ 116.8 \\ 114.3 \\ 122.8 \\ 125.6 \\ 132.5 \\ 127.4 \\ 147.8 \end{bmatrix} \quad \mathbf{X} = \begin{bmatrix} 1 & 33.1 & 0 & 0 & 0 & 0 \\ 1 & 42.0 & 0 & 0 & 0 & 0 \\ 1 & 47.8 & 0 & 0 & 0 & 0 \\ 1 & 53.4 & 0 & 0 & 0 & 0 \\ 1 & 59.6 & 0 & 0 & 0 & 0 \\ 1 & 63.9 & 1 & 0 & 63.9 & 0 \\ 1 & 68.4 & 1 & 0 & 68.4 & 0 \\ 1 & 72.3 & 1 & 0 & 72.3 & 0 \\ 1 & 77.8 & 1 & 0 & 77.8 & 0 \\ 1 & 80.8 & 1 & 0 & 80.8 & 0 \\ 1 & 96.5 & 0 & 1 & 0 & 96.5 \\ 1 & 101.8 & 0 & 1 & 0 & 101.8 \\ 1 & 106.2 & 0 & 1 & 0 & 106.2 \\ 1 & 112.6 & 0 & 1 & 0 & 112.6 \\ 1 & 120.5 & 0 & 1 & 0 & 120.5 \end{bmatrix}$$

The Minitab computer printout is in Figure 14.11, where C2–C6 refer to x_1, x_2, x_3, $x_1 x_2$, and $x_1 x_3$, correspondingly.

TABLE 14.27 Sample data for Example 14.9

Neighborhood A		Neighborhood B		Neighborhood C	
x	Y	x	Y	x	Y
33.1	42.5	63.9	75.2	96.5	122.8
42.0	36.8	68.4	83.4	101.8	125.6
47.8	42.6	72.3	83.3	106.2	132.5
53.4	41.2	77.8	116.8	112.6	127.4
59.6	48.6	80.8	114.3	120.5	147.8

FIGURE 14.11 Computer printout for Example 14.9

```
THE REGRESSION EQUATION IS
Y =   31.4   + 0.232 X1 − 129.X2
    + 1.89 X3    + 2.41 X4 + 0.679 X5
```

	COLUMN	COEFFICIENT	ST. DEV. OF COEF.	T−RATIO = COEF/S.D.
	—	31.37	14.66	2.14
X1	C2	0.2325	0.3050	0.76
X2	C3	−128.81	36.29	−3.55
X3	C4	1.89	38.82	0.05
X4	C5	2.4112	0.5481	4.40
X5	C6	0.6786	0.4518	1.50

```
THE ST. DEV. OF Y ABOUT REGRESSION LINE IS
S = 6.238
WITH (  15 − 6) = 9 DEGREES OF FREEDOM

R−SQUARED = 98.4 PERCENT

ANALYSIS OF VARIANCE
```

DUE TO	DF	SS	MS=SS/DF
REGRESSION	5	21577.96	4315.59
RESIDUAL	9	350.26	38.92
TOTAL	14	21928.22	

```
FURTHER ANALYSIS OF VARIANCE
SS EXPLAINED BY EACH VARIABLE WHEN ENTERED IN THE ORDER GIVEN
```

DUE TO	DF	SS
REGRESSION	5	21577.96
C2	1	19892.61
C3	1	698.16
C4	1	232.89
C5	1	666.52
C6	1	87.79

Notice that the null hypothesis

$$H_0: \beta_{12} = 0$$

can be rejected, but the hypothesis

$$H_0: \beta_{13} = 0$$

cannot. There is reason to believe the slopes for neighborhoods A and B are not the same. From the printout we determine that the estimated regression equations for each neighborhood are as follows:

Neighborhood A: $\hat{y} = 31.37 + 0.2325x_1$,
$(x_2 = x_3 = 0)$

Neighborhood B: $\hat{y} = -97.44 + 2.6437x_1$,
$(x_2 = 1, x_3 = 0)$

Neighborhood C: $\hat{y} = 33.26 + 0.9111x_1$.
$(x_2 = 0, x_3 = 1)$

References

1. S. Chatterjee and B. Price, *Regression analysis by example*, Wiley, New York, 1977.
2. C. Daniel and F. S. Wood, *Fitting equations to data*, Wiley, New York, 1971.
3. N. R. Draper and H. Smith, *Applied regression analysis*, 2nd ed., Wiley, New York, 1981.
4. F. A. Graybill, *Theory and application of the linear model*, Duxbury, North Scituate, Mass., 1976.
5. J. Neter, W. Wasserman, and M. H. Kutner, *Applied linear regression models*, Richard D. Irwin, Homewood, Ill., 1983.
6. *SAS users guide*, SAS Institute, Raleigh, N. C., 1982.

Exercises

14.1. Which of the following models are not cases of the general linear model and why?

    a. $Y = \beta_0 + \beta_1 \exp(\beta_2 x_1) + \beta_3 x_2 + \varepsilon$
    b. $Y = \beta_1 x_1 + \beta_2 x_2 + \beta_3 x_1^2 + \beta_4 x_1^2 x_2 + \varepsilon$
    c. $Y = \beta_0 + \beta_1/x_1 + \beta_2 x_2^{1/2} + \varepsilon$

14.2. An automobile rental agency has determined the estimated regression equation

$$\hat{y} = 0.75 + 1.2x_1 + 0.15x_2$$

to predict average annual cost Y in thousands of dollars as a function of the number of automobiles rented x_1 and average number of miles each car is driven x_2 in thousands of miles. Explain the meaning of the estimated regression coefficients.

14.3. Suppose the estimated regression equation depicting a mean response as a function of two predictor variables is

$$\hat{y} = 15 + 6x_1 - 2x_2 - 1.5x_1 x_2.$$

a. What is the effect on the mean response per unit change in x_1 when $x_2 = 2$?

b. What is the effect on the mean response per unit change in x_2 when $x_1 = 1$?

14.4. Using the Prater data, fit all linear models involving only x_1 and x_3 and illustrate the Extra Sum of Squares Principle by computing the following:

a. corresponding analysis of variance tables.

b. $SSR(x_3 \mid x_1)$ and $SSR(x_1 \mid x_3)$.

c. appropriate partial F tests.

14.5. An agency wants to estimate family expenditures for food based on family income and family size. The data in Table 14.28 represent monthly food expenditures Y in thousands of dollars versus monthly income x_1 and family size x_2 for fifteen families that were randomly selected in one geographic region.

TABLE 14.28 Sample data for Exercise 14.5

Y	x_1	x_2
0.43	2.1	3
0.31	1.1	4
0.32	0.9	5
0.46	1.6	4
1.25	6.2	4
0.44	2.3	3
0.52	1.8	6
0.29	1.0	5
1.29	8.9	3
0.35	2.4	2
0.35	1.2	4
0.78	4.7	3
0.43	3.5	2
0.47	2.9	3
0.38	1.4	4

a. Fit all linear models involving x_1 and/or x_2 and interpret the estimated regression coefficients.

b. Test the null hypothesis $H_0: \beta_1 = \beta_2 = 0$.

c. Compute $SSR(x_2 \mid x_1)$ and $SSR(x_1 \mid x_2)$ and perform appropriate partial F tests.

d. Compute and interpret the multiple correlation coefficient R^2.

e. Based on your preceding results, decide on the best equation to predict food expenditures and use it to estimate monthly average food expenses for a family of four with monthly income of \$2,500. Determine a 98% confidence interval for this quantity.

14.6. Referring to Exercise 14.5, do the following:

a. For the regression involving both x_1 and x_2, perform individual t tests for the regression coefficients β_1 and β_2. Use $\alpha = 0.05$.

b. Determine 95% confidence intervals for β_1 and β_2 and make appropriate conclusions.

14.7. Using the data of Exercise 14.5, set up the general linear model involving both x_1 and x_2 in matrix form, identify all matrices, and determine the normal equations.

14.8. In many governmental agencies and private corporations, the problem of identifying important factors to predict the job effectiveness of potential employees is a continuous process. The usual procedure is to administer to a potential employee a battery of appropriate tests and to base the hiring decision on the test scores. The key question is to know a priori which tests can predict the job effectiveness of an individual. Suppose the personnel office of a large corporation has developed four tests for a given job classification. These tests were administered to twenty individuals who were hired by the company. After a two-year period, each of these employees was rated for job effectiveness. The job effectiveness score Y and the scores on the four tests x_1, x_2, x_3, x_4 are given in Table 14.29.

TABLE 14.29 Sample data for Exercise 14.8

Employee	Y	x_1	x_2	x_3	x_4
1	94	122	121	96	89
2	71	108	115	98	78
3	82	120	115	95	90
4	76	118	117	93	95
5	111	113	102	109	109
6	64	112	96	90	88
7	109	109	129	102	108
8	104	112	119	106	105
9	80	115	101	95	88
10	73	111	95	95	84
11	127	119	118	107	110
12	88	112	110	100	87
13	99	120	89	105	97
14	80	117	108	99	100
15	99	109	125	108	95
16	116	116	122	116	102
17	100	104	83	100	102
18	96	110	101	103	103
19	126	117	120	113	108
20	58	120	77	80	74

a. Use PROC GLM from SAS (or some other comparable package) to fit the linear regression of Y on x_1, x_2, x_3, and x_4.

b. Based on the computer output for part a, prepare an analysis of variance table showing all possible partial F tests.

c. Interpret the estimated regression coefficients and the multiple correlation coefficient.

14.9. Use the data from Exercise 14.8 to do the following:

a. Determine all possible regression equations and for each compute the error sum of squares, the error mean square, the C_p value, and the R^2 value (see Exercise 14.12).

b. Show that stepwise regression and backward elimination procedures yield the same result for the best prediction equation.

c. Based on your preceding results, deduce the best prediction equation and use it to estimate the job effectiveness of an individual who has the following test scores: $x_1 = 105$, $x_2 = 110$, $x_3 = 99$, and $x_4 = 107$. Determine a 95% prediction interval for this quantity.

14.10. Recent interest has focused on the development of more rapid and economical methods for monitoring sediment and pollutant concentration in the nation's waters.

Of special concern to those charged with environmental monitoring is the need to quantify water surface concentration values based on remote sensing data. The use of remote sensing techniques to monitor various water quality parameters appears to be promising. One type of remote sensing system is the passive variety, which depends solely on the sun's radiation as the energy source and measures the total upwelled radiance emitted from the water-atmospheric system. A major component of the total upwelled radiance is the upwelled light emitted from the water, which under normal conditions is a function of the constituents in the water. To measure the upwelled radiance spectrum a number of multispectral scanner systems are currently available. However, each system has different band locations and band widths.

A change in pollutant concentration is believed to cause a change in the upwelled radiance value. Thus if the radiance values are known at different spectral bands, it is possible to predict the concentration of a pollutant in a given body of water. The problem is to identify which of several bands can predict the concentration of a pollutant. For a recent doctoral thesis, Whitlock* obtained actual remote sensing data from a laboratory, under controlled conditions, using five bands and several constituents, among which was feldspar sediment. Sample data are given in Table 14.30.

TABLE 14.30 Sample data for Exercise 14.10

Feldspar concentration Y	Radiance bands				
	x_1	x_2	x_3	x_4	x_5
17	0.297	0.310	0.290	0.220	0.156
17	0.360	0.390	0.369	0.297	0.205
35	0.075	0.058	0.047	0.034	0.023
69	0.114	0.100	0.081	0.058	0.042
69	0.229	0.213	0.198	0.142	0.102
173	0.315	0.304	0.267	0.202	0.147
173	0.477	0.518	0.496	0.395	0.285
17	0.072	0.063	0.047	0.036	0.024
17	0.099	0.092	0.074	0.056	0.038
73	0.420	0.452	0.425	0.332	0.235
17	0.189	0.178	0.153	0.107	0.076
35	0.369	0.391	0.364	0.286	0.200
69	0.142	0.124	0.105	0.077	0.056
35	0.094	0.087	0.072	0.049	0.032
35	0.171	0.161	0.145	0.094	0.068
52	0.378	0.420	0.380	0.281	0.200

a. Use the five bands as predictor variables and feldspar concentration as the response to fit a linear regression model.
b. Compute the correlation matrix for the five radiance bands. Interpret your output.
c. Use stepwise regression and backward elimination procedures to determine the best set of predictor variables. Are your results the same?
d. Based on the preceding results, discuss any concerns that are apparent to you about this problem for deciding on an adequate prediction equation.

*Charles H. Whitlock, Doctoral dissertation, Old Dominion University, May, 1977.

14.11. It was pointed out in Section 14.5 that the value of R^2 will increase as more terms are added to the regression equation because SSE always decreases as more terms are added and SST always remains the same. For this reason, an alternative relative measure that takes into account the number of terms in the model has been suggested. This measure is called the *adjusted multiple correlation coefficient* and is defined by

$$R_A^2 = 1 - \left(\frac{n-1}{n-p}\right)\frac{\text{SSE}}{\text{SST}}$$

where p is the number of terms in the model, including the constant term. Use the information in Table 14.10 to show that the adjusted multiple correlation coefficient for the linear regression containing x_1, x_2, and x_3 is smaller than that of the regression equation containing only x_2 and x_3.

14.12. Refer to Exercise 14.9, part a, and use the estimated regression equation involving only x_1, x_2, and x_4 to compute the standardized residuals. Then graph these residuals against the corresponding values of x_3. Explain your result.

14.13. Using the estimated simple linear regression equation in Exercise 13.14, compute and graph the standardized residuals against gross annual income x. What can you conclude? Fit a new regression equation as suggested by the residual plot and use it to show the danger of extrapolation by estimating percent taxes paid if gross annual income is $250,000.

14.14. Use the estimated regression equation in Exercise 13.18 to compute and graph the standardized residuals against years of experience. Determine a new regression equation, compute the new standardized residuals, and plot them against x. What can you conclude?

14.15. The data in Table 14.31 represent the average atmospheric temperature Y in January for 50 weather stations in Virginia, where each station is identified by latitude x_1, longitude x_2, and elevation x_3.

    a. Fit a complete second-order regression model and make appropriate analyses on your result.

    b. Use appropriate means to evaluate whether all terms in the estimated regression equation should be retained. If not, provide sufficient argument for your selection as an adequate prediction equation.

14.16. The data in Table 14.32 represent recent murder rates Y per 100,000 population for the 48 contiguous states in the U. S., and some potential predictor variables, such as percentage of urban population x_1, percentage of minority population x_2, unemployment rate x_3, percentage of population with four or more years of college x_4, and geographic region x_5.

    a. Use a stepwise procedure to determine the best set of predictor variables to include in a linear model.

    b. For the best prediction equation, compute the standardized residuals and plot these against the regions. Is the spread of the residuals essentially the same for all regions? If not, determine the weights for each region using the procedure suggested in Section 14.8 and use weighted least squares to determine estimates for the regression coefficients of the best set of predictor variables. Compare your results with those of ordinary least squares.

TABLE 14.31 Sample data for Exercise 14.15*

Station number	Y	x_1	x_2	x_3
1	37.9	37.35	79.52	975
2	28.7	38.52	78.43	3535
3	38.3	37.08	77.95	440
4	37.3	37.53	79.68	870
5	31.5	37.08	81.33	3300
6	35.0	37.38	80.08	1890
7	36.0	38.03	78.52	870
8	37.4	36.83	79.37	700
9	40.4	37.28	75.97	11
10	35.8	37.77	78.15	300
11	35.3	38.47	78.00	420
12	33.2	38.45	78.93	1400
13	39.3	36.58	79.38	410
14	41.3	36.90	76.20	25
15	34.7	38.45	77.67	300
16	38.0	37.33	78.38	450
17	34.2	36.93	80.30	2600
18	35.4	38.30	77.47	100
19	35.7	37.37	80.87	1524
20	39.7	36.68	76.78	80
21	40.5	37.30	77.30	40
22	31.6	38.00	79.83	2238
23	40.0	37.08	76.35	10
24	36.1	37.78	79.43	1060
25	34.1	39.12	77.72	500
26	36.1	38.03	78.00	420
27	33.9	38.67	78.38	1200
28	36.6	37.33	79.20	916
29	37.1	36.70	79.88	760
30	28.6	38.42	79.58	2910
31	29.3	39.07	77.88	1720
32	37.4	37.70	78.30	300
33	40.5	36.90	76.20	22
34	38.9	37.58	75.82	300
35	34.4	36.75	83.03	1510
36	35.3	38.50	77.32	12
37	37.5	37.50	77.33	164
38	36.4	37.32	79.97	1149
39	35.0	36.88	81.77	1735
40	34.0	38.15	79.03	1385
41	33.3	38.65	78.72	1000
42	38.6	37.65	76.57	25
43	37.5	37.75	77.05	50
44	36.2	37.85	75.48	9
45	32.1	38.95	77.45	291
46	35.6	38.85	77.03	10
47	39.3	37.30	76.70	70
48	33.7	39.20	78.17	760
49	34.4	38.88	78.52	887
50	34.4	36.93	81.08	2450

* *Source: Monthly normals of temperature, precipitation and heating and cooling degree days 1941–70,* No. 81, NOAA, U. S. Department of Commerce.

TABLE 14.32 Sample data for Exercise 14.16

State	Y	x_1	x_2	x_3	x_4	x_5
1	14.2	58.4	25.8	7.4	10.2	6
2	9.5	79.6	9.2	9.8	15.7	8
3	8.8	50.0	18.4	6.6	9.1	6
4	11.5	90.9	12.0	8.2	16.8	8
5	6.3	78.5	4.7	5.6	19.4	7
6	4.2	77.4	6.6	7.1	18.3	1
7	6.0	72.2	15.2	8.9	15.5	2
8	10.2	80.5	14.9	9.0	13.7	5
9	11.7	60.3	26.5	6.9	12.3	5
10	5.5	54.1	1.8	6.3	13.5	7
11	9.9	83.0	14.7	6.5	13.7	3
12	7.4	64.9	7.6	5.7	11.0	3
13	2.3	57.2	1.6	4.0	12.8	4
14	6.6	66.1	5.6	4.0	14.6	4
15	10.1	52.3	7.5	4.6	10.0	6
16	15.5	66.1	30.2	7.0	11.5	6
17	2.4	50.8	0.7	8.9	13.6	1
18	8.0	76.6	21.1	6.8	18.6	2
19	3.1	84.6	4.3	9.5	16.8	1
20	9.3	73.8	12.5	8.2	12.6	3
21	2.7	66.4	2.0	5.9	13.2	4
22	14.3	44.5	36.4	7.4	11.5	6
23	9.6	70.1	11.2	6.2	11.8	4
24	5.4	53.4	4.8	6.2	14.2	7
25	3.9	61.5	3.8	5.0	12.8	4
26	15.8	80.9	8.3	9.0	13.1	8
27	3.2	56.4	0.7	6.4	15.3	1
28	5.6	88.9	12.8	9.4	14.9	2
29	8.8	69.8	9.8	7.8	15.3	8
30	10.7	88.9	14.6	9.1	16.0	2
31	10.6	45.0	23.1	6.2	11.8	5
32	0.9	44.3	3.3	5.5	12.2	4
33	7.8	75.3	10.1	7.8	11.5	3
34	8.6	68.0	11.3	5.0	11.7	6
35	4.9	67.1	3.0	9.5	15.4	7
36	5.6	71.5	9.4	7.9	11.9	2
37	3.9	87.1	3.7	8.6	14.9	1
38	11.9	47.6	31.2	5.0	10.4	5
39	2.0	44.6	6.1	3.6	11.4	4
40	10.1	58.7	15.9	6.0	10.5	6
41	13.3	79.7	13.1	5.7	13.7	6
42	3.5	80.4	2.5	5.3	17.5	7
43	1.4	32.2	0.8	8.0	15.6	1
44	9.0	63.1	19.5	5.6	16.4	5
45	4.3	72.6	5.1	8.8	16.1	7
46	6.0	39.0	3.9	7.5	9.2	5
47	2.8	65.9	3.9	4.5	12.7	3
48	5.4	60.5	3.1	3.6	14.5	7

Source: World almanac, 1979

14.17. Use the data in Exercise 14.16 to determine a correlation matrix for all the potential predictor variables and the response. Which predictor variables are most correlated with the response? Is this result in line with that in part a of Exercise 14.16? Are any predictor variables highly correlated? Comment in terms of the problem of multicollinearity.

14.18. It is believed that academic year salaries Y of university professors in thousands of dollars are influenced by three variables: years of teaching experience x_1, academic rank x_2, and discipline x_3. The data in Table 14.33 are a random sample of eighteen professors in a large state-supported university. The ranks are identified by 1 for assistant professor, 2 for associate professor, and 3 for full professor. The disciplines are identified by 1 for sciences, 2 for humanities, 3 for arts, and 4 for business.

TABLE 14.33 Sample data for Exercise 14.18

Y	x_1	x_2	x_3
25.7	10	1	2
18.8	4	1	1
18.6	5	1	3
21.8	13	2	3
26.3	4	1	4
29.4	24	3	3
28.6	7	2	2
34.5	12	3	4
24.3	11	2	1
21.2	6	1	3
28.8	6	1	4
24.7	4	1	2
32.4	12	3	2
33.4	20	3	1
27.4	11	2	1
29.8	6	2	4
31.4	11	2	4
27.7	8	2	3

a. Define indicator variables for academic rank and discipline. Then fit a linear model with salary as the response, years of teaching experience as the quantitative variable, and indicator variables representing academic rank and discipline.
b. Interpret the estimated regression coefficients.
c. Fit a linear model that includes all cross-product terms between the indicator variables and x_1. Perform a complete analysis on this regression equation and draw appropriate conclusions.
d. For each discipline and academic rank, graph the estimated regression equation obtained in part c as a function of x_1.

CHAPTER FIFTEEN

Nonparametric Methods

15.1 Introduction

With the exceptions of the distribution-free tolerance limits, discussed in Chapter 8, and the Kolmogorov–Smirnov statistic, presented in Chapter 10, the inferential procedures we have examined so far required the specification of a distribution for the underlying population. For example, the analysis of variance procedure is made possible by assuming that the observations come from normal distributions. Thus for the most part, the inferential procedures we have discussed represent assessments about the parameters of the underlying distribution. For this reason, such inferences are known as *parametric methods*.

We have made an attempt to determine the robustness of many of the inferential methods we have presented, and in several instances the procedures have been found to be reasonably robust to the distributional assumptions. But it is generally true for parametric methods that they are sensitive to the assumptions for small sample sizes, and for the most part, their application is limited to observations that are quantitative. That is, what is being observed is assumed to be a continuous numerical quantity, such as the weekly sales volume, the amount being poured into a container, the strength of a metal specimen, and so on.

Quantitative observations are usually defined on an *interval* or on a *ratio* scale. Measurements defined on an interval scale can be numerically distinguished and ordered, and the differences among them are meaningful. A classic example of an interval scale involves the measurement of temperature. One may choose to record temperature in degrees Celsius (for which the freezing point of water is 0° C) or in degrees Fahrenheit (for which the freezing point is 32° F). Thus the origin differs; but the meaning of the difference between, say, 10° C and 15° C is the same as the meaning of the difference between 20° C and 25° C.

If a measurement meets the requirements of an interval scale and in addition has a true point of origin, then the measurement is defined on a ratio scale. For example, heights, weights, strengths, and so on are defined on a ratio scale because they have true zero points, regardless of the unit of measurement. The interval and ratio scales are the truly quantitative scales. For the most part, the parametric methods we have presented, such as constructing confidence intervals, testing statistical hypotheses, and fitting equations, are applicable to observations that are defined at least on an interval scale.

In many situations, however, what is being observed is qualitative, not quantitative, and therefore cannot be defined on an interval or ratio scale. Such situations are often found in the social sciences and in marketing surveys. For example, a consumer's evaluation of the taste characteristics of a soft drink is not likely to adhere to a meaningful numerical scale. And even if the consumer is asked to evaluate the drink on, say, a five-point scale where 1 and 5 may represent highly negative or highly positive reactions, the scale is arbitrary. In other words, the numbers have no physical meaning other than to signify that the greater the number, the more favorable the response for the drink.

Such observations can be defined on an *ordinal* scale because the distance between two numbers is of no consequence and only the *order* or *rank* of the numbers is important. Sometimes observations can only be defined on a *nominal* scale because either a name (symbol) or a number is used to classify a characteristic of interest, but the principle of order is of no consequence. For example, individuals may be classified according to sex. We may use the symbols F and M, or we may just as easily use the numbers, say, 122 and 48 to designate female and male, respectively. Observations defined on nominal scales are the weakest type of measurement.

Inferential procedures have been developed that are not subject to the form of the underlying population distribution and do not necessarily require that observations be defined at least on an interval scale. Such inferential procedures are known as *nonparametric methods*. Because these methods do not require that the form of the underlying population distribution be specified, they are also known as *distribution-free* methods (recall, for example, the distribution-free tolerance limits of Chapter 8). In a relative sense, nonparametric methods require fewer assumptions, and for the most part, they are easier to apply than comparable parametric procedures we have discussed in the preceding chapters. Moreover, nonparametric methods can be applied to situations in which the observations are defined at least on ordinal scales and on occasion on nominal scales. But if observations are defined at least on an interval scale and the distribution of the underlying population is normal, nonparametric methods are less efficient than comparable parametric procedures that are based on the normality assumption.

Many nonparametric methods have been developed, including methods for nonparametric analysis of variance and nonparametric regression. The references cited at the end of the chapter provide a thorough coverage of all nonparametric methods. Our purpose here will be only to introduce the basic nonparametric concepts to the reader and to discuss a few methods that are especially useful. These nonparametric procedures are comparable to the parametric methods for testing means of two independent normal distributions (Section 9.6.2), testing means for paired observations (Section 9.6.4), single-factor experiments in completely randomized designs and randomized block designs (Sections 12.4 and 12.5), and linear correlation (Section 13.8).

15.2 Nonparametric Tests for Comparing Two Populations Based on Independent Random Samples

In Section 9.6.2 we considered the problem of comparing the means of two population distributions when the distributions are assumed to be normal. In this section we will discuss two nonparametric procedures that compare the distributions of two populations. These are the Mann–Whitney U test and the Wald–Wolfowitz runs test. The only necessary assumption for their application is that the underlying distributions be continuous. Accordingly, we will assume that X_1, X_2, ..., X_{n_1} and Y_1, Y_2, ..., Y_{n_2} are independent random samples from two populations with continuous distributions.

15.2.1 Mann–Whitney Test

Given independent random samples from two populations, consider testing the null hypothesis that the populations have the same distribution. The hypothesis may be stated as

$$H_0: f_1(x) \equiv f_2(y), \tag{15.1}$$

where $f_1(x)$ and $f_2(y)$ are the corresponding probability density functions. The alternative hypothesis may be either two-sided or one-sided. The two-sided alternative hypothesis simply states that the distributions are not identical. But the alternative hypothesis implies only a displacement in the central tendency of one distribution relative to that of the other and does not suggest a difference in shape or dispersion. In other words, as for the Student's t procedure, it is assumed that the population distributions have the same shape and dispersion.

To test the null hypothesis as given by (15.1), a popular nonparametric procedure is the *Mann–Whitney U test.** This test is the nonparametric equivalent of the two-sample Student's t test covered in Section 9.6.2. The Mann–Whitney test is based on combining the n_1 and n_2 observations to form a single set of $n_1 + n_2$ observations and arranging the observations in order of increasing magnitude. Then a *rank* is assigned to each observation in the ordered sequence, beginning with rank 1 and terminating with rank $n_1 + n_2$. If the random samples come from populations with identical distributions, we would expect the ranks to be sufficiently interspersed when one sees to which sample the observations belong. Otherwise we would expect the ranks of the observations in each sample to be fairly bunched together at one end or the other. In essence, the Mann–Whitney statistic determines when an observed clustering of ranks is sufficient to conclude that the two random samples come from populations whose distributions differ in central tendency.

To implement the procedure we determine the sum of the ranks associated with the observations of one of the two samples, say sample 1, where the choice as to which sample is selected is arbitrary. Let this sum be denoted by R_1. Then the Mann–Whitney U statistic is given by

---

*This procedure is essentially the same as the Wilcoxon rank sum test.

$$U = n_1 n_2 + \frac{n_1(n_1 + 1)}{2} - R_1. \tag{15.2}$$

The statistic U is a function of the random variable R_1 and the sample sizes n_1 and n_2. If H_0 is true, the occurrence of any particular order for the observations of the combined set is equiprobable. Under H_0, therefore, R_1 is the sum of n_1 positive integers randomly selected from among the first $n_1 + n_2$. Accordingly, we can determine that

$$E(R_1) = n_1(n_1 + n_2 + 1)/2, \tag{15.3}$$

$$Var(R_1) = n_1 n_2(n_1 + n_2 + 1)/12. \tag{15.4}$$

It follows from (15.2) that

$$E(U) = n_1 n_2 + \frac{n_1(n_1 + 1)}{2} - E(R_1) = n_1 n_2/2, \tag{15.5}$$

and

$$Var(U) = Var(R_1) = n_1 n_2(n_1 + n_2 + 1)/12. \tag{15.6}$$

The exact distribution of U has been determined and tabulated. The reader is directed to [1] and [2] for details. For a two-sided alternative hypothesis, H_0 is likely to be rejected if either a very small value or a very large value of U is determined. This will occur whenever the value of R_1 is correspondingly very large or very small. However, when both n_1 and n_2 are greater than 10, the distribution of U is adequately approximated by a normal distribution with mean and variance as given by (15.5) and (15.6), respectively. That is, under H_0 the random variable

$$Z = \frac{U - E(U)}{\sqrt{Var(U)}}$$

is approximately $N(0, 1)$ for large n_1 and n_2.

We should note that although, theoretically, ties cannot occur in the ordered sequence, they often do in practice. When ties occur in the ordered sequence, it is suggested that the average of the ranks for the tied observations be assigned to them. For example, suppose the values of the eighth and ninth observations in the ordered sequence are the same. Then each of these observations is assigned the rank 8.5.

Example 15.1 A large corporation is suspected of sex discrimination in the salaries of its employees. From employees with similar responsibilities and work experience, 12 male and 12 female employees were randomly selected; their annual salaries in thousands of dollars are as follows:

Females	22.5	19.8	20.6	24.7	23.2	19.2	18.7	20.9	21.6	23.5	20.7	21.6
Males	21.9	21.6	22.4	24.0	24.1	23.4	21.2	23.9	20.5	24.5	22.3	23.6

Is there reason to believe that these random samples come from populations with different distributions? Use $\alpha = 0.05$.

We combine the salaries of the two samples to form a single set of 24 annual salaries. Then the salaries are ordered and ranked as follows:

Sex	F	F	F	M	F	F	F	M	M	F	F	M
Salary	18.7	19.2	19.8	20.5	20.6	20.7	20.9	21.2	21.6	21.6	21.6	21.9
Rank	1	2	3	4	5	6	7	8	10	10	10	12

Sex	M	M	F	F	M	F	M	M	M	M	M	F
Salary	22.3	22.4	22.5	23.2	23.4	23.5	23.6	23.9	24.0	24.1	24.5	24.7
Rank	13	14	15	16	17	18	19	20	21	22	23	24

To determine the sum of the ranks, say we select the sample of females. Then the sum of the ranks is

$$1 + 2 + 3 + 5 + 6 + 7 + 10 + 10 + 15 + 16 + 18 + 24 = 117,$$

and the value of the Mann–Whitney U statistic is

$$u = (12)(12) + \frac{12(13)}{2} - 117 = 105.$$

Since $E(U) = (12)(12)/2 = 72$ and $Var(U) = (12)(12)(25)/12 = 300$, using the normal approximation,

$$z = (105 - 72)/\sqrt{300} = 1.91$$

is a value of a standard normal random variable. For $\alpha = 0.05$, the critical values are ± 1.96. Therefore, the null hypothesis that the random samples come from populations with identical distributions cannot be rejected.

15.2.2   Wald–Wolfowitz Runs Test

Another nonparametric method that compares the distributions of two populations based on independent random samples is the *Wald–Wolfowitz runs test*. For this test the null hypothesis is that the two independent random samples come from populations with identical distributions. But unlike the Mann–Whitney U test, the alternative hypothesis does not suggest a difference only in central tendency. That is, the alternative hypothesis in the Wald–Wolfowitz test is broader. It simply states that the distributions differ in some respect, such as central tendency, dispersion, or skewness.

As in the Mann–Whitney U test, the observations of the two random samples are combined and ordered by their magnitudes. But instead of considering ranks, the Wald–Wolfowitz procedure looks at the number of *runs* in the ordered sequence.

Definition 15.1 A run of length j is defined as a sequence of j observations, all belonging to the same group, that is preceded or followed by observations belonging to a different group.

For illustration, recall the ordered sequence of Example 15.1. The ordered sequence by the sex of the employee is as follows:

$$\text{F} \quad \text{F} \quad \text{F} \quad \text{M} \quad \text{F} \quad \text{F} \quad \text{F} \quad \text{M} \quad \text{M} \quad \text{F} \quad \text{F} \quad \text{M}$$
$$\text{M} \quad \text{M} \quad \text{F} \quad \text{F} \quad \text{M} \quad \text{F} \quad \text{M} \quad \text{M} \quad \text{M} \quad \text{M} \quad \text{M} \quad \text{F}$$

For the sex of the employee the ordered sequence exhibits runs of F's and M's. In particular, the sequence begins with a run of length three, followed by a run of length one, followed by another run of length three, and so on. The total number of runs in this sequence is 11.

If the null hypothesis of identical distributions is true, the observations of the two samples in the ordered sequence should be well mixed, producing a fairly large number of runs. But if the underlying distributions differ in some respect, the ordered sequence is likely to contain runs of long lengths thereby yielding a fairly small total number of runs.

Let R be the total number of runs observed in an ordered sequence of $n_1 + n_2$ observations, where n_1 and n_2 are the respective sample sizes. The possible values of R are 2, 3, ..., $(n_1 + n_2)$. It can be shown that the probability function of R is

$$p(r) = \begin{cases} \dfrac{2\dbinom{n_1 - 1}{r/2 - 1}\dbinom{n_2 - 1}{r/2 - 1}}{\dbinom{n_1 + n_2}{n_1}} & r \text{ even,} \\[3em] \dfrac{\dbinom{n_1 - 1}{r/2 - 1/2}\dbinom{n_2 - 1}{r/2 - 3/2} + \dbinom{n_1 - 1}{r/2 - 3/2}\dbinom{n_2 - 1}{r/2 - 1/2}}{\dbinom{n_1 + n_2}{n_1}} & r \text{ odd.} \end{cases} \tag{15.7}$$

The mean and variance of R are determined to be

$$E(R) = \frac{2n_1 n_2}{n_1 + n_2} + 1, \tag{15.8}$$

$$Var(R) = \frac{2n_1 n_2 (2n_1 n_2 - n_1 - n_2)}{(n_1 + n_2)^2 (n_1 + n_2 - 1)}. \tag{15.9}$$

To test H_0 with probability of type I error α, we must find an integer r_0 such that as nearly as possible

$$\sum_{r=2}^{r_0} p(r) = \alpha.$$

The null hypothesis is rejected when the observed number of runs is less than or equal to r_0. Notice that the critical region is a lower one-sided region since H_0 ought to be rejected when the number of runs is fairly small.

The cumulative distribution of R is extensively tabulated; but if both n_1 and n_2 exceed 10, the distribution of R is adequately approximated by a normal distribution with mean and variance given by (15.8) and (15.9), respectively. For illustration, recall Example 15.1. The observed number of runs is 11, and for $n_1 = n_2 = 12$ the mean and variance of R are determined to be 13 and 5.7391, respectively. Then using the normal approximation,

$$z = (11 - 13)/\sqrt{5.7391} = -0.83$$

is a value of a standard normal random variable. For $\alpha = 0.05$, it is seen that the null hypothesis cannot be rejected.

A serious problem arises in the application of the Wald–Wolfowitz runs test when ties occur among observations that belong to different groups. It is a problem because the number of runs will depend on how one handles the ties in the ordered sequence. The suggested procedure is to order the tied observations in a way that is least favorable to rejecting H_0. But if there are many ties, the validity of the Wald–Wolfowitz test is questionable.

Because of the broader nature of the alternative hypothesis in the Wald–Wolfowitz test, it and the Mann–Whitney test are not truly comparable. If an investigator wishes to compare the central tendencies of two population distributions and only ordinal observations are available, the Mann–Whitney statistic is the most powerful nonparametric procedure for detecting differences in central tendency. If a broader comparison is to be made, the Wald–Wolfowitz runs test is a viable procedure but understandably less powerful.

15.3   Nonparametric Tests for Paired Observations

In Section 9.6.4 we considered comparing the means of two treatments when the observations are paired to remove the effect of external factors. Now we discuss two nonparametric tests that are equivalent to the Student's t procedure of Section 9.6.4. These are the *sign test* and the *Wilcoxon signed rank test*.

15.3.1   The Sign Test

The *sign test* is based on the signs of the differences between paired observations of two random variables X and Y. Let (X_1, Y_1), (X_2, Y_2), ..., (X_n, Y_n) be n paired sample observations from the distributions of X and Y, where the distributions are assumed to be continuous. Often there is a natural relationship between X and Y, and thus X and Y need not be independent. For example, X and Y may represent the responses of married couples.

For each pair in which X exceeds Y a plus sign $(+)$ is recorded; otherwise a minus sign $(-)$ is recorded. Since the distributions of X and Y are assumed to be continuous, ties theoretically cannot occur. Let the probability that X exceeds Y be p. Then if the null hypothesis is that X and Y are identically distributed, p must be equal to 0.5. It must be noted, however, that p can be equal to 0.5 even when X and Y are not identically distributed. In essence, therefore, the null hypothesis for the sign test is

$$H_0: \quad p = 0.5,$$

tested against either a two-sided or a one-sided alternative hypothesis, depending on the wishes of the investigator. Notice that if H_0 is true, we would expect about half of the n pairs to have $+$ signs.

The statistic for the sign test, denoted by S, is the number of $+$ signs among the n pairs. Since under H_0 each pair constitutes an independent trial with probability of a $+$ sign of 0.5, the statistic S is binomially distributed with $p = 0.5$. Accordingly, for a given n and $p = 0.5$, the binomial distribution is used to determine critical regions of size α for type I error. For large n we may use the normal approximation to the binomial distribution, as discussed in Section 5.2.

When ties occur in the application of the sign test, the recommended procedure is to ignore them and use the sign test only for those pairs in which there are no ties. This procedure may present a problem if ties are numerous and the original number of pairs is relatively small.

Example 15.2 Ten newly married couples were randomly selected, and each husband and wife were independently asked the question of how many children they would like to have. The following information was obtained.

Couple	1	2	3	4	5	6	7	8	9	10
Wife X	3	2	1	0	0	1	2	2	2	0
Husband Y	2	3	2	2	0	2	1	3	1	2

Using the sign test, is there reason to believe that wives want fewer children than husbands? Assume a maximum size of type I error of 0.05.

Consider testing the null hypothesis

$$H_0: \quad p = 0.5$$

against the alternative

$$H_1: \quad p < 0.5.$$

Notice that H_0 should be rejected if the number of $+$'s is fairly small. Subtracting each husband's response from that of the wife, and noticing that the responses for couple 5 are the same, we obtain the following $+$ and $-$ arrangement:

Couple	1	2	3	4	6	7	8	9	10
Sign	$+$	$-$	$-$	$-$	$-$	$+$	$-$	$+$	$-$

There are three $+$ signs, so the observed value of the statistic S is 3. Since under H_0, S is binomial with $n = 9$ and $p = 0.5$, the p-value, or the probability of observing three or less +'s, is determined from Table A of the Appendix to be

$$P(S \leqslant 3) = 0.2539.$$

Since 0.2539 is greater than $\alpha = 0.05$, the null hypothesis cannot be rejected. Notice that for this example the critical value of S would be one if the maximum size of type I error is 0.05.

15.3.2 Wilcoxon Signed Rank Test

The sign test considers only the sign of the differences between each pair of observations and ignores the magnitudes of the differences. If the observations are defined on an ordinal scale, the magnitudes of the differences are of little value. But if the observations are physical measurements, much information may be ignored by the sign test because the magnitudes of the differences are not taken into account. The *Wilcoxon signed rank test* considers both the sign and the magnitude of the differences between each pair of observations. On balance, therefore, it is the better nonparametric method to use for paired observations.

To implement the Wilcoxon test, differences are determined for the n pairs of observations. These differences are then ordered without regard to sign and ranked accordingly. That is, the smallest absolute difference receives rank one, and the largest absolute difference is assigned rank n. Then the sign of each difference is attached to the rank for that difference. Ties among the differences are handled in the same manner as in the Mann–Whitney test, but if a difference is exactly zero, the suggested procedure is to drop that pair and adjust n.

The Wilcoxon test statistic is the sum of the positive ranks and is denoted by T_+. Notice that T_+ contains not only the information provided by the sign test statistic but also information about the relative magnitude of the differences. If the null hypothesis that the observations in each pair come from identical distributions is true, the occurrence of any particular sequence of the signed ranks is equiprobable among the 2^n possible sequences of +'s and −'s. Under the null hypothesis we expect T_+ to be about the same as the sum of the magnitudes of the negative ranks. Depending on the nature of the alternative hypothesis, therefore, H_0 is rejected when an observed value of T_+ is sufficiently large or sufficiently small.

The exact distribution of T_+ has been determined and is tabulated. As for some other statistics, however, the sampling distribution of T_+ is adequately approximated by a normal distribution for $n > 10$, where

$$E(T_+) = n(n + 1)/4, \tag{15.10}$$

$$Var(T_+) = n(n + 1)(2n + 1)/24. \tag{15.11}$$

In other words, the random variable

$$Z = \frac{T_+ - E(T_+)}{\sqrt{Var(T_+)}}$$

is approximately $N(0, 1)$ for large n.

TABLE 15.1 Sample data for Example 15.3

Student	Test 1	Test 2	Difference	Rank	Signed rank
1	94	85	9	8	8
2	78	65	13	10	10
3	89	92	-3	4	-4
4	62	56	6	7	7
5	49	52	-3	4	-4
6	78	74	4	6	6
7	80	79	1	1	1
8	82	84	-2	2	-2
9	62	48	14	11	11
10	83	71	12	9	9
11	79	82	-3	4	-4

Example 15.3 Eleven students were randomly selected from a large statistics class, and their numerical grades on two successive examinations were recorded. For the grades indicated in Table 15.1 use the Wilcoxon signed rank test to determine whether the second test was more difficult than the first. Use $\alpha = 0.1$.

In the table we have determined the differences (Test 1 − Test 2), ranks, and signed ranks for the eleven students. Since we wish to determine whether the second test was more difficult than the first, the alternative hypothesis is one-sided, and the critical region is the upper tail of the sampling distribution of T_+. That is, if the observed value of the sum of the positive ranks is large, it would imply sufficiently lower scores for Test 2, and the null hypothesis of no difference should be rejected.

The sum of the positive ranks is $8 + 10 + 7 + 6 + 1 + 11 + 9 = 52$. For $n = 11$, the mean and variance of T_+ work out to be $E(T_+) = 33$ and $Var(T_+) = 126.5$. Then, using the normal approximation,

$$z = \frac{52 - 33}{\sqrt{126.5}} = 1.69.$$

For $\alpha = 0.1$, $z_{0.9} = 1.28$, and the null hypothesis is therefore rejected.

15.4 Kruskal–Wallis Test for *k* Independent Random Samples

Recall the parametric analysis of variance procedure in Section 12.4 in which we were interested in testing the null hypothesis

$$H_0: \quad \mu_1 = \mu_2 = \cdots = \mu_k,$$

based on *k* mutually independent random samples drawn from populations whose distributions were assumed to be normal. Nonparametric methods have been developed for essentially the same purpose so long as at least ordinal measurements are available and the underlying population distributions are continuous. One of these methods is the *Kruskal–Wallis* procedure, which tests the null hypothesis

TABLE 15.2 Observations of k random samples for Kruskal–Wallis test

1	2	$\cdots$	Sample j	$\cdots$	k
Y_{11}	Y_{12}	$\cdots$	Y_{1j}	$\cdots$	Y_{1k}
Y_{21}	Y_{22}	$\cdots$	Y_{2j}	$\cdots$	Y_{2k}
$\vdots$	$\vdots$		$\vdots$		$\vdots$
$Y_{n_1 1}$	$Y_{n_2 2}$	$\cdots$	$Y_{n_j j}$	$\cdots$	$Y_{n_k k}$

that the treatment effects are the same, or the k random samples come from populations with identical distributions.

Let the observations of the k random samples be as given in Table 15.2, where n_j is the size of the jth sample and $N = \Sigma_{j=1}^{k} n_j$ is the total number of observations over all samples.

The null hypothesis may be stated as

$$H_0: \quad f_1(y) \equiv f_2(y) \equiv \cdots \equiv f_k(y) \tag{15.12}$$

where $f_1(y), f_2(y), \cdots, f_k(y)$ are the corresponding probability density functions. The alternative hypothesis can be general and state only that the k distributions are not the same. However, the Kruskal–Wallis test is particularly sensitive to differences in central tendency and is very useful when one suspects that the underlying distributions may differ only in that regard. Accordingly, the Kruskal–Wallis procedure is generally regarded as an extension of the Mann–Whitney U test.

As in the Mann–Whitney test, the Kruskal–Wallis procedure is based on combining all observations in the random samples to form a single set of N observations. The observations are then arranged in order of increasing magnitude, and a rank is assigned to each observation beginning with rank 1 and terminating with rank N. When the ranking of all observations is completed, the sum of the ranks in each sample can be determined. Let R_j be the sum of the ranks of the jth sample. In essence the Kruskal–Wallis test determines whether the disparity among the R_j with respect to the sample sizes n_j is sufficient to warrant the rejection of the null hypothesis.

Under the assumption that the k samples come from populations with identical distributions, the Kruskal–Wallis test statistic is

$$H = \frac{12}{N(N+1)} \left[\sum_{j=1}^{k} \frac{R_j^2}{n_j} \right] - 3(N+1), \tag{15.13}$$

which for relatively large sample sizes n_j is adequately approximated by a chi-square distribution with $k-1$ degrees of freedom. For a specified size of type I error, the critical region is the upper portion of the chi-square distribution. Accordingly, the null hypothesis is rejected for large values of the Kruskal–Wallis statistic. It should be noted that the chi-square approximation is generally satisfactory except when $k = 3$ and none of the sample sizes n_j is larger than five.

TABLE 15.3 Sample data for Example 15.4

	Neighborhood		
1	*2*	*3*	*4*
1.19 (15)	1.08 (4.5)	0.98 (2)	1.12 (7.5)
1.05 (3)	1.23 (17.5)	1.19 (15)	1.14 (10)
1.14 (10)	1.26 (20)	1.08 (4.5)	1.31 (22)
1.25 (19)	1.10 (6)	0.93 (1)	1.12 (7.5)
1.29 (21)	1.18 (12.5)	1.23 (17.5)	1.19 (15)
	1.14 (10)	1.18 (12.5)	

The recommended procedure for handling ties is the same as in the Mann–Whitney test. If the number of ties is large, a correction factor has been proposed for the test statistic (15.13); see any of the references at the end of this chapter. Although the correction always increases the value of the test statistic, in most cases the effect is negligible, even if there are numerous ties.

Example 15.4 Independent random samples of recently sold houses were taken from four distinct residential neighborhoods in a large city. The problem was to determine whether differences exist among the neighborhoods in property valuation when compared to the sale price. The data in Table 15.3 are the ratios of sale price to property valuation as determined by the city's real estate assessor's office. For $\alpha = 0.05$, use the Kruskal–Wallis statistic to test whether these samples come from populations with identical distributions.

The values in parentheses in the table are the ranks of the observations after they are combined and ordered. Notice that $n_1 = n_4 = 5$, $n_2 = n_3 = 6$, and $N = 22$. The sums of the ranks for each sample are $R_1 = 68$, $R_2 = 70.5$, $R_3 = 52.5$, and $R_4 = 62$. Then the value of the Kruskal–Wallis statistic is

$$h = \frac{12}{(22)(23)} \left[\frac{(68)^2}{5} + \frac{(70.5)^2}{6} + \frac{(52.5)^2}{6} + \frac{(62)^2}{5} \right] - 3(23) = 1.70.$$

From Table E of the Appendix, for $\alpha = 0.05$ and $k - 1 = 3$ degrees of freedom the critical value is 7.82. Since $h = 1.70 < 7.82$, the null hypothesis cannot be rejected. There is no reason to believe that differences exist among the neighborhoods for property valuation when compared to sale price.

15.5 Friedman Test for *k* Paired Samples

The Wilcoxon signed rank test is regarded as the nonparametric equivalent of the Student's *t* method for paired observations, or of the analysis of variance procedure for a two-treatment experiment in a randomized complete block design. When $k \geqslant 3$ treatments of a single factor need to be investigated in the presence of an external factor and at least ordinal measurements are available, a useful nonparametric method to determine whether treatment effects are the same is the *Friedman test*.

TABLE 15.4   Arrangement of observations for the Friedman test

Block	Treatment					
	1	2	$\cdots$	j	$\cdots$	k
1	Y_{11}	Y_{12}	$\cdots$	Y_{1j}	$\cdots$	Y_{1k}
2	Y_{21}	Y_{22}	$\cdots$	Y_{2j}	$\cdots$	Y_{2k}
$\vdots$	$\vdots$	$\vdots$		$\vdots$		$\vdots$
n	Y_{n1}	Y_{n2}	$\cdots$	Y_{nj}	$\cdots$	Y_{nk}

Similar to the parametric procedure, a block is created for each of n conditions of the external factor such that each block contains one observation from each of the k treatments. In addition, it is assumed that treatments are assigned at random and there is no interaction between blocks and treatments. Let the nk observations be arranged as in Table 15.4, where the blocks are the rows and the treatments are the columns.

The null hypothesis for the Friedman procedure is that treatment effects are the same (that is, the underlying populations have identical distributions), and the alternative hypothesis is that treatment differences exist. As for the Kruskal–Wallis statistic, the uncovering of treatment differences through the Friedman statistic implies differences in central tendency.

As in other nonparametric procedures, the Friedman test is based on ranks. For each block (row), we rank the observations beginning with rank 1 and terminating with rank k; then we sum the ranks for each treatment. Let R_j be the sum of the ranks of the jth treatment (column). If within each block the treatment effects are the same, then for every block the ranks should be a random permutation of the integers 1 to k with each permutation being equally likely. Thus for each treatment we expect the ranks 1 to k to appear with approximately the same frequency. If treatment effects are identical, R_j should be about the same for all j. In substance, therefore, the Friedman procedure determines when an observed disparity among the R_j is sufficient to reject the null hypothesis.

The Friedman statistic is given by

$$S = \frac{12}{nk(k+1)}\left[\sum_{j=1}^{k} R_j^2\right] - 3n(k+1). \tag{15.14}$$

Probabilities for values of S are tabulated for small n and k (see [3]). But if the number of blocks n and the number of treatments k are not too small (say $n \geq$ 10 and $k \geq 4$), the statistic S is distributed approximately as a chi-square random variable with $k - 1$ degrees of freedom. As in the Kruskal–Wallis test, the critical region of size α is the upper portion of the chi-square distribution with $k - 1$ degrees of freedom. The null hypothesis is rejected when the value of S exceeds the critical value. As before, ties do occur and are handled by using average ranks.

Example 15.5   Four persons judge performance in a diving competition involving ten finalists. The data in Table 15.5 are the recorded scores, where a 10 indicates

TABLE 15.5 Sample data for Example 15.5

Competitor	*1*		*2*		*3*		*4*	
					Judge			
1	8.5	(3)	8.6	(4)	8.2	(1)	8.4	(2)
2	9.8	(4)	9.7	(3)	9.4	(1)	9.6	(2)
3	7.9	(2)	8.1	(3)	7.5	(1)	8.2	(4)
4	9.7	(3)	9.8	(4)	9.6	(1.5)	9.6	(1.5)
5	6.2	(1)	6.8	(3)	6.9	(4)	6.5	(2)
6	8.9	(3)	9.2	(4)	8.1	(1)	8.7	(2)
7	9.2	(3.5)	9.2	(3.5)	8.7	(1)	8.9	(2)
8	8.4	(1.5)	8.5	(3)	8.4	(1.5)	8.6	(4)
9	9.2	(2)	9.6	(4)	8.9	(1)	9.5	(3)
10	8.8	(2)	9.2	(3)	8.6	(1)	9.3	(4)

a perfect dive. For $\alpha = 0.01$, use the Friedman statistic to determine if there are discernible differences in scoring among the four judges.

We have determined the ranks of the observations for each competitor (block). They are the values in the parentheses in the table. Then for each judge the sum of the ranks is as follows: $R_1 = 25$, $R_2 = 34.5$, $R_3 = 14$, $R_4 = 26.5$. The value of the Friedman statistic is computed to be

$$s = \frac{12}{(10)(4)(5)}[25^2 + 34.5^2 + 14^2 + 26.5^2] - (3)(10)(5) = 12.81.$$

For $\alpha = 0.01$ and $k - 1 = 3$ degrees of freedom the critical value is determined from Table E of the Appendix to be 11.32. Since $s = 12.81 > 11.32$, the null hypothesis that the treatment effects are the same is rejected; differences in scoring among the four judges are statistically discernible.

15.6   Spearman Rank Correlation Coefficient

In Section 13.8 we defined the sample correlation coefficient as a measure of linear association between two variables X and Y. Our approach in that section was parametric since we assumed a bivariate normal distribution for X and Y. Here we wish to define a popular nonparametric measure of association when ranks are used, the *Spearman rank correlation coefficient*, denoted by r_S.

Let X and Y represent two characteristics of interest and suppose there exists a random sample of n pairs that consist only of ranks for X and Y. Spearman's rank correlation coefficient is the ordinary sample correlation coefficient that one can determine using either (13.27) or (13.28), except now the ranks are used instead of actual observations of X and Y. Like the sample correlation coefficient r, the rank correlation coefficient r_S is defined in the range $-1 \leq r_S \leq 1$; it measures the degree of linear association between *ranks* of X and Y. For the characteristics X and Y the interpretation of r_S is not entirely identical to that of r. If actual observations of X and Y were available, then the sample correlation coefficient r would measure the degree of *linear* association between X and Y.

But if ranks are used, r_S measures the tendency of X and Y to relate in a *monotone* way. That is, if r_S is close to $+1$ or -1, a monotonically increasing or decreasing association for X and Y is suggested. In a sense r_S is more meaningful than r because by measuring the degree of monotonic association between X and Y, r_S is not restricted to uncovering only a linear relation between them.

Let (X_i', Y_i'), $i = 1, 2, ..., n$ represent a sample of ranks for X and Y. Then from (13.28) the Spearman rank correlation coefficient is

$$r_S = \frac{\sum\limits_{i=1}^{n} X_i' Y_i' - \frac{\left(\sum\limits_{i=1}^{n} X_i'\right)\left(\sum\limits_{i=1}^{n} Y_i'\right)}{n}}{\left[\sum\limits_{i=1}^{n} X_i'^2 - \frac{\left(\sum\limits_{i=1}^{n} X_i'\right)^2}{n}\right]^{1/2}\left[\sum\limits_{i=1}^{n} Y_i'^2 - \frac{\left(\sum\limits_{i=1}^{n} Y_i'\right)^2}{n}\right]^{1/2}} \tag{15.15}$$

If there are no ties, an alternative and simpler relation for (15.15) can be developed by taking advantage of the nature of a rank. The ranks (X_i', Y_i') are arrangements of the first n positive integers. Since the sum of the first n positive integers is $n(n + 1)/2$, and the sum of their squares is $n(n + 1)(2n + 1)/6$,

$$\sum X_i' = \sum Y_i' = n(n + 1)/2 \tag{15.16}$$

and

$$\sum X_i'^2 = \sum Y_i'^2 = n(n + 1)(2n + 1)/6. \tag{15.17}$$

Moreover, since the relation

$$\sum X_i' Y_i' = \left[\sum X_i'^2 + \sum Y_i'^2 - \sum (X_i' - Y_i')^2\right]/2 \tag{15.18}$$

holds for any values, substitution of (15.16)–(15.18) in (15.15) and after some algebra yields the alternative expression

$$r_S = 1 - \frac{6\sum (X_i' - Y_i')^2}{n(n^2 - 1)}. \tag{15.19}$$

Example 15.6   Two wine judges were asked to rate ten different clarets on a scale from 1 (poor) to 10 (excellent). The ratings in Table 15.6 were obtained. Compute the Spearman rank correlation coefficient.

Since there are no ties, we can use (15.19) to compute r_S.

$$r_S = 1 - \frac{6[(5 - 3)^2 + (2 - 4)^2 + \cdots + (3 - 1)^2]}{10(100 - 1)} = 0.73,$$

which suggests a fairly strong agreement between the two judges.

TABLE 15.6 Sample data for Example 15.6

Wine	Judge 1 X'	Judge 2 Y'
1	5	3
2	2	4
3	8	7
4	9	6
5	10	9
6	7	9
7	1	3
8	4	6
9	4	7
10	3	1

15.7 Concluding Remarks

Three advantages emerge for nonparametric methods as discussed in this chapter:

1. Assumptions for their use are less rigid than those of comparable parametric methods.
2. Nonparametric methods can easily be applied to observations that are defined only on an ordinal scale.
3. The computations involved are easy when compared to corresponding parametric methods.

Because of the first advantage, nonparametric methods are particularly useful when small sample sizes are involved and there is concern about adherence to distributional assumptions for the parametric methods. In particular, the Mann–Whitney, Wilcoxon, Kruskal–Wallis, and Friedman tests compare relatively well in power with the corresponding parametric methods involving the Student's t distribution or the F statistic in analysis of variance. But as we indicated in Chapter 9, for sample sizes of 15 or more the Student's t distribution is largely robust to the normality assumption. Moreover, the T statistic is robust to the assumption of equal variances for large but equal sample sizes when comparing two means, as is the F statistic in analysis of variance so long as the treatment sample sizes are the same. Thus when large sample sizes are involved and observations are defined at least on an interval scale, important information may be lost by converting the observations to ranks or signs and using nonparametric methods. For such cases the power efficiency of the nonparametric methods is less than that of comparable parametric procedures. On balance, therefore, the clearest advantage nonparametric methods have over the parametric type is the second one on our list. The application of parametric methods to observations that are defined only on an ordinal scale is awkward because the interpretation of an interval has little substance.

References

1. J. D. Gibbons, *Nonparametric statistical inference*, McGraw-Hill, New York, 1971.
2. M. Hollander and D. A. Wolfe, *Nonparametric statistical methods*, Wiley, New York, 1973.
3. S. Siegel, *Nonparametric statistics for the behavioral sciences*, McGraw-Hill, New York, 1956.

Exercises

15.1. For the data in Example 15.1, test the null hypothesis of no difference in means using the Student's t procedure from Section 9.6.2. For the same size of type I error as in the example, is your conclusion different this time?

15.2. A five-year study was conducted to determine whether there is a difference in the number of colds experienced by smokers and nonsmokers. Based on random samples of 14 nonsmokers and 12 smokers, the following data represent the number of colds observed during the five-year period.

Nonsmokers	1	0	2	7	3	1	2	2	4	3	5	0	2	1
Smokers	4	2	6	5	8	10	8	7	6	4	9	3		

Use the Mann–Whitney U statistic to determine whether there is reason to believe these random samples come from populations with different distributions. Assume $\alpha = 0.05$. Are there any assumptions we may be violating?

15.3. A marketing research firm is interested in comparing consumer acceptance of two new products, A and B. Twelve randomly selected consumers were asked to rate their acceptance of product A using a scale from 1 (strongly dislike) to 5 (strongly like). An equal number of consumers rated product B. The following information was obtained.

Product A	1	2	5	5	4	3	5	4	4	3	5	2
Product B	2	2	1	1	3	1	2	2	4	3	1	3

Use the Mann–Whitney U statistic to determine whether the null hypothesis that these random samples come from populations with identical distributions can be rejected at the $\alpha = 0.05$ level.

15.4. The following information represents the daily number of finished units for two production workers, A and B, over a five-day period.

A	49	52	53	47	50
B	56	48	58	46	55

a. Use expression (15.7) to determine the probability function of the possible number of runs.

b. For $\alpha = 0.05$, use the Wald–Wolfowitz runs procedure to test the null hypothesis that these samples come from identical distributions.

15.5. The Wald–Wolfowitz runs procedure is often used as a test of randomness for a given sequence of observations. If randomness exists, then the number of runs for two distinct groups should be neither too large nor too small. Suppose the following is the sequence of residuals for an estimated regression equation:

−2.98	−4.19	−0.51	5.19	2.38	6.73	0.93	1.29	−3.18
−1.14	−0.54	−2.76	−1.89	−4.28	−0.18	0.32	0.48	1.48
−2.43	−4.69	3.18	0.64	0.89	2.08	0.98	−3.28	

Is there reason to believe that this sequence of residuals is not random? Use $\alpha = 0.05$.

15.6. A marketing research firm was interested in taste preferences for two competing brands of soft drink. Fourteen persons were randomly selected and asked to rate both soft drinks using the scale 1 (strongly dislike) to 10 (strongly like). The order of drink selection was randomized. The following information was obtained:

Person	*1*	*2*	*3*	*4*	*5*	*6*	*7*	*8*	*9*	*10*	*11*	*12*	*13*	*14*
Brand A	7	5	9	4	8	10	4	3	7	2	8	6	6	9
Brand B	3	2	7	6	9	3	5	1	4	2	4	7	5	4

Using the sign test, is there reason to believe there is a difference in taste preference for these two soft drinks? Assume $\alpha = 0.1$.

15.7. Use the Wilcoxon signed rank test for the data in Exercise 15.6. Are the conclusions the same?

15.8. Refer to the data in Example 9.10 and suppose the normality assumption cannot be made. Using the Wilcoxon signed rank test, determine whether the corresponding nonparametric null hypothesis can be rejected at the $\alpha = 0.01$ level.

15.9. On twelve randomly selected days the following number of units of the same product were sold by two competitors, A and B:

Day	*1*	*2*	*3*	*4*	*5*	*6*	*7*	*8*	*9*	*10*	*11*	*12*
A	42	58	47	39	41	56	59	37	38	46	43	51
B	64	57	48	59	64	52	65	59	37	65	68	49

Using the sign test, can the null hypothesis that the samples come from identical distributions be rejected at the $\alpha = 0.05$ level?

15.10. Use the Wilcoxon signed rank test for the data in Exercise 15.9 and compare your results.

15.11. We wish to determine whether a student's undergraduate field has an effect on his/her performance in law school. A random sample of 30 students is chosen from a graduating class of a certain law school. The law school class ranking and the undergraduate field are noted for each student; the findings are in Table 15.7. Use

TABLE 15.7 Sample data for Exercise 15.11

Business	*Science or engineering*	*Liberal arts*	*Other*
9	3	2	14
22	7	4	34
24	10	15	48
31	18	26	52
47	23	38	59
65	25	43	63
		45	67
		49	72
		55	79

the Kruskal–Wallis test to determine whether the undergraduate field has an effect on law school performance with $\alpha = 0.05$.

15.12. Refer to the data in Exercise 12.7. Use the Kruskal–Wallis procedure to test the null hypothesis of no brand differences in durability with $\alpha = 0.05$. Is your conclusion the same as in Exercise 12.7?

15.13. Twelve students were randomly selected from a very large undergraduate class; their scores on the four examinations administered to the class during the semester are listed in Table 15.8. Use the Friedman test to determine whether differences among the four examinations are statistically discernible at the 0.01 level. Are you comfortable with the assumption that there is no interaction between student and examination? Elaborate.

TABLE 15.8 Sample data for Exercise 15.13

Student	1	2	3	4
1	72	68	80	75
2	89	87	78	92
3	48	56	64	58
4	65	76	70	62
5	86	94	93	85
6	56	73	78	87
7	75	84	65	69
8	39	45	48	56
9	78	67	69	59
10	98	87	86	95
11	64	87	92	48
12	82	76	85	79

15.14. Refer to the data in Exercise 12.16. Use the Friedman procedure to determine whether differences among the four supermarkets are statistically discernible at the 0.01 level.

15.15. For Exercise 13.12, convert the data into ranks and compute the Spearman rank correlation coefficient.

15.16. Two judges rated the performances of eight figure skaters using the scale 1 (worst) to 10 (best). The following results were obtained.

Skater	1	2	3	4	5	6	7	8
Judge 1	3	4	8	8	4	6	4	7
Judge 2	2	4	9	7	2	8	7	9

Compute the Spearman rank correlation coefficient and comment on whether a relationship is apparent.

15.17. Using the same scale as in Exercise 15.16, two judges rated the talent performance of the ten semifinalists in a recent Miss America Pageant as follows:

Semifinalist	1	2	3	4	5	6	7	8	9	10
Judge 1	2	6	5	9	3	7	9	2	6	2
Judge 2	7	1	4	4	8	9	3	9	10	8

Compute the Spearman rank correlation coefficient and comment as in Exercise 15.16.

15.18. A group of investment analysts ranked ten companies for book value and growth potential as follows:

Company	1	2	3	4	5	6	7	8	9	10
Book value	8	3	10	1	6	2	5	7	4	9
Growth	4	8	6	5	9	3	7	1	10	2

Compute the Spearman rank correlation coefficient and comment on whether a relation between a company's book value and its growth potential is apparent.

Appendix

TABLE A Values of the binomial cumulative distribution function

$$P(X \le x) = F(x; n, p) = \sum_{i=0}^{x} \binom{n}{i} p^x (1-p)^{n-x}$$

							p					
n	x	0.01	0.05	0.10	0.15	0.20	0.25	0.30	0.35	0.40	0.45	0.50
2	0	0.9801	0.9025	0.8100	0.7225	0.6400	0.5625	0.4900	0.4225	0.3600	0.3025	0.2500
	1	0.9999	0.9975	0.9900	0.9775	0.9600	0.9375	0.9100	0.8775	0.8400	0.7975	0.7500
	2	1.0000	1.0000	1.0000	1.0000	1.0000	1.0000	1.0000	1.0000	1.0000	1.0000	1.0000
3	0	0.9703	0.8574	0.7290	0.6141	0.5120	0.4219	0.3430	0.2746	0.2160	0.1664	0.1250
	1	0.9997	0.9928	0.9720	0.9392	0.8960	0.8438	0.7840	0.7183	0.6480	0.5748	0.5000
	2	1.0000	0.9999	0.9990	0.9966	0.9920	0.9844	0.9730	0.9571	0.9360	0.9089	0.8750
	3	1.0000	1.0000	1.0000	1.0000	1.0000	1.0000	1.0000	1.0000	1.0000	1.0000	1.0000
4	0	0.9606	0.8145	0.6561	0.5220	0.4096	0.3164	0.2401	0.1785	0.1296	0.0915	0.0625
	1	0.9994	0.9860	0.9477	0.8905	0.8192	0.7383	0.6517	0.5630	0.4752	0.3910	0.3125
	2	1.0000	0.9995	0.9963	0.9880	0.9728	0.9492	0.9163	0.8735	0.8208	0.7585	0.6875
	3	1.0000	1.0000	0.9999	0.9995	0.9984	0.9961	0.9919	0.9850	0.9744	0.9590	0.9375
	4	1.0000	1.0000	1.0000	1.0000	1.0000	1.0000	1.0000	1.0000	1.0000	1.0000	1.0000
5	0	0.9510	0.7738	0.5905	0.4437	0.3277	0.2373	0.1681	0.1160	0.0778	0.0503	0.0313
	1	0.9990	0.9774	0.9185	0.8352	0.7373	0.6328	0.5282	0.4284	0.3370	0.2562	0.1875
	2	1.0000	0.9988	0.9914	0.9734	0.9421	0.8965	0.8369	0.7648	0.6826	0.5931	0.5000
	3	1.0000	1.0000	0.9995	0.9978	0.9933	0.9844	0.9692	0.9460	0.9130	0.8688	0.8125
	4	1.0000	1.0000	1.0000	0.9999	0.9997	0.9990	0.9976	0.9947	0.9898	0.9815	0.9688
	5	1.0000	1.0000	1.0000	1.0000	1.0000	1.0000	1.0000	1.0000	1.0000	1.0000	1.0000
6	0	0.9415	0.7351	0.5314	0.3771	0.2621	0.1780	0.1176	0.0754	0.0467	0.0277	0.0156
	1	0.9985	0.9672	0.8857	0.7765	0.6554	0.5339	0.4202	0.3191	0.2333	0.1636	0.1094
	2	1.0000	0.9978	0.9842	0.9527	0.9011	0.8306	0.7443	0.6471	0.5443	0.4415	0.3438
	3	1.0000	0.9999	0.9987	0.9941	0.9830	0.9624	0.9295	0.8826	0.8208	0.7447	0.6563
	4	1.0000	1.0000	0.9999	0.9996	0.9984	0.9954	0.9891	0.9777	0.9590	0.9308	0.8906
	5	1.0000	1.0000	1.0000	1.0000	0.9999	0.9998	0.9993	0.9982	0.9959	0.9917	0.9844
	6	1.0000	1.0000	1.0000	1.0000	1.0000	1.0000	1.0000	1.0000	1.0000	1.0000	1.0000

n	x											
7	0	0.0078	0.0152	0.0280	0.0490	0.0824	0.1335	0.2097	0.3206	0.4783	0.6983	0.9321
	1	0.0625	0.1024	0.1586	0.2338	0.3294	0.4449	0.5767	0.7166	0.8503	0.9556	0.9980
	2	0.2266	0.3164	0.4199	0.5323	0.6471	0.7564	0.8520	0.9262	0.9743	0.9962	1.0000
	3	0.5000	0.6083	0.7102	0.8002	0.8740	0.9294	0.9667	0.9879	0.9973	0.9998	1.0000
	4	0.7734	0.8471	0.9037	0.9444	0.9712	0.9871	0.9953	0.9988	0.9998	1.0000	1.0000
	5	0.9375	0.9643	0.9812	0.9910	0.9962	0.9987	0.9996	0.9999	1.0000	1.0000	1.0000
	6	0.9922	0.9963	0.9984	0.9994	0.9998	0.9999	1.0000	1.0000	1.0000	1.0000	1.0000
	7	1.0000	1.0000	1.0000	1.0000	1.0000	1.0000	1.0000	1.0000	1.0000	1.0000	1.0000
8	0	0.0039	0.0084	0.0168	0.0319	0.0576	0.1001	0.1678	0.2725	0.4305	0.6634	0.9227
	1	0.0352	0.0632	0.1064	0.1691	0.2553	0.3671	0.5033	0.6572	0.8131	0.9428	0.9973
	2	0.1445	0.2201	0.3154	0.4278	0.5518	0.6785	0.7969	0.8948	0.9619	0.9942	0.9999
	3	0.3633	0.4770	0.5941	0.7064	0.8059	0.8862	0.9437	0.9786	0.9950	0.9996	1.0000
	4	0.6367	0.7396	0.8263	0.8939	0.9420	0.9727	0.9896	0.9971	0.9996	1.0000	1.0000
	5	0.8555	0.9115	0.9502	0.9747	0.9887	0.9958	0.9988	0.9998	1.0000	1.0000	1.0000
	6	0.9648	0.9819	0.9915	0.9964	0.9987	0.9996	0.9999	1.0000	1.0000	1.0000	1.0000
	7	0.9961	0.9983	0.9993	0.9998	0.9999	1.0000	1.0000	1.0000	1.0000	1.0000	1.0000
	8	1.0000	1.0000	1.0000	1.0000	1.0000	1.0000	1.0000	1.0000	1.0000	1.0000	1.0000
9	0	0.0020	0.0046	0.0101	0.0207	0.0404	0.0751	0.1342	0.2316	0.3874	0.6302	0.9135
	1	0.0195	0.0385	0.0705	0.1211	0.1960	0.3003	0.4362	0.5995	0.7748	0.9288	0.9966
	2	0.0898	0.1495	0.2318	0.3373	0.4628	0.6007	0.7382	0.8591	0.9470	0.9916	0.9999
	3	0.2539	0.3614	0.4826	0.6089	0.7297	0.8343	0.9144	0.9661	0.9917	0.9994	1.0000
	4	0.5000	0.6214	0.7334	0.8283	0.9012	0.9511	0.9804	0.9944	0.9991	1.0000	1.0000
	5	0.7461	0.8342	0.9006	0.9464	0.9747	0.9900	0.9969	0.9994	0.9999	1.0000	1.0000
	6	0.9102	0.9502	0.9750	0.9888	0.9957	0.9987	0.9997	1.0000	1.0000	1.0000	1.0000
	7	0.9805	0.9909	0.9962	0.9986	0.9996	0.9999	1.0000	1.0000	1.0000	1.0000	1.0000
	8	0.9980	0.9992	0.9997	0.9999	1.0000	1.0000	1.0000	1.0000	1.0000	1.0000	1.0000
	9	1.0000	1.0000	1.0000	1.0000	1.0000	1.0000	1.0000	1.0000	1.0000	1.0000	1.0000
10	0	0.0010	0.0025	0.0060	0.0135	0.0282	0.0563	0.1074	0.1969	0.3487	0.5987	0.9044
	1	0.0107	0.0233	0.0464	0.0860	0.1493	0.2440	0.3758	0.5443	0.7361	0.9139	0.9957
	2	0.0547	0.0996	0.1673	0.2616	0.3828	0.5256	0.6778	0.8202	0.9298	0.9885	0.9999
	3	0.1719	0.2660	0.3823	0.5138	0.6496	0.7759	0.8791	0.9500	0.9872	0.9990	1.0000
	4	0.3770	0.5044	0.6331	0.7515	0.8497	0.9219	0.9672	0.9901	0.9984	0.9999	1.0000
	5	0.6230	0.7384	0.8338	0.9051	0.9527	0.9803	0.9936	0.9986	0.9999	1.0000	1.0000
	6	0.8281	0.8980	0.9452	0.9740	0.9894	0.9965	0.9991	0.9999	1.0000	1.0000	1.0000
	7	0.9453	0.9726	0.9877	0.9952	0.9984	0.9996	0.9999	1.0000	1.0000	1.0000	1.0000
	8	0.9893	0.9955	0.9983	0.9995	0.9999	1.0000	1.0000	1.0000	1.0000	1.0000	1.0000
	9	0.9990	0.9997	0.9999	1.0000	1.0000	1.0000	1.0000	1.0000	1.0000	1.0000	1.0000
	10	1.0000	1.0000	1.0000	1.0000	1.0000	1.0000	1.0000	1.0000	1.0000	1.0000	1.0000

TABLE A (continued)   Values of the binomial cumulative distribution function

							p					
n	x	0.01	0.05	0.10	0.15	0.20	0.25	0.30	0.35	0.40	0.45	0.50
11	0	0.8953	0.5688	0.3138	0.1673	0.0859	0.0422	0.0198	0.0088	0.0036	0.0014	0.0005
	1	0.9948	0.8981	0.6974	0.4922	0.3221	0.1971	0.1130	0.0606	0.0302	0.0139	0.0059
	2	0.9998	0.9848	0.9104	0.7788	0.6174	0.4552	0.3127	0.2001	0.1189	0.0652	0.0327
	3	1.0000	0.9984	0.9815	0.9306	0.8389	0.7133	0.5696	0.4256	0.2963	0.1911	0.1133
	4	1.0000	0.9999	0.9972	0.9841	0.9496	0.8854	0.7897	0.6683	0.5328	0.3971	0.2744
	5	1.0000	1.0000	0.9997	0.9973	0.9883	0.9657	0.9218	0.8513	0.7535	0.6331	0.5000
	6	1.0000	1.0000	1.0000	0.9997	0.9980	0.9924	0.9784	0.9499	0.9006	0.8262	0.7256
	7	1.0000	1.0000	1.0000	1.0000	0.9998	0.9988	0.9957	0.9878	0.9707	0.9390	0.8867
	8	1.0000	1.0000	1.0000	1.0000	1.0000	0.9999	0.9994	0.9980	0.9941	0.9852	0.9673
	9	1.0000	1.0000	1.0000	1.0000	1.0000	1.0000	1.0000	0.9998	0.9993	0.9978	0.9941
	10	1.0000	1.0000	1.0000	1.0000	1.0000	1.0000	1.0000	1.0000	1.0000	0.9998	0.9995
	11	1.0000	1.0000	1.0000	1.0000	1.0000	1.0000	1.0000	1.0000	1.0000	1.0000	1.0000
12	0	0.8864	0.5404	0.2824	0.1422	0.0687	0.0317	0.0138	0.0057	0.0022	0.0008	0.0002
	1	0.9938	0.8816	0.6590	0.4435	0.2749	0.1584	0.0850	0.0424	0.0196	0.0083	0.0032
	2	0.9998	0.9804	0.8891	0.7358	0.5583	0.3907	0.2528	0.1513	0.0834	0.0421	0.0193
	3	1.0000	0.9978	0.9744	0.9078	0.7946	0.6488	0.4925	0.3467	0.2253	0.1345	0.0730
	4	1.0000	0.9998	0.9957	0.9761	0.9274	0.8424	0.7237	0.5833	0.4382	0.3044	0.1938
	5	1.0000	1.0000	0.9995	0.9954	0.9806	0.9456	0.8822	0.7873	0.6652	0.5269	0.3872
	6	1.0000	1.0000	0.9999	0.9993	0.9961	0.9857	0.9614	0.9154	0.8418	0.7393	0.6128
	7	1.0000	1.0000	1.0000	0.9999	0.9994	0.9972	0.9905	0.9745	0.9427	0.8883	0.8062
	8	1.0000	1.0000	1.0000	1.0000	0.9999	0.9996	0.9983	0.9944	0.9847	0.9644	0.9270
	9	1.0000	1.0000	1.0000	1.0000	1.0000	1.0000	0.9998	0.9992	0.9972	0.9921	0.9807
	10	1.0000	1.0000	1.0000	1.0000	1.0000	1.0000	1.0000	0.9999	0.9997	0.9989	0.9968
	11	1.0000	1.0000	1.0000	1.0000	1.0000	1.0000	1.0000	1.0000	1.0000	0.9999	0.9998
	12	1.0000	1.0000	1.0000	1.0000	1.0000	1.0000	1.0000	1.0000	1.0000	1.0000	1.0000

n = 13

x											
0	0.8775	0.5133	0.2542	0.1209	0.0550	0.0238	0.0097	0.0037	0.0013	0.0004	0.0001
1	0.9928	0.8646	0.6213	0.3983	0.2336	0.1267	0.0637	0.0296	0.0126	0.0049	0.0017
2	0.9997	0.9755	0.8661	0.6920	0.5017	0.3326	0.2025	0.1132	0.0579	0.0269	0.0112
3	1.0000	0.9969	0.9658	0.8820	0.7473	0.5843	0.4206	0.2783	0.1686	0.0929	0.0461
4	1.0000	0.9997	0.9935	0.9658	0.9009	0.7940	0.6543	0.5005	0.3530	0.2279	0.1334
5	1.0000	1.0000	0.9991	0.9925	0.9700	0.9198	0.8346	0.7159	0.5744	0.4268	0.2905
6	1.0000	1.0000	0.9999	0.9987	0.9930	0.9757	0.9376	0.8705	0.7712	0.6437	0.5000
7	1.0000	1.0000	1.0000	0.9998	0.9988	0.9944	0.9818	0.9538	0.9023	0.8212	0.7095
8	1.0000	1.0000	1.0000	1.0000	0.9998	0.9990	0.9960	0.9874	0.9679	0.9302	0.8666
9	1.0000	1.0000	1.0000	1.0000	1.0000	0.9999	0.9993	0.9975	0.9922	0.9797	0.9539
10	1.0000	1.0000	1.0000	1.0000	1.0000	1.0000	0.9999	0.9997	0.9987	0.9959	0.9888
11	1.0000	1.0000	1.0000	1.0000	1.0000	1.0000	1.0000	1.0000	0.9999	0.9995	0.9983
12	1.0000	1.0000	1.0000	1.0000	1.0000	1.0000	1.0000	1.0000	1.0000	1.0000	0.9999
13	1.0000	1.0000	1.0000	1.0000	1.0000	1.0000	1.0000	1.0000	1.0000	1.0000	1.0000

n = 14

x											
0	0.8687	0.4877	0.2288	0.1028	0.0440	0.0178	0.0068	0.0024	0.0008	0.0002	0.0001
1	0.9916	0.8470	0.5846	0.3567	0.1979	0.1010	0.0475	0.0205	0.0081	0.0029	0.0009
2	0.9997	0.9699	0.8416	0.6479	0.4481	0.2811	0.1608	0.0839	0.0398	0.0170	0.0065
3	1.0000	0.9958	0.9559	0.8535	0.6982	0.5213	0.3552	0.2205	0.1243	0.0632	0.0287
4	1.0000	0.9996	0.9908	0.9533	0.8702	0.7415	0.5842	0.4227	0.2793	0.1672	0.0898
5	1.0000	1.0000	0.9985	0.9885	0.9561	0.8883	0.7805	0.6405	0.4859	0.3373	0.2120
6	1.0000	1.0000	0.9998	0.9978	0.9884	0.9617	0.9067	0.8164	0.6925	0.5461	0.3953
7	1.0000	1.0000	1.0000	0.9997	0.9976	0.9897	0.9685	0.9247	0.8499	0.7414	0.6047
8	1.0000	1.0000	1.0000	1.0000	0.9996	0.9978	0.9917	0.9757	0.9417	0.8811	0.7880
9	1.0000	1.0000	1.0000	1.0000	1.0000	0.9997	0.9983	0.9940	0.9825	0.9574	0.9102
10	1.0000	1.0000	1.0000	1.0000	1.0000	1.0000	0.9998	0.9989	0.9961	0.9886	0.9713
11	1.0000	1.0000	1.0000	1.0000	1.0000	1.0000	1.0000	0.9999	0.9994	0.9978	0.9935
12	1.0000	1.0000	1.0000	1.0000	1.0000	1.0000	1.0000	1.0000	0.9999	0.9997	0.9991
13	1.0000	1.0000	1.0000	1.0000	1.0000	1.0000	1.0000	1.0000	1.0000	1.0000	0.9999
14	1.0000	1.0000	1.0000	1.0000	1.0000	1.0000	1.0000	1.0000	1.0000	1.0000	1.0000

TABLE A (continued)   Values of the binomial cumulative distribution function

n	x						p					
		0.01	0.05	0.10	0.15	0.20	0.25	0.30	0.35	0.40	0.45	0.50
15	0	0.8601	0.4633	0.2059	0.0874	0.0352	0.0134	0.0047	0.0016	0.0005	0.0001	0.0000
	1	0.9904	0.8290	0.5490	0.3186	0.1671	0.0802	0.0353	0.0142	0.0052	0.0017	0.0005
	2	0.9996	0.9638	0.8159	0.6042	0.3980	0.2361	0.1268	0.0617	0.0271	0.0107	0.0037
	3	1.0000	0.9945	0.9444	0.8227	0.6482	0.4613	0.2969	0.1727	0.0905	0.0424	0.0176
	4	1.0000	0.9994	0.9873	0.9383	0.8358	0.6865	0.5155	0.3519	0.2173	0.1204	0.0592
	5	1.0000	0.9999	0.9978	0.9832	0.9389	0.8516	0.7216	0.5643	0.4032	0.2608	0.1509
	6	1.0000	1.0000	0.9997	0.9964	0.9819	0.9434	0.8689	0.7548	0.6098	0.4522	0.3036
	7	1.0000	1.0000	1.0000	0.9994	0.9958	0.9827	0.9500	0.8868	0.7869	0.6535	0.5000
	8	1.0000	1.0000	1.0000	0.9999	0.9992	0.9958	0.9848	0.9578	0.9050	0.8182	0.6964
	9	1.0000	1.0000	1.0000	1.0000	0.9999	0.9992	0.9963	0.9876	0.9662	0.9231	0.8491
	10	1.0000	1.0000	1.0000	1.0000	1.0000	0.9999	0.9993	0.9972	0.9907	0.9745	0.9408
	11	1.0000	1.0000	1.0000	1.0000	1.0000	1.0000	0.9999	0.9995	0.9981	0.9937	0.9824
	12	1.0000	1.0000	1.0000	1.0000	1.0000	1.0000	1.0000	1.0000	0.9997	0.9989	0.9963
	13	1.0000	1.0000	1.0000	1.0000	1.0000	1.0000	1.0000	1.0000	1.0000	0.9999	0.9995
	14	1.0000	1.0000	1.0000	1.0000	1.0000	1.0000	1.0000	1.0000	1.0000	1.0000	1.0000
	15	1.0000	1.0000	1.0000	1.0000	1.0000	1.0000	1.0000	1.0000	1.0000	1.0000	1.0000
16	0	0.8515	0.4401	0.1853	0.0743	0.0281	0.0100	0.0033	0.0010	0.0003	0.0001	0.0000
	1	0.9891	0.8108	0.5147	0.2839	0.1407	0.0635	0.0261	0.0098	0.0033	0.0010	0.0003
	2	0.9995	0.9571	0.7893	0.5614	0.3518	0.1971	0.0994	0.0451	0.0183	0.0066	0.0021
	3	1.0000	0.9930	0.9316	0.7899	0.5981	0.4050	0.2459	0.1339	0.0651	0.0281	0.0106
	4	1.0000	0.9991	0.9830	0.9209	0.7982	0.6302	0.4499	0.2892	0.1666	0.0853	0.0384
	5	1.0000	0.9999	0.9967	0.9765	0.9183	0.8103	0.6598	0.4900	0.3288	0.1976	0.1051
	6	1.0000	1.0000	0.9995	0.9944	0.9733	0.9204	0.8247	0.6881	0.5272	0.3660	0.2272
	7	1.0000	1.0000	0.9999	0.9989	0.9930	0.9729	0.9256	0.8406	0.7161	0.5629	0.4018
	8	1.0000	1.0000	1.0000	0.9998	0.9985	0.9925	0.9743	0.9329	0.8577	0.7441	0.5982
	9	1.0000	1.0000	1.0000	1.0000	0.9998	0.9984	0.9929	0.9771	0.9417	0.8759	0.7728
	10	1.0000	1.0000	1.0000	1.0000	1.0000	0.9997	0.9984	0.9938	0.9809	0.9514	0.8949
	11	1.0000	1.0000	1.0000	1.0000	1.0000	1.0000	0.9997	0.9987	0.9951	0.9851	0.9616
	12	1.0000	1.0000	1.0000	1.0000	1.0000	1.0000	1.0000	0.9998	0.9991	0.9965	0.9894
	13	1.0000	1.0000	1.0000	1.0000	1.0000	1.0000	1.0000	1.0000	0.9999	0.9994	0.9979
	14	1.0000	1.0000	1.0000	1.0000	1.0000	1.0000	1.0000	1.0000	1.0000	0.9999	0.9997
	15	1.0000	1.0000	1.0000	1.0000	1.0000	1.0000	1.0000	1.0000	1.0000	1.0000	1.0000
	16	1.0000	1.0000	1.0000	1.0000	1.0000	1.0000	1.0000	1.0000	1.0000	1.0000	1.0000

17

k											
0	0.0000	0.0000	0.0002	0.0007	0.0023	0.0075	0.0225	0.0631	0.1668	0.4181	0.8429
1	0.0001	0.0006	0.0021	0.0067	0.0193	0.0501	0.1182	0.2525	0.4818	0.7922	0.9877
2	0.0012	0.0041	0.0123	0.0327	0.0774	0.1637	0.3096	0.5198	0.7618	0.9497	0.9994
3	0.0064	0.0184	0.0464	0.1028	0.2019	0.3530	0.5489	0.7556	0.9174	0.9912	1.0000
4	0.0245	0.0596	0.1260	0.2348	0.3887	0.5739	0.7582	0.9013	0.9779	0.9988	1.0000
5	0.0717	0.1471	0.2639	0.4197	0.5968	0.7653	0.8943	0.9681	0.9953	0.9999	1.0000
6	0.1662	0.2902	0.4478	0.6188	0.7752	0.8929	0.9623	0.9917	0.9992	1.0000	1.0000
7	0.3145	0.4743	0.6405	0.7872	0.8954	0.9598	0.9891	0.9983	0.9999	1.0000	1.0000
8	0.5000	0.6626	0.8011	0.9006	0.9597	0.9876	0.9974	0.9997	1.0000	1.0000	1.0000
9	0.6855	0.8166	0.9081	0.9617	0.9873	0.9969	0.9995	1.0000	1.0000	1.0000	1.0000
10	0.8338	0.9174	0.9652	0.9880	0.9968	0.9994	0.9999	1.0000	1.0000	1.0000	1.0000
11	0.9283	0.9699	0.9894	0.9970	0.9993	0.9999	1.0000	1.0000	1.0000	1.0000	1.0000
12	0.9755	0.9914	0.9975	0.9994	0.9999	1.0000	1.0000	1.0000	1.0000	1.0000	1.0000
13	0.9936	0.9981	0.9995	0.9999	1.0000	1.0000	1.0000	1.0000	1.0000	1.0000	1.0000
14	0.9988	0.9997	0.9999	1.0000	1.0000	1.0000	1.0000	1.0000	1.0000	1.0000	1.0000
15	0.9999	1.0000	1.0000	1.0000	1.0000	1.0000	1.0000	1.0000	1.0000	1.0000	1.0000
16	1.0000	1.0000	1.0000	1.0000	1.0000	1.0000	1.0000	1.0000	1.0000	1.0000	1.0000
17	1.0000	1.0000	1.0000	1.0000	1.0000	1.0000	1.0000	1.0000	1.0000	1.0000	1.0000

18

k											
0	0.0000	0.0000	0.0001	0.0004	0.0016	0.0056	0.0180	0.0536	0.1501	0.3972	0.8345
1	0.0001	0.0003	0.0013	0.0046	0.0142	0.0395	0.0991	0.2241	0.4503	0.7735	0.9862
2	0.0007	0.0025	0.0082	0.0236	0.0600	0.1353	0.2713	0.4797	0.7338	0.9419	0.9993
3	0.0038	0.0120	0.0328	0.0783	0.1646	0.3057	0.5010	0.7202	0.9018	0.9891	1.0000
4	0.0154	0.0411	0.0942	0.1886	0.3327	0.5187	0.7164	0.8794	0.9718	0.9985	1.0000
5	0.0481	0.1077	0.2088	0.3550	0.5344	0.7175	0.8671	0.9581	0.9936	0.9998	1.0000
6	0.1189	0.2258	0.3743	0.5491	0.7217	0.8610	0.9487	0.9882	0.9988	1.0000	1.0000
7	0.2403	0.3915	0.5634	0.7283	0.8593	0.9431	0.9837	0.9973	0.9998	1.0000	1.0000
8	0.4073	0.5778	0.7368	0.8609	0.9404	0.9807	0.9957	0.9995	1.0000	1.0000	1.0000
9	0.5927	0.7473	0.8653	0.9403	0.9790	0.9946	0.9991	0.9999	1.0000	1.0000	1.0000
10	0.7597	0.8720	0.9424	0.9788	0.9939	0.9988	0.9998	1.0000	1.0000	1.0000	1.0000
11	0.8811	0.9463	0.9797	0.9938	0.9986	0.9998	1.0000	1.0000	1.0000	1.0000	1.0000
12	0.9519	0.9817	0.9942	0.9986	0.9997	1.0000	1.0000	1.0000	1.0000	1.0000	1.0000
13	0.9846	0.9951	0.9987	0.9997	1.0000	1.0000	1.0000	1.0000	1.0000	1.0000	1.0000
14	0.9962	0.9990	0.9998	1.0000	1.0000	1.0000	1.0000	1.0000	1.0000	1.0000	1.0000
15	0.9993	0.9999	1.0000	1.0000	1.0000	1.0000	1.0000	1.0000	1.0000	1.0000	1.0000
16	0.9999	1.0000	1.0000	1.0000	1.0000	1.0000	1.0000	1.0000	1.0000	1.0000	1.0000
17	1.0000	1.0000	1.0000	1.0000	1.0000	1.0000	1.0000	1.0000	1.0000	1.0000	1.0000
18	1.0000	1.0000	1.0000	1.0000	1.0000	1.0000	1.0000	1.0000	1.0000	1.0000	1.0000

TABLE A (continued)   Values of the binomial cumulative distribution function

n	x	p 0.01	0.05	0.10	0.15	0.20	0.25	0.30	0.35	0.40	0.45	0.50
19	0	0.8262	0.3774	0.1351	0.0456	0.0144	0.0042	0.0011	0.0003	0.0001	0.0000	0.0000
	1	0.9847	0.7547	0.4203	0.1985	0.0829	0.0310	0.0104	0.0031	0.0008	0.0002	0.0000
	2	0.9991	0.9335	0.7054	0.4413	0.2369	0.1113	0.0462	0.0170	0.0055	0.0015	0.0004
	3	1.0000	0.9868	0.8850	0.6841	0.4551	0.2631	0.1332	0.0591	0.0230	0.0077	0.0022
	4	1.0000	0.9980	0.9648	0.8556	0.6733	0.4654	0.2822	0.1500	0.0696	0.0280	0.0096
	5	1.0000	0.9998	0.9914	0.9463	0.8369	0.6678	0.4739	0.2968	0.1629	0.0777	0.0318
	6	1.0000	1.0000	0.9983	0.9837	0.9324	0.8251	0.6655	0.4812	0.3081	0.1727	0.0835
	7	1.0000	1.0000	0.9997	0.9959	0.9767	0.9225	0.8180	0.6656	0.4878	0.3169	0.1796
	8	1.0000	1.0000	1.0000	0.9992	0.9933	0.9713	0.9161	0.8145	0.6675	0.4940	0.3238
	9	1.0000	1.0000	1.0000	0.9999	0.9984	0.9911	0.9674	0.9125	0.8139	0.6710	0.5000
	10	1.0000	1.0000	1.0000	1.0000	0.9997	0.9977	0.9895	0.9653	0.9115	0.8159	0.6762
	11	1.0000	1.0000	1.0000	1.0000	1.0000	0.9995	0.9972	0.9886	0.9648	0.9129	0.8204
	12	1.0000	1.0000	1.0000	1.0000	1.0000	0.9999	0.9994	0.9969	0.9884	0.9658	0.9165
	13	1.0000	1.0000	1.0000	1.0000	1.0000	1.0000	0.9999	0.9993	0.9969	0.9891	0.9682
	14	1.0000	1.0000	1.0000	1.0000	1.0000	1.0000	1.0000	0.9999	0.9994	0.9972	0.9904
	15	1.0000	1.0000	1.0000	1.0000	1.0000	1.0000	1.0000	1.0000	0.9999	0.9995	0.9978
	16	1.0000	1.0000	1.0000	1.0000	1.0000	1.0000	1.0000	1.0000	1.0000	0.9999	0.9996
	17	1.0000	1.0000	1.0000	1.0000	1.0000	1.0000	1.0000	1.0000	1.0000	1.0000	1.0000
	18	1.0000	1.0000	1.0000	1.0000	1.0000	1.0000	1.0000	1.0000	1.0000	1.0000	1.0000
	19	1.0000	1.0000	1.0000	1.0000	1.0000	1.0000	1.0000	1.0000	1.0000	1.0000	1.0000
20	0	0.8179	0.3585	0.1216	0.0388	0.0115	0.0032	0.0008	0.0002	0.0000	0.0000	0.0000
	1	0.9831	0.7358	0.3917	0.1756	0.0692	0.0243	0.0076	0.0021	0.0005	0.0001	0.0000
	2	0.9990	0.9245	0.6769	0.4049	0.2061	0.0913	0.0355	0.0121	0.0036	0.0009	0.0002
	3	1.0000	0.9841	0.8670	0.6477	0.4114	0.2252	0.1071	0.0444	0.0160	0.0049	0.0013
	4	1.0000	0.9974	0.9568	0.8298	0.6296	0.4148	0.2375	0.1182	0.0510	0.0189	0.0059
	5	1.0000	0.9997	0.9887	0.9327	0.8042	0.6172	0.4164	0.2454	0.1256	0.0553	0.0207
	6	1.0000	1.0000	0.9976	0.9781	0.9133	0.7858	0.6080	0.4166	0.2500	0.1299	0.0577
	7	1.0000	1.0000	0.9996	0.9941	0.9679	0.8982	0.7723	0.6010	0.4159	0.2520	0.1316
	8	1.0000	1.0000	0.9999	0.9987	0.9900	0.9591	0.8867	0.7624	0.5956	0.4143	0.2517
	9	1.0000	1.0000	1.0000	0.9998	0.9974	0.9861	0.9520	0.8782	0.7553	0.5914	0.4119
	10	1.0000	1.0000	1.0000	1.0000	0.9994	0.9961	0.9829	0.9468	0.8725	0.7507	0.5881

n = 25

k											
11	1.0000	1.0000	1.0000	1.0000	0.9999	0.9991	0.9949	0.9804	0.9435	0.8692	0.7483
12	1.0000	1.0000	1.0000	1.0000	1.0000	0.9998	0.9987	0.9940	0.9790	0.9420	0.8684
13	1.0000	1.0000	1.0000	1.0000	1.0000	1.0000	0.9997	0.9985	0.9935	0.9786	0.9423
14	1.0000	1.0000	1.0000	1.0000	1.0000	1.0000	1.0000	0.9997	0.9984	0.9936	0.9793
15	1.0000	1.0000	1.0000	1.0000	1.0000	1.0000	1.0000	1.0000	0.9997	0.9985	0.9941
16	1.0000	1.0000	1.0000	1.0000	1.0000	1.0000	1.0000	1.0000	1.0000	0.9997	0.9987
17	1.0000	1.0000	1.0000	1.0000	1.0000	1.0000	1.0000	1.0000	1.0000	1.0000	0.9998
18	1.0000	1.0000	1.0000	1.0000	1.0000	1.0000	1.0000	1.0000	1.0000	1.0000	1.0000
19	1.0000	1.0000	1.0000	1.0000	1.0000	1.0000	1.0000	1.0000	1.0000	1.0000	1.0000
20	1.0000	1.0000	1.0000	1.0000	1.0000	1.0000	1.0000	1.0000	1.0000	1.0000	1.0000

n = 25

k											
0	0.7778	0.2774	0.0718	0.0172	0.0038	0.0008	0.0001	0.0000	0.0000	0.0000	0.0000
1	0.9742	0.6424	0.2712	0.0931	0.0274	0.0070	0.0016	0.0003	0.0001	0.0000	0.0000
2	0.9980	0.8729	0.5371	0.2537	0.0982	0.0321	0.0090	0.0021	0.0004	0.0001	0.0000
3	0.9999	0.9659	0.7636	0.4711	0.2340	0.0962	0.0332	0.0097	0.0024	0.0005	0.0001
4	1.0000	0.9928	0.9020	0.6821	0.4207	0.2137	0.0905	0.0320	0.0095	0.0023	0.0005
5	1.0000	0.9988	0.9666	0.8385	0.6167	0.3783	0.1935	0.0826	0.0294	0.0086	0.0020
6	1.0000	0.9998	0.9905	0.9305	0.7800	0.5611	0.3407	0.1734	0.0736	0.0258	0.0073
7	1.0000	1.0000	0.9977	0.9745	0.8909	0.7265	0.5118	0.3061	0.1536	0.0639	0.0216
8	1.0000	1.0000	0.9995	0.9920	0.9532	0.8506	0.6769	0.4668	0.2735	0.1340	0.0539
9	1.0000	1.0000	0.9999	0.9979	0.9827	0.9287	0.8106	0.6303	0.4246	0.2424	0.1148
10	1.0000	1.0000	1.0000	0.9995	0.9944	0.9703	0.9022	0.7712	0.5858	0.3843	0.2122
11	1.0000	1.0000	1.0000	0.9999	0.9985	0.9893	0.9558	0.8746	0.7323	0.5426	0.3450
12	1.0000	1.0000	1.0000	1.0000	0.9996	0.9966	0.9825	0.9396	0.8462	0.6937	0.5000
13	1.0000	1.0000	1.0000	1.0000	0.9999	0.9991	0.9940	0.9745	0.9222	0.8173	0.6550
14	1.0000	1.0000	1.0000	1.0000	1.0000	0.9998	0.9982	0.9907	0.9656	0.9040	0.7878
15	1.0000	1.0000	1.0000	1.0000	1.0000	1.0000	0.9995	0.9971	0.9868	0.9560	0.8852
16	1.0000	1.0000	1.0000	1.0000	1.0000	1.0000	0.9999	0.9992	0.9957	0.9826	0.9461
17	1.0000	1.0000	1.0000	1.0000	1.0000	1.0000	1.0000	0.9998	0.9988	0.9942	0.9784
18	1.0000	1.0000	1.0000	1.0000	1.0000	1.0000	1.0000	1.0000	0.9997	0.9984	0.9927
19	1.0000	1.0000	1.0000	1.0000	1.0000	1.0000	1.0000	1.0000	0.9999	0.9996	0.9980
20	1.0000	1.0000	1.0000	1.0000	1.0000	1.0000	1.0000	1.0000	1.0000	0.9999	0.9995
21	1.0000	1.0000	1.0000	1.0000	1.0000	1.0000	1.0000	1.0000	1.0000	1.0000	0.9999
22	1.0000	1.0000	1.0000	1.0000	1.0000	1.0000	1.0000	1.0000	1.0000	1.0000	1.0000
23	1.0000	1.0000	1.0000	1.0000	1.0000	1.0000	1.0000	1.0000	1.0000	1.0000	1.0000
24	1.0000	1.0000	1.0000	1.0000	1.0000	1.0000	1.0000	1.0000	1.0000	1.0000	1.0000
25	1.0000	1.0000	1.0000	1.0000	1.0000	1.0000	1.0000	1.0000	1.0000	1.0000	1.0000

TABLE B   Values of the Poisson cumulative distribution function

$$P(X \le x) = F(x; \lambda) = \sum_{i=0}^{x} \frac{e^{-\lambda}\lambda^i}{i!}$$

					λ					
x	0.1	0.2	0.3	0.4	0.5	0.6	0.7	0.8	0.9	1.0
0	0.9048	0.8187	0.7408	0.6703	0.6065	0.5488	0.4966	0.4493	0.4066	0.3679
1	0.9953	0.9825	0.9631	0.9384	0.9098	0.8781	0.8442	0.8088	0.7725	0.7358
2	0.9998	0.9989	0.9964	0.9921	0.9856	0.9769	0.9659	0.9526	0.9371	0.9197
3	1.0000	0.9999	0.9997	0.9992	0.9982	0.9966	0.9942	0.9909	0.9865	0.9810
4	1.0000	1.0000	1.0000	0.9999	0.9998	0.9996	0.9992	0.9986	0.9977	0.9963
5	1.0000	1.0000	1.0000	1.0000	1.0000	1.0000	0.9999	0.9998	0.9997	0.9994
6	1.0000	1.0000	1.0000	1.0000	1.0000	1.0000	1.0000	1.0000	1.0000	0.9999
7	1.0000	1.0000	1.0000	1.0000	1.0000	1.0000	1.0000	1.0000	1.0000	1.0000

					λ					
x	1.1	1.2	1.3	1.4	1.5	1.6	1.7	1.8	1.9	2.0
0	0.3329	0.3012	0.2725	0.2466	0.2231	0.2019	0.1827	0.1653	0.1496	0.1353
1	0.6990	0.6626	0.6268	0.5918	0.5578	0.5249	0.4932	0.4628	0.4338	0.4060
2	0.9004	0.8795	0.8571	0.8335	0.8088	0.7834	0.7572	0.7306	0.7037	0.6767
3	0.9743	0.9662	0.9569	0.9463	0.9344	0.9212	0.9068	0.8913	0.8747	0.8571
4	0.9946	0.9923	0.9893	0.9857	0.9814	0.9763	0.9704	0.9636	0.9559	0.9473
5	0.9990	0.9985	0.9978	0.9968	0.9955	0.9940	0.9920	0.9896	0.9868	0.9834
6	0.9999	0.9997	0.9996	0.9994	0.9991	0.9987	0.9981	0.9974	0.9966	0.9955
7	1.0000	1.0000	0.9999	0.9999	0.9998	0.9997	0.9996	0.9994	0.9992	0.9989
8	1.0000	1.0000	1.0000	1.0000	1.0000	1.0000	0.9999	0.9999	0.9998	0.9998
9	1.0000	1.0000	1.0000	1.0000	1.0000	1.0000	1.0000	1.0000	1.0000	1.0000

λ

x	2.1	2.2	2.3	2.4	2.5	2.6	2.7	2.8	2.9	3.0
0	0.1225	0.1108	0.1003	0.0907	0.0821	0.0743	0.0672	0.0608	0.0550	0.0498
1	0.3796	0.3546	0.3309	0.3084	0.2873	0.2674	0.2487	0.2311	0.2146	0.1991
2	0.6496	0.6227	0.5960	0.5697	0.5438	0.5184	0.4936	0.4695	0.4460	0.4232
3	0.8386	0.8194	0.7993	0.7787	0.7576	0.7360	0.7141	0.6919	0.6696	0.6472
4	0.9379	0.9275	0.9163	0.9041	0.8912	0.8774	0.8629	0.8477	0.8318	0.8153
5	0.9796	0.9751	0.9700	0.9643	0.9580	0.9510	0.9433	0.9349	0.9258	0.9161
6	0.9941	0.9925	0.9906	0.9884	0.9858	0.9828	0.9794	0.9756	0.9713	0.9665
7	0.9985	0.9980	0.9974	0.9967	0.9958	0.9947	0.9934	0.9919	0.9901	0.9881
8	0.9997	0.9995	0.9994	0.9991	0.9989	0.9985	0.9981	0.9976	0.9969	0.9962
9	0.9999	0.9999	0.9999	0.9998	0.9997	0.9996	0.9995	0.9993	0.9991	0.9989
10	1.0000	1.0000	1.0000	1.0000	0.9999	0.9999	0.9999	0.9998	0.9998	0.9997
11	1.0000	1.0000	1.0000	1.0000	1.0000	1.0000	1.0000	1.0000	0.9999	0.9999

λ

x	3.1	3.2	3.3	3.4	3.5	3.6	3.7	3.8	3.9	4.0
0	0.0450	0.0408	0.0369	0.0334	0.0302	0.0273	0.0247	0.0224	0.0202	0.0183
1	0.1847	0.1712	0.1586	0.1468	0.1359	0.1257	0.1162	0.1074	0.0992	0.0916
2	0.4012	0.3799	0.3594	0.3397	0.3208	0.3027	0.2854	0.2689	0.2531	0.2381
3	0.6248	0.6025	0.5803	0.5584	0.5366	0.5152	0.4942	0.4735	0.4533	0.4335
4	0.7982	0.7806	0.7626	0.7442	0.7254	0.7064	0.6872	0.6678	0.6484	0.6288
5	0.9057	0.8946	0.8829	0.8705	0.8576	0.8441	0.8301	0.8156	0.8006	0.7851
6	0.9612	0.9554	0.9490	0.9421	0.9347	0.9267	0.9182	0.9091	0.8995	0.8893
7	0.9858	0.9832	0.9802	0.9769	0.9733	0.9692	0.9648	0.9599	0.9546	0.9489
8	0.9953	0.9943	0.9931	0.9917	0.9901	0.9883	0.9863	0.9840	0.9815	0.9786
9	0.9986	0.9982	0.9978	0.9973	0.9967	0.9960	0.9952	0.9942	0.9931	0.9919
10	0.9996	0.9995	0.9994	0.9992	0.9990	0.9987	0.9984	0.9981	0.9977	0.9972
11	0.9999	0.9999	0.9998	0.9998	0.9997	0.9996	0.9995	0.9994	0.9993	0.9991
12	1.0000	1.0000	1.0000	0.9999	0.9999	0.9999	0.9999	0.9998	0.9998	0.9997
13	1.0000	1.0000	1.0000	1.0000	1.0000	1.0000	1.0000	1.0000	0.9999	0.9999

TABLE B (continued) Values of the Poisson cumulative distribution function

λ

x	4.1	4.2	4.3	4.4	4.5	4.6	4.7	4.8	4.9	5.0
0	0.0166	0.0150	0.0136	0.0123	0.0111	0.0101	0.0091	0.0082	0.0074	0.0067
1	0.0845	0.0780	0.0719	0.0663	0.0611	0.0563	0.0518	0.0477	0.0439	0.0404
2	0.2238	0.2102	0.1974	0.1851	0.1736	0.1626	0.1523	0.1425	0.1333	0.1247
3	0.4142	0.3954	0.3772	0.3595	0.3423	0.3257	0.3097	0.2942	0.2793	0.2650
4	0.6093	0.5898	0.5704	0.5512	0.5321	0.5132	0.4946	0.4763	0.4582	0.4405
5	0.7693	0.7531	0.7367	0.7199	0.7029	0.6858	0.6684	0.6510	0.6335	0.6160
6	0.8787	0.8675	0.8558	0.8436	0.8311	0.8180	0.8046	0.7908	0.7767	0.7622
7	0.9427	0.9361	0.9290	0.9214	0.9134	0.9050	0.8960	0.8867	0.8769	0.8666
8	0.9755	0.9721	0.9683	0.9642	0.9597	0.9549	0.9497	0.9442	0.9382	0.9319
9	0.9905	0.9889	0.9871	0.9851	0.9829	0.9805	0.9778	0.9749	0.9717	0.9682
10	0.9966	0.9959	0.9952	0.9943	0.9933	0.9922	0.9910	0.9896	0.9880	0.9863
11	0.9989	0.9986	0.9983	0.9980	0.9976	0.9971	0.9966	0.9960	0.9953	0.9945
12	0.9997	0.9996	0.9995	0.9993	0.9992	0.9990	0.9988	0.9986	0.9983	0.9980
13	0.9999	0.9999	0.9998	0.9998	0.9997	0.9997	0.9996	0.9995	0.9994	0.9993
14	1.0000	1.0000	1.0000	0.9999	0.9999	0.9999	0.9999	0.9999	0.9998	0.9998
15	1.0000	1.0000	1.0000	1.0000	1.0000	1.0000	1.0000	1.0000	0.9999	0.9999

λ

x	5.1	5.2	5.3	5.4	5.5	5.6	5.7	5.8	5.9	6.0
0	0.0061	0.0055	0.0050	0.0045	0.0041	0.0037	0.0033	0.0030	0.0027	0.0025
1	0.0372	0.0342	0.0314	0.0289	0.0266	0.0244	0.0224	0.0206	0.0189	0.0174
2	0.1165	0.1088	0.1016	0.0948	0.0884	0.0824	0.0768	0.0715	0.0666	0.0620
3	0.2513	0.2381	0.2254	0.2133	0.2017	0.1906	0.1801	0.1700	0.1604	0.1512
4	0.4231	0.4061	0.3895	0.3733	0.3575	0.3422	0.3272	0.3127	0.2987	0.2851
5	0.5984	0.5809	0.5635	0.5461	0.5289	0.5119	0.4950	0.4783	0.4619	0.4457
6	0.7474	0.7324	0.7171	0.7017	0.6860	0.6703	0.6544	0.6384	0.6224	0.6063
7	0.8560	0.8449	0.8335	0.8217	0.8095	0.7970	0.7842	0.7710	0.7576	0.7440
8	0.9252	0.9181	0.9106	0.9027	0.8944	0.8857	0.8766	0.8672	0.8574	0.8472
9	0.9644	0.9603	0.9559	0.9512	0.9462	0.9409	0.9352	0.9292	0.9228	0.9161
10	0.9844	0.9823	0.9800	0.9775	0.9747	0.9718	0.9686	0.9651	0.9614	0.9574
11	0.9937	0.9927	0.9916	0.9904	0.9890	0.9875	0.9859	0.9841	0.9821	0.9799
12	0.9976	0.9972	0.9967	0.9962	0.9955	0.9949	0.9941	0.9932	0.9922	0.9912
13	0.9992	0.9990	0.9988	0.9986	0.9983	0.9980	0.9977	0.9973	0.9969	0.9964
14	0.9997	0.9997	0.9996	0.9995	0.9994	0.9993	0.9991	0.9990	0.9988	0.9986
15	0.9999	0.9999	0.9999	0.9998	0.9998	0.9998	0.9997	0.9996	0.9996	0.9995
16	1.0000	1.0000	1.0000	0.9999	0.9999	0.9999	0.9999	0.9999	0.9999	0.9998
17	1.0000	1.0000	1.0000	1.0000	1.0000	1.0000	1.0000	1.0000	1.0000	0.9999

λ

x	6.1	6.2	6.3	6.4	6.5	6.6	6.7	6.8	6.9	7.0
0	0.0022	0.0020	0.0018	0.0017	0.0015	0.0014	0.0012	0.0011	0.0010	0.0009
1	0.0159	0.0146	0.0134	0.0123	0.0113	0.0103	0.0095	0.0087	0.0080	0.0073
2	0.0577	0.0536	0.0498	0.0463	0.0430	0.0400	0.0371	0.0344	0.0320	0.0296
3	0.1425	0.1342	0.1264	0.1189	0.1119	0.1052	0.0988	0.0928	0.0871	0.0818
4	0.2719	0.2592	0.2469	0.2351	0.2237	0.2127	0.2022	0.1920	0.1823	0.1730
5	0.4298	0.4141	0.3988	0.3837	0.3690	0.3547	0.3407	0.3270	0.3137	0.3007
6	0.5902	0.5742	0.5582	0.5423	0.5265	0.5108	0.4953	0.4799	0.4647	0.4497
7	0.7301	0.7160	0.7018	0.6873	0.6728	0.6581	0.6433	0.6285	0.6136	0.5987
8	0.8367	0.8259	0.8148	0.8033	0.7916	0.7796	0.7673	0.7548	0.7420	0.7291
9	0.9090	0.9016	0.8939	0.8858	0.8774	0.8686	0.8596	0.8502	0.8405	0.8305
10	0.9531	0.9486	0.9437	0.9386	0.9332	0.9274	0.9214	0.9151	0.9084	0.9015
11	0.9776	0.9750	0.9723	0.9693	0.9661	0.9627	0.9591	0.9552	0.9510	0.9467
12	0.9900	0.9887	0.9873	0.9857	0.9840	0.9821	0.9801	0.9779	0.9755	0.9730
13	0.9958	0.9952	0.9945	0.9937	0.9929	0.9920	0.9909	0.9898	0.9885	0.9872
14	0.9984	0.9981	0.9978	0.9974	0.9970	0.9966	0.9961	0.9956	0.9950	0.9943
15	0.9994	0.9993	0.9992	0.9990	0.9988	0.9986	0.9984	0.9982	0.9979	0.9976
16	0.9998	0.9997	0.9997	0.9996	0.9996	0.9995	0.9994	0.9993	0.9992	0.9990
17	0.9999	0.9999	0.9999	0.9999	0.9998	0.9998	0.9998	0.9997	0.9997	0.9996
18	1.0000	1.0000	1.0000	1.0000	0.9999	0.9999	0.9999	0.9999	0.9999	0.9999
19	1.0000	1.0000	1.0000	1.0000	1.0000	1.0000	1.0000	1.0000	1.0000	1.0000

TABLE B (continued) Values of the Poisson cumulative distribution function

λ

x	7.1	7.2	7.3	7.4	7.5	7.6	7.7	7.8	7.9	8.0
0	0.0008	0.0007	0.0007	0.0006	0.0006	0.0005	0.0005	0.0004	0.0004	0.0003
1	0.0067	0.0061	0.0056	0.0051	0.0047	0.0043	0.0039	0.0036	0.0033	0.0030
2	0.0275	0.0255	0.0236	0.0219	0.0203	0.0188	0.0174	0.0161	0.0149	0.0138
3	0.0767	0.0719	0.0674	0.0632	0.0591	0.0554	0.0518	0.0485	0.0453	0.0424
4	0.1641	0.1555	0.1473	0.1395	0.1321	0.1249	0.1181	0.1117	0.1055	0.0996
5	0.2881	0.2759	0.2640	0.2526	0.2414	0.2307	0.2203	0.2103	0.2006	0.1912
6	0.4349	0.4204	0.4060	0.3920	0.3782	0.3646	0.3514	0.3384	0.3257	0.3134
7	0.5838	0.5689	0.5541	0.5393	0.5246	0.5100	0.4956	0.4812	0.4670	0.4530
8	0.7160	0.7027	0.6892	0.6757	0.6620	0.6482	0.6343	0.6204	0.6065	0.5926
9	0.8202	0.8097	0.7988	0.7877	0.7764	0.7649	0.7531	0.7411	0.7290	0.7166
10	0.8942	0.8867	0.8788	0.8707	0.8622	0.8535	0.8445	0.8352	0.8257	0.8159
11	0.9420	0.9371	0.9319	0.9265	0.9208	0.9148	0.9085	0.9020	0.8952	0.8881
12	0.9703	0.9673	0.9642	0.9609	0.9573	0.9536	0.9496	0.9454	0.9409	0.9362
13	0.9857	0.9841	0.9824	0.9805	0.9784	0.9762	0.9739	0.9714	0.9687	0.9658
14	0.9935	0.9927	0.9918	0.9908	0.9897	0.9886	0.9873	0.9859	0.9844	0.9827
15	0.9972	0.9969	0.9964	0.9959	0.9954	0.9948	0.9941	0.9934	0.9926	0.9918
16	0.9989	0.9987	0.9985	0.9983	0.9980	0.9978	0.9974	0.9971	0.9967	0.9963
17	0.9996	0.9995	0.9994	0.9993	0.9992	0.9991	0.9989	0.9988	0.9986	0.9984
18	0.9998	0.9998	0.9998	0.9997	0.9997	0.9996	0.9996	0.9995	0.9994	0.9993
19	0.9999	0.9999	0.9999	0.9999	0.9999	0.9999	0.9998	0.9998	0.9998	0.9997
20	1.0000	1.0000	1.0000	1.0000	1.0000	1.0000	0.9999	0.9999	0.9999	0.9999
21	1.0000	1.0000	1.0000	1.0000	1.0000	1.0000	1.0000	1.0000	1.0000	1.0000

λ

x	8.1	8.2	8.3	8.4	8.5	8.6	8.7	8.8	8.9	9.0
0	0.0003	0.0003	0.0002	0.0002	0.0002	0.0002	0.0002	0.0002	0.0001	0.0001
1	0.0028	0.0025	0.0023	0.0021	0.0019	0.0018	0.0016	0.0015	0.0014	0.0012
2	0.0127	0.0118	0.0109	0.0100	0.0093	0.0086	0.0079	0.0073	0.0068	0.0062
3	0.0396	0.0370	0.0346	0.0323	0.0301	0.0281	0.0262	0.0244	0.0228	0.0212
4	0.0941	0.0887	0.0837	0.0789	0.0744	0.0701	0.0660	0.0621	0.0584	0.0550
5	0.1823	0.1736	0.1653	0.1573	0.1496	0.1422	0.1352	0.1284	0.1219	0.1157
6	0.3013	0.2896	0.2781	0.2670	0.2562	0.2457	0.2355	0.2256	0.2160	0.2068
7	0.4391	0.4254	0.4119	0.3987	0.3856	0.3728	0.3602	0.3478	0.3357	0.3239
8	0.5786	0.5647	0.5508	0.5369	0.5231	0.5094	0.4958	0.4823	0.4689	0.4557
9	0.7041	0.6915	0.6788	0.6659	0.6530	0.6400	0.6269	0.6137	0.6006	0.5874
10	0.8058	0.7956	0.7850	0.7743	0.7634	0.7522	0.7409	0.7294	0.7178	0.7060
11	0.8807	0.8731	0.8652	0.8571	0.8487	0.8400	0.8311	0.8220	0.8126	0.8030
12	0.9313	0.9261	0.9207	0.9150	0.9091	0.9029	0.8965	0.8898	0.8829	0.8758
13	0.9628	0.9595	0.9561	0.9524	0.9486	0.9445	0.9403	0.9358	0.9311	0.9262
14	0.9810	0.9791	0.9771	0.9749	0.9726	0.9701	0.9675	0.9647	0.9617	0.9585
15	0.9908	0.9898	0.9887	0.9875	0.9862	0.9848	0.9832	0.9816	0.9798	0.9780
16	0.9958	0.9953	0.9947	0.9941	0.9934	0.9926	0.9918	0.9909	0.9899	0.9889
17	0.9982	0.9979	0.9977	0.9973	0.9970	0.9966	0.9962	0.9957	0.9952	0.9947
18	0.9992	0.9991	0.9990	0.9989	0.9987	0.9985	0.9983	0.9981	0.9978	0.9976
19	0.9997	0.9997	0.9996	0.9995	0.9995	0.9994	0.9993	0.9992	0.9991	0.9989
20	0.9999	0.9999	0.9998	0.9998	0.9998	0.9998	0.9997	0.9997	0.9996	0.9996
21	1.0000	1.0000	0.9999	0.9999	0.9999	0.9999	0.9999	0.9999	0.9998	0.9998
22	1.0000	1.0000	1.0000	1.0000	1.0000	1.0000	1.0000	1.0000	0.9999	0.9999
23	1.0000	1.0000	1.0000	1.0000	1.0000	1.0000	1.0000	1.0000	1.0000	1.0000

TABLE B (continued) Values of the Poisson cumulative distribution function

x	λ									
	9.1	9.2	9.3	9.4	9.5	9.6	9.7	9.8	9.9	10.0
0	0.0001	0.0001	0.0001	0.0001	0.0001	0.0001	0.0001	0.0001	0.0001	0.0000
1	0.0011	0.0010	0.0009	0.0009	0.0008	0.0007	0.0007	0.0006	0.0005	0.0005
2	0.0058	0.0053	0.0049	0.0045	0.0042	0.0038	0.0035	0.0033	0.0030	0.0028
3	0.0198	0.0184	0.0172	0.0160	0.0149	0.0138	0.0129	0.0120	0.0111	0.0103
4	0.0517	0.0486	0.0456	0.0429	0.0403	0.0378	0.0355	0.0333	0.0312	0.0293
5	0.1098	0.1041	0.0987	0.0935	0.0885	0.0838	0.0793	0.0750	0.0710	0.0671
6	0.1978	0.1892	0.1808	0.1727	0.1650	0.1575	0.1502	0.1433	0.1366	0.1301
7	0.3123	0.3010	0.2900	0.2792	0.2687	0.2584	0.2485	0.2388	0.2294	0.2202
8	0.4426	0.4296	0.4168	0.4042	0.3918	0.3796	0.3676	0.3558	0.3442	0.3328
9	0.5742	0.5611	0.5480	0.5349	0.5218	0.5089	0.4960	0.4832	0.4705	0.4579
10	0.6941	0.6820	0.6699	0.6576	0.6453	0.6330	0.6205	0.6081	0.5956	0.5830
11	0.7932	0.7832	0.7730	0.7626	0.7520	0.7412	0.7303	0.7193	0.7081	0.6968
12	0.8684	0.8607	0.8529	0.8448	0.8364	0.8279	0.8191	0.8101	0.8009	0.7916
13	0.9210	0.9156	0.9100	0.9042	0.8981	0.8919	0.8853	0.8786	0.8716	0.8645
14	0.9552	0.9517	0.9480	0.9441	0.9400	0.9357	0.9312	0.9265	0.9216	0.9165
15	0.9760	0.9738	0.9715	0.9691	0.9665	0.9638	0.9609	0.9579	0.9546	0.9513
16	0.9878	0.9865	0.9852	0.9838	0.9823	0.9806	0.9789	0.9770	0.9751	0.9730
17	0.9941	0.9934	0.9927	0.9919	0.9911	0.9902	0.9892	0.9881	0.9870	0.9857
18	0.9973	0.9969	0.9966	0.9962	0.9957	0.9952	0.9947	0.9941	0.9935	0.9928
19	0.9988	0.9986	0.9985	0.9983	0.9980	0.9978	0.9975	0.9972	0.9969	0.9965
20	0.9995	0.9994	0.9993	0.9992	0.9991	0.9990	0.9989	0.9987	0.9986	0.9984
21	0.9998	0.9998	0.9997	0.9997	0.9996	0.9996	0.9995	0.9995	0.9994	0.9993
22	0.9999	0.9999	0.9999	0.9999	0.9999	0.9998	0.9998	0.9998	0.9997	0.9997
23	1.0000	1.0000	1.0000	1.0000	0.9999	0.9999	0.9999	0.9999	0.9999	0.9999
24	1.0000	1.0000	1.0000	1.0000	1.0000	1.0000	1.0000	1.0000	1.0000	1.0000
25	1.0000	1.0000	1.0000	1.0000	1.0000	1.0000	1.0000	1.0000	1.0000	1.0000

λ

x	11.0	12.0	13.0	14.0	15.0	16.0	17.0	18.0	19.0	20.0
0	0.0000	0.0000	0.0000	0.0000	0.0000	0.0000	0.0000	0.0000	0.0000	0.0000
1	0.0002	0.0001	0.0000	0.0000	0.0000	0.0000	0.0000	0.0000	0.0000	0.0000
2	0.0012	0.0005	0.0002	0.0001	0.0000	0.0000	0.0000	0.0000	0.0000	0.0000
3	0.0049	0.0023	0.0011	0.0005	0.0002	0.0001	0.0000	0.0000	0.0000	0.0000
4	0.0151	0.0076	0.0037	0.0018	0.0009	0.0004	0.0002	0.0001	0.0000	0.0000
5	0.0375	0.0203	0.0107	0.0055	0.0028	0.0014	0.0007	0.0003	0.0002	0.0001
6	0.0786	0.0458	0.0259	0.0142	0.0076	0.0040	0.0021	0.0010	0.0005	0.0003
7	0.1432	0.0895	0.0540	0.0316	0.0180	0.0100	0.0054	0.0029	0.0015	0.0008
8	0.2320	0.1550	0.0998	0.0621	0.0374	0.0220	0.0126	0.0071	0.0039	0.0021
9	0.3405	0.2424	0.1658	0.1094	0.0699	0.0433	0.0261	0.0154	0.0089	0.0050
10	0.4599	0.3472	0.2517	0.1757	0.1185	0.0774	0.0491	0.0304	0.0183	0.0108
11	0.5793	0.4616	0.3532	0.2600	0.1848	0.1270	0.0847	0.0549	0.0347	0.0214
12	0.6887	0.5760	0.4631	0.3585	0.2676	0.1931	0.1350	0.0917	0.0606	0.0390
13	0.7813	0.6815	0.5730	0.4644	0.3632	0.2745	0.2009	0.1426	0.0984	0.0661
14	0.8540	0.7720	0.6751	0.5704	0.4657	0.3675	0.2808	0.2081	0.1497	0.1049
15	0.9074	0.8444	0.7636	0.6694	0.5681	0.4667	0.3715	0.2867	0.2148	0.1565
16	0.9441	0.8987	0.8355	0.7559	0.6641	0.5660	0.4677	0.3751	0.2920	0.2211
17	0.9678	0.9370	0.8905	0.8272	0.7489	0.6593	0.5640	0.4686	0.3784	0.2970
18	0.9823	0.9626	0.9302	0.8826	0.8195	0.7423	0.6550	0.5622	0.4695	0.3814
19	0.9907	0.9787	0.9573	0.9235	0.8752	0.8122	0.7363	0.6509	0.5606	0.4703
20	0.9953	0.9884	0.9750	0.9521	0.9170	0.8682	0.8055	0.7307	0.6472	0.5591
21	0.9977	0.9939	0.9859	0.9712	0.9469	0.9108	0.8615	0.7991	0.7255	0.6437
22	0.9990	0.9970	0.9924	0.9833	0.9673	0.9418	0.9047	0.8551	0.7931	0.7206
23	0.9995	0.9985	0.9960	0.9907	0.9805	0.9633	0.9367	0.8989	0.8490	0.7875
24	0.9998	0.9993	0.9980	0.9950	0.9888	0.9777	0.9594	0.9317	0.8933	0.8432
25	0.9999	0.9997	0.9990	0.9974	0.9938	0.9869	0.9748	0.9554	0.9269	0.8878
26	1.0000	0.9999	0.9995	0.9987	0.9967	0.9925	0.9848	0.9718	0.9514	0.9221
27	1.0000	0.9999	0.9998	0.9994	0.9983	0.9959	0.9912	0.9827	0.9687	0.9475
28	1.0000	1.0000	0.9999	0.9997	0.9991	0.9978	0.9950	0.9897	0.9805	0.9657
29	1.0000	1.0000	1.0000	0.9999	0.9996	0.9989	0.9973	0.9941	0.9882	0.9782
30	1.0000	1.0000	1.0000	0.9999	0.9998	0.9994	0.9986	0.9967	0.9930	0.9865
31	1.0000	1.0000	1.0000	1.0000	0.9999	0.9997	0.9993	0.9982	0.9960	0.9919
32	1.0000	1.0000	1.0000	1.0000	1.0000	0.9999	0.9996	0.9990	0.9978	0.9953
33	1.0000	1.0000	1.0000	1.0000	1.0000	0.9999	0.9998	0.9995	0.9988	0.9973
34	1.0000	1.0000	1.0000	1.0000	1.0000	1.0000	0.9999	0.9998	0.9994	0.9985
35	1.0000	1.0000	1.0000	1.0000	1.0000	1.0000	1.0000	0.9999	0.9997	0.9992
36	1.0000	1.0000	1.0000	1.0000	1.0000	1.0000	1.0000	0.9999	0.9998	0.9996
37	1.0000	1.0000	1.0000	1.0000	1.0000	1.0000	1.0000	1.0000	0.9999	0.9998
38	1.0000	1.0000	1.0000	1.0000	1.0000	1.0000	1.0000	1.0000	1.0000	0.9999

TABLE C Values of the cumulative distribution and probability functions for the hypergeometric distribution

$$P(X \le x) = F(x; N, n, k) = \sum_{i=0}^{x} \frac{\binom{k}{i}\binom{N-k}{n-i}}{\binom{N}{n}} \qquad p(x) = \frac{\binom{k}{x}\binom{N-k}{n-x}}{\binom{N}{n}}$$

N	n	k	x	F(x)	p(x)		N	n	k	x	F(x)	p(x)
2	1	1	0	0.500000	0.500000		6	2	2	2	1.000000	0.066667
2	1	1	1	1.000000	0.500000		6	3	1	0	0.500000	0.500000
3	1	1	0	0.666667	0.666667		6	3	1	1	1.000000	0.500000
3	1	1	1	1.000000	0.333333		6	3	2	0	0.200000	0.200000
3	2	1	0	0.333333	0.333333		6	3	2	1	0.800000	0.600000
3	2	1	1	1.000000	0.666667		6	3	2	2	1.000000	0.200000
3	2	2	1	0.666667	0.666667		6	3	3	0	0.050000	0.050000
3	2	2	2	1.000000	0.333333		6	3	3	1	0.500000	0.450000
4	1	1	0	0.750000	0.750000		6	3	3	2	0.950000	0.450000
4	1	1	1	1.000000	0.250000		6	3	3	3	1.000000	0.050000
4	2	1	0	0.500000	0.500000		6	4	1	0	0.333333	0.333333
4	2	1	1	1.000000	0.500000		6	4	1	1	1.000000	0.666667
4	2	2	0	0.166667	0.166667		6	4	2	0	0.066667	0.066667
4	2	2	1	0.833333	0.666667		6	4	2	1	0.600000	0.533333
4	2	2	2	1.000000	0.166667		6	4	2	2	1.000000	0.400000
4	3	1	0	0.250000	0.250000		6	4	3	1	0.200000	0.200000
4	3	1	1	1.000000	0.750000		6	4	3	2	0.800000	0.600000
4	3	2	1	0.500000	0.500000		6	4	3	3	1.000000	0.200000
4	3	2	2	1.000000	0.500000		6	4	4	2	0.400000	0.400000
4	3	3	2	0.750000	0.750000		6	4	4	3	0.933333	0.533333
4	3	3	3	1.000000	0.250000		6	4	4	4	1.000000	0.066667
5	1	1	0	0.800000	0.800000		6	5	1	0	0.166667	0.166667
5	1	1	1	1.000000	0.200000		6	5	1	1	1.000000	0.833333
5	2	1	0	0.600000	0.600000		6	5	2	1	0.333333	0.333333
5	2	1	1	1.000000	0.400000		6	5	2	2	1.000000	0.666667
5	2	2	0	0.300000	0.300000		6	5	3	2	0.500000	0.500000
5	2	2	1	0.900000	0.600000		6	5	3	3	1.000000	0.500000
5	2	2	2	1.000000	0.100000		6	5	4	3	0.666667	0.666667
5	3	1	0	0.400000	0.400000		6	5	4	4	1.000000	0.333333
5	3	1	1	1.000000	0.600000		6	5	5	4	0.833333	0.833333

n	m	k	d	P_1	P_2		n	m	k	d	P_1	P_2
5	3	2	0	0.100000	0.100000		6	3	3	0	1.000000	0.166667
5	3	2	1	0.600000	0.700000		7	1	1	0	0.857143	0.857143
5	3	2	2	0.300000	1.000000		7	1	1	1	1.000000	0.142857
5	3	3	1	0.300000	0.300000		7	2	1	0	0.714286	0.714286
5	3	3	2	0.600000	0.900000		7	2	1	1	1.000000	0.285714
5	3	3	3	0.100000	1.000000		7	2	2	0	0.476190	0.476190
5	4	1	0	0.200000	0.200000		7	2	2	1	0.952381	0.476190
5	4	1	1	0.800000	1.000000		7	2	2	2	1.000000	0.047619
5	4	2	1	0.400000	0.400000		7	3	1	0	0.571429	0.571429
5	4	2	2	0.600000	1.000000		7	3	1	1	1.000000	0.428571
5	4	3	2	0.600000	0.600000		7	3	2	0	0.285714	0.285714
5	4	3	3	0.400000	1.000000		7	3	2	1	0.857143	0.571429
5	4	4	3	0.800000	0.800000		7	3	2	2	1.000000	0.142857
5	4	4	4	0.200000	1.000000		7	3	3	0	0.114286	0.114286
6	1	1	0	0.833333	0.833333		7	3	3	1	0.628571	0.514286
6	1	1	1	0.166667	1.000000		7	3	3	2	0.971428	0.342857
6	2	1	0	0.666667	0.666667		7	3	3	3	1.000000	0.028571
6	2	1	1	0.333333	1.000000		7	4	1	0	0.428571	0.428571
6	2	2	0	0.400000	0.400000		7	4	1	1	1.000000	0.571429
6	2	2	1	0.533333	0.933333		8	2	2	0	0.142857	0.142857
7	4	2	1	0.571429	0.714286		8	3	3	0	0.982143	0.267857
7	4	2	2	0.285714	1.000000		8	3	3	1	1.000000	0.017857
7	4	3	0	0.028571	0.028571		8	2	1	0	0.500000	0.500000
7	4	3	1	0.342857	0.371429		8	2	1	1	1.000000	0.500000
7	4	3	2	0.514286	0.885714		8	4	4	0	0.214286	0.214286
7	4	3	3	0.114286	1.000000		8	4	4	1	0.785714	0.571429
7	4	4	1	0.114286	0.114286		8	4	4	2	1.000000	0.214286
7	4	4	2	0.514286	0.628571		8	4	3	0	0.071429	0.071429
7	4	4	3	0.342857	0.971428		8	4	3	1	0.500000	0.428571
7	4	4	4	0.028571	1.000000		8	4	3	2	0.928571	0.428571
7	5	1	0	0.285714	0.285714		8	4	3	3	1.000000	0.071429
7	5	1	1	0.714286	1.000000		8	4	2	0	0.014286	0.014286
7	5	2	0	0.047619	0.047619		8	4	2	1	0.242857	0.228571
7	5	2	1	0.476190	0.523809		8	4	2	2	0.757143	0.514286
7	5	2	2	0.476190	1.000000		8	4	2	3	0.985714	0.228571
7	5	3	1	0.142857	0.142857		8	4	2	4	1.000000	0.014286
7	5	3	2	0.571429	0.714286		8	5	1	0	0.375000	0.375000
7	5	3	3	0.285714	1.000000		8	5	1	1	1.000000	0.625000
7	5	4	2	0.285714	0.285714		8	5	2	0	0.107143	0.107143
7	5	4	3	0.571429	0.857143		8	5	2	1	0.642857	0.535714

TABLE C (continued)   Values of the cumulative distribution and probability functions for the hypergeometric distribution

N	n	k	x	F(x)	p(x)	N	n	k	x	F(x)	p(x)
7	5	4	4	1.000000	0.142857	8	5	2	2	1.000000	0.357143
7	5	5	3	0.476190	0.476190	8	5	3	0	0.017857	0.017857
7	5	5	4	0.952381	0.476190	8	5	3	1	0.285714	0.267857
7	5	5	5	1.000000	0.047619	8	5	3	2	0.821429	0.535714
7	6	1	0	0.142857	0.142857	8	5	3	3	1.000000	0.178571
7	6	1	1	1.000000	0.857143	8	5	4	1	0.071429	0.071429
7	6	2	1	0.285714	0.285714	8	5	4	2	0.500000	0.428571
7	6	2	2	1.000000	0.714286	8	5	4	3	0.928571	0.428571
7	6	3	2	0.428571	0.428571	8	5	4	4	1.000000	0.071429
7	6	3	3	1.000000	0.571429	8	5	5	2	0.178571	0.178571
7	6	4	3	0.571429	0.571429	8	5	5	3	0.714286	0.535714
7	6	4	4	1.000000	0.428571	8	5	5	4	0.982143	0.267857
7	6	5	4	0.714286	0.714286	8	5	5	5	1.000000	0.017857
7	6	5	5	1.000000	0.285714	8	6	1	0	0.250000	0.250000
7	6	6	5	0.857143	0.857143	8	6	1	1	1.000000	0.750000
7	6	6	6	1.000000	0.142857	8	6	2	0	0.035714	0.035714
8	1	1	0	0.875000	0.875000	8	6	2	1	0.464286	0.428571
8	1	1	1	1.000000	0.125000	8	6	2	2	1.000000	0.535714
8	2	1	0	0.750000	0.750000	8	6	3	1	0.107143	0.107143
8	2	1	1	1.000000	0.250000	8	6	3	2	0.642857	0.535714
8	2	2	0	0.535714	0.535714	8	6	3	3	1.000000	0.357143
8	2	2	1	0.964286	0.428571	8	6	4	2	0.214286	0.214286
8	2	2	2	1.000000	0.035714	8	6	4	3	0.785714	0.571429
8	3	1	0	0.625000	0.625000	8	6	4	4	1.000000	0.214286
8	3	1	1	1.000000	0.375000	8	6	5	3	0.357143	0.357143
8	3	2	0	0.357143	0.357143	8	6	5	4	0.892857	0.535714
8	3	2	1	0.892857	0.535714	8	6	5	5	1.000000	0.107143
8	3	2	2	1.000000	0.107143	8	6	6	4	0.535714	0.535714
8	3	3	0	0.178571	0.178571	8	6	6	5	0.964286	0.428571
8	3	3	1	0.714286	0.535714	8	6	6	6	1.000000	0.035714

8	7	1	0	0.125000	0.125000	9	5	3	1	0.404762	0.357143
8	7	1	1	1.000000	0.875000	9	5	3	2	0.880952	0.476190
8	7	2	1	0.250000	0.250000	9	5	3	3	1.000000	0.119048
8	7	2	2	1.000000	0.750000	9	5	4	0	0.007936	0.007936
8	7	3	2	0.375000	0.375000	9	5	4	1	0.166667	0.158730
8	7	3	3	1.000000	0.625000	9	5	4	2	0.642857	0.476190
8	7	4	3	0.500000	0.500000	9	5	4	3	0.960317	0.317460
8	7	4	4	1.000000	0.500000	9	5	4	4	1.000000	0.039683
8	7	5	4	0.625000	0.625000	9	5	5	1	0.039683	0.039683
8	7	5	5	1.000000	0.375000	9	5	5	2	0.357143	0.317460
8	7	6	5	0.750000	0.750000	9	5	5	3	0.833333	0.476190
8	7	6	6	1.000000	0.250000	9	5	5	4	0.992063	0.158730
8	7	7	6	0.875000	0.875000	9	5	5	5	1.000000	0.007936
8	7	7	7	1.000000	0.125000	9	6	1	0	0.333333	0.333333
9	1	1	0	0.888889	0.888889	9	6	1	1	1.000000	0.666667
9	1	1	1	1.000000	0.111111	9	6	2	0	0.083333	0.083333
9	2	1	0	0.777778	0.777778	9	6	2	1	0.583333	0.500000
9	2	1	1	1.000000	0.222222	9	6	2	2	1.000000	0.416667
9	2	2	0	0.583333	0.583333	9	6	3	0	0.011905	0.011905
9	2	2	1	0.972222	0.388889	9	6	3	1	0.226190	0.214286
9	2	2	2	1.000000	0.027778	9	6	3	2	0.761905	0.535714
9	3	1	0	0.666667	0.666667	9	6	3	3	1.000000	0.238095
9	3	1	1	1.000000	0.333333	9	6	4	1	0.047619	0.047619
9	3	2	0	0.416667	0.416667	9	6	4	2	0.404762	0.357143
9	3	2	1	0.916667	0.500000	9	6	4	3	0.880952	0.476190
9	3	2	2	1.000000	0.083333	9	6	4	4	1.000000	0.119048
9	3	3	0	0.238095	0.238095	9	6	5	2	0.119048	0.119048
9	3	3	1	0.773809	0.535714	9	6	5	3	0.595238	0.476190
9	3	3	2	0.988095	0.214286	9	6	5	4	0.952381	0.357143
9	3	3	3	1.000000	0.011905	9	6	5	5	1.000000	0.047619
9	4	1	0	0.555556	0.555556	9	6	6	3	0.238095	0.238095
9	4	1	1	1.000000	0.444444	9	6	6	4	0.773809	0.535714
9	4	2	0	0.277778	0.277778	9	6	6	5	0.988095	0.214286
9	4	2	1	0.833333	0.555556	9	6	6	6	1.000000	0.011905
9	4	2	2	1.000000	0.166667	9	7	1	0	0.222222	0.222222
9	4	3	0	0.119048	0.119048	9	7	1	1	1.000000	0.777778
9	4	3	1	0.595238	0.476190	9	7	2	0	0.027778	0.027778
9	4	3	2	0.952381	0.357143	9	7	2	1	0.416667	0.388889
9	4	3	3	1.000000	0.047619	9	7	2	2	1.000000	0.583333
9	4	4	0	0.039683	0.039683	9	7	3	1	0.083333	0.083333

TABLE C (continued)   Values of the cumulative distribution and probability functions for the hypergeometric distribution

N	n	k	x	F(x)	p(x)	N	n	k	x	F(x)	p(x)
9	4	4	1	0.357143	0.317460	9	7	3	2	0.583333	0.500000
9	4	4	2	0.833333	0.476190	9	7	3	3	1.000000	0.416667
9	4	4	3	0.992063	0.158730	9	7	4	2	0.166667	0.166667
9	4	4	4	1.000000	0.007936	9	7	4	3	0.722222	0.555556
9	5	1	0	0.444444	0.444444	9	7	4	4	1.000000	0.277778
9	5	1	1	1.000000	0.555556	9	7	5	3	0.277778	0.277778
9	5	2	0	0.166667	0.166667	9	7	5	4	0.833333	0.555556
9	5	2	1	0.722222	0.555556	9	7	5	5	1.000000	0.166667
9	5	2	2	1.000000	0.277778	9	7	6	4	0.416667	0.416667
9	5	3	0	0.047619	0.047619	9	7	6	5	0.916667	0.500000
9	7	6	6	1.000000	0.833333	10	5	1	0	0.500000	0.500000
9	7	7	5	0.583333	0.583333	10	5	1	1	1.000000	0.500000
9	7	7	6	0.972222	0.388889	10	5	2	0	0.222222	0.222222
9	7	7	7	1.000000	0.027778	10	5	2	1	0.777778	0.555556
9	8	1	0	0.111111	0.111111	10	5	2	2	1.000000	0.222222
9	8	1	1	1.000000	0.888889	10	5	3	0	0.083333	0.083333
9	8	2	1	0.222222	0.222222	10	5	3	1	0.500000	0.416667
9	8	2	2	1.000000	0.777778	10	5	3	2	0.916667	0.416667
9	8	3	2	0.333333	0.333333	10	5	3	3	1.000000	0.083333
9	8	3	3	1.000000	0.666667	10	5	4	0	0.023810	0.023810
9	8	4	3	0.444444	0.444444	10	5	4	1	0.261905	0.238095
9	8	4	4	1.000000	0.555556	10	5	4	2	0.738095	0.476190
9	8	5	4	0.555556	0.555556	10	5	4	3	0.976190	0.238095
9	8	5	5	1.000000	0.444444	10	5	4	4	1.000000	0.023810
9	8	6	5	0.666667	0.666667	10	5	5	0	0.003968	0.003968
9	8	6	6	1.000000	0.333333	10	5	5	1	0.103175	0.099206
9	8	7	6	0.777778	0.777778	10	5	5	2	0.500000	0.396825
9	8	7	7	1.000000	0.222222	10	5	5	3	0.896825	0.396825
9	8	8	7	0.888889	0.888889	10	5	5	4	0.996032	0.099206
9	8	8	8	1.000000	0.111111	10	5	5	5	1.000000	0.003968

N	n	k	x	P(X ≤ x)	P(X = x)
10	1	1	0	0.900000	0.900000
10	1	1	1	1.000000	0.100000
10	2	1	0	0.800000	0.800000
10	2	1	1	1.000000	0.200000
10	2	2	0	0.622222	0.622222
10	2	2	1	0.977778	0.355556
10	2	2	2	1.000000	0.022222
10	3	1	0	0.700000	0.700000
10	3	1	1	1.000000	0.300000
10	3	2	0	0.466667	0.466667
10	3	2	1	0.933333	0.466667
10	3	2	2	1.000000	0.066667
10	3	3	0	0.291667	0.291667
10	3	3	1	0.816667	0.525000
10	3	3	2	0.991667	0.175000
10	3	3	3	1.000000	0.008333
10	4	1	0	0.600000	0.600000
10	4	1	1	1.000000	0.400000
10	4	2	0	0.333333	0.333333
10	4	2	1	0.866667	0.533333
10	4	2	2	1.000000	0.133333
10	4	3	0	0.166667	0.166667
10	4	3	1	0.666667	0.500000
10	4	3	2	0.966667	0.300000
10	4	3	3	1.000000	0.033333
10	4	4	0	0.071429	0.071429
10	4	4	1	0.452381	0.380952
10	4	4	2	0.880952	0.428571
10	4	4	3	0.995238	0.114286
10	4	4	4	1.000000	0.004762
10	6	1	0	0.400000	0.400000
10	6	1	1	1.000000	0.600000
10	6	2	0	0.133333	0.133333
10	6	2	1	0.666667	0.533333
10	6	2	2	1.000000	0.333333
10	6	3	0	0.033333	0.033333
10	6	3	1	0.333333	0.300000
10	6	3	2	0.833333	0.500000
10	6	3	3	1.000000	0.166667
10	6	4	0	0.004762	0.004762
10	6	4	1	0.119048	0.114286
10	6	4	2	0.547619	0.428571
10	6	4	3	0.928571	0.380952
10	6	4	4	1.000000	0.071429
10	6	5	1	0.023810	0.023810
10	6	5	2	0.261905	0.238095
10	6	5	3	0.738095	0.476190
10	6	5	4	0.976190	0.238095
10	6	5	5	1.000000	0.023810
10	6	6	2	0.071429	0.071429
10	6	6	3	0.452381	0.380952
10	6	6	4	0.880952	0.428571
10	6	6	5	0.995238	0.114286
10	6	6	6	1.000000	0.004762
10	7	1	0	0.300000	0.300000
10	7	1	1	1.000000	0.700000
10	7	2	0	0.066667	0.066667
10	7	2	1	0.533333	0.466667
10	7	2	2	1.000000	0.466667
10	7	3	0	0.008333	0.008333

TABLE D Values of the standard normal cumulative distribution function

$$P(Z \le z) = F(z; 0, 1) = \frac{1}{\sqrt{2\pi}} \int_{-\infty}^{z} \exp(-t^2/2)dt$$

z	.00	.01	.02	.03	.04	.05	.06	.07	.08	.09
−3.5	0.0002	0.0002	0.0002	0.0002	0.0002	0.0002	0.0002	0.0002	0.0002	0.0002
−3.4	0.0003	0.0003	0.0003	0.0003	0.0003	0.0003	0.0003	0.0003	0.0003	0.0002
−3.3	0.0005	0.0005	0.0005	0.0004	0.0004	0.0004	0.0004	0.0004	0.0004	0.0003
−3.2	0.0007	0.0007	0.0006	0.0006	0.0006	0.0006	0.0006	0.0005	0.0005	0.0005
−3.1	0.0010	0.0009	0.0009	0.0009	0.0008	0.0008	0.0008	0.0008	0.0007	0.0007
−3.0	0.0013	0.0013	0.0013	0.0012	0.0012	0.0011	0.0011	0.0011	0.0010	0.0010
−2.9	0.0019	0.0018	0.0018	0.0017	0.0016	0.0016	0.0015	0.0015	0.0014	0.0014
−2.8	0.0026	0.0025	0.0024	0.0023	0.0023	0.0022	0.0021	0.0021	0.0020	0.0019
−2.7	0.0035	0.0034	0.0033	0.0032	0.0031	0.0030	0.0029	0.0028	0.0027	0.0026
−2.6	0.0047	0.0045	0.0044	0.0043	0.0041	0.0040	0.0039	0.0038	0.0037	0.0036
−2.5	0.0062	0.0060	0.0059	0.0057	0.0055	0.0054	0.0052	0.0051	0.0049	0.0048
−2.4	0.0082	0.0080	0.0078	0.0075	0.0073	0.0071	0.0069	0.0068	0.0066	0.0064
−2.3	0.0107	0.0104	0.0102	0.0099	0.0096	0.0094	0.0091	0.0089	0.0087	0.0084
−2.2	0.0139	0.0136	0.0132	0.0129	0.0125	0.0122	0.0119	0.0116	0.0113	0.0110
−2.1	0.0179	0.0174	0.0170	0.0166	0.0162	0.0158	0.0154	0.0150	0.0146	0.0143
−2.0	0.0228	0.0222	0.0217	0.0212	0.0207	0.0202	0.0197	0.0192	0.0188	0.0183

z	.00	.01	.02	.03	.04	.05	.06	.07	.08	.09
-1.9	0.0287	0.0281	0.0274	0.0268	0.0262	0.0256	0.0250	0.0244	0.0239	0.0233
-1.8	0.0359	0.0351	0.0344	0.0336	0.0329	0.0322	0.0314	0.0307	0.0301	0.0294
-1.7	0.0446	0.0436	0.0427	0.0418	0.0409	0.0401	0.0392	0.0384	0.0375	0.0367
-1.6	0.0548	0.0537	0.0526	0.0516	0.0505	0.0495	0.0485	0.0475	0.0465	0.0455
-1.5	0.0668	0.0655	0.0643	0.0630	0.0618	0.0606	0.0594	0.0582	0.0571	0.0559
-1.4	0.0808	0.0793	0.0778	0.0764	0.0749	0.0735	0.0721	0.0708	0.0694	0.0681
-1.3	0.0968	0.0951	0.0934	0.0918	0.0901	0.0885	0.0869	0.0853	0.0838	0.0823
-1.2	0.1151	0.1131	0.1112	0.1093	0.1075	0.1056	0.1038	0.1020	0.1003	0.0985
-1.1	0.1357	0.1335	0.1314	0.1292	0.1271	0.1251	0.1230	0.1210	0.1190	0.1170
-1.0	0.1587	0.1562	0.1539	0.1515	0.1492	0.1469	0.1446	0.1423	0.1401	0.1379
-0.9	0.1841	0.1814	0.1788	0.1762	0.1736	0.1711	0.1685	0.1660	0.1635	0.1611
-0.8	0.2119	0.2090	0.2061	0.2033	0.2005	0.1977	0.1949	0.1922	0.1894	0.1867
-0.7	0.2420	0.2389	0.2358	0.2327	0.2297	0.2266	0.2236	0.2206	0.2177	0.2148
-0.6	0.2743	0.2709	0.2676	0.2643	0.2611	0.2578	0.2546	0.2514	0.2483	0.2451
-0.5	0.3085	0.3050	0.3015	0.2981	0.2946	0.2912	0.2877	0.2843	0.2810	0.2776
-0.4	0.3446	0.3409	0.3372	0.3336	0.3300	0.3264	0.3228	0.3192	0.3156	0.3121
-0.3	0.3821	0.3783	0.3745	0.3707	0.3669	0.3632	0.3594	0.3557	0.3520	0.3483
-0.2	0.4207	0.4168	0.4129	0.4090	0.4052	0.4013	0.3974	0.3936	0.3897	0.3859
-0.1	0.4602	0.4562	0.4522	0.4483	0.4443	0.4404	0.4364	0.4325	0.4286	0.4247
-0.0	0.5000	0.4960	0.4920	0.4880	0.4840	0.4801	0.4761	0.4721	0.4681	0.4641
0.0	0.5000	0.5040	0.5080	0.5120	0.5160	0.5199	0.5239	0.5279	0.5319	0.5359
0.1	0.5398	0.5438	0.5478	0.5517	0.5557	0.5596	0.5636	0.5675	0.5714	0.5753
0.2	0.5793	0.5832	0.5871	0.5910	0.5948	0.5987	0.6026	0.6064	0.6103	0.6141
0.3	0.6179	0.6217	0.6255	0.6293	0.6331	0.6368	0.6406	0.6443	0.6480	0.6517
0.4	0.6554	0.6591	0.6628	0.6664	0.6700	0.6736	0.6772	0.6808	0.6844	0.6879
0.5	0.6915	0.6950	0.6985	0.7019	0.7054	0.7088	0.7123	0.7157	0.7190	0.7224
0.6	0.7257	0.7291	0.7324	0.7357	0.7389	0.7422	0.7454	0.7486	0.7517	0.7549
0.7	0.7580	0.7611	0.7642	0.7673	0.7703	0.7734	0.7764	0.7794	0.7823	0.7852
0.8	0.7881	0.7910	0.7939	0.7967	0.7995	0.8023	0.8051	0.8078	0.8106	0.8133
0.9	0.8159	0.8186	0.8212	0.8238	0.8264	0.8289	0.8315	0.8340	0.8365	0.8389

TABLE D (continued)   Values of the standard normal cumulative distribution function

z	.00	.01	.02	.03	.04	.05	.06	.07	.08	.09
1.0	0.8413	0.8438	0.8461	0.8485	0.8508	0.8531	0.8554	0.8577	0.8599	0.8621
1.1	0.8643	0.8665	0.8686	0.8708	0.8729	0.8749	0.8770	0.8790	0.8810	0.8830
1.2	0.8849	0.8869	0.8888	0.8907	0.8925	0.8944	0.8962	0.8980	0.8997	0.9015
1.3	0.9032	0.9049	0.9066	0.9082	0.9099	0.9115	0.9131	0.9147	0.9162	0.9177
1.4	0.9192	0.9207	0.9222	0.9236	0.9251	0.9265	0.9279	0.9292	0.9306	0.9319
1.5	0.9332	0.9345	0.9357	0.9370	0.9382	0.9394	0.9406	0.9418	0.9429	0.9441
1.6	0.9452	0.9463	0.9474	0.9484	0.9495	0.9505	0.9515	0.9525	0.9535	0.9545
1.7	0.9554	0.9564	0.9573	0.9582	0.9591	0.9599	0.9608	0.9616	0.9625	0.9633
1.8	0.9641	0.9649	0.9656	0.9664	0.9671	0.9678	0.9686	0.9693	0.9699	0.9706
1.9	0.9713	0.9719	0.9726	0.9732	0.9738	0.9744	0.9750	0.9756	0.9761	0.9767
2.0	0.9772	0.9778	0.9783	0.9788	0.9793	0.9798	0.9803	0.9808	0.9812	0.9817
2.1	0.9821	0.9826	0.9830	0.9834	0.9838	0.9842	0.9846	0.9850	0.9854	0.9857
2.2	0.9861	0.9864	0.9868	0.9871	0.9875	0.9878	0.9881	0.9884	0.9887	0.9890
2.3	0.9893	0.9896	0.9898	0.9901	0.9904	0.9906	0.9909	0.9911	0.9913	0.9916
2.4	0.9918	0.9920	0.9922	0.9925	0.9927	0.9929	0.9931	0.9932	0.9934	0.9936
2.5	0.9938	0.9940	0.9941	0.9943	0.9945	0.9946	0.9948	0.9949	0.9951	0.9952
2.6	0.9953	0.9955	0.9956	0.9957	0.9959	0.9960	0.9961	0.9962	0.9963	0.9964
2.7	0.9965	0.9966	0.9967	0.9968	0.9969	0.9970	0.9971	0.9972	0.9973	0.9974
2.8	0.9974	0.9975	0.9976	0.9977	0.9977	0.9978	0.9979	0.9979	0.9980	0.9981
2.9	0.9981	0.9982	0.9982	0.9983	0.9984	0.9984	0.9985	0.9985	0.9986	0.9986
3.0	0.9987	0.9987	0.9987	0.9988	0.9988	0.9989	0.9989	0.9989	0.9990	0.9990
3.1	0.9990	0.9991	0.9991	0.9991	0.9992	0.9992	0.9992	0.9992	0.9993	0.9993
3.2	0.9993	0.9993	0.9994	0.9994	0.9994	0.9994	0.9994	0.9995	0.9995	0.9995
3.3	0.9995	0.9995	0.9995	0.9996	0.9996	0.9996	0.9996	0.9996	0.9996	0.9997
3.4	0.9997	0.9997	0.9997	0.9997	0.9997	0.9997	0.9997	0.9997	0.9997	0.9998
3.5	0.9998	0.9998	0.9998	0.9998	0.9998	0.9998	0.9998	0.9998	0.9998	0.9998

TABLE E Quantile values of the chi-square distribution

$$P(X \leq x_{1-\alpha,\nu}) = F(x_{1-\alpha}; \nu) = \frac{1}{\Gamma(\nu/2)\,2^{\nu/2}} \int_0^{x_{1-\alpha,\nu}} t^{\nu/2-1}\exp(-t/2)\,dt = 1-\alpha$$

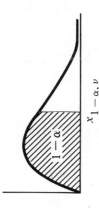

ν	$x_{0.005}$	$x_{0.010}$	$x_{0.025}$	$x_{0.050}$	$x_{0.100}$	$x_{0.900}$	$x_{0.950}$	$x_{0.975}$	$x_{0.990}$	$x_{0.995}$
1	0.00	0.00	0.00	0.00	0.02	2.71	3.84	5.02	6.64	7.90
2	0.01	0.02	0.05	0.10	0.21	4.60	5.99	7.38	9.22	10.59
3	0.07	0.11	0.22	0.35	0.58	6.25	7.82	9.36	11.32	12.82
4	0.21	0.30	0.48	0.71	1.06	7.78	9.49	11.15	13.28	14.82
5	0.41	0.55	0.83	1.15	1.61	9.24	11.07	12.84	15.09	16.76
6	0.67	0.87	1.24	1.63	2.20	10.65	12.60	14.46	16.81	18.55
7	0.99	1.24	1.69	2.17	2.83	12.02	14.07	16.02	18.47	20.27
8	1.34	1.64	2.18	2.73	3.49	13.36	15.51	17.55	20.08	21.94
9	1.73	2.09	2.70	3.32	4.17	14.69	16.93	19.03	21.65	23.56
10	2.15	2.55	3.24	3.94	4.86	15.99	18.31	20.50	23.19	25.15
11	2.60	3.05	3.81	4.57	5.58	17.28	19.68	21.93	24.75	26.71
12	3.06	3.57	4.40	5.22	6.30	18.55	21.03	23.35	26.25	28.25
13	3.56	4.10	5.01	5.89	7.04	19.81	22.37	24.75	27.72	29.88
14	4.07	4.65	5.62	6.57	7.79	21.07	23.69	26.13	29.17	31.38
15	4.59	5.23	6.26	7.26	8.55	22.31	25.00	27.50	30.61	32.86
16	5.14	5.81	6.90	7.96	9.31	23.55	26.30	28.86	32.03	34.32
17	5.69	6.40	7.56	8.67	10.08	24.77	27.59	30.20	33.43	35.77
18	6.25	7.00	8.23	9.39	10.86	25.99	28.88	31.54	34.83	37.21
19	6.82	7.63	8.90	10.11	11.65	27.21	30.15	32.87	36.22	38.63
20	7.42	8.25	9.59	10.85	12.44	28.42	31.42	34.18	37.59	40.05

TABLE E (continued)   Quantile values of the chi-square distribution

ν	$x_{0.005}$	$x_{0.010}$	$x_{0.025}$	$x_{0.050}$	$x_{0.100}$	$x_{0.900}$	$x_{0.950}$	$x_{0.975}$	$x_{0.990}$	$x_{0.995}$
21	8.02	8.89	10.28	11.59	13.24	29.62	32.68	35.49	38.96	41.45
22	8.62	9.53	10.98	12.34	14.04	30.82	33.93	36.79	40.31	42.84
23	9.25	10.19	11.69	13.09	14.85	32.01	35.18	38.09	41.66	44.23
24	9.87	10.85	12.40	13.84	15.66	33.20	36.42	39.38	43.00	45.60
25	10.50	11.51	13.11	14.61	16.47	34.38	37.66	40.66	44.34	46.97
26	11.13	12.19	13.84	15.38	17.29	35.57	38.89	41.94	45.66	48.33
27	11.79	12.87	14.57	16.15	18.11	36.74	40.12	43.21	46.99	49.69
28	12.44	13.55	15.30	16.92	18.94	37.92	41.34	44.47	48.30	51.04
29	13.09	14.24	16.04	17.70	19.77	39.09	42.56	45.74	49.61	52.38
30	13.77	14.94	16.78	18.49	20.60	40.26	43.78	46.99	50.91	53.71
35	17.16	18.49	20.56	22.46	24.79	46.06	49.81	53.22	57.36	60.31
40	20.67	22.14	24.42	26.51	29.06	51.80	55.75	59.34	63.71	66.80
45	24.28	25.88	28.36	30.61	33.36	57.50	61.65	65.41	69.98	73.20
50	27.96	29.68	32.35	34.76	37.69	63.16	67.50	71.42	76.17	79.52
60	35.50	37.46	40.47	43.19	46.46	74.39	79.08	83.30	88.40	91.98
70	43.25	45.42	48.75	51.74	55.33	85.52	90.53	95.03	100.44	104.24
80	51.14	53.52	57.15	60.39	64.28	96.57	101.88	106.63	112.34	116.35
90	59.17	61.74	65.64	69.13	73.29	107.56	113.14	118.14	124.13	128.32
100	67.30	70.05	74.22	77.93	82.36	118.49	124.34	129.56	135.82	140.19

TABLE F Quantile values of the Student's t distribution

$$P(T \le t_{1-\alpha,\nu}) = \frac{\Gamma[(\nu+1)/2]}{\sqrt{\pi\nu}\,\Gamma(\nu/2)} \int_{-\infty}^{t_{1-\alpha,\nu}} [1 + (t^2/\nu)]^{-(\nu+1)/2} dt = 1 - \alpha$$

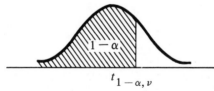

$t_{1-\alpha,\nu}$

ν	$t_{0.001}$	$t_{0.005}$	$t_{0.010}$	$t_{0.025}$	$t_{0.050}$	$t_{0.100}$	$t_{0.200}$
1	−318.309	−63.657	−31.821	−12.706	−6.314	−3.078	−1.376
2	−22.327	−9.925	−6.965	−4.303	−2.920	−1.886	−1.061
3	−10.215	−5.841	−4.541	−3.182	−2.353	−1.638	−0.978
4	−7.173	−4.604	−3.747	−2.776	−2.132	−1.533	−0.941
5	−5.893	−4.032	−3.365	−2.571	−2.015	−1.476	−0.920
6	−5.208	−3.707	−3.143	−2.447	−1.943	−1.440	−0.906
7	−4.785	−3.499	−2.998	−2.365	−1.895	−1.415	−0.896
8	−4.501	−3.355	−2.896	−2.306	−1.860	−1.397	−0.889
9	−4.297	−3.250	−2.821	−2.262	−1.833	−1.383	−0.883
10	−4.144	−3.169	−2.764	−2.228	−1.812	−1.372	−0.879
11	−4.025	−3.106	−2.718	−2.201	−1.796	−1.363	−0.876
12	−3.930	−3.055	−2.681	−2.179	−1.782	−1.356	−0.873
13	−3.852	−3.012	−2.650	−2.160	−1.771	−1.350	−0.870
14	−3.787	−2.977	−2.624	−2.145	−1.761	−1.345	−0.868
15	−3.733	−2.947	−2.602	−2.131	−1.753	−1.341	−0.866
16	−3.686	−2.921	−2.583	−2.120	−1.746	−1.337	−0.865
17	−3.646	−2.898	−2.567	−2.110	−1.740	−1.333	−0.863
18	−3.610	−2.878	−2.552	−2.101	−1.734	−1.330	−0.862
19	−3.579	−2.861	−2.539	−2.093	−1.729	−1.328	−0.861
20	−3.552	−2.845	−2.528	−2.086	−1.725	−1.325	−0.860
21	−3.527	−2.831	−2.518	−2.080	−1.721	−1.323	−0.859
22	−3.505	−2.819	−2.508	−2.074	−1.717	−1.321	−0.858
23	−3.485	−2.807	−2.500	−2.069	−1.714	−1.319	−0.858
24	−3.467	−2.797	−2.492	−2.064	−1.711	−1.318	−0.857
25	−3.450	−2.787	−2.485	−2.060	−1.708	−1.316	−0.856
26	−3.435	−2.779	−2.479	−2.056	−1.706	−1.315	−0.856
27	−3.421	−2.771	−2.473	−2.052	−1.703	−1.314	−0.855
28	−3.408	−2.763	−2.467	−2.048	−1.701	−1.313	−0.855
29	−3.396	−2.756	−2.462	−2.045	−1.699	−1.311	−0.854
30	−3.385	−2.750	−2.457	−2.042	−1.697	−1.310	−0.854
35	−3.340	−2.724	−2.438	−2.030	−1.690	−1.306	−0.852
40	−3.307	−2.704	−2.423	−2.021	−1.684	−1.303	−0.851
45	−3.281	−2.690	−2.412	−2.014	−1.679	−1.301	−0.850
50	−3.261	−2.678	−2.403	−2.009	−1.676	−1.299	−0.849
60	−3.232	−2.660	−2.390	−2.000	−1.671	−1.296	−0.848
70	−3.211	−2.648	−2.381	−1.994	−1.667	−1.294	−0.847
80	−3.195	−2.639	−2.374	−1.990	−1.664	−1.292	−0.846
90	−3.183	−2.632	−2.369	−1.987	−1.662	−1.291	−0.846
100	−3.174	−2.626	−2.364	−1.984	−1.660	−1.290	−0.845
200	−3.131	−2.601	−2.345	−1.972	−1.652	−1.286	−0.843
500	−3.107	−2.586	−2.334	−1.965	−1.648	−1.283	−0.842
1000	−3.098	−2.581	−2.330	−1.962	−1.646	−1.282	−0.842

TABLE F (continued)   Quantile values of the Student's t distribution

ν	$t_{0.800}$	$t_{0.900}$	$t_{0.950}$	$t_{0.975}$	$t_{0.990}$	$t_{0.995}$	$t_{0.999}$
1	1.376	3.078	6.314	12.706	31.820	63.656	318.294
2	1.061	1.886	2.920	4.303	6.965	9.925	22.327
3	0.978	1.638	2.353	3.182	4.541	5.841	10.214
4	0.941	1.533	2.132	2.776	3.747	4.604	7.173
5	0.920	1.476	2.015	2.571	3.365	4.032	5.893
6	0.906	1.440	1.943	2.447	3.143	3.707	5.208
7	0.896	1.415	1.895	2.365	2.998	3.499	4.785
8	0.889	1.397	1.860	2.306	2.896	3.355	4.501
9	0.883	1.383	1.833	2.262	2.821	3.250	4.297
10	0.879	1.372	1.812	2.228	2.764	3.169	4.144
11	0.876	1.363	1.796	2.201	2.718	3.106	4.025
12	0.873	1.356	1.782	2.179	2.681	3.055	3.930
13	0.870	1.350	1.771	2.160	2.650	3.012	3.852
14	0.868	1.345	1.761	2.145	2.624	2.977	3.787
15	0.866	1.341	1.753	2.131	2.602	2.947	3.733
16	0.865	1.337	1.746	2.120	2.583	2.921	3.686
17	0.863	1.333	1.740	2.110	2.567	2.898	3.646
18	0.862	1.330	1.734	2.101	2.552	2.878	3.610
19	0.861	1.328	1.729	2.093	2.539	2.861	3.579
20	0.860	1.325	1.725	2.086	2.528	2.845	3.552
21	0.859	1.323	1.721	2.080	2.518	2.831	3.527
22	0.858	1.321	1.717	2.074	2.508	2.819	3.505
23	0.858	1.319	1.714	2.069	2.500	2.807	3.485
24	0.857	1.318	1.711	2.064	2.492	2.797	3.467
25	0.856	1.316	1.708	2.060	2.485	2.787	3.450
26	0.856	1.315	1.706	2.056	2.479	2.779	3.435
27	0.855	1.314	1.703	2.052	2.473	2.771	3.421
28	0.855	1.313	1.701	2.048	2.467	2.763	3.408
29	0.854	1.311	1.699	2.045	2.462	2.756	3.396
30	0.854	1.310	1.697	2.042	2.457	2.750	3.385
35	0.852	1.306	1.690	2.030	2.438	2.724	3.340
40	0.851	1.303	1.684	2.021	2.423	2.704	3.307
45	0.850	1.301	1.679	2.014	2.412	2.690	3.281
50	0.849	1.299	1.676	2.009	2.403	2.678	3.261
60	0.848	1.296	1.671	2.000	2.390	2.660	3.232
70	0.847	1.294	1.667	1.994	2.381	2.648	3.211
80	0.846	1.292	1.664	1.990	2.374	2.639	3.195
90	0.846	1.291	1.662	1.987	2.368	2.632	3.183
100	0.845	1.290	1.660	1.984	2.364	2.626	3.174
200	0.843	1.286	1.652	1.972	2.345	2.601	3.131
500	0.842	1.283	1.648	1.965	2.334	2.586	3.107
1000	0.842	1.282	1.646	1.962	2.330	2.581	3.098

TABLE G   Quantile values of the *F* distribution

$$P(F \leqslant f_{1-\alpha,\nu_1,\nu_2}) = \frac{\Gamma[(\nu_1 + \nu_2)/2]\nu_1^{\nu_1/2} \nu_2^{\nu_2/2}}{\Gamma(\nu_1/2)\Gamma(\nu_2/2)} \int_0^{f_{1-\alpha,\nu_1,\nu_2}} t^{(\nu_1-2)/2} (\nu_2 + \nu_1 t)^{(\nu_1+\nu_2)/2} \; dt = 1 - \alpha$$

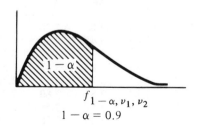

$$f_{1-\alpha,\nu_1,\nu_2}$$
$$1 - \alpha = 0.9$$

	$\nu_1 =$ degrees of freedom for the numerator									
ν_2	1	2	3	4	5	6	7	8	9	10
1	39.86	49.50	53.59	55.83	57.24	58.20	58.91	59.44	59.86	60.19
2	8.53	9.00	9.16	9.24	9.29	9.33	9.35	9.37	9.38	9.39
3	5.54	5.46	5.39	5.34	5.31	5.28	5.27	5.25	5.24	5.23
4	4.54	4.32	4.19	4.11	4.05	4.01	3.98	3.95	3.94	3.92
5	4.06	3.78	3.62	3.52	3.45	3.40	3.37	3.34	3.32	3.30
6	3.78	3.46	3.29	3.18	3.11	3.05	3.01	2.98	2.96	2.94
7	3.59	3.26	3.07	2.96	2.88	2.83	2.79	2.75	2.72	2.70
8	3.46	3.11	2.92	2.81	2.73	2.67	2.62	2.59	2.56	2.54
9	3.36	3.01	2.81	2.69	2.61	2.55	2.51	2.47	2.44	2.42
10	3.29	2.92	2.73	2.61	2.52	2.46	2.41	2.38	2.35	2.32
11	3.23	2.86	2.66	2.54	2.45	2.39	2.34	2.30	2.27	2.25
12	3.18	2.81	2.61	2.48	2.39	2.33	2.28	2.24	2.21	2.19
13	3.14	2.76	2.56	2.43	2.35	2.28	2.23	2.20	2.16	2.14
14	3.10	2.73	2.52	2.39	2.31	2.24	2.19	2.15	2.12	2.10
15	3.07	2.70	2.49	2.36	2.27	2.21	2.16	2.12	2.09	2.06
16	3.05	2.67	2.46	2.33	2.24	2.18	2.13	2.09	2.06	2.03
17	3.03	2.64	2.44	2.31	2.22	2.15	2.10	2.06	2.03	2.00
18	3.01	2.62	2.42	2.29	2.20	2.13	2.08	2.04	2.00	1.98
19	2.99	2.61	2.40	2.27	2.18	2.11	2.06	2.02	1.98	1.96
20	2.97	2.59	2.38	2.25	2.16	2.09	2.04	2.00	1.96	1.94
21	2.96	2.57	2.36	2.23	2.14	2.08	2.02	1.98	1.95	1.92
22	2.95	2.56	2.35	2.22	2.13	2.06	2.01	1.97	1.93	1.90
23	2.94	2.55	2.34	2.21	2.11	2.05	1.99	1.95	1.92	1.89
24	2.93	2.54	2.33	2.19	2.10	2.04	1.98	1.94	1.91	1.88
25	2.92	2.53	2.32	2.18	2.09	2.02	1.97	1.93	1.89	1.87
26	2.91	2.52	2.31	2.17	2.08	2.01	1.96	1.92	1.88	1.86
27	2.90	2.51	2.30	2.17	2.07	2.00	1.95	1.91	1.87	1.85
28	2.89	2.50	2.29	2.16	2.06	2.00	1.94	1.90	1.87	1.84
29	2.89	2.50	2.28	2.15	2.06	1.99	1.93	1.89	1.86	1.83
30	2.88	2.49	2.28	2.14	2.05	1.98	1.93	1.88	1.85	1.82
35	2.85	2.46	2.25	2.11	2.02	1.95	1.90	1.85	1.82	1.79
40	2.84	2.44	2.23	2.09	2.00	1.93	1.87	1.83	1.79	1.76
50	2.81	2.41	2.20	2.06	1.97	1.90	1.84	1.80	1.76	1.73
60	2.79	2.39	2.18	2.04	1.95	1.87	1.82	1.77	1.74	1.71
80	2.77	2.37	2.15	2.02	1.92	1.85	1.79	1.75	1.71	1.68
100	2.76	2.36	2.14	2.00	1.91	1.83	1.78	1.73	1.69	1.66
200	2.73	2.33	2.11	1.97	1.88	1.80	1.75	1.70	1.66	1.63
500	2.72	2.31	2.09	1.96	1.86	1.79	1.73	1.68	1.64	1.61
1000	2.71	2.31	2.09	1.95	1.85	1.78	1.72	1.68	1.64	1.61

TABLE G (continued)   Quantile values of the F distribution

$$1 - \alpha = 0.9$$

ν_1 = *degrees of freedom for the numerator*

ν_2	11	12	15	20	25	30	40	50	100	1000
1	60.47	60.71	61.22	61.74	62.06	62.26	62.53	62.69	63.00	63.29
2	9.40	9.41	9.42	9.44	9.45	9.46	9.47	9.47	9.48	9.49
3	5.22	5.22	5.20	5.19	5.17	5.17	5.16	5.15	5.14	5.13
4	3.91	3.90	3.87	3.84	3.83	3.82	3.80	3.80	3.78	3.76
5	3.28	3.27	3.24	3.21	3.19	3.17	3.16	3.15	3.13	3.11
6	2.92	2.90	2.87	2.84	2.81	2.80	2.78	2.77	2.75	2.72
7	2.68	2.67	2.63	2.59	2.57	2.56	2.54	2.52	2.50	2.47
8	2.52	2.50	2.46	2.42	2.40	2.38	2.36	2.35	2.32	2.30
9	2.40	2.38	2.34	2.30	2.27	2.25	2.23	2.22	2.19	2.16
10	2.30	2.28	2.24	2.20	2.17	2.16	2.13	2.12	2.09	2.06
11	2.23	2.21	2.17	2.12	2.10	2.08	2.05	2.04	2.00	1.98
12	2.17	2.15	2.10	2.06	2.03	2.01	1.99	1.97	1.94	1.91
13	2.12	2.10	2.05	2.01	1.98	1.96	1.93	1.92	1.88	1.85
14	2.07	2.05	2.01	1.96	1.93	1.91	1.89	1.87	1.83	1.80
15	2.04	2.02	1.97	1.92	1.89	1.87	1.85	1.83	1.79	1.76
16	2.01	1.99	1.94	1.89	1.86	1.84	1.81	1.79	1.76	1.72
17	1.98	1.96	1.91	1.86	1.83	1.81	1.78	1.76	1.73	1.69
18	1.95	1.93	1.89	1.84	1.80	1.78	1.75	1.74	1.70	1.66
19	1.93	1.91	1.86	1.81	1.78	1.76	1.73	1.71	1.67	1.64
20	1.91	1.89	1.84	1.79	1.76	1.74	1.71	1.69	1.65	1.61
21	1.90	1.87	1.83	1.78	1.74	1.72	1.69	1.67	1.63	1.59
22	1.88	1.86	1.81	1.76	1.73	1.70	1.67	1.65	1.61	1.57
23	1.87	1.84	1.80	1.74	1.71	1.69	1.66	1.64	1.59	1.55
24	1.85	1.83	1.78	1.73	1.70	1.67	1.64	1.62	1.58	1.54
25	1.84	1.82	1.77	1.72	1.68	1.66	1.63	1.61	1.56	1.52
26	1.83	1.81	1.76	1.71	1.67	1.65	1.61	1.59	1.55	1.51
27	1.82	1.80	1.75	1.70	1.66	1.64	1.60	1.58	1.54	1.50
28	1.81	1.79	1.74	1.69	1.65	1.63	1.59	1.57	1.53	1.48
29	1.80	1.78	1.73	1.68	1.64	1.62	1.58	1.56	1.52	1.47
30	1.79	1.77	1.72	1.67	1.63	1.61	1.57	1.55	1.51	1.46
35	1.76	1.74	1.69	1.63	1.60	1.57	1.53	1.51	1.47	1.42
40	1.74	1.71	1.66	1.61	1.57	1.54	1.51	1.48	1.43	1.38
50	1.70	1.68	1.63	1.57	1.53	1.50	1.46	1.44	1.39	1.33
60	1.68	1.66	1.60	1.54	1.50	1.48	1.44	1.41	1.36	1.30
80	1.65	1.63	1.57	1.51	1.47	1.44	1.40	1.38	1.32	1.25
100	1.64	1.61	1.56	1.49	1.45	1.42	1.38	1.35	1.29	1.22
200	1.60	1.58	1.52	1.46	1.41	1.38	1.34	1.31	1.24	1.16
500	1.58	1.56	1.50	1.44	1.39	1.36	1.31	1.28	1.21	1.11
1000	1.58	1.55	1.49	1.43	1.38	1.35	1.30	1.27	1.20	1.08

TABLE G (continued) Quantile values of the *F* distribution

$$1 - \alpha = 0.95$$

ν_2	$\nu_1 =$ degrees of freedom for the numerator									
	1	2	3	4	5	6	7	8	9	10
1	161.45	199.50	215.71	224.58	230.16	233.99	236.77	238.88	240.54	241.88
2	18.51	19.00	19.16	19.25	19.30	19.33	19.35	19.37	19.38	19.40
3	10.13	9.55	9.28	9.12	9.01	8.94	8.89	8.85	8.81	8.79
4	7.71	6.94	6.59	6.39	6.26	6.16	6.09	6.04	6.00	5.97
5	6.61	5.79	5.41	5.19	5.05	4.95	4.88	4.82	4.77	4.73
6	5.99	5.14	4.76	4.53	4.39	4.28	4.21	4.15	4.10	4.06
7	5.59	4.74	4.35	4.12	3.97	3.87	3.79	3.73	3.68	3.64
8	5.32	4.46	4.07	3.84	3.69	3.58	3.50	3.44	3.39	3.35
9	5.12	4.26	3.86	3.63	3.48	3.37	3.29	3.23	3.18	3.14
10	4.96	4.10	3.71	3.48	3.33	3.22	3.14	3.07	3.02	2.98
11	4.84	3.98	3.59	3.36	3.20	3.09	3.01	2.95	2.90	2.85
12	4.75	3.89	3.49	3.26	3.11	3.00	2.91	2.85	2.80	2.75
13	4.67	3.81	3.41	3.18	3.03	2.92	2.83	2.77	2.71	2.67
14	4.60	3.74	3.34	3.11	2.96	2.85	2.76	2.70	2.65	2.60
15	4.54	3.68	3.29	3.06	2.90	2.79	2.71	2.64	2.59	2.54
16	4.49	3.63	3.24	3.01	2.85	2.74	2.66	2.59	2.54	2.49
17	4.45	3.59	3.20	2.96	2.81	2.70	2.61	2.55	2.49	2.45
18	4.41	3.55	3.16	2.93	2.77	2.66	2.58	2.51	2.46	2.41
19	4.38	3.52	3.13	2.90	2.74	2.63	2.54	2.48	2.42	2.38
20	4.35	3.49	3.10	2.87	2.71	2.60	2.51	2.45	2.39	2.35
21	4.32	3.47	3.07	2.84	2.68	2.57	2.49	2.42	2.37	2.32
22	4.30	3.44	3.05	2.82	2.66	2.55	2.46	2.40	2.34	2.30
23	4.28	3.42	3.03	2.80	2.64	2.53	2.44	2.37	2.32	2.27
24	4.26	3.40	3.01	2.78	2.62	2.51	2.42	2.36	2.30	2.25
25	4.24	3.39	2.99	2.76	2.60	2.49	2.40	2.34	2.28	2.24
26	4.23	3.37	2.98	2.74	2.59	2.47	2.39	2.32	2.27	2.22
27	4.21	3.35	2.96	2.73	2.57	2.46	2.37	2.31	2.25	2.20
28	4.20	3.34	2.95	2.71	2.56	2.45	2.36	2.29	2.24	2.19
29	4.18	3.33	2.93	2.70	2.55	2.43	2.35	2.28	2.22	2.18
30	4.17	3.32	2.92	2.69	2.53	2.42	2.33	2.27	2.21	2.16
35	4.12	3.27	2.87	2.64	2.49	2.37	2.29	2.22	2.16	2.11
40	4.08	3.23	2.84	2.61	2.45	2.34	2.25	2.18	2.12	2.08
50	4.03	3.18	2.79	2.56	2.40	2.29	2.20	2.13	2.07	2.03
60	4.00	3.15	2.76	2.53	2.37	2.25	2.17	2.10	2.04	1.99
80	3.96	3.11	2.72	2.49	2.33	2.21	2.13	2.06	2.00	1.95
100	3.94	3.09	2.70	2.46	2.31	2.19	2.10	2.03	1.97	1.93
200	3.89	3.04	2.65	2.42	2.26	2.14	2.06	1.98	1.93	1.88
500	3.86	3.01	2.62	2.39	2.23	2.12	2.03	1.96	1.90	1.85
1000	3.85	3.01	2.61	2.38	2.22	2.11	2.02	1.95	1.89	1.84

TABLE G (continued)   Quantile values of the *F* distribution

$$1 - \alpha = 0.95$$

ν_2	ν_1 = degrees of freedom for the numerator									
	11	12	15	20	25	30	40	50	100	1000
1	242.98	243.91	245.96	248.01	249.26	250.08	251.15	251.77	253.01	254.17
2	19.40	19.41	19.43	19.45	19.46	19.46	19.47	19.48	19.49	19.50
3	8.76	8.74	8.70	8.66	8.63	8.62	8.59	8.58	8.55	8.53
4	5.94	5.91	5.86	5.80	5.77	5.74	5.72	5.70	5.66	5.63
5	4.70	4.68	4.62	4.56	4.52	4.50	4.46	4.44	4.41	4.37
6	4.03	4.00	3.94	3.87	3.84	3.81	3.77	3.75	3.71	3.67
7	3.60	3.57	3.51	3.44	3.40	3.38	3.34	3.32	3.27	3.23
8	3.31	3.28	3.22	3.15	3.11	3.08	3.04	3.02	2.97	2.93
9	3.10	3.07	3.01	2.94	2.89	2.86	2.83	2.80	2.76	2.71
10	2.94	2.91	2.85	2.77	2.73	2.70	2.66	2.64	2.59	2.54
11	2.82	2.79	2.72	2.65	2.60	2.57	2.53	2.51	2.46	2.41
12	2.72	2.69	2.62	2.54	2.50	2.47	2.43	2.40	2.35	2.30
13	2.63	2.60	2.53	2.46	2.41	2.38	2.34	2.31	2.26	2.21
14	2.57	2.53	2.46	2.39	2.34	2.31	2.27	2.24	2.19	2.14
15	2.51	2.48	2.40	2.33	2.28	2.25	2.20	2.18	2.12	2.07
16	2.46	2.42	2.35	2.28	2.23	2.19	2.15	2.12	2.07	2.02
17	2.41	2.38	2.31	2.23	2.18	2.15	2.10	2.08	2.02	1.97
18	2.37	2.34	2.27	2.19	2.14	2.11	2.06	2.04	1.98	1.92
19	2.34	2.31	2.23	2.16	2.11	2.07	2.03	2.00	1.94	1.88
20	2.31	2.28	2.20	2.12	2.07	2.04	1.99	1.97	1.91	1.85
21	2.28	2.25	2.18	2.10	2.05	2.01	1.96	1.94	1.88	1.82
22	2.26	2.23	2.15	2.07	2.02	1.98	1.94	1.91	1.85	1.79
23	2.24	2.20	2.13	2.05	2.00	1.96	1.91	1.88	1.82	1.76
24	2.22	2.18	2.11	2.03	1.97	1.94	1.89	1.86	1.80	1.74
25	2.20	2.16	2.09	2.01	1.96	1.92	1.87	1.84	1.78	1.72
26	2.18	2.15	2.07	1.99	1.94	1.90	1.85	1.82	1.76	1.70
27	2.17	2.13	2.06	1.97	1.92	1.88	1.84	1.81	1.74	1.68
28	2.15	2.12	2.04	1.96	1.91	1.87	1.82	1.79	1.73	1.66
29	2.14	2.10	2.03	1.94	1.89	1.85	1.81	1.77	1.71	1.65
30	2.13	2.09	2.01	1.93	1.88	1.84	1.79	1.76	1.70	1.63
35	2.07	2.04	1.96	1.88	1.82	1.79	1.74	1.70	1.63	1.57
40	2.04	2.00	1.92	1.84	1.78	1.74	1.69	1.66	1.59	1.52
50	1.99	1.95	1.87	1.78	1.73	1.69	1.63	1.60	1.52	1.45
60	1.95	1.92	1.84	1.75	1.69	1.65	1.59	1.56	1.48	1.40
80	1.91	1.88	1.79	1.70	1.64	1.60	1.54	1.51	1.43	1.34
100	1.89	1.85	1.77	1.68	1.62	1.57	1.52	1.48	1.39	1.30
200	1.84	1.80	1.72	1.62	1.56	1.52	1.46	1.41	1.32	1.21
500	1.81	1.77	1.69	1.59	1.53	1.48	1.42	1.38	1.28	1.14
1000	1.80	1.76	1.68	1.58	1.52	1.47	1.41	1.36	1.26	1.11

TABLE G (continued)   Quantile values of the *F* distribution

$$1 - \alpha = 0.99$$

ν_2	$\nu_1 = $ degrees of freedom for the numerator									
	1	2	3	4	5	6	7	8	9	10
2	98.50	99.00	99.17	99.25	99.30	99.33	99.36	99.37	99.39	99.40
3	34.12	30.82	29.46	28.71	28.24	27.91	27.67	27.50	27.34	27.22
4	21.20	18.00	16.69	15.98	15.52	15.21	14.98	14.80	14.66	14.55
5	16.26	13.27	12.06	11.39	10.97	10.67	10.46	10.29	10.16	10.05
6	13.75	10.92	9.78	9.15	8.75	8.47	8.26	8.10	7.98	7.87
7	12.25	9.55	8.45	7.85	7.46	7.19	6.99	6.84	6.72	6.62
8	11.26	8.65	7.59	7.01	6.63	6.37	6.18	6.03	5.91	5.81
9	10.56	8.02	6.99	6.42	6.06	5.80	5.61	5.47	5.35	5.26
10	10.04	7.56	6.55	5.99	5.64	5.39	5.20	5.06	4.94	4.85
11	9.65	7.21	6.22	5.67	5.32	5.07	4.89	4.74	4.63	4.54
12	9.33	6.93	5.95	5.41	5.06	4.82	4.64	4.50	4.39	4.30
13	9.07	6.70	5.74	5.21	4.86	4.62	4.44	4.30	4.19	4.10
14	8.86	6.51	5.56	5.04	4.69	4.46	4.28	4.14	4.03	3.94
15	8.68	6.36	5.42	4.89	4.56	4.32	4.14	4.00	3.89	3.80
16	8.53	6.23	5.29	4.77	4.44	4.20	4.03	3.89	3.78	3.69
17	8.40	6.11	5.18	4.67	4.34	4.10	3.93	3.79	3.68	3.59
18	8.29	6.01	5.09	4.58	4.25	4.01	3.84	3.71	3.60	3.51
19	8.18	5.93	5.01	4.50	4.17	3.94	3.77	3.63	3.52	3.43
20	8.10	5.85	4.94	4.43	4.10	3.87	3.70	3.56	3.46	3.37
21	8.02	5.78	4.87	4.37	4.04	3.81	3.64	3.51	3.40	3.31
22	7.95	5.72	4.82	4.31	3.99	3.76	3.59	3.45	3.35	3.26
23	7.88	5.66	4.76	4.26	3.94	3.71	3.54	3.41	3.30	3.21
24	7.82	5.61	4.72	4.22	3.90	3.67	3.50	3.36	3.26	3.17
25	7.77	5.57	4.68	4.18	3.85	3.63	3.46	3.32	3.22	3.13
26	7.72	5.53	4.64	4.14	3.82	3.59	3.42	3.29	3.18	3.09
27	7.68	5.49	4.60	4.11	3.78	3.56	3.39	3.26	3.15	3.06
28	7.64	5.45	4.57	4.07	3.75	3.53	3.36	3.23	3.12	3.03
29	7.60	5.42	4.54	4.04	3.73	3.50	3.33	3.20	3.09	3.00
30	7.56	5.39	4.51	4.02	3.70	3.47	3.30	3.17	3.07	2.98
35	7.42	5.27	4.40	3.91	3.59	3.37	3.20	3.07	2.96	2.88
40	7.31	5.18	4.31	3.83	3.51	3.29	3.12	2.99	2.89	2.80
50	7.17	5.06	4.20	3.72	3.41	3.19	3.02	2.89	2.78	2.70
60	7.08	4.98	4.13	3.65	3.34	3.12	2.95	2.82	2.72	2.63
80	6.96	4.88	4.04	3.56	3.26	3.04	2.87	2.74	2.64	2.55
100	6.90	4.82	3.98	3.51	3.21	2.99	2.82	2.69	2.59	2.50
200	6.76	4.71	3.88	3.41	3.11	2.89	2.73	2.60	2.50	2.41
500	6.69	4.65	3.82	3.36	3.05	2.84	2.68	2.55	2.44	2.36
1000	6.66	4.63	3.80	3.34	3.04	2.82	2.66	2.53	2.43	2.34

TABLE G (continued)   Quantile values of the *F* distribution

$$1 - \alpha = 0.99$$

ν_2	$\nu_1 = $ degrees of freedom for the numerator									
	11	12	15	20	25	30	40	50	100	1000
2	99.41	99.42	99.43	99.45	99.46	99.46	99.47	99.48	99.49	99.51
3	27.12	27.03	26.85	26.67	26.58	26.50	26.41	26.35	26.24	26.14
4	14.45	14.37	14.19	14.02	13.91	13.84	13.75	13.69	13.58	13.48
5	9.96	9.89	9.72	9.55	9.45	9.38	9.30	9.24	9.13	9.03
6	7.79	7.72	7.56	7.40	7.29	7.23	7.15	7.09	6.99	6.89
7	6.54	6.47	6.31	6.16	6.06	5.99	5.91	5.86	5.75	5.66
8	5.73	5.67	5.52	5.36	5.26	5.20	5.12	5.07	4.96	4.87
9	5.18	5.11	4.96	4.81	4.71	4.65	4.57	4.52	4.41	4.32
10	4.77	4.71	4.56	4.41	4.31	4.25	4.17	4.12	4.01	3.92
11	4.46	4.40	4.25	4.10	4.00	3.94	3.86	3.81	3.71	3.61
12	4.22	4.16	4.01	3.86	3.76	3.70	3.62	3.57	3.47	3.37
13	4.02	3.96	3.82	3.66	3.57	3.51	3.43	3.38	3.27	3.18
14	3.86	3.80	3.66	3.51	3.41	3.35	3.27	3.22	3.11	3.02
15	3.73	3.67	3.52	3.37	3.28	3.21	3.13	3.08	2.98	2.88
16	3.62	3.55	3.41	3.26	3.16	3.10	3.02	2.97	2.86	2.76
17	3.52	3.46	3.31	3.16	3.07	3.00	2.92	2.87	2.76	2.66
18	3.43	3.37	3.23	3.08	2.98	2.92	2.84	2.78	2.68	2.58
19	3.36	3.30	3.15	3.00	2.91	2.84	2.76	2.71	2.60	2.50
20	3.29	3.23	3.09	2.94	2.84	2.78	2.69	2.64	2.54	2.43
21	3.24	3.17	3.03	2.88	2.78	2.72	2.64	2.58	2.48	2.37
22	3.18	3.12	2.98	2.83	2.73	2.67	2.58	2.53	2.42	2.32
23	3.14	3.07	2.93	2.78	2.69	2.62	2.54	2.48	2.37	2.27
24	3.09	3.03	2.89	2.74	2.64	2.58	2.49	2.44	2.33	2.22
25	3.06	2.99	2.85	2.70	2.60	2.54	2.45	2.40	2.29	2.18
26	3.02	2.96	2.81	2.66	2.57	2.50	2.42	2.36	2.25	2.14
27	2.99	2.93	2.78	2.63	2.54	2.47	2.38	2.33	2.22	2.11
28	2.96	2.90	2.75	2.60	2.51	2.44	2.35	2.30	2.19	2.08
29	2.93	2.87	2.73	2.57	2.48	2.41	2.33	2.27	2.16	2.05
30	2.91	2.84	2.70	2.55	2.45	2.39	2.30	2.24	2.13	2.02
35	2.80	2.74	2.60	2.44	2.35	2.28	2.19	2.14	2.02	1.90
40	2.73	2.66	2.52	2.37	2.27	2.20	2.11	2.06	1.94	1.82
50	2.62	2.56	2.42	2.27	2.17	2.10	2.01	1.95	1.82	1.70
60	2.56	2.50	2.35	2.20	2.10	2.03	1.94	1.88	1.75	1.62
80	2.48	2.42	2.27	2.12	2.01	1.94	1.85	1.79	1.65	1.51
100	2.43	2.37	2.22	2.07	1.97	1.89	1.80	1.74	1.60	1.45
200	2.34	2.27	2.13	1.97	1.87	1.79	1.69	1.63	1.48	1.30
500	2.28	2.22	2.07	1.92	1.81	1.74	1.63	1.57	1.41	1.20
1000	2.27	2.20	2.06	1.90	1.79	1.72	1.61	1.54	1.38	1.16

TABLE H   *k*-values for two-sided tolerance limits when sampling from normal distributions

n \ d	$\gamma = 0.75$					$\gamma = 0.90$				
	0.75	0.90	0.95	0.99	0.999	0.75	0.90	0.95	0.99	0.999
6	1.704	2.429	2.889	3.779	4.802	2.196	3.131	3.723	4.870	6.188
7	1.624	2.318	2.757	3.611	4.593	2.034	2.902	3.452	4.521	5.750
8	1.568	2.238	2.663	3.491	4.444	1.921	2.743	3.264	4.278	5.446
9	1.525	2.178	2.593	3.400	4.330	1.839	2.626	3.125	4.098	5.220
10	1.492	2.131	2.537	3.328	4.241	1.775	2.535	3.018	3.959	5.046
11	1.465	2.093	2.493	3.271	4.169	1.724	2.463	2.933	3.849	4.906
12	1.443	2.062	2.456	3.223	4.110	1.683	2.404	2.863	3.758	4.792
13	1.425	2.036	2.424	3.183	4.059	1.648	2.355	2.805	3.682	4.697
14	1.409	2.013	2.398	3.148	4.016	1.619	2.314	2.756	3.618	4.615
15	1.395	1.994	2.375	3.118	3.979	1.594	2.278	2.713	3.562	4.545
16	1.383	1.977	2.355	3.092	3.946	1.572	2.246	2.676	3.514	4.484
17	1.372	1.962	2.337	3.069	3.917	1.552	2.219	2.643	3.471	4.430
18	1.363	1.948	2.321	3.048	3.891	1.535	2.194	2.614	3.433	4.382
19	1.355	1.936	2.307	3.030	3.867	1.520	2.172	2.588	3.399	4.339
20	1.347	1.925	2.294	3.013	3.846	1.506	2.152	2.564	3.368	4.300
21	1.340	1.915	2.282	2.998	3.827	1.493	2.135	2.543	3.340	4.264
22	1.334	1.906	2.271	2.984	3.809	1.482	2.118	2.524	3.315	4.232
23	1.328	1.898	2.261	2.971	3.793	1.471	2.103	2.506	3.292	4.203
24	1.322	1.891	2.252	2.959	3.778	1.462	2.089	2.489	3.270	4.176
25	1.317	1.883	2.244	2.948	3.764	1.453	2.077	2.474	3.251	4.151
26	1.313	1.877	2.236	2.938	3.751	1.444	2.065	2.460	3.232	4.127
27	1.309	1.871	2.229	2.929	3.740	1.437	2.054	2.447	3.215	4.106
28	1.305	1.865	2.222	2.920	3.728	1.430	2.044	2.435	3.199	4.085
29	1.301	1.860	2.216	2.911	3.718	1.423	2.034	2.424	3.184	4.066
30	1.297	1.855	2.210	2.904	3.708	1.417	2.025	2.413	3.170	4.049
31	1.294	1.850	2.204	2.896	3.699	1.411	2.017	2.403	3.157	4.032
32	1.291	1.846	2.199	2.890	3.690	1.405	2.009	2.393	3.145	4.016
33	1.288	1.842	2.194	2.883	3.682	1.400	2.001	2.385	3.133	4.001
34	1.285	1.838	2.189	2.877	3.674	1.395	1.994	2.376	3.122	3.987
35	1.283	1.834	2.185	2.871	3.667	1.390	1.988	2.368	3.112	3.974
36	1.280	1.830	2.181	2.866	3.660	1.386	1.981	2.361	3.102	3.961
37	1.278	1.827	2.177	2.860	3.653	1.381	1.975	2.353	3.092	3.949
38	1.275	1.824	2.173	2.855	3.647	1.377	1.969	2.346	3.083	3.938
39	1.273	1.821	2.169	2.850	3.641	1.374	1.964	2.340	3.075	3.927
40	1.271	1.818	2.166	2.846	3.635	1.370	1.959	2.334	3.066	3.917
41	1.269	1.815	2.162	2.841	3.629	1.366	1.954	2.328	3.059	3.907
42	1.267	1.812	2.159	2.837	3.624	1.363	1.949	2.322	3.051	3.897
43	1.266	1.810	2.156	2.833	3.619	1.360	1.944	2.316	3.044	3.888
44	1.264	1.807	2.153	2.829	3.614	1.357	1.940	2.311	3.037	3.879
45	1.262	1.805	2.150	2.826	3.609	1.354	1.935	2.306	3.030	3.871
46	1.261	1.802	2.148	2.822	3.605	1.351	1.931	2.301	3.024	3.863
47	1.259	1.800	2.145	2.819	3.600	1.348	1.927	2.297	3.018	3.855
48	1.258	1.798	2.143	2.815	3.596	1.345	1.924	2.292	3.012	3.847
49	1.256	1.796	2.140	2.812	3.592	1.343	1.920	2.288	3.006	3.840
50	1.255	1.794	2.138	2.809	3.588	1.340	1.916	2.284	3.001	3.833

TABLE H (continued) k-values for two-sided tolerance limits when sampling from normal distributions

n \ d	$\gamma = 0.95$					$\gamma = 0.99$				
	0.75	0.90	0.95	0.99	0.999	0.75	0.90	0.95	0.99	0.999
6	2.604	3.712	4.414	5.775	7.337	3.743	5.337	6.345	8.301	10.548
7	2.361	3.369	4.007	5.248	6.676	3.233	4.613	5.488	7.187	9.142
8	2.197	3.136	3.732	4.891	6.226	2.905	4.147	4.936	6.468	8.234
9	2.078	2.967	3.532	4.631	5.899	2.677	3.822	4.550	5.966	7.600
10	1.987	2.839	3.379	4.433	5.649	2.508	3.582	4.265	5.594	7.129
11	1.916	2.737	3.259	4.277	5.452	2.378	3.397	4.045	5.308	6.766
12	1.858	2.655	3.162	4.150	5.291	2.274	3.250	3.870	5.079	6.477
13	1.810	2.587	3.081	4.044	5.158	2.190	3.130	3.727	4.893	6.240
14	1.770	2.529	3.012	3.955	5.045	2.120	3.029	3.608	4.737	6.043
15	1.735	2.480	2.954	3.878	4.949	2.060	2.945	3.507	4.605	5.876
16	1.705	2.437	2.903	3.812	4.865	2.009	2.872	3.421	4.492	5.732
17	1.679	2.400	2.858	3.754	4.791	1.965	2.808	3.345	4.393	5.607
18	1.655	2.366	2.819	3.702	4.725	1.926	2.753	3.279	4.307	5.497
19	1.635	2.337	2.784	3.656	4.667	1.891	2.703	3.221	4.230	5.399
20	1.616	2.310	2.752	3.615	4.614	1.860	2.659	3.168	4.161	5.312
21	1.599	2.286	2.723	3.577	4.567	1.833	2.620	3.121	4.100	5.234
22	1.584	2.264	2.697	3.543	4.523	1.808	2.584	3.078	4.044	5.163
23	1.570	2.244	2.673	3.512	4.484	1.785	2.551	3.040	3.993	5.098
24	1.557	2.225	2.651	3.483	4.447	1.764	2.522	3.004	3.947	5.039
25	1.545	2.208	2.631	3.457	4.413	1.745	2.494	2.972	3.904	4.985
26	1.534	2.193	2.612	3.432	4.382	1.727	2.469	2.941	3.865	4.935
27	1.523	2.178	2.595	3.409	4.353	1.711	2.446	2.914	3.828	4.888
28	1.514	2.164	2.579	3.388	4.326	1.695	2.424	2.888	3.794	4.845
29	1.505	2.152	2.554	3.368	4.301	1.681	2.404	2.864	3.763	4.805
30	1.497	2.140	2.549	3.350	4.278	1.668	2.385	2.841	3.733	4.768
31	1.489	2.129	2.536	3.332	4.256	1.656	2.367	2.820	3.706	4.732
32	1.481	2.118	2.524	3.316	4.235	1.644	2.351	2.801	3.680	4.699
33	1.475	2.108	2.512	3.300	4.215	1.633	2.335	2.782	3.655	4.668
34	1.468	2.099	2.501	3.286	4.197	1.623	2.320	2.764	3.632	4.639
35	1.462	2.090	2.490	3.272	4.179	1.613	2.306	2.748	3.611	4.611
36	1.455	2.081	2.479	3.258	4.161	1.604	2.293	2.732	3.590	4.585
37	1.450	2.073	2.470	3.246	4.146	1.595	2.281	2.717	3.571	4.560
38	1.446	2.068	2.464	3.237	4.134	1.587	2.269	2.703	3.552	4.537
39	1.441	2.060	2.455	3.226	4.120	1.579	2.257	2.690	3.534	4.514
40	1.435	2.052	2.445	3.213	4.104	1.571	2.247	2.677	3.518	4.493
41	1.430	2.045	2.437	3.202	4.090	1.564	2.236	2.665	3.502	4.472
42	1.426	2.039	2.429	3.192	4.077	1.557	2.227	2.653	3.486	4.453
43	1.422	2.033	2.422	3.183	4.065	1.551	2.217	2.642	3.472	4.434
44	1.418	2.027	2.415	3.173	4.053	1.545	2.208	2.631	3.458	4.416
45	1.414	2.021	2.408	3.165	4.042	1.539	2.200	2.621	3.444	4.399
46	1.410	2.016	2.402	3.156	4.031	1.533	2.192	2.611	3.431	4.383
47	1.406	2.011	2.396	3.148	4.021	1.527	2.184	2.602	3.419	4.367
48	1.403	2.006	2.390	3.140	4.011	1.522	2.176	2.593	3.407	4.352
49	1.399	2.001	2.384	3.133	4.002	1.517	2.169	2.584	3.396	4.337
50	1.396	1.969	2.379	3.126	3.993	1.512	2.162	2.576	3.385	4.323

Source: C. Eisenhart, M. W. Hastay, and W. A. Wallis, *Techniques of statistical analysis,* McGraw-Hill, New York, 1947. Reprinted with permission.

TABLE I   *k*-values for one-sided tolerance limits when sampling from normal distributions

d n	γ = 0.75					γ = 0.90				
	0.75	0.90	0.95	0.99	0.999	0.75	0.90	0.95	0.99	0.999
6	1.087	1.860	2.336	3.243	4.273	1.540	2.494	3.091	4.242	5.556
7	1.043	1.791	2.250	3.126	4.118	1.435	2.333	2.894	3.972	5.201
8	1.010	1.740	2.190	3.042	4.008	1.360	2.219	2.755	3.783	4.955
9	0.984	1.702	2.141	2.977	3.924	1.302	2.133	2.649	3.641	4.772
10	0.964	1.671	2.103	2.927	3.858	1.257	2.065	2.568	3.532	4.629
11	0.947	1.646	2.073	2.885	3.804	1.219	2.012	2.503	3.444	4.515
12	0.933	1.624	2.048	2.851	3.760	1.188	1.966	2.448	3.371	4.420
13	0.919	1.606	2.026	2.822	3.722	1.162	1.928	2.403	3.310	4.341
14	0.909	1.591	2.007	2.796	3.690	1.139	1.895	2.363	3.257	4.274
15	0.899	1.577	1.991	2.776	3.661	1.119	1.866	2.329	3.212	4.215
16	0.891	1.566	1.977	2.756	3.637	1.101	1.842	2.299	3.172	4.164
17	0.883	1.554	1.964	2.739	3.615	1.085	1.820	2.272	3.136	4.118
18	0.876	1.544	1.951	2.723	3.595	1.071	1.800	2.249	3.106	4.078
19	0.870	1.536	1.942	2.710	3.577	1.058	1.781	2.228	3.078	4.041
20	0.865	1.528	1.933	2.697	3.561	1.046	1.765	2.208	3.052	4.009
21	0.859	1.520	1.923	2.686	3.545	1.035	1.750	2.190	3.028	3.979
22	0.854	1.514	1.916	2.675	3.532	1.025	1.736	2.174	3.007	3.952
23	0.849	1.508	1.907	2.665	3.520	1.016	1.724	2.159	2.987	3.927
24	0.845	1.502	1.901	2.656	3.509	1.007	1.712	2.145	2.969	3.904
25	0.842	1.496	1.895	2.647	3.497	0.999	1.702	2.132	2.952	3.882
30	0.825	1.475	1.869	2.613	3.454	0.966	1.657	2.080	2.884	3.794
35	0.812	1.458	1.849	2.588	3.421	0.942	1.623	2.041	2.833	3.730
40	0.803	1.445	1.834	2.568	3.395	0.923	1.598	2.010	2.793	3.679
45	0.795	1.435	1.821	2.552	3.375	0.908	1.577	1.986	2.762	3.638
50	0.788	1.426	1.811	2.538	3.358	0.894	1.560	1.965	2.735	3.604

Table I (continued) *k*-values for one-sided tolerance limits when sampling from normal distributions

d n	γ = 0.95 0.75	0.90	0.95	0.99	0.999	γ = 0.99 0.75	0.90	0.95	0.99	0.999
6	1.895	3.006	3.707	5.062	6.612	2.849	4.408	5.409	7.334	9.540
7	1.732	2.755	3.399	4.641	6.061	2.490	3.856	4.730	6.411	8.348
8	1.617	2.582	3.188	4.353	5.686	2.252	3.496	4.287	5.811	7.566
9	1.532	2.454	3.031	4.143	5.414	2.085	3.242	3.971	5.389	7.014
10	1.465	2.355	2.911	3.981	5.203	1.954	3.048	3.739	5.075	6.603
11	1.411	2.275	2.815	3.852	5.036	1.854	2.897	3.557	4.828	6.284
12	1.366	2.210	2.736	3.747	4.900	1.771	2.773	3.410	4.633	6.032
13	1.329	2.155	2.670	3.659	4.787	1.702	2.677	3.290	4.472	5.826
14	1.296	2.108	2.614	3.585	4.690	1.645	2.592	3.189	4.336	5.651
15	1.268	2.068	2.566	3.520	4.607	1.596	2.521	3.102	4.224	5.507
16	1.242	2.032	2.523	3.463	4.534	1.553	2.458	3.028	4.124	5.374
17	1.220	2.001	2.486	3.415	4.471	1.514	2.405	2.962	4.038	5.268
18	1.200	1.974	2.453	3.370	4.415	1.481	2.357	2.906	3.961	5.167
19	1.183	1.949	2.423	3.331	4.364	1.450	2.315	2.855	3.893	5.078
20	1.167	1.926	2.396	3.295	4.319	1.424	2.275	2.807	3.832	5.003
21	1.152	1.905	2.371	3.262	4.276	1.397	2.241	2.768	3.776	4.932
22	1.138	1.887	2.350	3.233	4.238	1.376	2.208	2.729	3.727	4.866
23	1.126	1.869	2.329	3.206	4.204	1.355	2.179	2.693	3.680	4.806
24	1.114	1.853	2.309	3.181	4.171	1.336	2.154	2.663	3.638	4.755
25	1.103	1.838	2.292	3.158	4.143	1.319	2.129	2.632	3.601	4.706
30	1.059	1.778	2.220	3.064	4.022	1.249	2.029	2.516	3.446	4.508
35	1.025	1.732	2.166	2.994	3.934	1.195	1.957	2.431	3.334	4.364
40	0.999	1.697	2.126	2.941	3.866	1.154	1.902	2.365	3.250	4.255
45	0.978	1.669	2.092	2.897	3.811	1.122	1.857	2.313	3.181	4.168
50	0.961	1.646	2.065	2.863	3.766	1.096	1.821	2.296	3.124	4.096

Source: G. J. Lieberman, *Table for one-sided statistical tolerance limits,* Industrial Quality Control **XIV,** 1958, 7–9. Reprinted with permission.

TABLE J Upper quantile values of the distribution of the Kolmogorov–Smirnov statistic D_n

n	$1 - \alpha$				
	0.80	0.85	0.90	0.95	0.99
1	.900	.925	.950	.975	.995
2	.684	.726	.776	.842	.929
3	.565	.597	.642	.708	.828
4	.494	.525	.564	.624	.733
5	.446	.474	.510	.565	.669
6	.410	.436	.470	.521	.618
7	.381	.405	.438	.486	.577
8	.358	.381	.411	.457	.543
9	.339	.360	.388	.432	.514
10	.322	.342	.368	.410	.490
11	.307	.326	.352	.391	.468
12	.295	.313	.338	.375	.450
13	.284	.302	.325	.361	.433
14	.274	.292	.314	.349	.418
15	.266	.283	.304	.338	.404
16	.258	.274	.295	.328	.392
17	.250	.266	.286	.318	.381
18	.244	.259	.278	.309	.371
19	.237	.252	.272	.301	.363
20	.231	.246	.264	.294	.356
25	.21	.22	.24	.27	.32
30	.19	.20	.22	.24	.29
35	.18	.19	.21	.23	.27
Formula for large n	$\dfrac{1.07}{\sqrt{n}}$	$\dfrac{1.14}{\sqrt{n}}$	$\dfrac{1.22}{\sqrt{n}}$	$\dfrac{1.36}{\sqrt{n}}$	$\dfrac{1.63}{\sqrt{n}}$

Source: F. J. Massey, Jr., *The Kolmogorov–Smirnov test for goodness of fit*, J. Amer. Statistical Assoc. **46** (1951), 68–78. Reprinted with permission.

TABLE K   Bounds of the Durbin–Watson statistic

	$1 - \alpha = 0.95$									
	$k = 1$		$k = 2$		$k = 3$		$k = 4$		$k = 5$	
n	d_L	d_U	d_L	d_U	d_L	d_U	d_L	d_U	d_L	d_U
15	1.08	1.36	0.95	1.54	0.82	1.75	0.69	1.97	0.56	2.21
16	1.10	1.37	0.98	1.54	0.86	1.73	0.74	1.93	0.62	2.15
17	1.13	1.38	1.02	1.54	0.90	1.71	0.78	1.90	0.67	2.10
18	1.16	1.39	1.05	1.53	0.93	1.69	0.82	1.87	0.71	2.06
19	1.18	1.40	1.08	1.53	0.97	1.68	0.86	1.85	0.75	2.02
20	1.20	1.41	1.10	1.54	1.00	1.68	0.90	1.83	0.79	1.99
21	1.22	1.42	1.13	1.54	1.03	1.67	0.93	1.81	0.83	1.96
22	1.24	1.43	1.15	1.54	1.05	1.66	0.96	1.80	0.86	1.94
23	1.26	1.44	1.17	1.54	1.08	1.66	0.99	1.79	0.90	1.92
24	1.27	1.45	1.19	1.55	1.10	1.66	1.01	1.78	0.93	1.90
25	1.29	1.45	1.21	1.55	1.12	1.66	1.04	1.77	0.95	1.89
26	1.30	1.46	1.22	1.55	1.14	1.65	1.06	1.76	0.98	1.88
27	1.32	1.47	1.24	1.56	1.16	1.65	1.08	1.76	1.01	1.86
28	1.33	1.48	1.26	1.56	1.18	1.65	1.10	1.75	1.03	1.85
29	1.34	1.48	1.27	1.56	1.20	1.65	1.12	1.74	1.05	1.84
30	1.35	1.49	1.28	1.57	1.21	1.65	1.14	1.74	1.07	1.83
31	1.36	1.50	1.30	1.57	1.23	1.65	1.16	1.74	1.09	1.83
32	1.37	1.50	1.31	1.57	1.24	1.65	1.18	1.73	1.11	1.82
33	1.38	1.51	1.32	1.58	1.26	1.65	1.19	1.73	1.13	1.81
34	1.39	1.51	1.33	1.58	1.27	1.65	1.21	1.73	1.15	1.81
35	1.40	1.52	1.34	1.58	1.28	1.65	1.22	1.73	1.16	1.80
36	1.41	1.52	1.35	1.59	1.29	1.65	1.24	1.73	1.18	1.80
37	1.42	1.53	1.36	1.59	1.31	1.66	1.25	1.72	1.19	1.80
38	1.43	1.54	1.37	1.59	1.32	1.66	1.26	1.72	1.21	1.79
39	1.43	1.54	1.38	1.60	1.33	1.66	1.27	1.72	1.22	1.79
40	1.44	1.54	1.39	1.60	1.34	1.66	1.29	1.72	1.23	1.79
45	1.48	1.57	1.43	1.62	1.38	1.67	1.34	1.72	1.29	1.78
50	1.50	1.59	1.46	1.63	1.42	1.67	1.38	1.72	1.34	1.77
55	1.53	1.60	1.49	1.64	1.45	1.68	1.41	1.72	1.38	1.77
60	1.55	1.62	1.51	1.65	1.48	1.69	1.44	1.73	1.41	1.77
65	1.57	1.63	1.54	1.66	1.50	1.70	1.47	1.73	1.44	1.77
70	1.58	1.64	1.55	1.67	1.52	1.70	1.49	1.74	1.46	1.77
75	1.60	1.65	1.57	1.68	1.54	1.71	1.51	1.74	1.49	1.77
80	1.61	1.66	1.59	1.69	1.56	1.72	1.53	1.74	1.51	1.77
85	1.62	1.67	1.60	1.70	1.57	1.72	1.55	1.75	1.52	1.77
90	1.63	1.68	1.61	1.70	1.59	1.73	1.57	1.75	1.54	1.78
95	1.64	1.69	1.62	1.71	1.60	1.73	1.58	1.75	1.56	1.78
100	1.65	1.69	1.63	1.72	1.61	1.74	1.59	1.76	1.57	1.78

TABLE K (continued) Bounds of the Durbin–Watson Statistic

	\multicolumn{10}{c}{$1 - \alpha = 0.99$}									
	$k = 1$		$k = 2$		$k = 3$		$k = 4$		$k = 5$	
n	d_L	d_U	d_L	d_U	d_L	d_U	d_L	d_U	d_L	d_U
15	0.81	1.07	0.70	1.25	0.59	1.46	0.49	1.70	0.39	1.96
16	0.84	1.09	0.74	1.25	0.63	1.44	0.53	1.66	0.44	1.90
17	0.87	1.10	0.77	1.25	0.67	1.43	0.57	1.63	0.48	1.85
18	0.90	1.12	0.80	1.26	0.71	1.42	0.61	1.60	0.52	1.80
19	0.93	1.13	0.83	1.26	0.74	1.41	0.65	1.58	0.56	1.77
20	0.95	1.15	0.86	1.27	0.77	1.41	0.68	1.57	0.60	1.74
21	0.97	1.16	0.89	1.27	0.80	1.41	0.72	1.55	0.63	1.71
22	1.00	1.17	0.91	1.28	0.83	1.40	0.75	1.54	0.66	1.69
23	1.02	1.19	0.94	1.29	0.86	1.40	0.77	1.53	0.70	1.67
24	1.04	1.20	0.96	1.30	0.88	1.41	0.80	1.53	0.72	1.66
25	1.05	1.21	0.98	1.30	0.90	1.41	0.83	1.52	0.75	1.65
26	1.07	1.22	1.00	1.31	0.93	1.41	0.85	1.52	0.78	1.64
27	1.09	1.23	1.02	1.32	0.95	1.41	0.88	1.51	0.81	1.63
28	1.10	1.24	1.04	1.32	0.97	1.41	0.90	1.51	0.83	1.62
29	1.12	1.25	1.05	1.33	0.99	1.42	0.92	1.51	0.85	1.61
30	1.13	1.26	1.07	1.34	1.01	1.42	0.94	1.51	0.88	1.61
31	1.15	1.27	1.08	1.34	1.02	1.42	0.96	1.51	0.90	1.60
32	1.16	1.28	1.10	1.35	1.04	1.43	0.98	1.51	0.92	1.60
33	1.17	1.29	1.11	1.36	1.05	1.43	1.00	1.51	0.94	1.59
34	1.18	1.30	1.13	1.36	1.07	1.43	1.01	1.51	0.95	1.59
35	1.19	1.31	1.14	1.37	1.08	1.44	1.03	1.51	0.97	1.59
36	1.21	1.32	1.15	1.38	1.10	1.44	1.04	1.51	0.99	1.59
37	1.22	1.32	1.16	1.38	1.11	1.45	1.06	1.51	1.00	1.59
38	1.23	1.33	1.18	1.39	1.12	1.45	1.07	1.52	1.02	1.58
39	1.24	1.34	1.19	1.39	1.14	1.45	1.09	1.52	1.03	1.58
40	1.25	1.34	1.20	1.40	1.15	1.46	1.10	1.52	1.05	1.58
45	1.29	1.38	1.24	1.42	1.20	1.48	1.16	1.53	1.11	1.58
50	1.32	1.40	1.28	1.45	1.24	1.49	1.20	1.54	1.16	1.59
55	1.36	1.43	1.32	1.47	1.28	1.51	1.25	1.55	1.21	1.59
60	1.38	1.45	1.35	1.48	1.32	1.52	1.28	1.56	1.25	1.60
65	1.41	1.47	1.38	1.50	1.35	1.53	1.31	1.57	1.28	1.61
70	1.43	1.49	1.40	1.52	1.37	1.55	1.34	1.58	1.31	1.61
75	1.45	1.50	1.42	1.53	1.39	1.56	1.37	1.59	1.34	1.62
80	1.47	1.52	1.44	1.54	1.42	1.57	1.39	1.60	1.36	1.62
85	1.48	1.53	1.46	1.55	1.43	1.58	1.41	1.60	1.39	1.63
90	1.50	1.54	1.47	1.56	1.45	1.59	1.43	1.61	1.41	1.64
95	1.51	1.55	1.49	1.57	1.47	1.60	1.45	1.62	1.42	1.64
100	1.52	1.56	1.50	1.58	1.48	1.60	1.46	1.63	1.44	1.65

Source: J. Durbin and G. S. Watson, *Testing for serial correlation in least squares regression, II,* Biometrika **38** (1951), 159–178. Reprinted with permission of the Biometrika Trustees.

Answers to Selected
Odd-Numbered Exercises

Chapter 1

1.1. a., b.

True limits	Class frequency	Relative frequency	Cumulative relative frequency
(0.15, 1.55)	17	0.34	0.34
(1.55, 2.95)	11	0.22	0.56
(2.95, 4.35)	7	0.14	0.70
(4.35, 5.75)	6	0.12	0.82
(5.75, 7.15)	4	0.08	0.90
(7.15, 8.55)	3	0.06	0.96
(8.55, 9.95)	2	0.04	1.00
Totals	50	1.00	

c. Interquartile and interdecile ranges are about 3.8 min. and 6.5 min., respectively.

d. $\bar{x} = 3.258$; *Median* = 2.6182; *Mode* = 0.85; $s = 2.4986$; *M.D.* = 2.081; and *Md.D.* = 2.0042

e. $\bar{x} = 3.26$; *Median* = 2.75; *Mode* = 0.4; $s = 2.4819$; *M.D.* = 2.0056; and *Md.D.* = 1.948

1.3. $\bar{x} = 3.5$; the variances are $s_1^2 = 3.5$, $s_2^2 = 7.5$, and $s_3^2 = 109.9$

1.5. a.

True limits	Frequency	Relative frequency
(−1.875, −1.125)	5	0.1667
(−1.125, −0.375)	5	0.1667
(−0.375, 0.375)	8	0.2667
(0.375, 1.125)	8	0.2667
(1.125, 1.875)	4	0.1333
Totals	30	1.0001

No change in the relative frequency distribution

1.7. b. $\bar{x} = 18.82$; *Mode* = 14.0
c. $s^2 = 123.4196$; $s = 11.11$; *M.D.* = 9.27

Chapter 2

2.1. a. Events are not mutually exclusive.
b. 1. 180/400; 2. 150/400; 3. 30/400; 4. 60/180; 5. 60/200
c. $P(S \mid M) = 50/220$; $P(S) = 150/400$; not statistically independent
d. No; $P(A \mid F) = 0.1111$, $P(A) = 0.125$
e. 1. 240/400; 2. 210/400; 3. 60/400; 4. 30/50

2.3. When either one or both of the events are empty

2.5. The permutations are GGG, GGB, GBG, BGG, GBB, BBG, BGB, and BBB. Probability of two children of the same sex is 6/8; probability of one boy and two girls is 3/8; probability of all of same sex is 2/8.

2.7. $(1/2)^{10}$; 1/2

2.9. 13/30

2.11. a. Four possible outcomes: both components work; both do not; and one works, the other does not (two ways)
b. 0.99

2.13. $n = 4$

2.15. 0.6571

2.17. 0.41

Chapter 3

3.1. a., c.

x	$p(x)$	$F(x)$
0	0.0498	0.0498
1	0.1494	0.1992
2	0.2240	0.4232
3	0.2240	0.6472
4	0.1680	0.8152
5	0.1008	0.9160
6	0.0504	0.9664
7	0.0216	0.9880

3.3. a. 3/2; b. $(x^3 + 1)/2$; c. 7/16, 1/8

3.5. a. $(1/100)\exp(-x/100)$; b. 0.8187

3.7. $E(X) = 4$; $Var(X) = 4.1$

3.9. a. 1/3; b. 1/18

3.11. a. 4; b. 16; c. 2; d. 9
e. The distribution in Exercise 3.10 is symmetrical and is centered about the value 5, has variance of 8.33 and standard deviation of 2.8868, and is flat-topped. This distribution is positively skewed, is relatively high-peaked, and has the larger relative dispersion.

3.13. a. $\sigma^2 + (\mu - c)^2$; b. $c = \mu$

3.15. $M.D.(X) = 0.19753$, $s.d.(X) = 0.2357$

3.17. a. Mean = 800, median = 554.52; b. 878.89 c. 1757.78; d. 0.3679

3.19. a. $(1 - 4t)^{-2}$ b. $E(X) = 8$, $Var (X) = 32$

Chapter 4

4.5. a. 0.6562, 0.9346; b. 0.5696, 0.9391

4.7. $P(X = 4) = 0.0049$, $P(X \geq 4) = 0.0055$; inclined to conclude the claim is incorrect

4.9. 0.2122

4.11. Six or more

4.15. 0.7601, 0.9718

4.17. 0.0488

4.19. 0.0803, 0.9862

4.21. 0.6767

4.23. 0.0293, yes

4.25. 0.1837, no

4.27. a. 0.5973; b. 5987; c. 0.6065

4.31.

x	Relative frequency	Theoretical probability
0	0.715	0.7201
1	0.179	0.1689
2	0.063	0.0630
3	0.019	0.0263
4	0.010	0.0116
5	0.010	0.0053
6	0.002	0.0025
7	0.000	0.0012
8	0.002	0.0006

4.33. a. 0.0189; b. 0.0180; occurrence is not likely

Chapter 5

5.3. a. 0.4649; b. 0.2204; c. 0.0228; d. 0.8643

5.5. a. 1.775; b. 18.225; c. 21.65; d. −1.65; e. 0.2; f. 19.8

5.7. 1018

5.9. 0.00069

5.11. 0.000008; occurrence is highly unlikely

5.13. $228,000

5.15. a. 0.0256; b. ≈0; c. ≈0

5.17. Yes, probability of occurrence is virtually zero.

5.19. a. 0.5774; b. no

5.21. $a = 4$, $b = 16$

5.23. b. $E(X) = 0.75$, $Var(X) = 0.0375$, $M.D.(X) = 0.1582$, $\alpha_3(X) = -0.8607$,
$\alpha_4(X) = 3.0952$
c. 0.6679, 0.9523; d. 0.63, 0.7937, 0.9086

5.25. 0.64, 0.9728

5.27. 0.1314, 0.0582

5.29. a. 0.594; b. 0.0466; c. 0.2642

5.31. $\alpha = 3.75$, $\theta = 8$

5.35. 0.9409

5.37. a. $E(X) = 44.3113$; 16.23, 23.62, 29.86, 35.74, 41.63, 47.86, 54.86, 63.43, 75.87
b. 0.1054

5.39. a. 0.3679; b. 0.8647, 0.9502

5.41. a. 0.1353; b. 433

5.45. Exponential with scale parameter θ^α

Chapter 6

6.1. 0.0022; occurrence is unlikely

6.3. a. $F(x, y) = (3x^2y - xy^2 - 3x^2 + x - 3y + y^2 + 2)/10$
b. 0.225
c. $F_X(x) = (3x - 1)(x - 1)/5$, $F_Y(y) = (9y - y^2 - 8)/10$
d. $f_X(x) = (6x - 4)/5$, $f_Y(y) = (9 - 2y)/10$

6.5. a. $p_X(x) = p_Y(y) = 5/16, 6/16, 5/16$, $x = y = -1, 0, 1$, respectively
b. no; c. 0

6.7. a. 0.69; b. $f_{T_1}(t_1) = (1/5) \exp(-t_1/5)$, $f_{T_2}(t_2) = 10\exp(-10t_2)$

6.9. 1029.2152

6.13. If $Cov(X, Y) > 0$, $Var(X + Y) > Var(X) + Var(Y)$ and $Var(X - Y) < Var(X) +$
$Var(Y)$; if $Cov(X, Y) < 0$, $Var(X + Y) < Var(X) + Var(Y)$, and $Var(X - Y) >$
$Var(X) + Var(Y)$

6.15. 11/27

6.17. a. $\mu = 0.04$, $\sigma^2 = 0.0014769$; b. $f(p \mid x) = 1260p(1 - p)^{34}$
c. $\mu = 0.054$, $\sigma^2 = 0.0013456$; d. 0.5432

6.19. a. 1/2; b. 50
c. $f(x \mid y) = \exp\{-(1/150)[x - 50 - (y - 25)/2]^2\}/\sqrt{150\pi}$
d. $f(x \mid Y = 30) = \exp[-(1/150)(x - 52.5)^2]/\sqrt{150\pi}$, 0.9251

Chapter 7

7.3. a. $\lambda^{\Sigma x_i} \exp(-n\lambda)/\Pi x_i!$; b. $p^n(1 - p)^{\Sigma x_i}$
c. $1/(b - a)^n$; d. $(1/\sigma\sqrt{2\pi})^n \exp[-\Sigma(x_i - \mu)^2/2\sigma^2]$

7.5. Parts (c), (d), and (f)

7.11. 0.0075

7.15. a. 0.7698; b. 0.9986; c. 0.0548; d. 0.0228

7.17. ≈ 0; inspector should take appropriate action

7.19. 255.82

7.23. 0.99

7.25. Highly unlikely; $P(T > 3.429) < 0.005$

7.27. Yes; $P(T < -3.516) < 0.001$

7.29. Doubtful; $P(F_{15,20} > 1.999) < 0.10$

Chapter 8

8.1.   a. $\text{MSE}(T_1) = p(1 - p)/n$; $\text{MSE}(T_2) = [np(1 - p) + (2p - 1)^2]/(n + 2)^2$
      b. No. For $n = 10$, if $0.138 < p < 0.862$, $\text{MSE}(T_2) < \text{MSE}(T_1)$; otherwise, $\text{MSE}(T_1) < \text{MSE}(T_2)$. For $n = 25$, if $0.142 < p < 0.858$, $\text{MSE}(T_2) < \text{MSE}(T_1)$; otherwise, $\text{MSE}(T_1) < \text{MSE}(T_2)$

8.5. T_3; $Var(T_3)/Var(T_1) = 0.9$

8.9. $\hat{\lambda} = \overline{X}$

8.11. $\hat{\sigma}^2 = \Sigma X_i^2/2n$; yes

8.13. Sample shape factors are -0.0028 and 2.21, respectively; the distribution is apparently symmetrical and slightly flat-topped.

8.15. a. $\hat{\theta} = 100.0696$;   b. yes, $\tilde{\theta} = 103.575$;   c. 0.1057

8.17. a. 2532.7;   b. 0.2061

8.19. a. 214.9289;   b. 0.8410, 0.5340

8.21. $(20.1191, 20.6434)$

8.27. $(151.31, 165.69)$, $(149.75, 167.25)$, $(147.82, 169.18)$

8.31. $(-3.89, -1.51)$, $(-4.12, -1.28)$, $(-4.58, -0.82)$, yes

8.33. $(4.84, 21.16)$, $(2.07, 23.93)$, yes

8.35. $(146.98, 645.69)$

8.39. $(0.2048, 4.0744)$, yes

8.41. $(0.0172, 0.0628)$, $(0.0128, 0.0672)$, $(0.0043, 0.0757)$; there may be reason to doubt the claim.

8.43. 663   8.45. a. 88;   b. $(66.40, 109.60)$

8.47. $(2.98514, 3.01486)$ 8.49. 0.8609, 299   8.51. 152

Chapter 9

9.1.   Test b

9.3.   a. H_0: $p = 0.05$ against H_1: $p > 0.05$; b. 0.2642
      c. 0.3396, 0.4831, 0.6083, 0.8244, 0.9308, and 0.9757, respectively
      d. $\alpha = 0.0755$, power is 0.1150, 0.2120, 0.3231, 0.5951, 0.7939, and 0.9087, respectively

9.5.   Critical values for Test 1 are 19.8333 and 20.1667; for Test 2, they are 19.7917 and 20.2083.

						Power					
μ	19.5	19.6	19.7	19.8	19.9	20.0	20.1	20.2	20.3	20.4	20.5
Test 1	$\approx 1-$	0.9974	0.9452	0.6554	0.2126	0.0456	0.2126	0.6554	0.9452	0.9974	≈ 1
Test 2	0.9998	0.9893	0.8643	0.4602	0.0968	0.0124	0.0968	0.4602	0.8643	0.9893	0.9998

9.7. The left tail of the sampling distribution of $\overline{X}$

9.9. a. $H_0: \lambda = 2.5$ against $H_1: \lambda < 2.5$
 b. For the four weeks, critical value is 5
 c. 0.8088

9.11. Cannot reject H_0 since $\bar{x} = 145 < \bar{x}_0 = 233.8$

9.13. 30

9.15. 7

9.17. 100.62; H_0 cannot be rejected if claimed value is ≥ 100.62

9.19. a. Relatively large value so as to easily reject H_0
 b. $t = 0.667$; H_0 cannot be rejected with $\alpha = 0.1$; the p-value exceeds 0.2
 c. Yes; tail values could become critical.

9.21. $t = 0.54$; H_0 cannot be rejected

9.23. a. Yes; critical value is three, p-value is 0.0755
 b. $z = 2.05$ and H_0 is rejected, p-value is 0.0202

9.25. $z = -3.54$, H_0 is rejected

9.27. $z = 1.62$, H_0 cannot be rejected; p-value is 0.1052

9.29. $[(z_{1-\beta} + z_{1-\alpha})^2(\sigma_X^2 + \sigma_Y^2)]/(\delta_0 - \delta_1)^2$

9.31. $t = -1.36$, H_0 cannot be rejected; p-value is 0.19

9.33. $t = -1.729$, H_0 cannot be rejected

9.37. a. $t = 2.11$, H_0 is rejected; b. p-value is 0.039; c. (1.66, 7.84)

9.39. $\chi^2 = 17.28$, H_0 cannot be rejected

9.41. Approximately 0.1

9.43. a. $\chi^2 = 47.04$, H_0 is rejected
 b. values in the interval $(1.8083, 7.1666)$; not equidistant because sampling distribution is not symmetrical

9.45. a. $f = 3.24$, H_0 is rejected; b. 0.1374

9.47. $z = 3.03$, H_0 is rejected; p-value is 0.0012

9.49. $z = 1.33$, H_0 cannot be rejected; p-value is 0.1836

Chapter 10

10.1. $\chi^2 = 12$, H_0 is rejected; p-value is about 0.008

10.3. a. $\chi^2 = 400$, H_0 is rejected; conclusion is different from that in Exercise 10.2

10.5. $\chi^2 = 40$, H_0 is rejected

10.7. $\chi^2 = 4.25$, H_0 cannot be rejected

10.9. a. $\chi^2 = 5.8501$, H_0 cannot be rejected
 b. $\hat{\lambda} = 2.673$, $\chi^2 = 5.8969$, and H_0 still cannot be rejected

10.11. Maximum deviation is 0.1263, H_0 cannot be rejected

10.13. $\chi^2 = 1.0097$ (for $k = 5$ classes), H_0 cannot be rejected

10.15. $\chi^2 = 7.8628$, H_0 cannot be rejected

10.17.

2.16	3.78	2.70	1.36
2.60	4.54	3.24	1.62
3.24	5.68	4.06	2.02

10.19. $\chi^2 = 22.04$, H_0 is rejected

10.21. $\chi^2 = 2.69$, H_0 cannot be rejected

Chapter 11

11.1. a. (4.3292, 5.6708), sample average for eleventh week exceeds upper control limit
    b. probability ≈ 0;   c. 0.0301

11.3. a. (475.5051, 524.4949), no;   b. 0.9884;   c. (0.574, 37.486)

11.5. a. (378.36, 422.04), (0, 31.96);   b. 16.28

11.7. a. (0, 0.0797);   b. (0, 0.0758);   c. 0.0013

11.9. a. 0.6767;   b. 0.5438

11.11. 0.5526

11.13. Approximately 0.175

11.15. $n = 99$, $c = 4$; $n = 131$, $c = 5$; $n = 100$, $c = 4$; $n = 116$, $c = 5$

11.17. a. 0.3679;   b. 0.019;   c. 0.3971;   d. 0.216

11.19. $n = 65$, $\bar{x}_a = 71.53$

Chapter 12

12.5.

Source	d.f.	SS	MS	F value
Treatments	2	0.492	0.246000	43.41
Error	12	0.068	0.005667	
Total	14	0.560	$f_{0.95,2,12} = 3.89$	

12.7. a.

Source	d.f.	SS	MS	F value
Treatments	3	2305.5	768.50	2.75
Error	28	7838.0	279.93	
Total	31	10143.5	$f_{0.95,3,28} = 2.95$	

b. The standardized residuals do not suggest unequal variances.

12.9. a.

Source	d.f.	SS	MS	F value
Treatments	4	522,744	130,686	66.41
Error	20	39,360	1,968	
Total	24	562,104	$f_{0.99,4,20} = 4.43$	

b. Some contrasts and their confidence intervals are: $L_1 = \mu_5 - \mu_4$, (41.87, 278); $L_2 = 3\mu_5 - \mu_2 - \mu_3 - \mu_4$, (406.65, 985.35); $L_3 = \mu_2 - \mu_1$, (33.87, 270.13); $L_4 = 2\mu_5 - \mu_3 - \mu_4$, (205.39, 614.61); $L_5 = \mu_3 - \mu_2$, (−82.13, 154.13)

12.11. The use of analysis of variance is questionable because the within region variation is much too large to be attributed only to random error.

12.13. b. $Y_{ij} = \mu + \beta_i + \tau_j + \varepsilon_{ij}$, $i = 1, 2, ..., 5, j = 1, 2, 3, 4$; H_0: $\tau_j = 0$ for all j;

Source	d.f.	SS	MS	F value
Blocks	4	1026.2875		
Treatments	3	17.6260	5.8753	41.09
Error	12	1.7165	0.1430	
Total	19	1045.6300	$f_{0.95,3,12} = 3.49$	

c. Some contrasts and their confidence intervals are: $L_1 = 3\mu_4 - \mu_1 - \mu_2 - \mu_3$, (4.48, 8.28); $L_2 = \mu_4 - \mu_1$, (1.57, 3.11); $L_3 = \mu_2 + \mu_3 - 2\mu_1$, $(-0.70, 1.98)$; $L_4 = \mu_3 - \mu_2$, $(-0.41, 1.13)$

12.15. a. $Y_{ij} = \mu + \beta_i + \tau_j + \varepsilon_{ij}$, $i = 1, 2, ..., 7, j = 1, 2, 3, 4$

b.

Source	d.f.	SS	MS	F value
Blocks	6	1,471,772.429		
Treatments	3	44,826.572	14,942.19	16.48
Error	18	16,316.428	906.47	
Total	27	1,532,915.429	$f_{0.95,3,18} \doteq 3.16$	

c. $f = 16.48 > f_{0.95,1,6} = 5.99$; H_0 is still rejected

d. Two contrasts and their confidence intervals are: $L_1 = \mu_1 - \mu_3$, (12.01, 111.13); $L_2 = \mu_2 - \mu_4$, $(-29.13, 69.99)$

12.17. a. $Y_{ijk} = \mu + \alpha_i + \beta_j + (\alpha\beta)_{ij} + \varepsilon_{ijk}$, $i = 1, 2, j = 1, 2, k = 1, 2, 3$

b. H_0: $(\alpha\beta)_{ij} = 0$ for all i and j; H_0: $\alpha_i = 0$ for all i; H_0: $\beta_j = 0$ for all j

c.

Source	d.f.	SS	MS	F value
Oven	1	0.022534	0.022534	3.92
Temperature	1	0.005634	0.005634	0.98
Oven × Temp.	1	0.554699	0.554699	96.47
Error	8	0.046000	0.005750	
Total	11	0.628867	$f_{0.95,1,8} = 5.32$	

12.19. a. $Y_{ijk} = \mu + \alpha_i + \beta_j + (\alpha\beta)_{ij} + \varepsilon_{ijk}$, $i = 1, 2, 3, 4, j = 1, 2, 3, k = 1, 2, 3, 4$

b. H_0: $\sigma_{\alpha\beta}^2 = 0$; H_0: $\alpha_i = 0$ for all i; H_0: $\sigma_\beta^2 = 0$

c.

Source	d.f.	SS	MS	F value
Varieties	3	331.750	110.58	0.64
Fertilizers	2	22,764.875	11,382.44	230.65
Varieties × Fert.	6	1,052.125	173.35	3.51
Error	36	1,776.500	49.35	
Total	47	25,925.250	$f_{0.95,3,6} = 4.76$	

$f_{0.95,2,36} = 3.27$ $f_{0.95,6,36} = 2.37$

Chapter 13

13.3. a. $\Sigma Y_i x_i / \Sigma x_i^2$; b. $E(B) = \beta$

13.5. a. To some degree; b. $\hat{y} = 2.50 + 1.7774x$
c. For every \$1,000 increase in family income, life insurance coverage increases by \$1,777.
d. A quadratic equation should be fitted.

13.7. a.

x	45	20	40	40	47	30	25	20	15
residuals	-12.48	11.95	-13.60	-23.60	3.96	-0.82	8.06	-3.05	10.84
x	35	40	55	50	60	15	30	35	45
residuals	0.29	1.40	4.74	18.63	10.85	0.84	-15.82	0.29	-2.48

c. 124.7; d. 7.727, 0.2021; e. (1.3489, 2.2059); f. Yes, $t = 8.79$

g.

x_p	Confidence interval	x_p	Confidence interval
45	(75.67, 89.29)	35	(59.11, 70.31)
20	(29.23, 46.87)	40	(67.75, 79.45)
40	(67.75, 79.45)	55	(90.38, 110.14)
40	(67.75, 79.45)	50	(83.17, 99.57)
47	(78.73, 93.35)	60	(97.43, 120.87)
30	(49.69, 61.95)	15	(18.60, 39.72)
25	(39.65, 54.23)	30	(49.69, 61.95)
20	(29.23, 46.87)	35	(59.11, 70.31)
15	(18.60, 39.72)	45	(75.67, 89.29)

13.9.

x_p	$\hat{y}_{part}$	95% prediction interval
18	34.49	(8.98, 60.00)
28	52.27	(27.71, 76.83)
38	70.04	(45.70, 94.38)
48	87.82	(62.95, 112.69)
58	105.59	(79.50, 131.68)

13.11. b. 0.2262; linear association is vague

13.13. a. $(\sigma^2/n) \le Var(\hat{Y}_p) \le 2(\sigma^2/n)$;
b. $[(n + 1)\sigma^2/n] \le Var(\hat{Y}_{part}) \le [(n + 2)\sigma^2/n]$;
c. $b_0 = 15.5$, $b_1 = 5.1$

13.15. b. $\hat{y} = 12.75 + 19.875x$; c. yes, $t = 14.24$; d. (16.881, 22.869)

13.17. a. $r = -0.8829$

b.

Source	d.f.	SS	MS	F value
Regression	1	5.64305	5.64305	63.65
Error	18	1.59595	0.08866	
Total	19	7.23900	$f_{0.99,1,18} = 8.29$	

13.19. a. $\hat{y} = -53.119 + 0.6639x$; b. yes
c. positive autocorrelation is detected, $d = 0.7075$
d. $\hat{y} = -45.116 + 0.6704x$

Chapter 14

14.1. a. β_2 is nonlinear

14.3. a. 3; b. -3.5

14.5. a.

Variable in the model	b_0	b_1	b_2
x_1	0.1619	0.1342	
x_2	0.6713		-0.0363
x_1, x_2	-0.1605	0.1487	0.0769

b. $f = 113.14$, reject H_0
c. $\text{SSR}(x_2 \mid x_1) = 0.0879, f = 14.63$; $\text{SSR}(x_1 \mid x_2) = 1.3366, f = 222.47$
d. $R^2 = 0.9496$
e. $\hat{y} = -0.1605 + 0.1487x_1 + 0.0769x_2$, $\hat{y}_p = \$518.85$, ($\$462.7, \$575.0$)

14.7. $\begin{bmatrix} 15 & 42.00 & 55.0 \\ 42 & 188.08 & 140.8 \\ 55 & 140.80 & 219.0 \end{bmatrix} \begin{bmatrix} b_0 \\ b_1 \\ b_2 \end{bmatrix} = \begin{bmatrix} 8.070 \\ 32.063 \\ 28.960 \end{bmatrix}$

14.9. a.

Variable in the model	R^2	SSE	MSE	C_p
x_1	0.000	7326	407.02	114.07
x_2	0.229	5648	313.77	84.27
x_3	0.784	1581	87.82	12.06
x_4	0.748	1846	102.53	16.76
x_1, x_2	0.230	5641	332.00	86.20
x_1, x_3	0.802	1451	85.34	11.75
x_1, x_4	0.754	1800	106.00	17.97
x_2, x_3	0.785	1576	92.73	13.99
x_2, x_4	0.774	1653	97.20	15.36
x_3, x_4	0.869	958	56.34	3.00
x_1, x_2, x_3	0.802	1451	90.70	13.77
x_1, x_2, x_4	0.778	1624	102.00	16.85
x_1, x_3, x_4	0.885	846	52.88	3.02
x_2, x_3, x_4	0.870	950	59.38	4.87
x_1, x_2, x_3, x_4	0.885	845	56.33	5.00

c. $\hat{y} = -114.988 + 1.2657x_3 + 0.8414x_4$, $\hat{y}_{\text{part}} = 100.35$, ($82.05, 118.64$)

14.11. 0.0654, 0.0952

14.13. Plot reveals a quadratic trend; $\hat{y} = 8.238 + 0.3126x - 0.001823x^2$; $\hat{y} = -27.55\%$, which is absurd.

14.15. a. $\hat{y} = 5284.28 - 114.85x_1 - 78.67x_2 + 0.129x_3 + 0.189x_1^2 + 0.201x_2^2 + 2.63 \times 10^{-7}x_3^2 + 1.268x_1x_2 - 0.0017x_1x_3 - 0.0008x_2x_3$
b. Choice for best equation is between the following two:
$\hat{y} = 2163.98 - 56.47x_1 - 26.17x_2 + 0.0162x_3 + 0.6952x_1x_2 - 0.0005x_1x_3$
$\hat{y} = 1676.19 - 43.57x_1 - 19.77x_2 + 0.526x_1x_2 - 5.91 \times 10^{-5}x_1x_3$

14.17.

	Y	x_1	x_2	x_3	x_4	x_5
Y	1.00	0.18	0.78	0.15	-0.29	0.45
x_1	0.18	1.00	-0.05	0.41	0.55	-0.04
x_2	0.78	-0.05	1.00	0.08	-0.30	0.16
x_3	0.15	0.41	0.08	1.00	0.27	-0.14
x_4	-0.29	0.55	-0.30	0.27	1.00	-0.11
x_5	0.45	-0.04	0.16	-0.14	-0.11	1.00

Chapter 15

15.1. Yes, $t = -2.12$ and H_0 is rejected

15.3. $z = -2.51$, H_0 is rejected

15.5. $z = -2.80$ and there is reason to believe that the sequence is not random

15.7. $z = 2.24$ and H_0 of no difference in taste preference is rejected. Conclusion differs from that in Exercise 15.6.

15.9. $s = 4$, critical values are 2 and 10, H_0 cannot be rejected

15.11. $h = 11.40$ and H_0 of identical distributions for the disciplines is rejected

15.13. $s = 1.1$ and differences among the four tests are not statistically discernible

15.15. $r_S = 0.7915$

15.17. $r_S = -0.4667$; there is some tendency for one judge to give a high score when the other judge gives a low score

Index